The RSGB Amateur Radio Operating Manual

SIXTH EDITION

by Don Field, G3XTT

Radio Society of Great Britain

The RSGB Amateur Radio Operating Manual
6th edition

Published by the Radio Society of Great Britain, Lambda House, Cranborne Rd, Potters Bar, Herts EN6 3JE.
Tel 0870 904 7373. Web www.rsgb.org

First published 2004.

ISBN 1-905086-00-8

Cover design: Jodie Escott, M3TPQ

Design and layout: Mike Dennison, G3XDV, Emdee Publishing

Production: Mark Allgar, M1MPA

Printed in Great Britain by Nuffield Press Ltd

Contents

Preface

The *RSGB Operating Manual* was first published in 1979 and, since then, has been a valuable source of advice for many amateurs, both experienced and newly licensed. Recent editions have very much been updates of earlier ones, reflecting changes in band plans, equipment, ideas on operating and so on, but also the introduction of completely new modes of operation, made possible by the digital revolution.

However, even since the last edition was published in 2000 much has happened. The Internet has become much more a feature of the hobby, and computers are now firmly established as almost a must-have part of the modern amateur radio shack. Perhaps more significantly though, the radical restructuring of the licensing system in the UK and elsewhere, along with the changes at the 2003 World Administrative Radio Conference, which effectively remove the previous demarcation between VHF/UHF only licences and those which also include HF, mean that there is probably a greater need than ever before for a handbook of this sort.

With these changes in mind, the author has taken the opportunity both to rewrite a substantial amount of what appeared in earlier editions as well as to add a significant volume of new material. Even if you owned an earlier edition of the *Manual,* it is hoped that you will find enough in here that is new or that offers a new perspective that you will feel it a worthwhile addition to your bookshelf. It must be said, though, that the subject area is a broad one and this *Manual* can do no more than be a general guide. If you decide to specialise, for example in Very Low Frequency (VLF) operating or, perhaps, in chasing contacts via the moon or operating Amateur Television, while this book will give you some useful pointers, you will need to supplement it with more focused sources. The good news is that many such sources are available on the Internet, and there should be sufficient suggestions in these pages to help your search. In any case, this makes absolute sense. While the basics of amateur radio operating stay much the same as the years go by, some of those specialisms change very rapidly, for example with the introduction of new software, and a book will always lag behind, whereas most Internet resources are updated almost on a daily basis.

An attempt was made with the last edition to link it with a web page which would carry new and relevant information, as appropriate. Sadly, this didn't really happen. It is inevitable that quite a lot will change before the next edition appears. This has been solved to some extent by removing some of the appendices that appeared in previous editions, given that this information (bandplans, prefix lists, etc) appears and is updated annually in the *RSGB Yearbook*. The *RSGB Prefix Guide*, compiled and maintained by Fred Handscombe, G4BWP, remains the most comprehensive source of prefix data. In addition, the existing Operating Manual Webpage will be replaced by an area on my own web pages (www.g3xtt.com/opmanual) dedicated specifically to any corrections, additions and other amendments to this manual. It is hoped that this will be updated more frequently than was the case with the previous edition, and the author would welcome any input from readers on corrections, additions or other suggestions which could usefully be posted there, or archived for use in a subsequent edition of this Manual.

It should be noted that, although in strict scientific usage the terms LF, MF and HF refer to the frequency ranges 30 - 300kHz, 300kHz - 3MHz and 3MHz - 30MHz respectively, this book uses the amateur radio shorthand of VLF (136kHz band), LF (1.8, 3.5 and 7MHz bands) and HF (10MHz to 28MHz bands). Similarly, the amateur radio term Microwaves is used to denote all bands above 1000MHz, even though the lower microwave bands are strictly UHF and the rest are SHF and EHF. The amateur radio terminology is used to group bands with similar propagation characteristics.

References specific to each chapter appear at the end of the relevant chapter, but are reproduced along with more extensive suggestions for further reading and a large number of useful website URLs in an appendix. Readers will be aware that websites come and go, though all these were working at the time of writing.

Finally, thanks are due to all who contributed to this revision, as well as to those who laid the groundwork in previous editions, in particular Ray Eckersley G4FTJ who edited the Fifth Edition. Without their efforts this current edition would have been impossible. My particular thanks also to those who have kindly helped with this edition, by providing information, reading drafts, and generally helping out in areas where my own expertise is sadly lacking. These include Mark Taylor G0LGJ, David Bowman G0MRF, Don Beattie G3BJ, Mike Dixon G3PFR, Bob Whelan G3PJT, Colin Thomas G3PSM, Ian White G3SEK, Roger Western G3SXW, Allan Robinson G3TQA, John Linford G3WGV, John Gould G3WKL, Mike Dennison G3XDV (who has also sub-edited and typeset this edition), Dave Pick G3YXM, Martin Atherton G3ZAY,, Fred Handscombe G4BWP, Bill Pechey, G4CUE, Chris Lorek G4HCL, Steve Telenius-Lowe G4JVG, Andy Cook G4PIQ, Justin Snow G4TSH, John Heath G7HIA, Trevor Brown G8CJS, Geoffrey Foster G8UKT, Phil Cooper GU0SUP, Mark Allgar M1MPA and last but not least to Jodie Escott for the design of the front cover. However, any errors or omissions should be laid at the door of the author. Thanks also to my wife Janet for putting up with yet another long-running amateur radio project.

Don Field G3XTT
September 2004
don@g3xtt.com

1 An Introduction to Amateur Radio Operating

THE AMATEUR SERVICE and Amateur Satellite Service, as they tend to be referred to in official documents, have always been about self-training in the art of communications by radio. As radio amateurs we are privileged to have the use of a wide range of frequencies throughout the electromagnetic spectrum, many of which are regarded with interest by commercial users who would like to get their hands on them. In return for that privilege, we are expected to use those frequencies to enhance our knowledge and skills in radio communication. Of course, it's only reasonable that, in the process, we should have fun too!

There are two areas in which we develop our skills. One is through the technical aspects of the hobby, setting up our station and ensuring it works effectively without causing annoyance and interference to other users of the radio spectrum. Even if your station consists entirely of commercial equipment, you will need to exercise at least some skills in connecting everything up, with attention to various factors such as effective earthing. Beyond this, many amateurs take pleasure in designing or, at least, building their own equipment, often to extremely high standards. The other area of self-training is in learning to operate effectively, and this book is aimed at that area. There are many aspects to consider if you are to be able to establish communication with another station or stations, pass information in an accurate and timely way and, in the process, do so with the least inconvenience to fellow amateurs and others with whom we share our bands.

Historically, there has been a line drawn at 30MHz between the HF spectrum and VHF/UHF. This is largely because HF propagation is characterised by ionospheric refraction, allowing radio waves to travel long distances, whereas VHF/UHF is essentially line-of-sight. Of course, anyone who has operated on 6m, or even on the higher bands when there is any sort of enhanced propagation, knows that this is far from the truth. But the split has also, over time, been written into our rules and licensing system, with HF operators being required to pass a test of proficiency in Morse code, while those happy to operate only on the VHF/UHF bands have not had to do so. That somewhat arbitrary distinction has now gone as a result of decisions made at the 2003 World Radio Conference, so that it is likely most countries will allow their licensed amateurs access to all frequencies, albeit with certain restrictions applying to particular introductory or intermediate forms of licence. Although operating practices vary to some extent according to waveband, they vary too according to the mode of operation. This book sets out to cover all aspects.

The effective station of GW4ALG

The chapter headings should be self-explanatory. The breakdown is largely by type of operating, but don't assume the book only addresses competitive operating (DXing and contesting). This is by no means the case. Many of the general principles are covered in this chapter and in Chapter 7, and will get you started if your interest is in casual day-to-day operating, whatever the band. There are plenty of tips in other chapters which you will find helpful, even if you don't expect to be chasing DXpeditions or entering contests.

Why an operating manual?

IF YOU HAVE SPENT any time listening on the amateur bands, you may wonder why an operating manual is necessary at all. Surely anyone who can hold a conversation, use a telephone or conduct a business meeting, ought to be able to sit in front of a radio and start operating? To some extent this is true. Some radio links are full duplex, where both parties can hear each other the whole time, just as with a telephone. This certainly makes operating much simpler, though there are still many factors to be borne in mind, such as the possibilities of interfering with users of other services, the necessity of identifying yourselves at regular intervals, and so on. Most radio links are half-duplex, in other words they operate in only one direction at a time. This requires a further level of operating procedure, to avoid losing contact or, on the other hand, both ends transmitting at once, neither hearing the other. Then there are net operations, which are a form of round-table discussion. There needs to be some understanding of the order in which the participants make their transmissions, how and when others can join the net and similar matters. This is complicated by the fact that, radio propagation being what it is, it is quite possible that not all net participants can necessarily hear each other.

All this goes to demonstrate that, whether consciously or not, we need a set of procedures to establish, maintain and finally end our various communications. Commercial and military users of radio communications have always recognised the need for this. If a commander, in the field of battle, issues an order, it needs to be absolutely clear to whom that order is addressed and the commander needs to know not only that the message has been sent but that it has been received accurately at the far end and will be acted upon. Fortunately the demands on amateur radio communications are usually less onerous, though those amateurs who offer their services in emergency situations, such as after 'September 11th', have to be extremely conscious of the need for accuracy and accountability at all times.

Types of operating

OF COURSE, operating interests vary widely. Some use amateur radio to keep in touch with friends at the local radio club, perhaps through a well-sited repeater. Others maintain regular schedules with a friend overseas. For the technically-minded, operating may simply be a way of checking out that newly-built piece of kit. For others, their operating may focus on a net of like-minded enthusiasts, maybe sharing a common interest in fishing or motor cars. It has been noticeable in recent years, though, that the amount of 'ragchewing' on the bands, in other words chatting away at length about a variety of subjects, has decreased dramatically. Unless there is some DX (long-distance) propagation, bands such as 6m can appear dead for long periods. In contrast, competitive operating, in the sense of DXing and contesting, appears to be growing in popularity. Perhaps this is a sign of the times, with radio amateurs finding less time in their busy diaries for casual operating, but able to mark out specific slots for contests, or to get on the air briefly to make a short DX contact. It may also be that the Internet has, to an extent, replaced radio communications for ragchewing, providing, as it does, more consistent communications without the vagaries of propagation.

These are signs of the times, but there are other signs that digital technology is, in its turn, helping to revive amateur radio in other ways. The digital modes (RTTY, PSK, WSJT and the like) are on the ascendant, and Echolink is providing a way of interconnecting radio and the Internet to achieve the best of both worlds, allowing communications while on the move, but benefiting from the ubiquity of the fixed Internet network.

Whatever your operating preferences, there should be something in these pages of interest, but one of the great joys of amateur radio as a hobby is that it encompasses so many different facets in terms of bands and modes. When one type of operating starts to grow stale, there is always something new to try, so do use these pages as a resource when trying out new operating experiences.

What is a contact?

AN AMATEUR RADIO contact, often referred to as a QSO (see Chapter 7 for an explanation of Q codes, and a list of the commonly used ones), consists of establishing two-way communications, maintaining them long enough to pass whatever information is appropriate (which may be a pleasant chat or, for example in the case of a contest, a set of data defined by the sponsors which will enable them to validate that a contact has taken place), and ending communications. If the contact is to count for the various operating awards or, as mentioned, as a valid contest QSO, then this complete cycle must take place, even if it's all over in a matter of seconds. If communications are lost part-way through, then no contact is deemed to have taken place (how can you be sure, for example, if you haven't heard the other party confirm the exchange, that he has received your greetings, contest exchange, or whatever?).

Having said this, amateur radio is a hobby and there are no hard and fast rules as to what that contact should include. For the most popular operating award, such as the RSGB's

Some like their amateur radio al fresco

IOTA Awards and the ARRL's DXCC (see Chapter 14), there is no requirement even to exchange signal reports, though this is usually considered appropriate. All that is necessary is to copy each other's callsign accurately. Even for awards such as Worked All Britain (based on NGR grid squares) or the various VHF awards based on QTH Locator squares, it's not actually necessary to pass the locator information during the contact. It can be written or printed on the QSL card which you send to confirm the contact. In practice, you'll almost certainly wish to exchange that information, but that's for personal interest only.

Establishing contact

THERE ARE THREE WAYS of establishing a contact. The first is to put out a call, inviting others to call you. The second is to answer such a call. Finally, you can call in as another contact is just finishing, often referred to as 'tail-ending'. Let's deal with these in turn.

In the first instance, you might put out a general call (usually referred to as a CQ call – "seek you"), or you may make a directed call. You might, for example, call "CQ VK/ZL" if you are looking specifically for contacts with Australia and New Zealand (VK being the internationally

A portable VHF-UHF expedition station

There's no age barrier to amateur radio operating

assigned callsign prefix for Australia, and ZL similarly for New Zealand). Or in the extreme, you might call only for a specific station "NK1G, this is G3XTT". Of course, before putting out any of those calls, you will first have checked that the frequency you are using is free. On the VHF and UHF bands, FM (frequency modulation) activity is usually channelised. In other words, rather than tune your radio to anywhere in the band, communications take place on discrete channels, widely recognised and listed in the various band plans (see the *RSGB Yearbook* [1] or the RSGB web site [2] for a complete list).

If, perhaps, you have a schedule (a pre-arranged contact, often referred to as a "sked") with a friend, you may have chosen a suitable channel beforehand, in which case you will call on that channel. Ideally, though, you will have made some sort of pre-arrangement that, if the channel is in use by others you will, for example, use the first clear channel above that one. Remember, this is amateur radio, and none of us, whether an individual, a club or even a national radio society, has any greater call on a specific frequency than any other. If you have no pre-arrangement, the usual practice where channelised operation is the norm, is to make your call on the designated calling channel and, once communication has been established, vacate that channel and move to a free channel elsewhere in the band.

Outside the channelised parts of the VHF/UHF bands and almost universally on the HF bands (there are certain exceptions), no defined channels exist. You can, quite simply, transmit anywhere (though the band plans designate certain sectors of the bands for specific modes, eg. SSB, CW and data modes). The trick is to find a slot wide enough for your transmission, which is not already in use, and make your CQ call. This may be easier said than done, and even when you have conscientiously done this and established your contact, propagation may change such that others who were using the frequency but inaudible to you may suddenly be interfering with you and you with them, as propagation changes. In such a case, it's not a matter of arguing right and wrong, as no 'wrong' has taken place. It's a matter of courtesy to sort matters out, with one pair of operators agreeing to move to an alternative frequency.

Already you may be realising that there is more to even the simple matter of establishing a contact than you might previously have thought. Let's turn, now, to answering someone else's call (which you will probably have heard by tuning around the band, or using the scanning facility on your transceiver). Firstly, if he (or she – the male pronoun is used in this book for convenience, but there are of course many female amateur radio operators) is making a directional call, then do not answer if you are not included. If no one replies from the specific area, club or whatever that he is calling for, then by all means make a short call to see if he is prepared to have a contact with you. But if you are within the scope of his call, or if he is making a general CQ call, then feel free to answer. However, make it short. Don't launch into "M0AIM, this is G3XTT in Reading, you are 59 and my equipment is ..." as I sometimes hear. After all, you may not be the only one calling, and you could simply be causing unnecessary interference. Instead, make a short call, and hand the transmission back to determine whether you have been heard and acknowledged. Normally, your call will be of the form "M0AIM, this is G3XTT, over" or, on Morse (CW) "`M0AIM DE G3XTT KN`". Incidentally, the word "over" isn't always used. The word "break" might be used instead, or perhaps nothing at all, as it's usually, but not always, obvious when you've stopped transmitting. If there is interference or signals are weak, you may send your callsign two or three times, and do so phonetically. There is no need to make a meal of sending the other station's callsign repeatedly; he already knows what it is! In a DX or contest situation, to save time, it is normal not to send his callsign, only your own. This is covered in more detail in the relevant chapters.

Finally, calling at the end of an existing contact. If you have been listening to what has gone before, it should be obvious which of the stations is likely to stay on frequency and who will move off (by convention, the station who originally found the frequency clear and called CQ will continue to use it until he's ready to close down). Call as you would when answering a CQ call, but do be absolutely sure that the previous contact really has ended and that you are not causing interference.

The meat of the contact

ONCE CONTACT HAS been established, pretty well anything goes. A so-called 'rubber stamp' QSO usually consists of an exchange of signal reports, name and location (QTH). You might also exchange details about equipment or maybe the weather. But there is absolutely no need to limit your exchange to that. Apart from certain licence restrictions regarding conducting business over the air, conducting a political campaign, etc. pretty much anything goes, and one of the joys of the hobby is making new friends and sharing experiences well outside amateur radio. Just because we use the technology of radio to make the communication possible, doesn't mean that's all we should talk about, any more than using a mobile phone means that you can only talk about mobile phones! Of course, if the other operator doesn't have English as his native language, there may be limitations on how deeply you can discuss existentialism (for example!), but there again you might even find that amateur radio becomes an excellent medium to practice your language skills.

Ending the contact

ENDING THE CONTACT is straightforward, but it is always helpful to make it clear to anyone listening as to whose frequency it is (following the convention described above, that the frequency remains with whoever was there first. No one 'owns' the frequency of course), in case anyone wants to call either you or the station you have been in contact with. Actually, it's surprising how often DX stations seem to leave some ambiguity as to whether or not the contact is complete (remember, those listening in may not be able to hear both sides of the QSO), and then get upset when others start calling when their QSO partner is still transmitting. So try to make it clear when you are signing. For example, "Thanks for the contact. Listening for any final comments from you before checking the frequency. M0AIM, this is G3XTT, over", thus making it clear that you aren't ready yet for other callers. When your QSO partner has finished, you might then say, "73, this is G3XTT listening for any further calls". On CW, it should be clear from the way you end your transmission. "... M0AIM DE G3XTT KN" clearly indicates that you are going back specifically to M0AIM. "... M0AIM DE G3XTT SK" is somewhat more ambiguous. It indicates this is your last transmission but, of course, it may not be your frequency and your QSO partner may still be expecting to make a final transmission. A DX or contest station often ends a QSO with TU (Thank you), indicating that he is now ready for other callers as in "... M0AIM DE G3XTT TU". "... M0AIM DE G3XTT CL" indicates that your have finished and are closing down. More on these abbreviations and procedure signals in the section on Morse operating in Chapter 7.

Net operations

MUCH HAS BEEN SAID about List and Net operations over the years, mainly because in the DXing context they are controversial. Making a DX contact with any sort of perceived assistance from an MC (Master of Ceremonies) or Net Controller is, in the view of many DX chasers, a form of assistance too far. But Net operations are common in other contexts in amateur radio, and an excellent way of bringing together operators with a common interest and using spectrum in an efficient way. An example might be a club net, where club members can meet on the air and exchange news and views. For a net to work, though, there needs to be a level of discipline above that necessary for the sort of two-way contact described above.

Military operators have very strict guidelines for net operations so that in the heat of battle, for example, everyone is absolutely clear what is going on, which messages are intended for which stations, when it is permissible to transmit, and so on. As radio amateurs, we certainly don't need to be so formal, but without some structure a net can quickly deteriorate, especially if not every station can hear every other station.

A transceiver covering both VHF and UHF

The simplest solution for net operations is to have a designated net controller, ideally one who every participant can hear and who, in turn, can hear every participant. He can then make clear to everyone the order in which they should transmit, ask them to stand by from time to time to allow others to join the net, and whatever else is required. Of course, this also requires that he will be there when the net starts and still there when it closes. Alternatively, the role of Net Controller can be passed from individual to individual as time goes on, if this is convenient. For small nets of just a handful of stations it is of course, possible to dispense with a Net Controller altogether, with the participants imposing their own discipline. Usually they will follow some obvious sort of system, such as passing the transmission progressively to the next one who joined the net, and allowing a short break between transmissions for others to join. As long as every participant knows who to hand over to at the end of his own transmission, this is usually sufficient to avoid confusion. As participants leave the net, they simply need to ensure that the station preceding them in order of transmission is aware of who the next station is down the line.

FM and repeater operations

MANY NEW OPERATORS start with some sort of VHF or UHF handheld transceiver, and their first experience of operating is via the channelised approach found in the FM bands. Such a transceiver will also give access to the repeater network, allowing contacts to be made over greater distances.

The earlier discussion has focused in general terms on how to establish, conduct and conclude an amateur radio contact. But it hasn't dealt with actually finding people to speak with, or the protocols associated with using frequencies which are shared with thousands of other users, unlike most commercial operations where each group of users is allocated its own frequency.

By convention, parts of the VHF and UHF bands, as well as part of the 10m band, are allocated to channelised operation. In other words, rather than treating the radio spectrum as a continuous entity, operations take place on discrete frequencies which are far enough apart to avoid mutual interference. Given that VHF/UHF propagation is limited in distance, and there may be relatively few users within your coverage area, picking a channel at random to call CQ could be very unproductive, unless someone else just happened to be tuning from channel to channel and ran across you. Instead, the usual approach is to recommend calling channels.

This is where you are much more likely to make a contact, as those who are looking for contacts will have their transceivers tuned to this channel. For this very reason, though, once contact is established it is normal procedure to move to a nearby channel (one not already in use) to continue the contact, rather than hog the calling channel. Of course, if you have a prearranged con-

QSL cards are fun to collect, brighten up the shack and are invaluable if you collect awards

tact, for example a club net, this can start on any pre-arranged channel though, again, courtesy demands that if that channel is already in use you should move elsewhere, probably to the first clear channel above or below. After all, as radio amateurs we all have equal rights to the frequencies covered by our licences, so no-one has precedence and the usual rule is that the first users to arrive on a channel have use of it for as long as they need it.

Repeater operation is slightly different. In any given part of the country, there may only be one or two repeaters accessible. Each has a single channel (they actually use two frequencies, one for input, a second for output, but your transceiver should take care of this automatically, along with generating any access tone required at the beginning of each transmission). A single channel means that all repeater users need to make suitable allowances for each other. If the station you make contact with through the repeater turns out to be within range of a direct contact, once again take the approach of moving to a clear simplex (non-repeater) frequency. If not, by all means continue to use the repeater as long as no one else wishes to. But allow pauses between your transmissions in case someone else is trying to access it, maybe a mobile station trying to get hold of a friend. Incidentally, repeaters were first set up essentially for the purpose of enabling mobile operators to make longer-distance contacts, and mobile stations should always be accorded priority. Within reason, several stations can use a repeater simultaneously, always keeping transmissions short and allowing everyone to have their turn. This doesn't have to be a formal net operation as described in previous sections, provided common sense prevails.

Non-channelised operation

THOSE PARTS OF the VHF/UHF bands used for DX working, and most of the HF amateur spectrum, are treated as continuous spectrum rather than channels. For anyone who has become used to channelised operation, this can be daunting at first. Except in specific instances (for example particular interest groups like Islands on the Air (IOTA) or Slow Scan Television (SSTV)), there are no recognised calling channels. Standard procedure is to find someone who is calling CQ and to answer him, or to find a frequency that isn't in use and call CQ yourself. The constantly changing nature of HF propagation also means that a frequency that is clear when you start a contact may not be clear a few minutes later, so you must be prepared to make allowances for this, maybe even to move frequency if there is too much mutual interference. It is this very unpredictability of HF propagation which makes it interesting to so many amateurs as, even with the best propagation-prediction tools, you can never be sure just where you may be speaking to next. It is also that unpredictability which means that you have to be prepared to be flexible as propagation changes. Of course, it is that same unpredictability which has driven commercial and broadcast users increasingly to other means such as satellite, as they need to be able to plan their schedules well ahead of time and with a high degree of confidence.

To QSL or not to QSL

IN THIS INTRODUCTORY discussion, a word about QSLing seems worthwhile. From the earliest days of the hobby it has been common to exchange QSL cards, some sort of written confirmation of the contact that has taken place. Indeed, a typical 1930s QSL card would be perfectly recognisable today, though improvements in printing technology mean that many contemporary QSL cards are quite elaborate compared with their predecessors.

A QSL card serves several purposes. Firstly, it is an ongoing memento of a contact. This may seem rather unnecessary nowadays, as contacts are easy to come by and, if desired, it's actually quite easy to record your contacts for posterity (many logging programs offer this option, so that a digital recording of the QSO is permanently associated with the corresponding log entry). In the early years of amateur radio, of course, every contact was an achievement, and the QSL card was very much valued. The other purpose of exchanging QSL cards is to have some sort of proof of contact for claiming operating awards. This is also becoming less relevant with the advent of the ARRL's Logbook of the World, an electronic database of QSO information with an Internet-friendly front-end, which not only allows you to gain credits for the ARRL's DXCC Awards Programme but will, in due course, also be available to other organisations such as RSGB for their own awards programmes. However, at the time of writing, and almost certainly for the foreseeable future, QSL cards will remain a popular way of providing a permanent memento of contacts, not necessarily all contacts but certainly those which are worthy of commemoration, such as a special event station or a rare DX station.

Which begs the question, what should you do about QSLing? The subject is covered in more detail in Chapter 14. But it is one which often comes up in the course of a contact. Your QSO partner may ask you for a QSL to confirm the contact, perhaps because he needs your card for an award. This is the time to give a clear reply, indicating perhaps that you will send him one with your own next batch to the QSL bureau, that you will reply on receipt of his, or whatever is appropriate.

Technical and related considerations

THERE WILL BE MORE to say later in this manual with regard to station and antennas. However, it's worth mentioning a few areas that relate directly to what has been said so far.

Firstly, do remember that the nature of radio transmissions is that they can be heard by anyone within range, and they are therefore insecure. The good operator is aware of this and not only avoids bad operating practices, but actual-

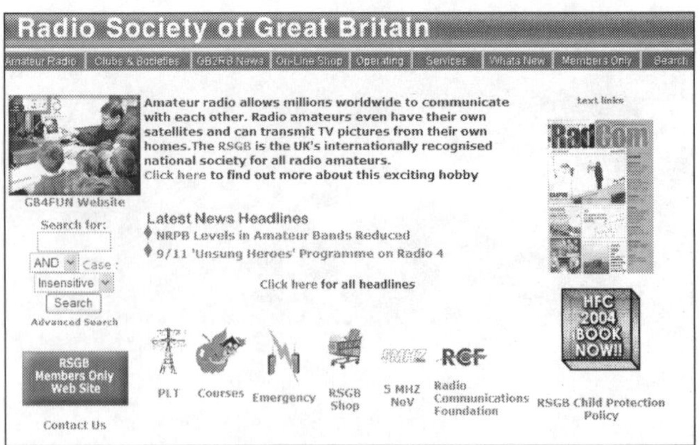

A mine of news and information: the RSGB's web site at www.rsgb.org

ly goes out of his way to operate well at all times. Not only does this avoid the censure of others, but serves as an example of how they themselves should operate.

Secondly, amateurs are encouraged at all times to use the minimum power appropriate for effective communications. This helps to reduce the potential for interference to other band users and, possibly, breakthrough to other electronic devices in the vicinity. Of course, it's almost impossible to determine what that level of power should be, especially on HF where signal strengths can vary enormously in the course of a single contact. But, equally, if you are engaged in a contact across town on 70cm, with huge signals at both ends, then it is quite clear that a reduction in power would be entirely appropriate. As always, experience and good sense help to decide the best power level to use at any given time.

Thirdly, be aware of the capabilities and limitations of your own equipment. For example, an older transceiver may drift significantly on switch-on, which can make it difficult to stay on a single frequency until thermal stability has been achieved. At the other extreme, many modern transceivers allow quite sophisticated tailoring of the transmitted waveform, which you can vary according to whether you want maximum 'punch' for DX working or best quality for local ragchewing. And, of course, even the best equipment can be abused, for example by excessive use of speech processing or by using break-in on CW with equipment that hasn't been specifically designed for the task. The moral is to get know your equipment and how it sounds on the air, perhaps by running tests with another local amateur. By not doing so, you run the risk of causing interference to other band users, of transmitting signals which are unintelligible and of causing problems for your neighbours. If problems do arise during your communications, always be prepared to reduce power or close down until they can be resolved.

Structure of this book

THIS CHAPTER HAS given a brief overview of amateur radio operations and the need for a structured approach to operating. The remainder of the book goes on to flesh out these considerations, starting with a more formal look at the amateur service. There follows some basic advice on setting up a station, including a chapter devoted to the use of PCs in the shack. This is followed by a comprehensive look at operating procedures, as they apply to the majority of amateur radio operations. However, each mode of operation has its special requirements, so these are covered in more detail in a separate chapter. There is a chapter describing each of the amateur bands, from Very Low Frequency through to the microwave region. This is followed by a general discussion of propagation modes, though it must be emphasized that a full treatment of propagation is well beyond the scope of this book. The purpose is to discuss propagation as to how it affects operating techniques, rather than to instil a detailed technical understanding. The book ends with chapters covering several relevant topics that don't sit conveniently elsewhere, such as QSLing and Operating Awards, and DXpedition and Special Event station operation. There is certainly no need to read the book in sequential order; it is intended more as a reference and refresher. There is a certain amount of overlap between sections. For example, the descriptions of the bands will make reference to modes commonly used and the chapter dealing with modes will refer to specific bands.

It is worth noting that, whereas in previous editions data communications have been treated separately from the historic modes of phone and CW operation, this *Manual* considers the majority of data modes to be mainstream nowadays, so all modes are treated equally. Also, although it is recognised that some amateurs will not have a PC as part of their station, by far the majority do. Much has changed in this respect since the previous edition of the *Operating Manual*, especially in the context of the Internet. This edition therefore puts much more emphasis on both PC and Internet.

The *RSGB Yearbook* has, over the years, become much more than a list of callsigns and addresses, and now includes a huge amount of data such as an international prefix list, UK repeaters, currently available satellites, IARU bandplans, beacon lists, etc. This data is updated annually. A decision has been made, therefore, to omit much of that data from this *Manual*, where it would be more likely to become out of date. Many of those tables and data sources are also available on the RSGB Web site [2]. The ARRL Operating Manual [3] is also an invaluable resource, though some sections are less relevant in the UK.

You should also ensure that you read and understand the operating instructions for your station equipment (transceiver, amplifier, etc.) and software (logging program, PSK31 or whatever). Each one is different, and it is impossible to give anything but generic advice in a manual of this kind.

Wherever possible in the following chapters, suggestions are given for further reading and, perhaps more importantly nowadays, useful web sites. Bear in mind though, that web sites come and go on a regular basis. If there is a specific topic that you want to follow up, it is always worth putting a query into one of the popular search engines (*Google*, *Ask Jeeves*, etc.) and see what you come up with. There is a vast amount of helpful information available.

References

[1] *RSGB Yearbook*, RSGB (published annually).

[2] RSGB: www.rsgb.org

[3] *ARRL Operating Manual*, ARRL

2 The Amateur Service and Your Licence

AMATEUR RADIO IS unusual as a hobby in that it is an officially recognised service, the Amateur Service, bound and protected by both national and international legislation. While it is possible to engage in two way radio communications without a licence, through the Family Radio Service, or via Citizens Band, which requires a licence but no examination, radio amateurs are required to demonstrate a minimum level of proficiency before they can apply for a licence. In return, they gain privileges which are unavailable to those other types of radio communications, in terms of the range of frequencies available for their use, the power levels they may use, the modes of operation allowed and the opportunity to use home-built equipment. The necessity of achieving a level of proficiency is twofold. Firstly, many amateur bands are shared with other services, and it is important that radio amateurs understand this and understand how to co-exist with those other services without causing problems to their users. Secondly, due to the power levels and wide variations in frequency allowable to radio amateurs, there is always a risk of electromagnetic incompatibility, in other words of breakthrough to other electronic devices in the neighbourhood, such as telephones or broadcast receivers, both radio and TV. Radio amateurs need to understand how to handle any such electromagnetic compatibility (EMC) issues which may arise.

The need for radio licensing to be covered not only by national but also by international legislation is self-evident, in that radio waves do not recognise national boundaries, and it is therefore crucial to harmonise the rules between countries. There are, of course, instances where certain wavebands, such as the 4m (70MHz) band, are only available in certain countries. Even in these cases, though, power levels and frequency limits will have been set by the national administration after consultation with foreign administrations which may be affected.

In terms of the international arena, amateur radio is governed, as are all radio services, by the International Telecommunication Union (ITU). Nationally, it is governed by a telecommunications administration, which in the UK is the Office of Communications (OFCOM). Within the hobby, there are bodies which match those official ones. All major countries have a national amateur radio society, and those societies work together through the International Amateur Radio Union (IARU).

The official bodies lay down regulations which must be followed by radio amateurs. These regulations govern both the issuing of an amateur licence and the rules which apply to that licence once in force. The amateur radio bodies lobby the official bodies as appropriate, to influence the rules and regulations which govern the hobby. They also agree voluntary codes of practice, band plans and other operating guidelines which, while not mandatory, help radio amateurs to coexist amicably.

This chapter gives the background to each of those bodies involved in governing and running amateur radio. It goes on to look at the mandatory rules and regulations as set out in the licence, and the voluntary codes recommended by the IARU through the national societies.

Article 25

(Definition of Amateur Service and Amateur-Satellite Service, currently in the process of being rewritten, so some of the following, including numbering, may be subject to change)

Section I – Amateur service

25.1 § 1 Radiocommunication between amateur stations of different countries shall be permitted unless the administration of one of the countries concerned has notified that it objects to such radiocommunications.

25.2 § 2 1) Transmissions between amateur stations of different countries shall be limited to communications incidental to the purposes of the amateur service, as defined in No. 1.56 and to remarks of a personal character.

25.2A 1A) Transmissions between amateur stations of different countries shall not be encoded for the purpose of obscuring their meaning, except for control signals exchanged between earth command stations and space stations in the amateur-satellite service.

25.3 2) Amateur stations may be used for transmitting international communications on behalf of third parties only in case of emergencies or disaster relief. An administration may determine the applicability of this provision to amateur stations under its jurisdiction.

25.5 § 3 1) Administrations shall determine whether or not a person seeking a licence to operate an amateur station shall demonstrate the ability to send and receive texts in Morse code signals.

25.6 2) Administrations shall verify the operational and technical qualifications of any person wishing to operate an amateur station. Guidance for standards of competence may be found in the most recent version of Recommendation ITU-R M.1544.

25.7 § 4 The maximum power of amateur stations shall be fixed by the administrations concerned.

25.8 § 5 1) All pertinent Articles and provisions of the Constitution, the Convention and of these Regulations shall apply to amateur stations.

25.9A § 5A Administrations are encouraged to take the necessary steps to allow amateur stations to prepare for and meet communication needs in support of disaster relief.

25.9B § 5B An administration may determine whether or not to permit a person who has been granted a licence to operate an amateur station by another administration to operate an amateur station while that person is temporarily in its territory, subject to such conditions or restrictions it may impose.

Section II – Amateur-satellite service

25.11 § 7 Administrations authorizing space stations in the amateur-satellite service shall ensure that sufficient earth command stations are established before launch to ensure that any harmful interference caused by emissions from a station in the amateur-satellite service can be terminated immediately (see No. 22.1).

International Telecommunication Union

THE ITU IS THE intergovernmental agency responsible for the coordination, standardisation and planning of world telecommunications. This United Nations organisation, founded in 1865, unites the telecommunication administrations of over 150 member countries. Its headquarters are located in Switzerland [1].

ITU regulations cover the activities of all telecommunication services, including amateur radio, and are published by the general secretariat of the ITU [2]. These regulations define international telecommunication law, and are therefore the cornerstone of amateur licence conditions in all countries.

From time to time, the ITU organises conferences attended by delegates from national administrations where aspects of the current regulations are reviewed to take into account developments in communications techniques. Major conferences used to be held every 20 years or so, and the last of this series took place in 1992 (the 1992 World Administrative Radio Conference). At this conference it was realised that such conferences in future were going to have to take place more frequently because technology was changing so rapidly and more countries were requiring access to sections of the spectrum. It was also realised that they would have to be more specialised, either in subject or range of frequencies under consideration. It was therefore decided to hold conferences every two years in future.

It is important that amateurs understand the basis of the service that they use.

Definitions

WITHIN THE ITU Radio Regulations the Amateur Service is defined as:

A radiocommunication service for the purpose of self training, intercommunication and technical investigations carried out by amateurs, that is, by duly authorised persons interested in radio technique solely with a personal aim and without pecuniary interest.

It should be noted that the ITU considers amateur satellite activities as a separate Amateur Satellite Service defined as:

A radiocommunication service using space stations on earth satellites for the same purposes as those of the Amateur Service.

The section of the regulations dealing specifically with amateur radio is Article 25, and this is shown in the panel on the previous page. It should be noted that, at the time of writing, Article 25 was still subject to minor changes.

This Indonesian IOTA expedition used a special prefix to create even more interest. Special prefixes are ones not normally used by amateur stations, but they must still conform with ITU regulations.

Callsigns

IT IS A REQUIREMENT of the regulations that all radio amateurs identify themselves by transmitting an identification code, known as the callsign, at short intervals during their transmissions.

The initial characters of the callsign denote the country to which the amateur station belongs and is operating from. The ITU allocates the telecommunication administration of each country blocks of letters and numbers in order to form callsigns, not just for amateur stations but for all radio stations in that country. The ITU allocation blocks are of three types:

(a letter-letter-letter, eg LAA-LNZ;

(b) digit-letter-letter, eg 2AA-2ZZ; and

(c) letter-digit-letter, eg H4A-H4Z.

Amateur callsigns are normally made up of the first two characters from the allocation, followed by a single digit and then a group of not more than three letters. However, if a country has the whole of a letter-letter-letter block, eg WAA-WZZ, then it is also entitled to form callsigns consisting of the first letter in front of the digit (in this case W).

For example, the UK has been allocated GAA-GZZ, MAA-MZZ and 2AA-2ZZ. This means that UK amateur callsigns can have GA, GB, GC etc as the first two characters. (As the UK has the whole GAA-GZZ block, it is also entitled to use the single letter G.) Similarly, it can form callsigns starting with MA, MB, MC etc and 2A, 2B, 2C etc.

The first two characters of the allocation are usually unique to a country but the ITU occasionally allocates 'half-series': eg 3DA-3DM to Swaziland and 3DN-3DZ to Fiji. In practice, Swaziland amateur radio callsigns commence with 3DA and Fiji amateur radio callsigns with 3D2.

Certain limitations are imposed by the ITU to ensure that callsigns issued cannot be confused with internationally agreed distress signals such as SOS (eg G4SOS was not issued) or the international Q code (QAA-QZZ was not allocated by the ITU and, for example, G4QAA was not issued in the UK).

Further information on the allocation of callsigns is given in the later section dealing with the work of the national telecommunications administration.

Designation of emissions

THERE ARE VERY MANY ways in which a radio signal can be modulated so as to convey information. In order to define the types of emission a code has been internationally agreed and implemented by the ITU.

The code is in two parts, the first specifying the necessary bandwidth and the second the classification of emission.

The necessary bandwidth is specified as follows: between 0.001 and 999Hz in Hertz (H); between 10 and 999kHz in kilohertz (K); between 1.00 and 999MHz in megahertz (M); between 100 and 999GHz in gigahertz (G). For example, 400Hz would be '400H', 2.4kHz as '2K40' and 12.5kHz as '12K5'.

The classification is specified by three symbols. The first denotes the type of modulation of the main carrier, the second the nature of the modulating signal(s) and the third the

Table 2.1: Classification of emissions

FIRST SYMBOL: Type of modulation of main carrier

1. Emission of unmodulated carrier: N.
2. Emission in which the main carrier is amplitude modulated including cases where subcarriers are angle modulated. Double sideband: A. Single sideband, full carrier: H. Single sideband, reduced or variable carrier: R. Single sideband, suppressed carrier: J. Independent sideband: B. Vestigial sideband: C.
3. Emission in which the main carrier is angle modulated. Frequency modulation: F. Phase modulation: G.
4. Emission in which the main carrier is amplitude or angle modulated either simultaneously or in a prearranged sequence: D.
5. Emission of pulses. Unmodulated sequence of pulses: P. A sequence of pulses (a) modulated in amplitude: K, (b) modulated in width/duration: L, (c) modulated in position/phase: M, (d) in which the carrier is angle modulated during the period of the pulse: Q, (e) which is a combination of the foregoing or is produced by other means: V.
6. Cases not covered above, in which an emission consists of the main carrier modulated, either simultaneously or in a preestablished sequence, in a combination of two or more of the following modes amplitude, angle, pulse: W.
7. Cases not otherwise covered: X.

Note: Emissions where the main carrier is directly modulated by a signal which has been coded into quantised form (e.g. pulse code modulation) should be designated by A, H, R, J, B, C, F, or G as appropriate.

SECOND SYMBOL: Nature of signal(s) modulating main carrier

1. No modulating signal: 0.
2. A single channel containing quantised or digital information without the use of a modulating subcarrier (excluding timedivision multiplex): 1.
3. A single channel containing quantised or digital information with the use of a modulating subcarrier (excluding timedivision multiplex): 2.
4. A single channel containing analogue information: 3.
5. Two or more channels containing quantised or digital information: 7.
6. Two or more channels containing analogue information: 8.
7. Composite system with one or more channels containing quantised or digital information, together with one or more channels containing analogue information: 9.
8. Cases not otherwise covered: X.

THIRD SYMBOL Type of information to be transmitted

1. No information transmitted: N.
2. Telegraphy for aural reception: A
3. Telegraphy for automatic reception: B.
4. Facsimile: C.
5. Data transmission, telemetry, telecommand: D.
6. Telephony (including sound broadcasting): E.
7. Television (video): F.
8. Combination of the above: W.
9. Cases not otherwise covered: X.

Note: In this context the word 'information' does not include information of a constant, unvarying nature such as provided by standard frequency emissions, continuous wave and pulse radars etc.

EXAMPLES OF THE USE OF EMISSION CODES

Telephony (speech)	
Single sideband, suppressed carrier (SSB)	J3E
Frequency modulation (FM)	F3E
Phase modulation (PM)	G3E
Amplitude modulation (AM)	A3E
Morse code	
Hand sent, on/off keying of carrier	A1A
Hand sent, on/off keying of the audio tone (FM transmitter)	F2A
RTTY/AmTOR/PSK	
Direct frequency shift keying of carrier	F1B
Frequency shift keyed audio tone (FM transmitter)	F2B
Frequency shift keyed audio tone (SSB transmitter)	J2B
Packet/Data	
Direct frequency shift keying of carrier	F1D
Frequency shift keyed audio tone (FM transmitter)	F2D
Frequency shift keyed audio tone (SSB transmitter)	J2D
Television	
Vestigial sideband (AM transmitter)	C3F
Slow scan TV (SSB transmitter)	J2F
Facsimile	
Frequency shift keyed audio tone (SSB transmitter)	J2C

type of information to be transmitted. **Table 2.1** gives the symbols and their meanings. Some examples relevant to amateur radio are also shown.

Note that for the purposes of the UK licence, modulation used only for short periods and for incidental purposes, such as identification or calling, may be ignored when calculating the emission designator. Double sideband emissions with reduced or suppressed carrier are included in the first character A.

Frequency allocations

ONE OF THE MOST important tasks of the ITU is to allocate parts of the radio spectrum to various radio services in such a way that the spectrum is used as efficiently as possible without mutual interference. The claims on the available frequency space are many and are continually changing.

The range of frequencies covered by the present ITU regulations is 9kHz-400GHz. For the allocation of these frequencies, and for various administrative reasons, the world has been divided into three regions (see **Fig 2.1** overleaf).

Region 1 comprises Europe and Africa, and including Mongolia, Turkey and the whole of the CIS. Region 2 comprises North and South America, while Region 3 comprises Asia, Australasia and Oceania.

The more formal ITU definitions of these areas are given in Fig 2.1. Note that these three ITU regions should not be confused with the ITU broadcasting zones, which are used for scoring purposes in some amateur radio contests.

Sometimes the ITU finds it necessary to allocate part of the radio spectrum to two or more radio services. Where this is done it is always specified which if any of the services has priority over the others, by placing the service in one of three categories: primary, permitted or secondary.

Permitted and primary services have equal status except that in the preparation of ITU frequency plans the primary service has prior choice of frequencies.

Services allocated a band on a secondary basis must not cause harmful interference to stations within that allocation having primary or permitted status, and cannot claim protection from harmful interference caused by the latter. They can, however, claim protection from interference generated by stations in the same service or other secondary services.

What this means is that primary and permitted services have the 'right of way' over secondary services. When operating in a shared allocation in which the Amateur Service is

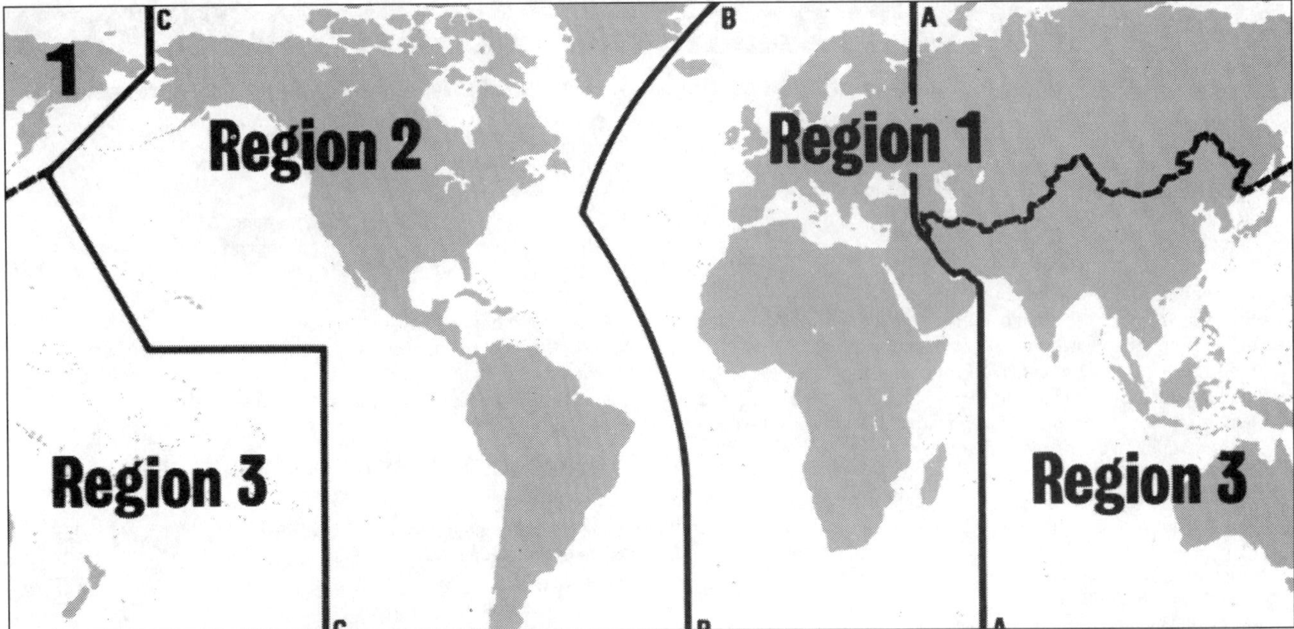

Fig 2.1: The three ITU regions. Region 1 includes the area limited on the east by line A (lines A, B and C are defined below) and on the west by line B, excluding any of the territory of Iran which lies between these limits. It also includes that part of the territory of Turkey and the former USSR lying outside of these limits, the territory of the Mongolian People's Republic, and the area to the north of the former USSR which lies between lines A and C.
Region 2 includes the area limited on the east by line B and on the west by line C.
Region 3 includes the area limited on the east by line C and on the west by line A, except the territories of the Mongolian People's Republic, Turkey, the former USSR, and the area to the north of the former USSR. It also includes that part of the territory of Iran lying outside of those limits. Lines A, B and C are defined as follows:
Line A extends from the North Pole along meridian 40°E to parallel 40°N, thence by great-circle arc to the intersection of meridian 60°E and the Tropic of Cancer; thence along the meridian 60°E to the South Pole.
Line B extends from the North Pole along meridian 10°W to its intersection with parallel 72°N, thence by great-circle arc to the intersection of meridian 20°W and parallel 10°S; thence along meridian 20°W to the South Pole.
Line C extends from the North Pole by great-circle arc to the intersection of parallel 65° 30'N with the international boundary in Behring Strait, thence by great-circle arc to the intersection of meridian 165°E and parallel 50°N; thence by great-circle arc to the intersection of meridian 170°W and parallel 10°N, thence along parallel 10°N to its intersection with meridian 120°W; thence along meridian 120°W to the South Pole

a secondary service, the amateur operator must take care not to cause interference to primary users. If these start transmitting on the same frequency, even while an amateur contact is already in progress, the amateurs must change frequency and leave the channel clear.

The *RSGB Yearbook* [4] shows all amateur allocations between 9kHz and 275GHz in the three ITU regions, the status of these allocations and the nature of services (if any) sharing the allocations. The information is shown in generalised form, and may not apply to particular countries within each ITU region. Major variations from these allocations are however mentioned in Chapter 5 in this book, on a band-by-band basis.

National telecommunication administration

THIS IS THE government department in each country which has the responsibility of controlling all its telecommunication services and the issue of licences. This same body usually represents that government at the ITU conferences.

In the UK this function is undertaken by OFCOM, the newly-formed Office of Communications.

Although based on the ITU regulations, the amateur licence conditions for each country can be quite different: some countries do not allow amateur radio at all, while in others its operation is restricted.

The national telecommunication administration assigns callsigns to individual amateur stations using its ITU-allocated character blocks as previously noted. It may choose to use these to denote the geographical area or licence category of the station. Similarly the single digit following the ITU characters is sometimes used to denote licence category or geographical area, while in other cases it has no particular significance and may be regarded as part of the serial letter group.

The serial letters following the single digit (the callsign suffix) are the part of the callsign which identifies individual stations. In a few countries the first or last letter of this group indicates geographical area or licence category. The serial letters are usually assigned in strict alphabetical order, but in some countries it is possible to request specific letter combinations, for example to correspond with the licensee's initials. A recent ITU agreement makes provision for callsign suffixes of up to four letters.

The part of the callsign which precedes the serial letters is known as the prefix. If the single digit is simply part of the serial allocation it is not included in the prefix, though it is customary in

amateur usage not to split two consecutive figures, eg C31 (not C3, which is more correct) is often given as the Andorran prefix.

Sometimes the administration will temporarily allocate special callsign prefixes outside its normal series to stations commemorating some national event or celebration, and this results in some strange callsigns being heard on the air from time to time which may be difficult to identify. The important thing to note is that any prefix so used must conform to the ITU block allocation(s) for the country concerned, and the list of these in the *RSGB Yearbook* or the *RSGB Prefix Guide* should be consulted in cases of doubt.

It is also possible for a callsign to have a suffix, which is always separated from the rest of the callsign by a solidus or 'forward slash' (/), usually spoken as "stroke". A suffix usually indicates temporary operation away from the registered address of the station. In the UK, for example, '/M' denotes a mobile station and '/P' a temporary location. Another use for a suffix is to denote a licence issued to a foreign amateur (see below).

Operation abroad

MOST COUNTRIES ALLOW foreign amateurs to operate within their boundaries, but the conditions are set by the national administration and vary widely. In some cases, the administration acts unilaterally and permits amateurs from certain countries to apply for licences while in others there must exist a formal reciprocal agreement with the amateur's country.

A welcome development is the increasing number of countries worldwide which permit temporary operation (generally taken to be one to two months at the most) according to Recommendation T/R6101 of the European Conference of Postal and Telecommunication Administrations (CEPT), which is a group of national telecommunication administrations from over 40 European countries. Once an administration has confirmed that its amateur radio licence conforms to the CEPT minimum standard, its amateurs may operate within the other participating countries with the minimum of formality. However, it should be noted that T/R61-01 applies only to Full UK licence holders, not to Foundation and Intermediate licensees. The text of the Recommendation is shown in the panel overleaf. It should be noted that not all member administrations have implemented this Recommendation but the list is growing all the time [5]. In addition, some non-CEPT countries such as Canada, Israel, New Zealand, Peru and the USA are prepared to authorise operation on similar lines.

Note the CEPT Radio Amateur Licence has been incorporated into the UK licence, and is not a separate document.

The temporary callsigns issued to foreign amateurs vary. Usually the foreign country prefix is added before the amateur's own call (but sometimes after it in non-CEPT countries) and separated by a solidus (/). For example, G3XTT may become OE/G3XTT in Austria but G3XTT/VP9 in Bermuda. In some smaller countries, or in other cases for extended operating periods, a separate callsign may be issued.

Several changes were made to the text of T/R 61-01 following WRC 2003. These include:

- The deletion of the Morse code requirement for access to frequencies below 30MHz,
- The merging of the old CEPT Class A and B licences into a single class, the "CEPT radio amateur licence",
- Removal of an ambiguity concerning portable and mobile operation,
- Freedom to use any amateur station in the country visited, not just the visitor's 'own' station.

The addition of a prefix converts this British callsign into a Bermudan one.

In practice a visitor now has to:

- Check that his national licence class does qualify for a CEPT Licence and that his national licence document confirms this. If not, confirmation that the licence held is equivalent to the CEPT licence is needed from his national licence authority.
- Check what national licence class in the country to be visited is equivalent to the CEPT Licence.
- Check what are the operating privileges and regulations covering the use of that national licence class in the country to be visited.
- Use the appropriate prefix which has to be appended to his own national callsign.

The key point is that the operating privileges for the visitor operating under the CEPT Licence are defined by the *country being visited*, not the privileges in his own country.

The following should be noted:

1. Not all of the countries who implemented the previous versions of T/R 61-01 have implemented the revised and current version. In such cases it is reasonable to assume that the requirement for Morse code for operation below 30MHz and any other restrictions still stand.
2. Not all members of CEPT have implemented any version of T/R 61-01.
3. Any country can add extra conditions to T/R 61-01. These conditions will be shown as footnotes in T/R 61-01 Appendix II.
4. The situation will change over time as countries update their internal legislation following WRC2003. The definitive website is that of the European Radiocommunications Office (ERO) [8].
5. Please also note that special conditions often apply to overseas territories such as those of France. Local permission will often be required in such locations.

Recommendation T/R 61-01 (Nice 1985, Paris 1992, August 1992, Nicosia 2003)
CEPT RADIO AMATEUR LICENCE

Recommendation proposed by the "Radio Regulatory" Working Group (RR). Text of the Recommendation adopted by the "Electronic Communications Committee" (ECC):

INTRODUCTION

The Recommendation as approved in 1985 makes it possible for radio amateurs from CEPT countries to operate during short visits in other CEPT countries without obtaining an individual temporary licence from the visited CEPT country. Good experience with this system is gained.

The Recommendation as revised in 1992 has the aim to make it possible for non-CEPT countries to participate in this licensing system. The appropriate provisions for this are found mainly in the new Appendices III and IV. The original Recommendation had to be adapted slightly, but it retains the same applicability within CEPT as before.

The Recommendation as revised in 2003 reflects the outcome of WRC-03 concerning Article 25 of the ITU Radio Regulations. The mandatory Morse code requirement has been removed and the number of amateur classes has been reduced from two to one.

"The European Conference of Postal and Telecommunications Administrations,

considering

a) that the Amateur Service and Amateur Satellite Service are Radiocommunications Services according to Article 1 of the ITU Radio Regulations and governed by other provisions of the ITU Radio Regulations as well as national regulations,

b) that it is necessary to harmonise licensing procedures for temporary use of radio amateur stations in CEPT countries and non-CEPT countries,

c) that Administrations are responsible, in accordance with Article 25 of the ITU Radio Regulations to verify the operational and technical qualifications of any person wishing to operate an amateur station.

d) that in accordance with Article 25 of the ITU Radio Regulations (rev WRC-03), administrations shall determine whether or not a person seeking a licence to operate an amateur station shall demonstrate the ability to send and receive texts in Morse code signals;

e) that the ability to send and receive texts in Morse code signals is not required for the purpose of this Recommendation;

f) that the issue and administration of temporary licences to foreign visitors based on bilateral agreements involves a considerable increase in work for Administrations,

g) that the International Amateur Radio Union (IARU) supports the simplification of procedures to obtain temporary operational privileges for foreign visitors in CEPT countries and in other countries,

noting that

this Recommendation bears no relation to the import and export of amateur radio equipment, which is subject only to relevant customs regulations,

noting further that

despite the procedures of this Recommendation, Administrations always have the right to require separate bilateral agreements when recognising the radio amateur licences issued by foreign Administrations,

recommends

1) that CEPT member Administrations recognise the principle of the CEPT radio amateur licence issued under the conditions specified in Appendices I and II, on which the Administrations of the countries visited will not levy administrative charges or spectrum fees.

2) that Administrations, not being members of CEPT, accepting the provisions of this Recommendation, may apply for participation in accordance with the conditions laid down in Appendices III and IV".

Please check the ERO web site (http//:www.ERO.dk) for the up to date position on the implementation of this and other ECC and ERC Recommendations

Appendix I

GENERAL CONDITIONS FOR THE ISSUE OF THE "CEPT RADIO AMATEUR LICENCE"

1. GENERAL PROVISIONS RELATING TO "CEPT RADIO AMATEUR LICENCE"

The "CEPT radio amateur licence" can be included in the national licence or be a special document issued by the same authority, and will be drafted in the national language and in German, English and French; it will be valid for non-residents only, for the duration of their temporary stays in countries having adopted the Recommendation, and within the limit of validity of the national licence. Radio amateurs holding a temporary licence issued in a foreign country may not benefit from the provisions of the Recommendation.

The minimum requirements for a "CEPT radio amateur licence" will be:

i) indication that the document is a CEPT amateur licence;
ii) a declaration according to which the holder is authorised to utilise an amateur radio station in accordance with this Recommendation in countries where the latter applies;
iii) the name and address of the holder;
iv) the call sign;
v) the validity;
vi) the issuing authority.

A list may be added or provided indicating the Administrations applying the Recommendation.

The CEPT Licence permits utilisation of all frequency bands allocated to the Amateur Service and Amateur Satellite Service and authorised in the country where the amateur station is to be operated.

2. CONDITIONS OF UTILISATION

2.1 On request the licence holder shall present his CEPT radio amateur licence to the appropriate authorities in the country visited.

2.2 The licence holder shall observe the provisions of the ITU Radio Regulations, this Recommendation and the regulations in force in the country visited. Furthermore, any restrictions concerning national and local conditions of a technical nature or regarding the public authorities must be respected. Special attention should be paid to the difference in frequency allocations to the radio amateur services in the three ITU Regions.

2.3 When transmitting in the visited country the licence holder must use his national call sign preceded by the call sign prefix of the visited country as indicated in Appendices II and IV. The call sign prefix and the national call sign must be separated by the character "/" (telegraphy) or the word "stroke" (telephony).

2.4 The licence holder cannot request protection against harmful interference.

3. EQUIVALENCE BETWEEN THE CEPT LICENCE AND NATIONAL LICENCES

3.1 The equivalence between the CEPT licence and national licences in CEPT countries is given in Appendix II.

3.2 The equivalence between the CEPT licence and national licences in non-CEPT countries is given in Appendix IV.

6. T/R 61-01 bears no relation to the import and export of amateur radio equipment, which is subject only to relevant customs regulations.

For the radio amateur who is moving permanently to another country use can sometimes be made of another CEPT document namely T/R 61-02. This covers the Harmonised Amateur Radio Examination Certificate or HAREC for short.

The HAREC is recognised by countries who are signatories to T/R 61-02 and provides automatic exemption from

Promoting amateur radio: the IARU stand at an ITU Conference

national amateur radio examinations relevant to some of the licence classes in the country to which you are moving. The ERO website is the place to look for more information but OFCOM issues the HAREC. For some countries you may also need to show you have passed a Morse test. This can be organised through the RSGB if necessary. For other countries the possession of a UK licence is enough for a local licence to be granted. It is worth noting in passing that you may need to show that you have made a bona fide move to a country in order to be issued with a local call.

The most useful website for licensing information is that of OH2MCN [6]. Further information on operating abroad is given in Chapter 11.

International Amateur Radio Union

THE AMATEUR SERVICE and Amateur Satellite Service have their own international organisation, the International Amateur Radio Union (IARU) [3,7] which has the specific objective of promoting, protecting and advancing these services within the framework of regulations established by the International Telecommunication Union. It also provides support to member societies in the pursuit of these objectives at the national level, with special reference to the following:

(a) representation of the interests of amateur radio at and between conferences and meetings of international telecommunications organisations;

(b) encouragement of agreements between national amateur radio societies on matters of common interest:

(c) enhancement of amateur radio as a means of technical self training for young people;

(d) promotion of technical and scientific investigations in the field of radio communication;

(e) promotion of amateur radio as a means of providing relief in the event of natural disasters;

(f) encouragement of international goodwill and friendship;

(g) support of member societies in developing amateur radio as a valuable national resource, particularly in developing countries; and

(h) development of amateur radio in those countries not represented by member societies.

The officers of IARU Region 1 (l to r): Andreas Thiemann, HB9JOE (Treasurer); Ole Garpestad, LA2RR (Chairman); Tafa Diop, 6W1KJ (Vice-Chairman); Don Beattie, G3BJ (Secretary)

The IARU was founded in 1925 and its International Secretariat is located at ARRL HQ in Newington, Connecticut, USA; it has separate organisations in each of the three ITU regions.

Membership is restricted to national societies just as the members of the ITU are national administrations, not radio services or individuals. There are nearly 150 national societies which are members of the IARU. The largest region is Region 1 which contains more than 80 societies located in Europe, Africa, the Middle East and the Commonwealth of Independent States.

In a similar way to that in which the ITU regulates and coordinates frequency allocations as a whole, the IARU regulates and coordinates amateur activities within individual amateur bands. This is on a voluntary basis within the UK but mandatory in some other countries. Whether mandatory or voluntary, they should always be obeyed because they have resulted from long debate and discussion within the world's national amateur radio societies. Band plans are discussed in Chapter 5, and the UK plans are detailed in the *RSGB Yearbook* [4].

The IARU operates several specialist Working Groups (WGs), to help in achieving its overall mission. These include the EMC WG, the Eurocom WG (to monitor, advise, influence and interact with those parts of the European Commission who have authority in areas of interest to radio amateurs), HF and VHF Working Groups, the ARDF WG (to encourage participation in Amateur Radio Direction Finding activities) and STARS (Support for The Amateur Radio Service, which provides help to amateur radio in developing countries).

Another valuable service, the IARU Monitoring System (IARUMS), monitors unauthorised transmissions by other services within amateur allocations. Volunteers located throughout the world record the characteristics of the signal and if possible identify the country of origin. These reports are collected and collated, and the administrations notified that they are causing problems. This can be very effective. More details of the RSGB Intruder Watch, which forms part of the IARU Monitoring System, are given in the *RSGB Yearbook* [4].

National society

THE FOURTH ARBITER of operating standards and practice is the national society of the country concerned. In the UK this is the Radio Society of Great Britain (RSGB). Recommendations may come from the specialist committees within each society whose recommendations are considered and debated at IARU regional conferences. Within the UK these areas are represented by the RSGB Spectrum Forum, which replaces the previous Microwave Committee, VHF Committee and HF Committee.

The Amateur Radio Observation Service is an advisory and reporting service of the RSGB which is intended to assist radio amateurs and others who may be affected by problems which occur within the amateur bands or which develop on other frequencies as a result of amateur transmissions. The Service investigates reports of licence infringements, or instances of poor operating practice which might bring the Amateur Service into disrepute. After investigation and where there is evidence of deliberate malpractice or malicious abuse of Amateur Radio facilities, a formal report may be made to the appropriate authorities. This report will contain sufficient detail and evidence to enable further investigations to be made and the authorities may take such action as is appropriate. However, AROS prefers to settle problems - great or small - within the Amateur Service. Problems arising are referred to the authorities as a last resort. For more details, see the *RSGB Yearbook* [4].

Your amateur licence

AMATEUR LICENCES VARY considerably from country to country. For example, in the USA band plans are a mandatory aspect of the licence whereas in many other countries nothing is said within the licence about how amateurs should divide up the bands which are allocated to them. This section looks specifically at the UK amateur licence, and any overseas readers are recommended to check the differences between this and their own licence.

The main provisions of the UK amateur licence are set out in *BR68*, an OFCOM document. There are essentially three versions of *BR68*, relating to the three classes of licence, Foundation, Intermediate and Full. These may from time to time be amended by a Notice of Variation (NoV). If you are recently licensed, you may well be familiar with the terms and conditions of *BR68*, but those of us who have been licensed for many years may not have read it closely of late, just as many drivers pay little heed to the Highway Code once they have safely passed their driving test. However, the terms of *BR68* have changed quite significantly over time, so it is worth going through the major sections in some detail. You might like to have your copy to hand while reading through the following sections (the headings reflect those in *BR68*). The references are to the paragraph number in the current *BR68* (Full Licence), the 2002 edition revised by an NoV dated September 2003.

Purpose

The amateur licence starts (para 1(1-3)) by setting out the purpose of the hobby. This is defined as being self-training, including technical investigations, and this is the major justification for radio amateurs maintaining their extensive frequency allocations. The following sub-paragraphs expand on this by discussing the use of amateur radio in support of User Services. These are defined elsewhere in the document, but include bodies such as the Red Cross, local Emergency Planning Officers, Police, Fire and Ambulance. Radio amateurs are also authorised to help in international disaster communications, but only on certain designated wavebands. The clear message is that amateur radio is considered a public service, and is encouraged to stand up and be counted when there is a specific community need.

Messages

The next section (para 1(4-9)) deals with the sort of communications which may be exchanged via amateur radio. Most of this section is self-explanatory. Obviously it reflects the modes commonly in use by radio amateurs, though the specific mention of RTTY and AMTOR suggests that the licence was drafted before the advent of the wide range of other data modes that are appearing, almost by the day. The use of abbreviations and recognised codes is also permitted, recognising that amateurs make wide use of both, to overcome language barriers and to save transmission time (especially on Morse). However, codes intended to hide the meaning of the communication (in other words, any form of encryption) are not allowed. There is nothing, incidentally, to

www.radio.gov.uk

Amateur Radio Licence (A) or (B)
Terms, Provisions and Limitations Booklet BR68

These terms, provisions and limitations shall be read as an integral part of the Amateur Radio Licence (A) or (B).

Conditions of use

Purpose

1(1) The Licensee shall use the Station for the purpose of self-training in communication by radio telecommunications, which use (without limiting the generality of the foregoing) includes technical investigations.

1(2) The Licensee may use or permit the use of the Station, as part of his self-training in communication by radio telecommunications, during any operation conducted by a User Service [defined in sub-clause 12(1) (o)] or during any exercise relating to such an operation for the purpose of sending Messages on behalf of the User Service to other licensed amateur stations. It is recommended that the Licensee follows a formal emergency communications training scheme, details of which are available from the Radiocommunications Agency.

1(2A) The Licensee may use or permit the use of the Station, as part of his self-training in communication by radio, during any community event where the Licensee has been requested in writing by a User Service [defined in sub-clause 12(1) (o)] to provide communication without pecuniary gain for the purpose of sending Messages relating to the event to other licensed amateur stations.

1(3) Notwithstanding sub-clauses 1(1) and 1(4) (a) of this Licence and subject to the limitations in paragraphs 2, 3, 4, 5, 6 and 8 of Resolution 640 of the Radio Regulations of the International Telecommunication Union, the Licensee may use the following frequency bands to meet the needs of international disaster communications: 3.5 MHz to 3.8 MHz, 7.0 MHz to 7.1 MHz, 10.10 MHz to 10.15 MHz, 14.00 MHz to 14.35 MHz, 18.068 MHz to 18.168 MHz, 21.00 MHz to 21.45 MHz, 24.89 MHz to 24.99 MHz and 144 MHz to 146 MHz.

Messages

1(4) The Licensee shall address Messages only to other licensed amateurs or the stations of licensed amateurs and shall send only:

(a) Messages relating to technical investigations or remarks of a personal character; or

(b) Signals (not enciphered) which form part of, or relate to, the transmission of Messages.

FOL 781

The Radiocommunications Agency is an Executive Agency of the Department of Trade and Industry
The Agency General Enquiry Point/Switchboard telephone number: 020 7211 0211

BR68 (Rev 11) JANUARY 2002

prevent you holding contacts in languages other than your own. This section also makes it clear that amateur radio is about communication with specific other stations, and is not intended as a broadcast medium. As you would expect, there is a sub-paragraph dealing with transmitting speeches or music. And there is a section detailing the terms under which greetings messages may be sent. This is important, as these are the only types of messages which may be passed by non-licensed persons, and organisers of special event stations in particular should be very familiar with the provisions of this section. In some countries the rules on carrying traffic of this sort are very different. For example, in the USA phone-patch has been legal for many, many years, whereby radio amateurs are allowed to connect a phone line to their transceiver and handle telephone traffic originating from and intended for non-licensed members of the public. However, in the UK this is definitely not the case. Perhaps the most important recent innovation, though, is the provision for non-licensed persons to operate an amateur radio station when undergoing a formal training course to become an amateur. Given that radio operating, like driving or flying, is not something you can actually learn from a book, this is very much to be welcomed.

Location

Para 1(10-12) specifies where your station may be set up. You will see that you may operate from a number of locations in addition to your home. However, and this is covered later in *BR68*, you may need to change your callsign. For example, from a so-called temporary location you should add the suffix /P, when mobile /M and when Maritime Mobile /MM. From other parts of the British Isles you should also change your prefix. So G3XTT, operating from a temporary location in Jersey, would become GJ3XTT/P. To avoid the necessity of signing /P, it is necessary to notify the local branch of OFCOM in advance of the dates and location of your temporary operation. This can be done by e-mail, so is not an onerous requirement.

Portable operation by the South Birmingham Radio Society

Standard Frequency Service

The next section (para 1(13)) of *BR68* specifically authorises licensed amateurs to receive transmissions in the Standard Frequency Service which may seem an unnecessary level of permission, but it should be borne in mind that the reception of radio transmissions is not an automatic right and, strictly speaking, unauthorised listeners are not permitted to listen in to many commercial transmissions that take place throughout the radio spectrum.

Limitations on use

The section headed Limitations on Use (para 2(1-7)) is quite extensive. The first paragraph reiterates the obvious point that amateurs are only allowed to operate within the frequency bands, power limits and types of transmission specified in their licence. It might be worth pointing out that, in some instances, these and other limitations within the licence may be overcome through a Notice of Variation (NoV), for example to be able to use higher power in pursuit of specific technical investigations such as moonbounce. Another example might be remote control of a transceiver over a telephone line or Internet link. However, these NoVs are issued on an individual basis, and only if a convincing case can be made to OFCOM both for the need to operate outside the normal restrictions of the licence and also of the way in which the additional privileges will be managed. In the case of a high power permit, for example, are there likely to be any incompatibilities with nearby electronic devices?

Unattended operation

Section 2(4) deals specifically with Unattended Operation. There was a time when all unattended operation required an NoV (see above), but this is no longer the case, and certain types of unattended operation are permitted as a matter of course. These operations are mainly confined to the VHF and UHF bands, and are intended to allow such services as beacon transmitters and low power control devices. Mailbox operations, however, are not covered (see "Recorded or retransmitted messages", below) and require an NoV. It should be noted that, even where unattended operations are allowed, there are geographical restrictions in a number of cases, principally within frequency bands which are shared in certain parts of the country with other users. Anyone intending to operate any sort of unattended transmitter should study this section of BR68 with care.

Operators

There follows a significant section (para 2(8-11)) on who may operate an amateur radio station. In essence, this allows not only the licensee, but other authorised users under his direct supervision, to operate the station. These authorised users include not only holders of an amateur radio licence, but also holders of an amateur radio examination certificate who have yet to be issued a licence of their own. It is up to the licensee, however, to assure himself that the person(s) concerned is suitably qualified and not subsequently disqualified, for example by having had his licence revoked.

It is also worth noting that the licence applies to the licensee and not to the station. This is different to the situation that exists in some countries where a different distinction is drawn and the licence can be used from the licensee's address without the licensee being present. In the UK, if your station is to be used by another amateur in your absence, he is required to use his own callsign as though operating from a temporary location (by adding the suffix /P).

The final paragraphs of this section refer to the situation where the licence concerned is held by the individual on behalf of a club, when slightly different restrictions apply in that the licence may indeed be used by another, properly qualified club member in the absence of the licensee.

Vessels

There then follow sections regarding the use of the licence from vessels (meaning seagoing) and aircraft. They are pretty much self-explanatory. Essentially, any maritime operation can only take place with the permission of the Master of the vessel, and airborne operation is specifically prohibited (again, this is not universal, some countries allowing aeronautical mobile operation by their amateurs).

Apparatus

After some paragraphs which might best be described as "the small print" *BR68* moves on to some other aspects which are directly relevant to the topics covered in this book. The first (para 4(1-5)) is to do with the station's equipment. This is one of those rather grey areas, in that some of these requirements are open to interpretation. What, for example, does "The Licensee shall conduct tests from time to time .." actually mean? How often is "from time to time". But the underlying message is clear, which is that it is the licensee's responsibility to ensure that his station is operating effectively, and not creating unnecessary emissions. Paragraph 4(1)(a) also recognises that amateur radio equipment will not be required to meet the technical standards that might be applied to commercial equipment. Gone are the days when every UK amateur radio station was required to own and use a separate frequency standard, and nowadays it might reasonably be expected that any piece of commercially manufactured equipment for the amateur radio market would meet the spirit of what *BR68* requires. Quite clearly, though, no home built transmitter should be used on-air without some initial tests to check for bandwidth and spurious emissions.

Recorded or retransmitted messages

While it is relatively uncommon to hear amateurs recording and retransmitting messages, it is clear from this section (para 5(1-4)) that there is no restriction provided that care is taken to avoid confusion as to who is actually controlling the transmission and whose message is being retransmitted at any given time. Often it's simply a case of an amateur recording his QSO partner's transmission and playing it back, so

Operation on board ship must be with the permission of the Ship's Master. Here G3SEM relaxes with his radio on board the *Queen Elizabeth II*

that the originator can hear what it sounds like. What is very clear, though, is that any retransmitted message must have originated from a licensed amateur. We are not allowed to send messages originated by non-amateurs. This section also makes it clear that the basic licence does not cover the operation of a data communications mailbox or a telephony repeater. These must be the subject of separate licence applications.

Log

The subject of logging causes a remarkable amount of confusion, so it is important to understand the implications of para 6(1-5). Many of us were first licensed when a logbook was exactly that. A properly bound, as against loose-leaf (still mentioned – para 6(3)(b) - because pages could be added or removed) book in which every contact was recorded. But nowadays probably the majority of amateurs use electronic means of logging, and the licence terms reflect this. Nothing is said about the exact format in which electronic log data is held (many commercial programs use proprietary log formats), but there is a requirement to keep back-ups, for obvious reasons.

#	Call	Time	Band	RS
QSO		GMT	MHz	
1	RK4LXD	14.20	14	59\59
2	UA1UPC	14.21	[illegible]	59\59
3	RV9MM/9	14.25		59\59
4	UA3BT	14.		[illegible]\59
5	RA3DCU	14		58
6	RK4CXK	14		9
7	RW9AS	14		9
8	UA0AX	14		8
9	UA1NCX	14.		57
10	UA9FLD	14.4		8\59
11	RW4UU	14.49		59\59
12	UA4SX	14.56	14	59\55

A log can be kept in a book or on a computer disk

From the licensing authority's point of view, the main purpose of the log is as an audit trail should any complaints be made against you, the licensee, or any problems arise. Therefore, what is important is the logging of each transmission, irrespective of whether you made a contact. As long as you are radiating energy, there is the possibility of EMC problems, and these can be tracked back at a later date if the band and power level are recorded. Although there is a requirement to log the callsigns of stations worked, this is of rather less importance, and you do not even have to record the exact time of each contact, just the times when you change band, mode or power level. After all, these are the changes which could affect nearby electronic appliances or other band users. Of course, there is nothing to stop you recording the times of each contact, along with other information (name, details of rig, IOTA reference, QSL manager, etc), and most amateurs will do exactly that. But this data is not required by your licence. On the other hand, data which is required, like CQ calls, times of opening up and closing down the station, and so on are not always catered for by some of the commercial logging programs. It is probably safe to say that UK-sourced station logging programs offer the necessary facilities, but many from overseas, where licensing requirements may be different, don't always do so.

As you will also note, your log should be kept for at least six months though, again, most amateurs preserve their log for their lifetime and it forms a fascinating history of their amateur radio activities over the years.

Identification

Station identification is another area occupied by myth and folklore. So, as with logging, it is well worth reading what BR68 has to say on the matter (para 7(1-8)). The requirement is to identify at the beginning and end of each contact and when undertaking any other transmission such as a CQ call. This identification should take the form of your full callsign (which may differ according to where you are: G3XTT, G3XTT/M, GW3XTT, etc.). So 'partial calls', often used when calling DX stations, are inappropriate (this is covered in more detail in Chapter 9). If a contact lasts for more than 15 minutes, the callsign should be repeated at least every 15 minutes, but need not be given at the beginning and end of each "over". When giving the callsign, it should be in the same mode as the actual transmission (CW, SSB, SSTV, etc.) and on the same frequency. But there is a further caveat that, on modes other than CW or SSB (such as RTTY or SSTV) the callsign should be given after at least every 30 minutes in either SSB or CW. This, of course, is because others listening to your signals and perhaps having interference from them, may not be able to copy those specialist modes, but are assumed to be able to copy SSB or CW. Now that the mandatory requirement for CW skills on HF has been dropped, it can only be assumed that this requirement will change in the next revision of BR68. The other main item of note is that if you are operating away from home, unless you have previously notified the relevant OFCOM office, you must sign /P and give your location, to the nearest 5km, at least every 30 minutes.

Inspection and close down

The final section I will deal with here relates to station close-down (para 8(1-4)). Hopefully none of us ever have to face this, but it is as well to be aware of the circumstances under which this might happen, and how it should be dealt with. Except when at sea, where the vessel's Master has authority to close you down, the only person who can ask for your station to be closed down is a person suitably authorised by the Secretary of State or by the Secretary of State himself, through a notice sent to individual amateurs or published in certain recognised media. That suitably authorised person should also be granted access to your station on request, in order to inspect your licence, log and equipment. Other than under extreme circumstances, such a request would only be made at "reasonable times" and, in practice, you would almost certainly be contacted beforehand to make an appointment, for example if a neighbour has suffered break-through and a station inspection is necessary.

References

[1] International Telecommunication Union, Place des Nations, CH1211 Geneva 20, Switzerland.

[2] Radio Regulations, ITU, Geneva.

[3] International Amateur Radio Union, Box 310 905, Newington, Connecticut 061310905, USA.

[4] *RSGB Yearbook*, RSGB (published annually).

[5] Latest T/R 61-01 countries summary table: www.ero.dk/documentation/docs/implement.asp?docid=1802

[6] OH2MCN: www.qsl.net/oh2mcn/license.htm

[7] IARU: www.iaru.org

[8] European Radiocommunications Office: www.ero.dk

3 Setting up a Station

SETTING UP AN amateur radio station is a task which can vary from choosing a handheld transceiver and reading up on its facilities, to building an extensive and competitive station with multiple towers and antennas. There are some aspects which are common, others which you will only face as you become more ambitious. This chapter is intended to walk you through some of the decisions and steps involved, not in a technical way (there are plenty of books about designing and building antennas, for example), but by way of some practical advice. You will learn a lot with time. Like most hobbies, it is likely you will start small, perhaps with second-hand equipment, but as time goes on you will want to build on what you already have.

Goals

YOU WILL PROBABLY be tempted to start by perusing the dealer advertisements, catalogues and websites, imagining yourself with the latest transceiver and maybe a substantial array of antennas in the garden. In practice, the starting point should be to ask yourself, "What is it I want to achieve?" If you are newly licensed, this may be easier to ask than to answer.

Although you may have done some listening on the bands, or visited another amateur's shack, you probably won't know at this stage exactly which bands are likely to appeal to you. Nor will you know whether your interests are more likely to lie with chatting to friends around town or chasing contacts with remote islands around the world. Do you see yourself operating on voice, or might you fancy trying out CW or data modes? Do you plan to make your PC an integral part of your station, for logging and other purposes? You can probably see where this line of reasoning is going, because the equipment and antennas you need for one are going to be rather different to what you need for the other.

The author's station, when he first became licensed in 1968. The transmitter, a Codar AT5, was a popular UK-manufactured model, with an input power of 10 watts of AM and CW on 160 and 80m. The receiver, a Lafayette, was built from a kit and covered the whole of the medium and shortwave bands

Nowadays it's getting easier to cover all the bases. Many modern transceivers, unlike their predecessors, cover a wide range of bands from 160m through to UHF, for example. And some facilities, such as a linear amplifier, can easily be added later. On the one hand, there is little sense in spending large amounts of money on facilities which you are unlikely ever to use. On the other hand, to give just one example, if you have just gained a licence with limited frequency and power privileges, does it make sense to buy a transceiver limited to those frequencies and power levels, or are you planning to upgrade in the near future? Even if you are only at the listening stage, without a transmitting licence yet, buying a transceiver rather than a communications receiver may be just the incentive you need to crack on and gain your licence. Do you want a compact radio for portable operating, perhaps, or maybe nowadays you are looking for something that can be hidden in a cupboard and operated via a software interface on your computer.

Choosing equipment

THE HEART OF ANY amateur radio station is the transceiver. Prior to late 1960s or thereabouts that statement wouldn't have been true as it was far more common to have a separate receiver and transmitter. Some amateurs still use 'separates', especially those who enjoy refurbishing and using classic equipment.

If your motivation for becoming a radio amateur is to be able to make contacts using equipment you have constructed yourself, then the choice of transceiver may be obvious. There have been some excellent designs published in the amateur radio press in recent years, both by specialist organisations such as the G-QRP Club and also in leading journals such as the RSGB's *RadCom*. And nowadays there is, once again, a wide selection of kits you can buy. These range from basic, easy to put together, kits offering limited facilities, power and frequency coverage, to top of the range transceivers with specifications at least as good as anything you might buy commercially.

If you do decide to follow the commercial route, the choice nowadays is quite overwhelming, and even modestly priced radios boast a huge range of features. A lot of debate has centred on the design compromises between offering additional features and focusing on good, basic RF performance. To a large extent that debate is now irrelevant. To all intents and purposes, most transceivers offer both to a level at which you are unlikely either to push its RF performance to the limit or to want additional features. The usual basic rule applies: you are likely to get what you pay for. A low-priced radio, perhaps designed primarily for mobile operation, may start to show its limitations if you use it in your home station with a large Yagi antenna. But that's not a fault of the radio, of course, as it's being used outside its original design brief. Given, though, that performance and reliability can largely be taken for granted nowadays, your choice is just as likely to be

Something to aspire to. The top of the range IC-7800 covers all bands from 136kHz to 50MHz, runs 200 watts and has a spectrum scope, two receivers and DSP

driven by ergonomics, in other words whether you are comfortable with actually operating the set. This is an area which is very much a matter of personal preference, and can only really be answered by using the equipment concerned.

Where to begin?

NONE OF THIS answers the question about where you should start. There's a lot to be said for trying out a transceiver in your home station before you lay out large amounts of money, just as you would want to test drive a car before entering in to a binding contract. If a friend can lend you a transceiver to use at home, so much the better, as you can then see whether it suits your requirements or whether you need something different. A dealer is unlikely to offer you this facility but most do the next best thing, which is to allow you to try out different transceivers on their premises.

Another solution is to buy second-hand, which minimises your financial exposure, especially as you can probably sell on in due course for close to what you paid. But this does have disadvantages. You are unlikely to be buying the latest model and, unless you buy second-hand from a dealer, there is always the risk that you may be sold a pup.

Transceivers are like cars, in that they tend to fall into fairly clearly defined classes. But, again like cars, manufacturers occasionally try to break the mould by trying to package things differently in terms of bands, facilities, or perhaps output power.

The starting point for many amateurs is a handheld VHF/UHF transceiver, or HT (Handy Talkie) as it's referred to in many parts of the world. This will usually cover one or more of the VHF and UHF amateur bands, using FM, perhaps also offering a general coverage receiver allowing you to listen to the VHF broadcast bands and the like. Most use rechargeable batteries, and offer a range of facilities for repeater operation, memory storage of your popular channels, scanning, etc. They should be rugged for portable use, some even boast of being waterproof. All will come with a small whip aerial. In some cases this can be removed to allow you to connect the transceiver to a car-mounted or even base-station aerial, but receive performance may suffer if it becomes overloaded with incoming signals. Prices range from £50 or so for a single-band, low power radio intended for short-range use or access to a very local repeater, to several hundred pounds for a multiband, fully-featured model.

The next category of VHF/UHF transceivers comprises those which are intended for mobile operation. These will usually be of a similar size to a car radio, intended to be fitted into the dash, or perhaps boot-mounted with a remote dash-mounted front panel. Their facilities will be very similar to those described above for handheld radios, but power output will normally be significantly higher, DC power will be drawn from the car battery, and there will be an antenna socket for connection to an external aerial mounted somewhere on the car body. There is nothing to stop one of these transceivers being used in your home station. However, for home use you may also want SSB and CW capabilities, for chasing longer-distance contacts when the bands are open. Some mobile transceivers offer alternative modes. However, in the past it was more typical to find a range of VHF/UHF transceivers designed specifically for home use, with a full range of facilities including SSB, CW and data modes, selectable filters, dual-band working for satellite operation, and much else. In recent years many of these have been withdrawn from the market, being replaced by a new generation of combined HF/VHF/UHF transceivers at similar prices. Incidentally, perhaps of more use on VHF than on the HF bands is the spectral display featured in some modern transceivers. You will be able to leave this on your favourite band and see immediately if there is a band opening, and signals start to appear on the display.

This bring us nicely to HF transceivers. The entry point nowadays seems to consist of a range of small, lightweight transceivers designed primarily for portable and mobile operation, able to be battery powered (some have internal, rechargeable batteries). These are designed to be used with temporary antennas, though most require an external tuner if the antenna is anything other than a resonant length. Some cover only the HF bands, but increasingly these transceivers also cover some of the VHF and UHF bands. It is worth mentioning at this point that very few commercial transceivers, whether VHF only, or combined HF/VHF, cover the 4m band as, until recently, this band has only been available in a handful of countries, so it hasn't been worthwhile for manufacturers to include it. Expect most of these transceivers to offer general coverage HF receive capability, DSP filtering and much else.

There are a number of HF transceivers on the market designed primarily for mobile operation. This may be surprising, as HF mobile isn't that common in the UK, but it is huge in Japan where home stations are frequently limited for

G3GIQ's fine collection of classic Collins equipment, all restored and in full working order. Many amateurs enjoy restoring old equipment and using it for their day-to-day operating" [photo G3GIQ]

antenna space. Beware that some of these sets may overload when used on a large home-station antenna. This is not a fault; they were simply not designed for that purpose.

Base station HF transceivers cover a very wide range of price and specification. Prices start around the £500 mark and go up to several thousand pounds for the latest generation of HF/VHF/UHF radios. The latter might incorporate dual receivers, large LCD displays, multiple filter options, built-in ATU, 200 watts or more power output, and a huge range of menu-selectable options so that the owner can set them up exactly to suit his operating preferences. The lower-priced radios will usually require an external power supply, and will generally offer a limited range of user options. Some, though, can be enhanced considerably through the retrospective fitting of additional filters, ATU, internal keyer or other options. It is also worth checking that your chosen transceiver is 'future proofed' in the sense of, for example, being able to add new bands if and when they become available, or downloading new software (many modern transceivers allow the operating software to be upgraded via an Internet download).

Given that all modern transceivers are hugely more capable than their predecessors of even ten or fifteen years ago, the final choice may well come down to price and usability. The latter is very much a case of personal preference. The layout and functions of the controls, the styling of the display, the general appearance and colour, all these may come into play in your selection, just as they might in choosing a car. But it is also sensible to get hold of product literature and read some of the reviews. The major magazines such as *RadCom* have extensive equipment reviews of most new transceivers, undertaken by competent reviewers using standardised test methods, so that the results can be compared. You can also find user reviews on the Internet at sites such as *eHam.net*.

Buying new

IF YOU DECIDE to buy a new transceiver, by all means shop around for the best price. But remember that you may need back-up, in the case of failure under warranty or later. Check that your dealer has suitable facilities. Nowadays it is often tempting to order over the Internet, perhaps from abroad, but do bear in mind that you may not get the same warranty with such equipment and it may also have a different specification (US mains voltage is 110V, as against 230V in Europe, VHF and UHF band limits, repeater shifts and channel spacings also vary from country to country).

Buying second-hand

MANY DEALERS OFFER a wide range of second-hand transceivers, usually from equipment that has been traded in. This will usually be offered with a limited warranty of a few months. Alternatively, large numbers of transceivers exchange hands privately, typically after being advertised in the amateur radio press but increasingly via Internet sites, either privately run or commercial (such as eBay). When buying privately, always take the usual precautions. Understand exactly what is being advertised, preferably go and see it, try it on the air, and maybe take another, more experienced amateur along for a second opinion. The *RSGB Rig Guide* [1] is a ready source of key data about many of the transceivers sold in recent years.

Wherever you buy second-hand equipment, you will want to understand exactly what condition it is in (a scratched case, for example, reduces a transceiver's value) and exactly what options are fitted (a CW filter might cost you up to £100 extra to buy). In some cases it is also important to know the serial number; as with most equipment, transceivers go through design upgrades during their lifetime and early models may have known problems that were eliminated later on.

Many amateurs, when they buy second-hand equipment, look for it to be in pristine condition and with the original box and packaging. If you expect to re-sell the equipment later, these aspects may be important in your purchase decision. This author takes rather a different view, which is that what matters is that the equipment does the job it was intended for, and that outward appearances are less important. A transceiver with a few scuff marks may well be telling the tale of a good life, with plenty of Field Days, DXpeditions and other travels behind it!

Modifying equipment

AS I HAVE SAID, most modern amateur radio equipment is of a high standard, and will do the job far better than its predecessors of, say, 20 years ago. That's not to say that equipment from earlier generations is unsuitable for use on the amateur bands, and many amateurs actually get their pleasure from renovating and using older equipment. If you choose to go this route, it is important to check the quality of the signals you are radiating, to ensure that there are no spurious carriers, no serious distortion of the audio, and suchlike.

Modern transceivers undoubtedly have better performance than some of their predecessors in terms of third-order intercept point and dynamic range (which affect the ability of the receiver to handle both strong and weak signals in close proximity), probably the main change that you might want to bear in mind from a usability point of view is that almost all modern transceivers have a PC interface. Some earlier mod-

It may look complex, but the Elekraft K2 has been built successfully by many amateurs

els had such an interface, but requiring an external level converter. The popular Kenwood TS-930S HF transceiver (we are, of course, going back around 25 years to the launch of that model) had no such interface, but it is a measure of the popularity of that particular radio that it is now possible to buy a new main board, which incorporates the necessary circuitry to work with a PC.

Indeed, it is the most popular models which attract post-release modifications and improvements. The successor to the TS930S, the TS940S, was transformed by a simple phase-noise modification developed by one of the UK amateur radio retailers. Several other models from around that period also benefited from modifications developed and introduced by UK dealers. The FT-1000D, still a favourite with many DXers and contesters, can be improved by a simple modification to reduce key clicks and another to reduce distortion caused by the noise blanker circuit. Its successor, the FT-1000MP, can now be fitted with new first-IF roofing filters to improve receive performance on SSB, data modes and CW, at the expense of FM operation which is irrelevant to most DXers and contesters. These are all examples of how a competent transceiver can be improved even further. There are many such examples on the Internet. However, you may well be reluctant to delve inside your transceiver for several reasons. Modifications made during the warranty period may render the warranty invalid. Modifications may also reduce the resale value of the radio at a later date, although most of those I have mentioned can be removed without affecting the transceiver in any way.

Building your own

MANY AMATEURS ARE in the hobby because they enjoy the technical challenge of building equipment. Home construction has gone through many cycles over the years. The earliest radio amateurs had to build their own equipment because, quite simply, there was no alternative. This included winding their own coils, often even fabricating their own capacitors. After WWII, a huge amount of surplus equipment came onto the amateur market at affordable prices. Most of the equipment was general coverage in nature, and could easily be pressed into service on the amateur bands with minimal modification. By the 1960s SSB was emerging, but many amateurs still started out on 160m AM or, if they had a Class B licence, 70cm FM. There were plenty of suitable designs for home construction, the main challenge being chassis bending and drilling to take the valve holders, transformers and other major components. This was also an era of kit building, with Heathkit dominating the market. By going the kit route, the metal-bashing had already been done, and most of the work was in soldering the components into place.

As affordable ready-built transceivers started to become available, especially from Japan, interest in kit building waned. Circuitry was starting to become more complex and unless you really were an experienced builder, it was difficult to match the performance of commercial equipment with something home-built. By the 1980s the reaction to this was an interest in home-construction for QRP operation. This provided simple designs such as direct conversion receivers where receive performance might be limited but, as you were running low power, you could probably hear anything you were likely to work. Very few felt they could begin to build anything equivalent to a typical commercial transceiver, with its frequency synthesiser, solid-state output stage, and multiple modes. The increasing miniaturisation of components, including surface-mount devices, seemed to put home construction of all but the simplest equipment out of range of the amateur. There was still an interest in building test gear and ancillary equipment and even linear amplifiers which, while involving high voltages, have relatively simple circuitry.

Interestingly, the tables have turned yet again, with a number of kits now available for what are very sophisticated transceivers. By far the best-known examples are the products from US company Elekraft. Their K2 transceiver can be built without substantial amounts of test equipment, yet its performance appears to be on a par with the best of the ready-built transceivers. So once again, building your own appears to be a very real option for those who want to have the satisfaction of making contacts with equipment they have put together themselves.

Other equipment

THERE IS A PLETHORA of other items you may want for your shack, either when starting up or at some later stage. A linear amplifier to boost the power of your transceiver, for example. This might be a small, solid state unit to boost a low power transceiver to the 100 watt level. It may be a high power, possibly valve-based amplifier, to boost a typical 100 watt transceiver to whatever your licence allows.

There is also a wide range of test equipment you might like to have, especially for measuring and setting up antennas. There may be data interfaces for DSP-based multimode operation, power supplies for your transceiver or ancillary equipment, specialist equipment for the microwave bands not covered by the main equipment manufacturers, microphones, headphones, Morse key and so on.

Much the same advice applies to choosing and buying these items as to transceivers. It is worth mentioning, though, that many of the ancillary items that would have been found in the shack in the past may no longer be necessary. Data terminals have largely been replaced by a combination of PC sound card and software. Most transceivers incorporate a keyer, SWR measurement, even antenna switching. One particularly useful accessory, though, is a Monitor Scope, whereby you can keep an eye on the quality of your CW waveform and check whether you are overdriving your transceiver on SSB.

Equipment for the VLF, VHF/UHF and the Microwave Bands

MANY COMMERCIAL transceivers cover frequencies up to the 430MHz band and, in a few cases, the 1300MHz band. A few models, such as the popular FT-847, cater for the specialist requirements of satellite working. Serious VHF and UHF DXers generally consider that, while commercial equipment is adequate for day-to-day operating, it falls short of their demanding requirements. Many, therefore build much of their own equipment, perhaps opting for transverters for the higher bands, which can work with a fully-featured HF transceiver to get the best of both worlds. This is even more true for the microwave bands, where there is very little commercial equipment available either to use directly or to adapt, although some specialist suppliers offer kits and modules.

High-specification designs appear in specialist publications such as the respected *DUBUS* magazine [2], often with provision made for readers to be able to source the necessary components. The RSGB Microwave Components Service [3] is also a valuable source of key items. Similar considerations apply at the other end of the spectrum, the VLF bands (136kHz in the UK), where it is very much a case of "roll your own". Again, a number of suitable designs have appeared in the literature in recent years.

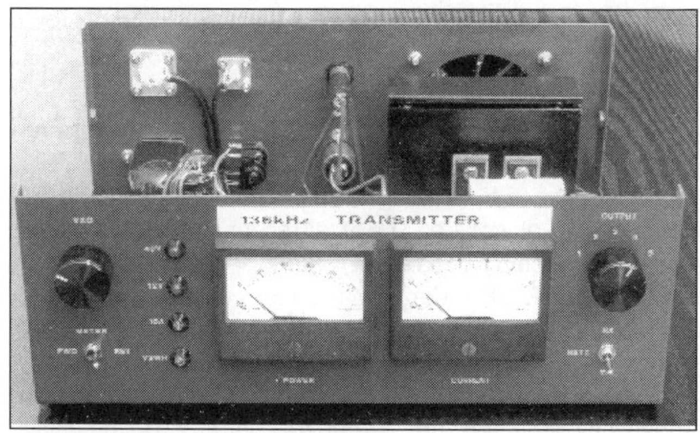

This design for a home-made 136kHz transmitter was published in the RSGB's magazine *RadCom*

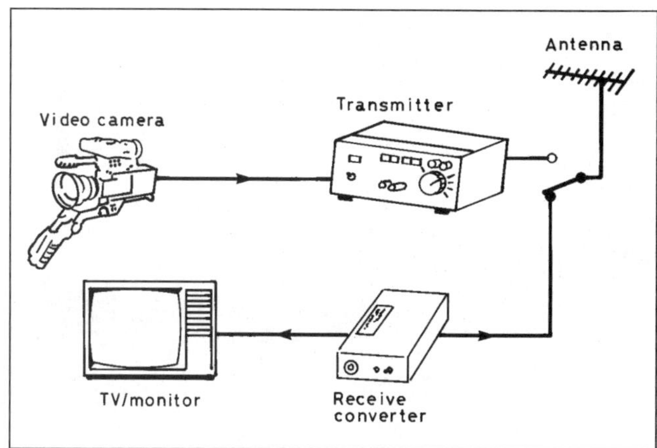

Fig.3.1: Block diagram of a basic fast-scan amateur TV station

Setting up an amateur TV Station

AN AMATEUR TV station need be only as complex as the individual desires. Many stations employ no more equipment than a camera, transmitter, receiver and a TV set. This basic system is adequate for normal communication and has the advantage of being easy to use and maintain. The block diagram of such a basic amateur TV station is shown in **Fig 3.1.** Amateurs who do not wish to put together a complete TV station often set up a simple receiving system in order to 'eavesdrop' on ATV pictures in their area. This can be very rewarding, especially if they live in a high-activity area, and particularly when lifts in propagation conditions occur. Looking in on a local ATV repeater is a common pastime for many stations. In addition, they can often still participate via the 2m talkback channel.

Transmitters and receivers

For ATV receive on 24cm, analogue satellite TV set-top boxes (STBs) are very popular and the change to digital satellite means they are readily available at give-away prices. The outdoor section of a satellite TV receiving system consists of a microwave down-converter (the LNB), mounted at the focus of a dish. The LNB converts the received satellite signals to an IF of around 950 - 2000MHz. The required channel is selected by the STB which is essentially an FM TV receiver, tunable across the full IF range. The amateur 24cm band falls nicely within this range. The output of the STB will drive a domestic TV set either using its AV input or, using the STB's RF modulator, directly into the aerial socket. STBs have two drawbacks for ATV use: Because they are designed to be connected to a high-gain down-converter they tend to be rather 'deaf' (perhaps 'blind' would be a better word!) so a preamplifier is usually needed. Be careful - the aerial input socket carries a DC supply for the LNB so you may need a DC block of some sort if your preamp output is a DC short. STBs tend to have two methods of indicating a short circuit on the input: The clever ones give a flashing warning screen on the TV monitor, the less clever ones produce clouds of black smoke! The second problem is that analogue satellite TV signals use about twice the FM deviation of an amateur transmission so the pictures can be rather dark. This can sometimes be improved by adjusting the contrast control on the TV or monitor but a simple video amplifier connected between the STB and TV is better. Several designs have been published in *CQTV* (see BATC website [4]).

A typical state-of-the-art HF station, with Yaesu FT-1000 MkV transceiver, Yaesu Quadra amplifier and, of course, PCs for logging and other functions. This station belongs to Bob Beebe, GU4YOX

Commercial ATV receiver "modules" are available from several sources and are advertised in *CQTV* and on websites. These are simple boards produced by Comtech to demonstrate their TV receive modules which have been adapted to be suitable for use as ATV receivers. They come in many forms from simple bare-board receivers, with DIL switches to set the frequency, to fully-built with push-button tuning, LCD display, memories, scanning and all the bells and whistles you would expect from an amateur radio voice transceiver.

The most popular 24cm FM ATV transmitter for many years was a 1W unit marketed as a kit by the Worthing and District Video Repeater Group. These are no longer available but many thousands have been sold and they often turn up second hand. They are good, simple, reliable transmitters and are still in use in many ATV stations in the UK. Companion transmitters to the Comtech units mentioned above are also available though their low power output of around 50mW means you will also need a power amplifier.

An article in *RadCom* [5] described how to build a 24cm ATV transceiver around commercially available modules.

Video sources

The most obvious video source is a camcorder, though more professional cameras do turn up at rallies from time to time. A video recorder or DVD player can, of course, also be used, for example to transmit regularly-used material which you have pre-recorded. Computers can also be used as video sources, although certain models are difficult to modify so as to extract the necessary composite video and blanking signal (CVBS) - this unfortunately includes the PC. However, many modern PC graphics cards offer CVBS output alongside the familiar monitor socket. Also available are external VGA to TV converter units which produce a CVBS output when connected between the PC graphics card output and monitor. Some units include a 'genlock' function which allows computer-generated text and graphics to be overlaid on an existing video signal; useful for adding a callsign caption to your transmitted picture.

Several designs for electronically-generated test cards have been published over the years and these have tended to get simpler as time has gone on, reflecting the increasing complexity of digital ICs. The most recent incarnation has all the digital circuitry condensed onto a single programmable logic device [6]. The data for the test card is stored in an EPROM and the latest design has room for 16 different patterns. As an alternative to the EEPROM programmed test card generator, some designs use RAM to store the pattern. These have the advantage that the pattern can be easily changed by downloading new information via a serial link from a PC.

Another useful piece of ATV video equipment is the overlay generator. This simple little unit is connected in line between your video source and the transmitter. Its function is to add (or overlay) text onto the transmitted video and is usually used to add the station callsign in one corner of the image for identification. Various designs have been published for home-built designs and they are also available as complete units.

Setting up your shack

UNLESS YOU ARE planning to confine your amateur radio activity to portable or mobile operations, one of your first priorities will be to set up an operating location or 'shack'. In the days when an amateur radio station consisted of one or more racks of valve equipment, the shack would almost inevitably be one room, set aside specifically for that purpose. Nowadays that need not be the case. Most modern transceivers would not look out of place in the corner of the living room, and take up relatively little space. But there are a number of practical considerations to take into account, largely determined by the amount of equipment you are likely to be using and the type of operating you plan on doing. The main factors, each needing to be considered in choosing a suitable location, are:

- Accessibility, privacy and security
- Acoustics and acoustic noise
- Comfort
- Position relative to the antenna
- Power
- Telecommunications
- Space

Accessibility, privacy and security

If you want to be able to check the bands at frequent intervals, it's not helpful to have to walk to a shed at the bottom of the garden every time. If, on the other hand, you plan to be active in 24 hour contests or even to invite friends to operate your station in such events, then it may be best to select a shack location which is remote from the rest of the household. Wherever your shack is located, there is a responsibility to ensure it is both safe and secure. Your equipment is valuable, it can potentially cause interference to other services if accessed and operated by an unqualified person and, given that it involves high voltages and RF, may cause injury to perhaps a child or elderly person.

Taken together, these factors suggest that, in most cases, your station should be set up in a separate room from the rest of the household, ideally one which can be locked and one which is not overlooked by neighbours or passers-by. In practice it may be necessary to use the same room for other purposes too, such as a study or general hobbies room, in which case other users of the room need to be made aware of the radio equipment and asked to leave it well alone.

Acoustics and acoustic noise

Data modes and CW operation can be almost silent, especially if headphones are used when operating. Phone operation is another matter. It can be very disturbing to other members of the household, especially at night when they are trying to sleep and there are very few other noises around. With

The contest station of IC8WUC on the Isle of Capri

the windows open at night, or if operating from a garden shed, the sound can carry not only through your own house but to neighbours' ears as well. The watchword is to be considerate, using sound insulation to deaden the effects, which will also help to reduce echo on your transmitted signal. Judicious use of heavy curtains, acoustic tiles on the walls, suitable carpets and perhaps double-glazing can all help in this respect. Remember, also, that your rig has a microphone gain control, so it isn't actually necessary to shout at the microphone as many operators invariably do, especially in the heat of chasing some rare DX!

Comfort

For occasional operating, comfort may not be a big issue, but can be of paramount importance when sitting in the same operating chair for hours on end, perhaps operating a contest. Temperature, humidity, draughts, the operating chair, and the positioning of the equipment relative to the operator all have an impact. Ideally your operating shack should be kept at a temperature between 19 and 24°C (65-75°F) summer or winter, especially when in use. Loft spaces and garden sheds, for example, can be subject to much greater extremes of temperature, which is not only uncomfortable for the operator, but does nothing for the equipment either. Electronic equipment can easily be damaged by condensation or by overheating. Most amateur radio equipment is designed for use in normal domestic environments, unlike military equipment which is usually designed (at great expense) for much wider environmental extremes.

You need to be aware of how the equipment itself will affect the environment. In a busy radio environment, such as a contest, where several items of equipment may be operating simultaneously (one or more PCs, transceiver, linear amplifier, etc), this equipment will generate substantial amounts of heat, helping to raise the shack temperature. In the UK very few homes have air conditioning and, in the extreme, it may even be worth investing in some sort of portable AC device for use on such occasions.

The operating chair should be chosen with care, as you could be spending many hours in one position, and back pain is unfortunately much easier to acquire than to eradicate. Many amateurs choose typist chairs, able to be adjusted for height, angle, etc. Equally important, though, is the position of the equipment relative to the operator (you). You will need to be able to reach items such as the PC keyboard, main tuning control (and other controls) of the transceiver,

Morse key or microphone, antenna rotator controller and other items without undue strain. What might work fine for the casual operator may lead to fatigue and discomfort after several hours. Factors to take into account include height of the main operating desk, and reach to the main items of equipment. Unfortunately most home office furniture, as sold in DIY stores, isn't deep enough to take a full-size transceiver and PC keyboard, and still leave room to rest your arms comfortably. The main alternatives are good quality office furniture (which can often be bought second-hand for affordable prices) or building your own operating desk.

Finally, but by no means to be forgotten, your shack should have suitable access to bathroom facilities. Those who have undertaken 24 hour Field Day operations from remote spots will understand the importance of this recommendation!

Position relative to the antenna

Usually there will be more flexibility in siting the shack than in siting the antenna. Therefore the location of the antenna may be important in determining the best location for the shack. You need to consider both the length and geometry of the feed lines and, possibly, rotator cables. Feeder loss, especially at VHF and UHF, can be very substantial and although you can go some way to countering this by using more expensive cable, it is best to keep feeder lengths to a minimum if at all possible. On the LF bands this is less of an issue, but even on 21 and 28MHz feeder losses over 50m or so can be several decibels, depending on the quality of the cable used. There are also good reasons for trying to run cables underground or, at least, close to the ground, if at all possible. This helps to reduce the potential for unwanted radiation from the feeder and unwanted pickup by the feeder of local noise. It is also worth mentioning that an upstairs shack brings problems of effective earthing, which can lead to equipment becoming 'hot' in the RF sense, and may exacerbate any EMC problems, such as TV breakthrough.

Power

Obviously it is necessary for the shack to have adequate electricity supplies. Not only should the circuits be able to supply the sort of current you expect to be drawing but, ideally, there should be enough individual sockets to cater for the number of appliances you will be connecting. In practice this is rarely the case. A well-equipped shack may easily have a dozen or more items which require direct connection to mains power (PC, rotator, HF transceiver, linear amplifier, VHF transceiver, 12V PSU for ancillary equipment, table lamp, etc) and this can result in the use of several trailing leads with extension sockets, which are potentially dangerous and untidy. Ideally, when setting up your shack, time should be taken to wire in enough sockets in a professional way.

Continuity of power may also be an issue, both for shack PC and for the transceiver. Uninterruptible power supplies are useful, and can keep a low power station on the air for several hours in the event of a power failure. Some amateurs also ensure they have generator power available in the event of mains failure, but this requires great caution in ensuring that the generator is never directly connected to an unisolated mains circuit.

Telecommunications

Most shacks nowadays will require access to a phone line and/or Internet. In many ways, the latter is better provided by way of a wireless LAN from an access point elsewhere in the house, as wireless LANs appear to be less susceptible to RF breakthrough than wired (UTP) networks. If the phone network is provided by overhead distribution this can be a problem, especially if those overhead spans are close to your antennas. This is more a factor when considering antenna location, but in any case you may need to plan for the installation of filters on the incoming telephone line.

ON4UN's QSL card records his amateur radio (and family) history over more than 40 years

Space

When planning a shack, it is obviously a good idea to consider not only the immediate needs, but how the amount of equipment might expand as time goes on. If you expect to be engaging in home construction, this is likely to require a bench in its own right (but such work doesn't necessarily have to take place in the shack). Many amateurs have been highly innovative in their use of space, managing to squeeze large amounts of equipment into tiny spaces, for example under the stairs, by judicious use of custom-made shelving. Do allow space for ventilation, though.

It is also important to consider rear access to equipment. One of the recurring irritations is having to disassemble much of the station in order to wire in one more rear connection, perhaps for a new data modem. In an ideal world, we would all be able to walk to the rear of our operating tables to do this sort of work. In practice, this rarely seems to be possible.

Developing your station

LATER, ONCE YOU have actually spent time on the bands, you will start thinking about upgrading your station. The usual experience of operators new to a particular band is that you will hear much more than you can work. Either you are running modest power levels, or your antenna system is limited (or both). You may decide to deal with the power issue by buying or building a linear amplifier, or you may work your way through the planning process to put up a tower and Yagi.

Eventually you may get to the stage where you are able to work everything you can hear. This is the point at which to think about upgrading your receiving capability. It really doesn't make sense to do so before this point is reached. I am forever amazed at the number of amateurs who upgrade a perfectly good transceiver to a later model, and yet are still using something like a half-size G5RV antenna. To my way of thinking, this defies all logic. Improving your antenna system will always have the dual benefit of improving both transmit and receive. But improving your receive ability can also come from installing specialist receiving antennas (especially for the LF bands, for example with a Beverage if you have space or a K9AY loop if you don't). If local noise is a problem, one of the modern noise cancelling devices may be of help. On the VHF, UHF and microwave bands, where the challenge is to squeeze extra every last fraction of a decibel out of the system, your focus will also be on the quality of feeder you use as well as the need for siting a receive preamplifier and perhaps your power amplifier at or close to the antenna.

If you take up a particular speciality such as contest operating, there will be other changes and additions you want to make to your station. For example, as a contester you may want a second transceiver in order to be able to look for multipliers on one transceiver while calling CQ on the other. This may then dictate the use of external bandpass filters to avoid interactions. If you decide to go in for satellite operation, you will not only want a transceiver that can handle the special requirements, but you may need to modify your antenna system to track elevation as well as azimuth heading.

And so, as with most hobbies, there is always room for improvement, as moving forward in one aspect of your station brings you face to face with its limitations in another area. Rest assured, you are unlikely ever to be finally satisfied!

Station layout

ASSUMING A SUITABLE site for the shack has been found, the next question is how the equipment can be arranged in the most convenient manner. Obviously this depends upon the type of operation envisaged, and the quantity of equipment to be accommodated, but there are some basic rules common to most situations.

In general, the equipment should be arranged so that all controls in frequent use are within reach of the comfortably seated operator, without any need to bend very far forward. Similarly, it should be possible to read meters and displays accurately without straining to one side, or peering. Units which generate appreciable heat should not be stacked on top of one another, and care should be taken that any ventilation holes in the cabinets are unobstructed. Solid-state transceivers may have cooling fins on the rear of the cabinet, which should have unobstructed air flow. No heating radiator should be located in the vicinity.

Sufficient clearance behind the equipment should be allowed for the connecting leads, especially if large-diameter coaxial cable is in use (see **Fig 3.2**). Adequate lengths of cable should be used to connect equipment together, so as to permit the sliding forward of any unit for inspection or adjustment while it remains connected to the rest of the station. Any strain in connecting leads will lead to failure sooner or later (Murphy's law).

The transceiver is the most important item of electronic equipment in an amateur radio station, and it is recommended that the rest of the operating area be built around it. It should be placed on a large firm table which allows plenty of space in front for a logbook, scrap pad and any other material, and so positioned that its tuning knob can be turned easily with the elbow resting lightly on the table. If a

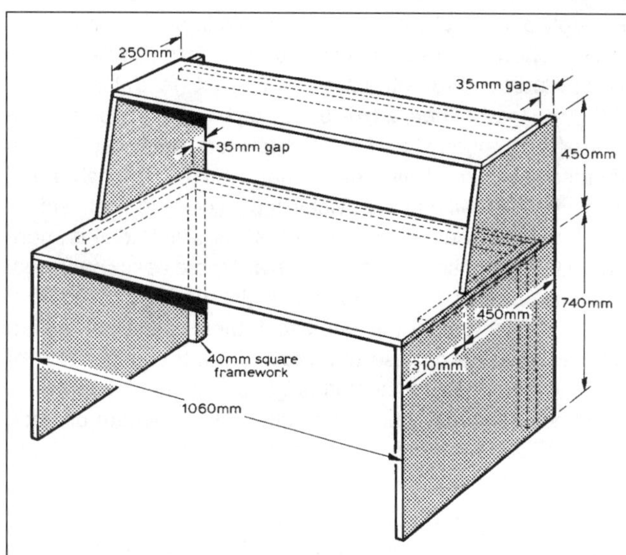

Fig 3.3: A customised radio desk design. The dimensions are approximate, and the distance between table-top and shelf may be reduced when using compact equipment. Note the 35mm clearance between desk shelf and wall to allow for cabling

Maps and lists can be conveniently pinned up above the operating position, or perhaps underneath a glass top to the desk

PC is pivotal to your station, for logging and other purposes, as is commonly the case nowadays, its location is also vital in deciding where everything goes. There are two aspects. The monitor needs to be easy to see without straining your neck. Monitors are designed to be at desk height. However, you will also need to be able to see the display on your transceiver. It is therefore tempting to mount the PC monitor above the transceiver, but this can lead to neck fatigue after long periods of operating. Similarly, you will need access to both the keyboard and the main transceiver controls. One solution it to have the keyboard on a pull-out tray, fixed below the operating desk. Unfortunately, very few office desks or computer tables have enough depth for a transceiver and a PC keyboard, and many amateurs resort to building their own operating table. The advent of affordable LCD PC monitors is a big step forward, as they require very much less space on which to stand. They are also easier on the eyes during long periods of use.

Opinion varies as to whether the transceiver should be placed to the left or right of the operator or dead centre. Possibly one could get used to it placed in any of these positions. If, however, the set is placed to the left, the right-handed operator can tune the set with the left hand, leaving the right free to write notes, type at the keyboard and operate the key or microphone. Some CW operators deliberately train themselves to send with the left hand, so that the right hand is available for all other activities. It may be found convenient to tilt the transceiver slightly so that its tuning dial is more easily visible, or so that its controls are more easily operated. Some transceivers have extensions already fitted to the front pair of rubber feet for this purpose. If there is still insufficient tilt, packing can be inserted under the front rubber feet of the set. Such packing should not obstruct ventilation holes, and should provide a firm mounting. A scrap length of wood about 150mm wide should be suitable, with a strip of foam rubber on top to deaden vibration.

Other equipment such as an antenna tuning unit, linear amplifier and computer may be positioned either side of the transceiver as convenient, preferably in a U-shaped layout as this ensures all displays are facing the operator. The power/SWR meter, monitor oscilloscope and clock are best arranged on a shelf above the operating position, but low enough to be easily viewed. All equipment which does not need to be adjusted or monitored while routinely operating, such as a low-pass filter or frequency meter, does not really belong to the operating area, and can be positioned elsewhere in the shack to save space. Conversely, equipment which you will need to adjust while operating, such as rotator controllers and antenna switches, should be within easy reach.

A suggested line-up on the table in front of the electronics is (from left to right) microphone, logbook/keyboard, scrap pad and Morse key, but the operator will no doubt have individual preferences. The main thing to ensure is that these items can be used with the minimum of effort. Over time, you will find what works and what doesn't and probably end up moving items around. So it is best to anticipate the need for flexibility when designing and setting up your operating position.

The best place for maps and lists constantly in use is the wall immediately above the operating position, but if this is not possible then the material can be laid out on the table and a thin sheet of glass placed on top to keep it clean and in position. Last, but not least, a comfortable chair with adequate back support should be chosen, for this will allow the operator to concentrate properly on the job without any fears of aches and pains when a long operating session is over. Typist chairs, with height and other adjustments are popular for this purpose. Those with castors allow you to move easily to the edges of your operating table if you need to reach other equipment in a hurry. Some contesters choose specially-designed ergonomic chairs to avoid back pain as a result of prolonged operating periods.

One of the potential problems you will face is noise and vibration from cooling fans in your transceiver and linear amplifier, and in your PC. For prolonged operating, noise cancelling headphones can be beneficial in reducing the scale of the problem. It is also worth noting that vibration from fans can easily be carried through walls and floors, especially if the operating bench is fixed directly to the wall, for example. Sitting equipment on some sort of flexible matting can help to reduce vibration, and therefore minimise any nuisance to the rest of the household.

Routing antenna cables

ONE OF THE UNIQUE problems faced by radio amateurs is how to bring cables into the shack from outside. This is something you need to plan carefully, as it is best to anticipate future requirements right from the start. Think about how many cables you are likely to need to bring in, and plan accordingly. This author drilled the shack wall (an upstairs bedroom) to take a standard piece of PVC drain pipe (about 7cm diameter). This is (just) sufficient to accommodate low-loss feeder (H100) from two HF and two VHF antennas, two rotator control cables, a control line for a remote antenna switch, and a couple of small diameter coaxial cables for backup purposes. I have also continued the drainage pipe underground to the base of my two towers, with inspection hatches at each bend and at the tower bases, to allow access. The small 'manholes' are concrete-lined and large enough for items such as a remote antenna switch. Draw strings are left in place so that cables can be pulled in or removed as required. An alternative is to run cables above ground, in which case they should be attached to posts or the house wall at regular intervals, with other members of the household familiar with their location so that they are not likely to be damaged, for example during gardening work.

Choosing antennas

THE CHOICE OF antenna is governed by many things. Obviously there are technical considerations about the performance required and the frequencies to be covered. There may also be physical constraints to do with the site, especially on the HF bands where a half wavelength (the typical starting point for most antennas is a half-wave dipole) may be more than the available space. Or you may be planning on a mast or tower which has limited weight or wind-loading capabilities. And last but by no means least, there may well be planning constraints, restricting the sort of antennas which can be erected at your location.

It is also worth bearing in mind that any sort of directional antenna will need to rotated, unless you want to use it only in one direction. This adds to both the cost and the complexity, though anyone who has upgraded from a vertical or dipole antenna to a multi-element Yagi or other antenna with significant amounts of gain will testify to the huge impact this will make to your station's capabilities, both on receive and transmit.

Commercially-made antennas are available from a wide range of suppliers. Nowadays it is reasonable to expect an antenna to have the gain specified, as most are designed using sophisticated computer modelling to arrive at an optimum combination of gain, front-to-back ratio and radiation pattern. The main difference between two antennas of similar design and claimed performance is likely to be in the mechanical construction, both in the quality of the materials used (are the fasteners and mounting hardware made of stainless steel, for example?) and the way it is all put together. For portable operation you would be looking for something lightweight and easy to erect. For home station use, you would want an antenna which will survive the worst the weather can throw at it at your location.

VHF and UHF antennas are almost all of aluminium construction, though many collinear verticals are encased in weatherproofing material to protect the more delicate loading and matching components. While the larger HF antennas are of similar construction, one of the joys of the HF bands is that a wide range of antennas can be constructed from wire, starting with simple dipoles, loops and verticals. A resonant antenna such as a half-wave dipole is easy to build and should work first time. It can be built for minimal expense (a few metres of wire and some insulators), and will be almost invisible when erected.

If you decide to buy an antenna, most of the major dealers can help you to decide what is most suitable for your location. Buying second-hand is fine, but bear in mind that antennas will have been exposed to the elements, so will have suffered deterioration. Trapped antennas are particularly prone to weather damage, so check out the condition before parting with your money. A trap may look fine externally but, on removing the cover, you may find that the connections are heavily corroded. Also ensure that any antenna comes with full instructions as it will almost certainly be broken down for transportation, and you will need to know how to put it back together on site!

This detail from DJ3JD's QSL card shows a typical antenna system - HF triband Yagi with a VHF beam above it, and a vertical on the house, probably for packet radio

One of the best investments you can make is in the antenna feedline. Why spend a lot of money on a good transceiver and a high-gain antenna, and then throw away power in the feedline? Always use low-loss cable, remembering that the higher the frequency the greater the losses will be.

For further discussion of antennas, you will need to turn to one of the many excellent antenna books. Antenna experimentation remains one of the most popular aspects of the hobby, because there is no ideal solution and every location has its own challenges.

Siting the antenna

FOR MAXIMUM efficiency, the antenna should be sited as high as possible, away from the ground, buildings and other obstructions. The advantages of even a hill-top site will not be realised unless this is done. For this purpose distances and heights should be thought of in terms of wavelengths rather than metres or feet, and the various publications describing particular antennas often give useful information on their performance at varying heights. Transmitting antennas should be kept away from metalwork, such as iron drainpipes. This can influence the directional properties of the antenna, and can also lead to radiation of harmonics of the transmitted signal if the metalwork contains joints capable of acting as metal-oxide diodes (the 'rusty bolt effect'). TV sets radiate timebase interference on harmonics of 15kHz in the HF bands, and antennas intended for HF reception should be kept as far as possible from such equipment. Transmitting antennas should also be located as far as possible from TV antennas and their feeders to avoid electromagnetic compatibility problems (see later). TV feeders usually run vertically, and are therefore particularly prone to RF pick-up from vertical transmitting antennas.

Unfortunately TV equipment is not the only category susceptible to high RF field strengths. Hi-fi equipment, domestic radios, amplified external PC speakers, electronic organs and solid-state switching circuits can all be adversely affected. Similarly other domestic equipment can also radiate interference. Electric motors, thermostats, and fluorescent or neon lighting are frequent culprits. If the antenna is fixed in position and thereby unable to rotate, it may be advantageous to position it so that equipment susceptible to RF (or generating interference) is in a position of minimum antenna gain. This is particularly important where high transmitter powers or high-gain antennas are in use. The safety and social aspects of the antenna site should not be forgotten. Antennas such as dipoles have dangerous RF voltages at their ends when high-power transmissions are being made, and it should not be possible for children or animals to reach up and touch them. It might even be appropriate to post warning signs. While you are not likely to be in the vicinity yourself when you are transmitting, as you will be in the shack, others may not be aware that you are on the air.

The aesthetic aspect is more a function of the type of antenna used than its location, but it may sometimes be better to have an antenna located lower than optimum to avoid antagonising neighbours or drawing attention to the presence of a radio station.

By far the best book on antenna design, location and installation is the ARRL Antenna Book [7], though there are many other excellent publications on the subject.

Planning permission for amateur radio masts and antennas

Town and Country Planning legislation is aimed at securing "the proper use of land" and, as part of this, to safeguard amenities, natural and otherwise, enjoyed by local inhabitants. In the UK, permission is required before undertaking "development" which is defined as "carrying out of building, engineering, mining or other operations in, on, over or under land, or the making of any material change in the use of any buildings or other land". Such applications are considered by Local Planning Authorities (usually the District Council in the case of amateur radio masts or antennas) and will entail an assessment of the pros and cons, balancing the issues involved and making a final judgement upon the merits of the proposal. The Secretary of State for the Environment and his opposite numbers for Wales, Scotland and Northern Ireland have appellate roles over these decisions and can also issue guidance on procedures. Councils also may publish guidance policies, either in the form of "Local Plans" relating to all or part of their areas or on specific topics. Look out for them.

The overall definition of "development" in the first paragraph is subject to some exclusions set out in Section 55 of the Town and Country Planning Act 1990 (as amended). Two are relevant to radio amateurs. Firstly the carrying out for the maintenance, improvement or other alteration of any building of works which (i) affect only the interior of the building or (ii) do not materially affect the external appearance of the building are not "development". Secondly, the use of any buildings or other land within the curtilage (usually the garden) of a dwelling for any purpose incidental to the enjoyment of the dwelling as such is not "development" and therefore does not require planning permission. Amateur radio, as a hobby, falls within this - thus the 'transmitting' component of the hobby cannot be challenged in the way that, say, a PMR base station might be.

In addition to the exclusions set out above, the Act provides for General Development Orders (GDOs), to be prepared which in effect represent automatic permission for things which may not warrant developers or local authorities having to go to the trouble and cost of preparing and processing applications of little moment to the community or where the 'benefits', in a national context, will override any possible costs. Such GDO permissions can be qualified in a variety of ways not practicable in general legislation. This Secondary Statutory Regulation system has a more simple Parliamentary procedure and thus can be revised more easily. The provisions which allow the extensions to a dwelling by 10 or 15% of its cubic capacity, subject to not coming in front of the forward-most part, nor exceeding the maximum height of the roof of the original dwelling, for many years allowed substantial dormer windows to be built on the front and/or back faces of dwelling roofs and so provided a very cheap way of enlarging dwellings. However, in 1988 this provision was changed to preclude such dormers on roofs facing a public highway and thus reducing some unsightly alterations to street scenes.

Satellite antennas on houses have also caused much criticism, more so on blocks of flats (where in fact the GDO permissions do not apply), but also because the 90cm size constraint produced difficulties in those northern parts of the British Isles where the satellite footprints were less strong. Adverse amenity impacts from the numerous dishes in street schemes and the adverse picture effects were dealt with in July 1991 by changes which varied the size according to the location in the country, allowing smaller (45cm) dishes on the chimney and 70cm elsewhere on the building but retained the 90cm below the roof top in the South West and the area North of the Humber.

There are also two other parts of the GDO which relate specifically to telecommunications; one is the Telecom Code Systems (telecommunication providers) and the other deals with other commercial microwave systems. Neither is relevant to radio amateurs as, apart from these limitations to commercial systems, they specifically exclude siting on dwelling houses.

Essential reading for RSGB members wishing to apply for planning permission to erect an antenna or mast

The Christmas tree of antennas at K6JL (formerly W6MKB), starting with a full-size 3-element 80m Yagi, right through to 70cm. The highest antenna is at 175ft, and the whole system was built and installed by Terry himself

The 'exclusions', set out in the third paragraph above, together with the automatic permissions referred to in the fourth paragraph may well meet the needs of many amateurs. Remember that neighbours and others may not regard a mast and antenna as a thing of beauty!

In other cases it will be necessary to make an application for permission. A study of the brochure *Planning Permission - Advice to Members*, which is available free to members from RSGB Headquarters, is strongly recommended. Think carefully what you really need - not what you would like, just because a local amateur has received permission for a pair of 17m telescopic masts with a variety of HF, VHF and UHF antennas, for example. Don't forget that his house is set in a pocket of woodland and that your corner bungalow on an estate will pose a very different set of 'costs' when your application is being considered. Do make sure that your application sets out fully why you need whatever it is that you show on the application forms and plans. Think about the siting and design of your proposal. Slimline (box-section or tubular) masts are more acceptable than square or triangular lattice masts although they won't carry such high wind loads at such heights. Some antennas are of better visual design than others - they don't have so many excrescences or breaks in their general lines which draw attention to them in an irritating way. Look at your proposal as if through a neighbour's eyes and show them where and why you want it. If you want a high mast to get antennas up to reduce EMC problems already existing, can you get help to have a report prepared to illustrate how the new set-up will reduce close-in field strengths? Don't try to mislead with antenna details. The Planning Authority is fully entitled to require details and a failure to supply them may result in permission subject to a condition which requires approval of detail drawings of the antenna before the mast is erected! At least one inspector endorsed this course of action; others have dismissed appeals because of the absence of clear information about antennas.

Make sure the mast, any guys and the antenna elements are entirely within your own land and do not trespass onto next door's airspace; if you do encroach, you must get his permission in writing and refer to this in supporting material, saying why the space is needed. Remember that an antenna which cannot be accommodated on your own land invites the comment "It's too big for this site". Make good plans and fair copies of any explanatory material and show them to your neighbours; the Council has to consult your neighbours and it is better if you get to them first and explain things. Ask the Case Officer in the Planning Department if he or his chief has any query. If so, offer to come into the office and explain things.

Some amateurs believe in erecting things first and hoping that nobody will notice them! If you are lucky, you may get away with this for four years after which the Council cannot serve an enforcement notice. It often happens, however, that a new neighbour arrives after three years and can cause problems. In any event, if you have altered the antenna at all within the four years, you may well have put the mast and all at risk. This is currently a grey area and the enforcement law is being steadily tightened. The four-year rule now only applies to building or engineering works and changes of use can now be challenged for longer periods from the change taking place.

One final point. You will know, if you have got the planning permission brochure mentioned above, that the RSGB has a panel of advisers who may be able to help you, perhaps to avoid problems or to overcome them by negotiation with the authority or to appeal to the Secretary of State if you have been refused permission.

Safety precautions

SAFETY IS OF paramount importance and every precaution should be taken to ensure that the equipment is perfectly safe, not only for the operator himself but also for the other members of the household or visitors. Double-pole switches should be used for all AC supply circuits, and interconnected switches should be fitted to home-constructed equipment so that no part of it can have high voltage applied until the valve heaters and low-power stages have been switched on. This precaution may not only save the life of the operator, but also protects the transmitter against damage.

Linear amplifiers using valves should have a microswitch fitted so that the EHT is switched off when the cabinet is opened. Where interconnecting plugs and sockets are used for high voltages, ensure that the female connector is connected to the supply unit, and the male to the unit to be supplied. It should be possible to turn off power to the entire station by operating one master switch, located in a very prominent position, and all members of the household should know that in the event of an emergency this must be switched off before anything is touched.

The antenna may require the provision of a lightning conductor in the immediate vicinity, or the use of lightning arresters. The most satisfactory type of arrester is the gas-filled type fitted in an adequately insulated mounting which includes a parallel air spark gap. Arresters for coaxial cable are also available. Lightning protection should always be located outside the building, providing as direct a path to earth as possible - "lightning doesn't go round corners!" Great care should be exercised before touching feeders have been disconnected before a thunderstorm as they may hold a dangerous charge for a considerable time after the storm. Further information on lightning protection is given in [8].

Safety recommendations for the amateur radio station

1. All equipment should be controlled by one master switch, the position of which should be well known to others in the house or club.

1. All equipment should be properly connected to a good and permanent earth (but see box on PME later in this chapter and Note A).

2. Wiring should be adequately insulated, especially where voltages greater than 500V are used. Terminals should be suitably protected.

3. Transformers operating at more than 100V RMS should be fitted with an earthed screen between the primary and secondary windings or have them in separate slots in the bobbin.

4. Capacitors of more than 0.01 F capacitance operating in power packs, modulators, etc (other than for RF bypass or coupling) should have a bleeder resistor connected directly across their terminals. The value of the bleeder resistor should be low enough to ensure rapid discharge. A value of 1/ C megohms (where C is in microfarads) is recommended. The use of earthed probe leads for discharging capacitors in case the bleeder resistor is defective is also recommended. (Note B). Low-leakage capacitors, such as paper and oil-filled types, should be stored with their terminals short-circuited to prevent static charging.

5. Indicator lamps should be installed showing that the equipment is live. These should be clearly visible at the operating and test position. Faulty indicator lamps should be replaced immediately. Gas-filled (neon) lamps and LEDs are more reliable than filament types.

6. Double-pole switches should be used for breaking mains circuits on equipment. Fuses of correct rating should be connected to the equipment side of each switch in the live lead only. (Note C.) Always switch off before changing a fuse. The use of AC/DC equipment should be avoided.

7. In metal-enclosed equipment install primary circuit breakers, such as micro-switches, which operate when the door or lid is opened. Check their operation frequently.

8. Test prods and test lamps should be of the insulated pattern.

9. A rubber mat should be used when the equipment is installed on a floor that is likely to become damp.

10. Switch off before making any adjustments. If adjustments must be made while the equipment is live, use one hand only and keep the other in your pocket. Never attempt two-handed work without switching off first. Use good-quality insulated tools for adjustments.

11. Do not wear headphones while making internal adjustments on live equipment.

12. Ensure that the metal cases of microphones, Morse keys etc are properly connected to the chassis.

13. Do not use meters with metal zero-adjusting screws in high-voltage circuits. Beware of live shafts projecting through panels, particularly when metal grub screws are used in control knobs.

14. Antennas should not, under any circumstances, be connected to the mains or other HT source. Where feeders are connected through a capacitor, which may have HT on the other side, a low resistance DC path to earth should be provided (RF choke).

15. Antennas must be designed with due allowance for wind loading. For this, guidance from the antenna manufacturer is necessary and British Standard (BS) CP3 Chapter 5 for guyed masts and BS 8100 for self-supporting masts should be consulted.

16. Certain chemicals occur in electronic devices which are harmful. Notable amongst these are the polychlorinated biphenyls (PCBs) which have been used in the past to fill transformers and high-voltage capacitors and beryllium oxide (BeO) which is used as an insulator inside the case of some high-power semiconductors. In the case of PCBs, the names to look out for on capacitors are: ARACLOR, PYROCHLOR, PYRANOL, ASBESTOL, NO-FLAMOL, SAFT- KUL and others. If one of these is present in a device, it must be disposed of carefully. The local Health and Safety Authority will advise. In the case of beryllium oxide, the simple rule is DON'T OPEN ANY DEVICE THAT MAY CONTAIN IT.

Note A. - Owing to the common use of plastic water main and sections of plastic pipe in effecting repairs, it is no longer safe to assume that a mains water pipe is effectively connected to earth. Steps must be taken, therefore, to ensure that the earth connection is of sufficiently low resistance to provide safety in the event of a fault. Checks should be made whenever repairs are made to the mains water system in the building.

Note B. - A 'wandering earth lead' or an 'insulated earthed probe lead' is an insulated lead permanently connected via a high-power 1k resistor or a 15W 250V lamp at one end to the chassis of the equipment; at the other end a suitable length of bare wire with an insulated handle is provided for touch contacting the high-potential terminals to be discharged.

Note C. - Where necessary, surge-proof fuses can be used.

An often-overlooked precaution concerns the current carrying capability of the mains supply to the station. An amateur station fully equipped with ancillary apparatus can draw quite a heavy current from the supply, and when assembling the equipment it is important to calculate the current that will be drawn when everything is in use and to check that the house wiring will carry this amount. If there is any doubt new wiring should be installed.

It is most important that every amateur should develop a strict code of safety discipline for use when handling his radio equipment. It should be the rule never to work on equipment which is plugged into the AC supply if this can possibly be avoided. However, there are occasions when this is unavoidable and under these circumstances the following precautions should be followed:

1. Keep one hand in a pocket.
2. Remove metal bracelets or watch straps.
3. Never wear headphones.
4. Be certain that no part of the body is touching an object which is earthed and use a non-conductive (eg rubber) covering over concrete floors.
5. Use insulated tools.

Before working on equipment of any kind, plugged into the mains or not, it is vital to make sure that all filter capacitors are fully discharged - these are capable of retaining what could be a lethal charge for a considerable time. Use an insulated screwdriver to short each capacitor in turn.

The vast majority of shocks sustained from electrical apparatus are derived from the 230V mains line lead. Every year there are 100 or more deaths in the UK due to electrocution, mostly as a result of accidental contact with mains voltage. There is evidence to suggest that because of the different physiological effects, those who receive shocks from voltages of more than 1000V have a better chance of survival than those subjected to severe medium-voltage shocks. Voltages as low as 32V have been known to cause death, provided there is sufficient current - as the jingle says: "It's volts that jolts but mils that kills". The danger of electrocution is increased where the victim's skin resistance is lowered by dampness or perspiration, or where he grips an extensive area of 'live' metal while in good contact with earth. It is against this second possibility that particular care is needed in amateur stations.

A particular hazard is equipment which has a chassis connected to the mains which is being used under conditions for which it was not intended. Some old British TV sets and domestic broadcast receivers fall into this category; not only the 'AC/DC' sets but also - and this is not always appreciated - a large proportion of 'AC only' models. If there is any such equipment in your station, the exposed parts should be checked with a neon screwdriver to make certain that they are not 'live' with the on/off switch in either position. Remember that a single-pole switch in the neutral lead will leave the chassis 'live' even with the set apparently turned off. After such checks have been carried out non-reversible plugs should be fitted to AC supply leads.

It is wise to check all three-pin supply sockets in the house to see whether they have been correctly wired; all too often this is not the case. The author recalls buying a second-hand valve receiver (from an experienced radio amateur!) and, on plugging it in, the house power went off. The earth leakage trip had been activated because neutral and earth were reversed in the receiver's mains plug. A three-pin plug with the 'earth' contact at the top should have the 'neutral' contact on the bottom left, and the live 'line' contact on the bottom right - these directions apply when looking at the back of the plug for wiring purposes (see **Fig 3.3**). Correct colour coding of leads in the UK has been for many years: 'live' or 'line', brown ; 'neutral', blue; 'earth', yellow and green. It is very important to note that this coding may not apply to the wiring on some imported equipment, and the manufacturer's instructions should be very carefully studied before plugging into the supply. The use of modern fused plugs is recommended. An even greater hazard, because it is seldom anticipated, can arise under fault conditions on equipment fitted with a double wound (i.e. 'isolating') transformer of the type so often used in amateur equipment. It is by no means unusual or unknown for the primary winding to short circuit to the screen between the primary and secondary, the core, or to one of the secondary windings, so that the chassis of the equipment becomes 'live'. Such equipment will often continue to operate quite normally and can thus represent a very real danger over a considerable period. The best safeguard against this danger is to ensure that the screen between the primary and the other windings, the core and the chassis are all effectively earthed.

The earth connection must be of very low resistance otherwise the supply fuses may not blow. These fuses should be of the minimum practicable rating - it is no use having a 50 ohm resistance to earth and a 10A fuse - if this should be the case the size of the electricity bills may be surprising, but the hazard is likely to remain undetected!

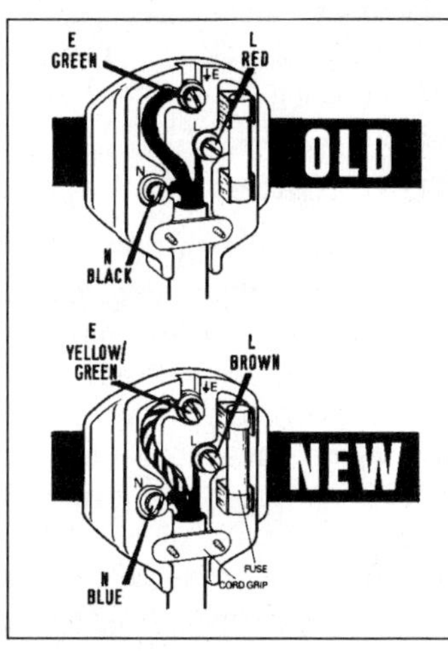

Fig 3.3: The correct wiring for three-pin plugs in the UK. To test that a socket is correctly wired, a lamp should light when connected between 'L' and 'N' or 'L' and 'E', but not when connected between 'N' and 'E'. A neon bulb will glow when touched against 'L'.

WARNING: Protective Multiple Earthing (PME)

Some houses, particularly those built or wired since the middle 'seventies, are wired on what is known as the PME system. In this system the earth conductor of the consumer's installation is bonded to the neutral close to where the supply enters the premises, and there is no separate earth conductor going back to the sub-station.

With a PME system a small voltage may exist between the consumer's earth conductor, and any metal work connected to it, and the true earth (the earth out in the garden). Under certain very rare supply system faults this voltage could rise to a dangerous level. Because of this supply companies advise certain precautions relating to the bonding of metal work inside the house, and also to the connection of external earths.

WHERE A HOUSE IS WIRED ON THE PME SYSTEM DO NOT CONNECT ANY EXTERNAL (i.e. radio) EARTHS TO APPARATUS INSIDE THE HOUSE unless suitable precautions are taken.

A free leaflet *EMC 07 Protective Multiple Earthing* is available on request from RSGB.

Another source of danger is the electric tool which has developed a fault and which has a 'live' casing. This can happen, for example, with soldering irons and electric drills. A very careful check should be kept on the leads to all such tools, and any 'tingles' felt when they are in use must be investigated immediately.

Many amateurs fit extra power sockets in their stations and the control arrangements may call for quite a lot of semi-permanent AC wiring and switching. In the UK these should always conform to the high standards laid down in the IEE Wiring Regulations. These are rather formidable reading for the non-professional but a number of books giving sound advice on modern wiring practice, based on the IEE recommendations, have been published and can often be obtained from local libraries. Advice can also be obtained from the offices of local electricity boards. In most countries overseas, similar regulations exist and operators in these areas are recommended to obtain copies or seek the advice of the supply authorities.

Another problem is the use of protective multiple earthing (PME) in some UK houses (see panel above). Finally, taking the worst possible event into consideration the operator and members of his household are advised to familiarise themselves with the procedures for the treatment of electric shock.

It is often not realised that low-voltage, high-current equipment can also have dangerous aspects. Some recent solid-state transceivers have power supply requirements of some 20-30A at 12V. It is vital that suitable cable is used to connect any external power supply and that all electrical connections are of low resistance, otherwise there could be a fire risk. There is also a considerable personal danger through hot or molten metal if the user inadvertently short-circuits such a power supply - the resultant current through, say, a wedding ring could cause severe burns. It is a wise precaution to have a fire extinguisher of the type suitable for use on electrical equipment in the shack. The best type is that which directs a stream of carbon dioxide gas on to the burning area; the powder and Halon types may be used but are liable to cause further damage to electrical equipment with which they come into contact.

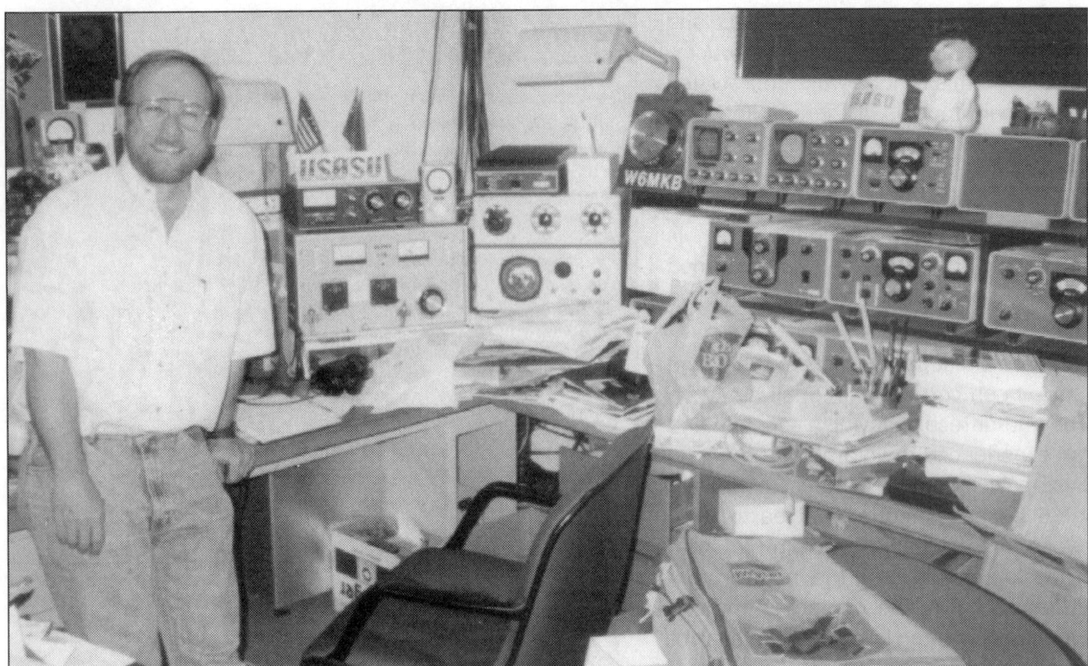

Terry Dubson, K6JL (formerly W6MKB) shows off his fine collection of classic equipment, some of which used to belong to the legendary W6AM

A word, too, about working on antennas. Firstly, in siting antennas do ensure that they are well clear of power cables and cannot fall across these cables in the event of structural failure. Many UK amateurs use tilt over masts and towers, which avoids having to climb them to work on antennas. Never try to climb a telescopic tower when it is extended, a potentially lethal activity. If you have a fixed tower, or need to climb a telescopic tower when retracted, always use a good-quality climbing belt, wear a safety helmet and, if at all possible, have a friend or relative nearby in case of injury. In the USA and other countries where fixed towers are more common, there are all too many climbing accidents each year, most of which were would have been avoidable if proper safety precautions had been observed. If your antennas are roof or chimney-mounted, again care should be taken when doing installation or maintenance work. You can always employ a professional antenna installer but, sadly, most TV antenna installers have little understanding of the particular requirements of radio amateurs, so the usual solution is to do the work ourselves. If you don't feel competent to handle the job, it may be that an amateur at your local club is willing to step into the breach.

A further comment regarding wind-up towers is perhaps appropriate at this stage. Be aware of the manufacturer's specifications. If the tower is unguyed, you will need to know the wind loading of your antenna(s) and rotator, and be prepared to lower the tower if strong winds are forecast. The guying of towers is a specialist subject which it is not intended to cover here. Be aware, though, that many failures of amateur towers have been due to twisting, due to the antenna itself not being balanced with respect to wind loading. Simple three-point guying cannot prevent this, and additional precautions may need to be taken.

Security

MANY AMATEUR stations contain easily portable equipment worth thousands of pounds. Sometimes this is located in a shack remote from the house, possibly on view to the passer-by. It is not surprising that an amateur station can attract attention the of the wrong sort of person. Some elementary precautions should always be taken.

Make a note of the model number, serial number and distinguishing features of each item of equipment and keep this somewhere in the house (not in the shack) where it is unlikely to be seen by an intruder. Make sure the shack is secure by checking (and using) the locks on windows and doors. Consider fitting a burglar alarm, especially if a separate shack in the garden is in use.

If in doubt on these matters, seek the advice of the crime prevention officer at the local police station. When going on holiday, let the police know.

Equipment left in cars is at particular risk. Never leave hand-portable transceivers (or any other valuables, for that matter) lying around on the seats of cars. Keep them with you or, if this is not convenient, locked up in the boot. Remove mobile transceivers when the car is left parked outside the house. Make sure the car is fitted with an alarm. If the worst comes to the worst, make it difficult for the thief to dispose of the equipment. Give the details of the theft and the equipment to the local radio club(s) and the RSGB (or appropriate national society) as well as the police and insurers. The local radio shops should also be warned, particularly any dealing in second-hand equipment.

Insurance

WHILST EVERY AMATEUR will try to construct and maintain his station so that it is completely safe for himself and any others who may visit it, there is always the possibility that an accident may occur. Owing to a component failure a visitor may receive an electric shock, or an antenna or mast may fall and injure someone or damage property. Such an occurrence may result in a legal action, and these days it can result in the award of very substantial damages against the person held to be responsible for the accident. This risk can, and should, be insured against, either by an extension to the

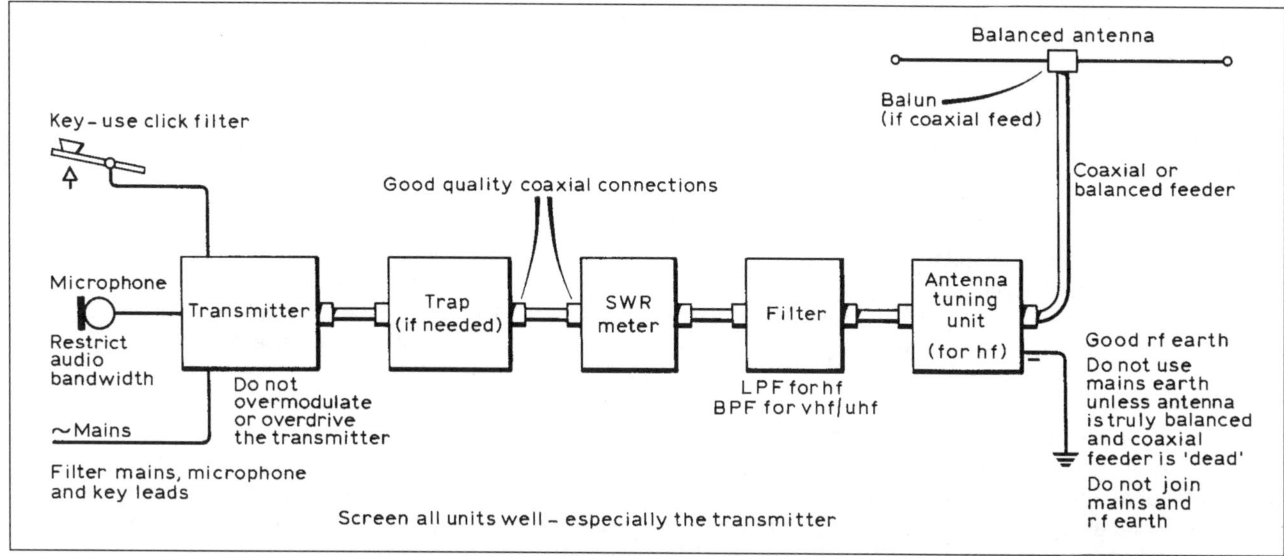

Fig 3.4: An example of station layout that leads to good electromagnetic compatibility (EMC)

existing Householder's Comprehensive policy or by taking out a separate public liability policy if only fire insurance is held. The annual premium for this will be quite a small amount and readers cannot be too strongly urged to consult their insurance advisers over this matter.

The other insurance risk is theft. Again, the existing household insurance should be checked to ensure that the equipment is covered and the cover should be increased if necessary. General household insurers do not always understand the special requirements of amateur radio. One story is of the amateur who had specialist microwave band equipment stolen and was offered a voucher for a replacement microwave cooker by his insurance company! Do, therefore, ensure that your insurance company fully understands what it is covering, with a list if equipment, replacement values, serial numbers and other relevant information.

Insurance is also important for special event and DXpedition operations. The same considerations apply.

Transmitter checks and adjustments

THE UK LICENCE stipulates that transmitters should be tested from time to time to ensure that the licence requirements concerning non-interference to other telecommunications can be met; details of such tests must be recorded in the station Log. Adverse comments made on the air concerning modulation quality (including that of CW signals) should be treated with concern, and the fault or incorrect adjustment traced before further transmissions are made. Most amateurs tend to be uncritical of other stations' signals out of politeness, and therefore when comments are made it is often the case that something is quite seriously wrong.

Most transceivers have built-in calibrators or digital frequency readouts. As with any other frequency measuring equipment, these should be checked periodically.

If available, the manufacturer's handbook should be carefully consulted for details of adjustments and tuning up procedure, and the operator should be fully conversant with these before putting the transmitter on the air.

The standard handbooks should be consulted for test methods and circuits. Most test gear required is either inexpensively obtainable on the second-hand market or easy to construct at home. Its regular use is not only the mark of a responsible operator, but also one who is sure that his transmitter is really giving peak performance in those DX pile-ups!

EMC - dealing with breakthrough

ONE OF THE MOST troublesome problems in amateur radio is breakthrough caused by the fundamental transmission getting into all types of electronic equipment. The term 'breakthrough' rather than 'interference' is normally used to describe this phenomenon, emphasising the fact that it is really a shortcoming on the part of the equipment being interfered with, and not a transmitter fault.

A good starting point is to adhere to the practices shown in **Fig 3.4**.

Good radio housekeeping

The main object of good radio housekeeping is to minimise breakthrough, by making sure that as little as possible of the precious RF energy finds its way into neighbouring TVs, videos, PCs, telephones, and the multitude of electronic gadgets which are part and parcel of the modern home. It could be argued that the immunity of the domestic equipment is inadequate, but this does not absolve the amateur from the responsibility of keeping his RF under reasonable control. Many of the features which contribute to minimising breakthrough also help in reducing received interference, so that the virtue of good neighbourliness has the bonus of better all-round station performance.

Antennas

By far the most important factor in preventing both breakthrough and received interference problems is the antenna and its siting. The aim is to site the antenna as high as you can, and as far as possible from your own house and from neighbouring houses (see **Fig 3.5**). If there is any choice to be made in this regard, give your neighbours the benefit of the increased distance - it is usually much easier to deal with any problems in your own home. It is a sad fact that many amateurs are persuaded by social pressures into using low, poorly sited, antennas only to find that breakthrough problems sour the local relations far more than fears of obtrusive antennas would have done. It is probably true to say that many neighbourly objections to planning applications for antennas are rooted more in fear of interference than in concern about the appearance of the antenna system. Therefore it is worth spending time helping them to understand, in layman's terms, the way in which near-field radiation falls off as the square of the distance or, to put it in simple terms, "twice as far away, one quarter as much signal level".

HF antennas

The question of which antenna to use is a perennial topic and the last thing that anyone would want to do is to discourage experimentation, but there is no doubt that certain types of antenna are more likely to cause breakthrough than others. It is simply a question of horses for courses; what you can get away with in a large garden, or on HF Field Day, may well be unsuitable for a confined city location. Where EMC is of prime importance, the antenna system should be:

(a) Horizontally polarised. TV down leads and other household wiring tend to look like an earthed vertical antenna so far as HF is concerned, and are more susceptible to vertically polarised radiation.

(b) Balanced. This avoids out-of-balance currents in feeders giving rise to radiation which has a large vertically polarised component. Generally, end-fed antennas are unsatisfactory from the EMC point of view and are best kept for portable and low-power operation. Where a balanced antenna is fed with coaxial feeder, a balun must be used.

(c) Compact. This ensures that neither end comes close to the house, and consequently to TV down leads and mains wiring. Antennas to be careful with are the extended types such as the W3DZZ trap dipole or the G5RV, because almost inevitably in restricted situations one end is close to the house. Even in quite a small garden, on frequencies of 14MHz upwards it is not too difficult to arrange an antenna fulfilling these requirements. A half-wave dipole or small beam up as high as possible and 15m or more from the house is the sort of thing to aim for. At lower frequencies compromise becomes inevitable, and at 3.5MHz most of us have no choice but to have one end of the antenna near the house, or to go for a loaded vertical antenna which can be mounted farther away. A small loop antenna is another possibility, but in general any antenna which is very small compared to a wavelength will have a narrow bandwidth and possibly a relatively low efficiency. Many stations use a G5RV or W3DZZ trap dipole for the lower frequencies but have separate dipoles (or a beam) for the higher frequencies, sited as far down the garden as possible.

VHF/UHF antennas

The main problem with VHF and UHF is that large beams can cause very high field strengths. For instance 100W fed to an isotropic transmitting antenna in free space would give a field strength of about 3.6V/m at a distance of 15m. The same transmitter into a beam with a gain of 20dBi (17.86dBd) would give a field strength, in the direction of the beam, of 36V/m the same distance away. Again, it comes down to the fact that if you want to run high power to a high-gain beam, the antenna must be kept as far from neighbouring houses as possible, and as high as practical.

Operation in adverse situations

The obvious question arises as to what to do if your garden is small or non-existent, or domestic conditions make a simple wire tuned against ground the only possibility. First of all, and most important, don't get discouraged - many amateurs operate very well from amazingly unpromising locations. It is really a question of cutting your coat according to your cloth. If there is no choice but to have antennas very close to the house, or even in the loft, it will almost certainly be necessary to restrict the transmitted power. It is worth remembering that it is good radio operating practice not to use more power than is required for satisfactory communication. In many cases, relations with neighbours could be significantly improved by observance of this simple rule.

Not all modes are equally 'EMC friendly', and it is worth looking at some of the more frequently used modes from this point of view.

SSB: This is one of the least EMC friendly modes, particularly where audio breakthrough is concerned.

FM: This is a very EMC friendly mode, mainly because in most cases the susceptible equipment sees only a constant carrier turned on and off every minute or so.

CW: This is the old faithful for those with breakthrough problems because it has two very big advantages. First, providing the keying waveform is well shaped with rise and fall times of about 10ms or so, the rectified carrier is not such a problem to audio equipment as SSB. Secondly it is a very

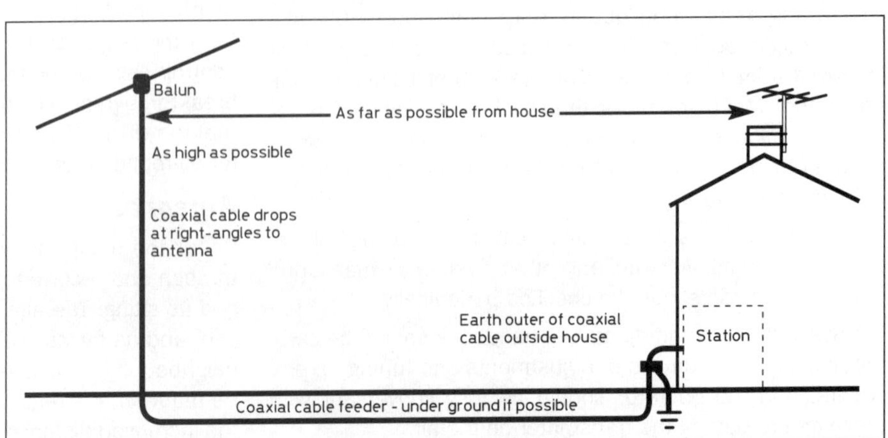

Fig 3.5: Good radio housekeeping - site your antenna and feeder system well away from the house

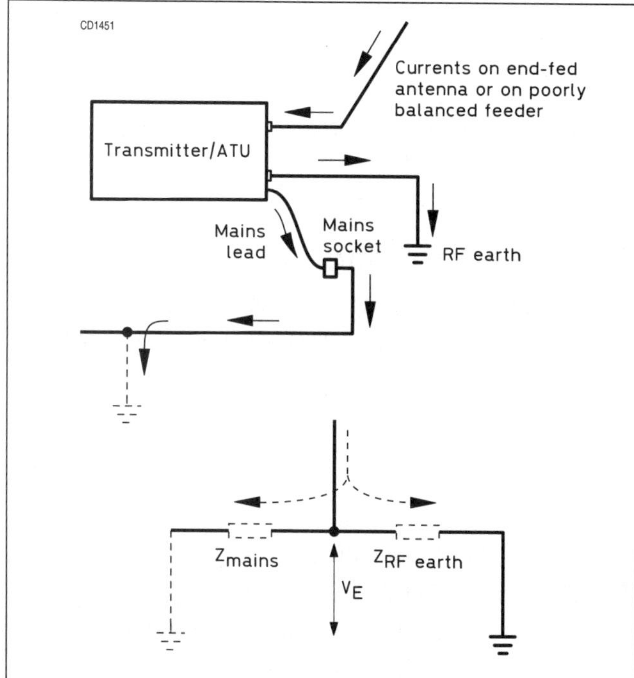

Fig 3.6: Earth current divides between RF earth and mains. The current down each path will depend on the impedances. The transmitter earth terminal will be at V_E relative to 'true' earth potential

'power efficient' mode, so that it is possible to use much lower power for a given contact.

Data: Generally the data modes used by amateurs are based on frequency shift keying (FSK) and phase shift keying (PSK), and should be EMC friendly. All data systems involve the carrier being keyed on and off - when going from receive to transmit, and vice versa - and consideration should be given to the carrier rise and fall times, just as in CW. Some of the new data modes which can now be generated from your PC rival CW in their ability to 'get through' with minimum power. These open up new horizons to amateurs living in difficult locations.

Earths

From the EMC point of view, the purpose of an earth is to provide a low impedance path for RF currents which would otherwise find their way into household wiring, and hence into susceptible electronic equipment in the vicinity. As shown in **Fig 3.6**, the RF earth is effectively in parallel with the mains earth path. Good EMC practice dictates that any earth currents should be reduced to a minimum by making sure that antennas are balanced as well as possible. An inductively coupled ATU can be used to improve the isolation between the antenna/RF earth system and the mains earth. The impedance of the mains earth path can be increased by winding the mains lead supplying the transceiver and its ancillaries onto ferrite cores to form a common-mode choke.

Antennas which use the earth as part of the radiating system - that is, antennas tuned against earth - should be avoided since these inevitably involve large RF currents flowing in the earth system. If this type of antenna must be used, arrange for it to be fed through coaxial cable so that the earth or, better, some form of counterpoise, can be arranged at some distance from the house.

The minimum requirement for an RF earth is several copper pipes 1.5m long or more, driven into the ground at least 1m apart and connected together by thick cable. The connection to the station should be as short as possible using thick cable or flat copper strip/braid.

Where the shack is installed in an upstairs room, the provision of a satisfactory RF earth is a difficult problem, and sometimes it may be found that connecting an RF earth makes interference problems worse. In such cases it is probably best to avoid the need for an RF earth by using a well-balanced antenna system - but don't forget to provide lightning protection.

Harmonics

Harmonics are much less of a problem than formerly, partly due to the closing down of VHF television in the UK and partly to the much greater awareness by home-brewers and commercial manufacturers alike of the importance of good design and construction.

Notwithstanding this, if there is any doubt about the harmonic performance of a transceiver, a low-pass filter should be used. Care should be taken where harmonics can fall into broadcast radio or TV bands. In particular:

1. The harmonics of some HF bands fall into the VHF broadcast band, 88-108MHz, as does the second harmonic of 50MHz.
2. The fourth harmonic from the 144MHz band could cause problems on TV channels 34 and 35 and the fifth on channels 52 and 53.
3. The second harmonic of 18MHz falls into the IF band of TV receivers.

Interference to amateur reception

While breakthrough causes the most problems so far as the relationship between an amateur and his (or her) neighbours is concerned, the most serious long-term threat to the future of amateur radio is the pollution of the spectrum by the increasing number of interference sources. Interference generated by motors and similar devices is still with us, but by far the most serious problem is the broad-band noise generated by digital electronic equipment. The RSGB and other amateur radio bodies have also become increasingly concerned about the proposed introduction of broadband networking via power lines (BPL) which has the potential to cause severe disruption to amateur radio communications.

The EC EMC Standards put limits on permissible emissions from all types of electrical equipment but these are intended to protect relatively large signal services such as broadcasting. They are not stringent enough to prevent interference to amateur reception. Fortunately most products are nowhere near the maximum limit for emissions, or may be so only on specific frequencies, so in practice the situation is not as bad as it appears at first sight.

Techniques for the distribution of high-speed data signals over telephone lines, and even over the electricity mains, are being pushed forward as an economical way of distribution of data for the Internet. This raises entirely different problems. Systems operating at relatively low frequencies are unlikely to give problems unless there is a system fault, but the demand for higher data speeds will mean pressure to move to frequencies in the HF band. Inevitably the signals will be broad-band and there is a risk that the competitive pressures will force providers to push emissions to the limit to minimise costs. The RSGB, in co-operation with other national societies, is lobbying for tight limits on permissible emissions from such systems, to ensure that the spectrum is protected for the use of small-signal services such as amateur radio.

Dealing with interference to reception is too big a question to be addressed in these notes. The RSGB EMC Committee also publishes a leaflet EMC 04 *Interference to Amateur Reception*. Up to date information on EMC issues can be found in the 'EMC' column in *RadCom*. Information on leaflets and filters available from RSGB can be found in the *RSGB Yearbook*, and on the EMC Committee web site [9] where copies of the various leaflets can also be downloaded in PDF format.

Station Notebook

To close this chapter, one piece of advice I would offer is, right from the start, to get into the habit of maintaining a station notebook. In this you might record the routing and labelling of your various antenna feeders, a note of antenna SWR curves (when they change it is a sign that something may be wrong), details of modifications to any of the equipment (and maybe a note of serial numbers, plus date purchased and amount paid), and so on. This sort of data can be invaluable at a later date, when you decide to make changes to the station, for example, and can't recall why you originally made a particular design decision. It's never too early to start with this valuable habit.

Further information

[1] *The Rig Guide*, Steve White G3ZVW, RSGB 2003

[2] *DUBUS* Magazine: http://www.marsport.demon.co.uk/dubus.htm

[3] RSGB Microwave Committee Components Service: http://www.g3wdg.free-online.co.uk/

[4] BATC: www.batc.org.uk

[5] 'A Modular 24cm ATV transceiver', Simon Lewis GM4PLM, *RadCom*, May 2003, p.26

[6] *CQTV* 201, Feb 2003

[7] *ARRL Antenna Book*, ARRL (available from RSGB)

[8] *Radio Communication Handbook*, RSGB.

[9] RSGB EMC Committee: http://www.qsl.net/rsgb_emc/

4 Computers in the Shack, and the Internet

THERE IS CERTAINLY no requirement to have a personal computer (PC) in your shack, and many amateurs continue to manage perfectly well without one. But for the majority, in the 20 years or so since the advent of so-called "personal" computing, PCs have become an essential element of a modern amateur radio station.

This chapter isn't intended to cover programming or the various technical issues you might face in interfacing your PC to your transceiver and other equipment in your shack. Rather, it will provide an overview of the ways in which a PC can enhance the operating experience, with some suggestions for further reading and research.

Undoubtedly the first PC-based application which found its way into many amateur radio stations was logging. Keeping a log-book is not only a licence requirement, but also a pleasurable activity. Over the years it is a joy to be able to look back and use the logbook entries as an *aide memoire* to recall special QSOs. But the reality is that if you are especially active, perhaps because you are a regular contester or simply because you have been licensed for a long time, those logbooks start to accumulate and it becomes harder and harder to keep track of what you have worked or to find a particular QSO. This is where PCs really come into their own. PCs are ideally suited for handling large quantities of data, allowing the user to index that data and retrieve it in a variety of ways. Frankly, any popular spreadsheet or database program can serve well as a computerised logbook, and all offer a variety of ways of searching for specific data. For example, you might enter QSOs into a spreadsheet in chronological order, but then sort the data alphabetically to be able to retrieve it. And if you are at all experienced in writing macros or programming in, for example, VB, then you can easily keep track of statistics such as countries worked.

Of course, you don't actually have to go to such trouble at all. There are many custom-made logging programs for both day-to-day logging and contest logging, some which you have to pay for and some are available as freeware or shareware. The benefit of commercial software is that you can usually expect a significantly higher level of customer support. The section on logging and station management programs goes into more detail.

As well as handling data, the other thing that PCs are particularly good at is undertaking calculations. So it wasn't long before programs became available for propagation prediction and for antenna modelling, both of which are computationally demanding. As PCs have become more powerful,

Murray Greenman, ZL1BPU, makes extensive use of computers in his shack for data communications

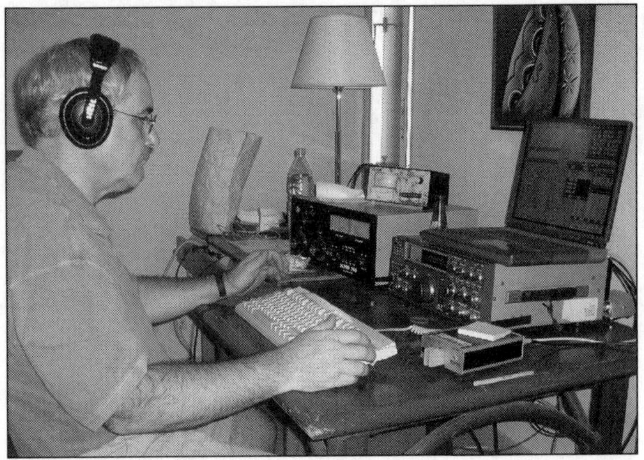

Lee, KY7M, operates 5U5Z with the Voodoo contest group in the 2003 *CQWW* contest. Note that the laptop computer is fully integrated into the station and networked to the other operating positions

later versions of such software have become more and more effective. Propagation prediction will always be subject to the vagaries of the ionosphere, just as weather forecasting remains something of a black art, but antenna modelling has now reached the stage where the calculated parameters are usually as close to final performance as measurements allow, at least for HF and above.

Computers have also taken over the data modes, covered in Chapter 8. RTTY, PSK, SSTV and the many emerging data modes all lend themselves to the world of computers. The PC sound card acts as the interface between the digital world appropriate to these modes and the analogue world of HF radio, where data is normally sent by modulating a carrier with audio tones. Of course, the same approach can also be taken to voice transmissions. Nowadays many logging programs provide such an interface, for example allowing the user to record incoming audio so that individual contacts or even a whole contest can be saved to the hard disc while, on the transmit side, CQ calls and other frequently-used phrases can be pre-recorded and played as required.

The distinction between transceiver and PC has become ever more blurred in recent years. While the PC can receive and generate audio tones, as discussed above, more and more of the circuitry in amateur transceivers is digital in nature. The first commonly-implemented interface was for frequency readout and control. This is extremely useful in the logging environment. On the one hand, it means that you need never mis-log the band on which you make a QSO, as the PC will automatically capture the frequency information from the transceiver. On the other hand, it can be extremely useful to control the transceiver's frequency from the PC, for example by capturing a 'spot' from the Cluster system and moving the transceiver instantly to the frequency. But nowadays the level of interaction between PC and transceiver can be very much more than this, to the extent that several transceiver models can be remotely controlled in every respect over a telephone or Internet link. This is ideal for anyone wanting to set up their station at, say, a remote rural location but operate it from their suburban home. As an alternative approach, some recent transceivers have been designed without external controls, but simply a PC interface, so that the front panel now becomes a virtual front panel displayed on the PC screen and controlled by keyboard and mouse. The ultimate reflection of this approach is those transceivers which have been reduced to a PC card, plugged into your desktop PC in exactly the same way as, say, a sound or games card. The main limitation is power availability and heat dissipation, so such cards tend to be suitable only for low transmit power levels.

Internet

IN MANY WAYS the real revolution has come through networking, especially in the context of the Internet. As in almost every other area of life, the Internet has opened up a plethora of opportunities for amateur radio, and new ideas are coming along all the time. As well as being an almost universal source of information, from circuit designs, equipment reviews, contest rules, and pretty much anything else you might need, the Internet's ubiquity allows many interactive applications which can enhance the pleasure of our hobby. The subject is one which could fill a book in its own right, so it is easiest here just to give a few examples. Log keeping again comes to the fore. Many DXpeditions have taken to posting their logs on the Internet in something close to real-time, which has become very popular with DX chasers. Most contest organisers now encourage submission of contest logs via the Internet, for speed, security (logs are less likely to go astray than in the international postal system) and also because electronic logs lend themselves to checking by PC, speeding up and improving contest adjudication whilst reducing the burden of manual log checking. And for awards purposes the advent of the ARRL's *Logbook of the World* (LoTW) is set to have a huge impact in the coming years. Amateurs will undoubtedly still wish to collect traditional QSL cards, but will no longer have to subject them to the vagaries of the postal service in order to claim awards.

There have been several instances in recent years where contest stations have linked their logs directly over the Internet, the best example being in the annual IARU HF Championship, where each IARU member society is encouraged to run an HQ station which others can work for multi-

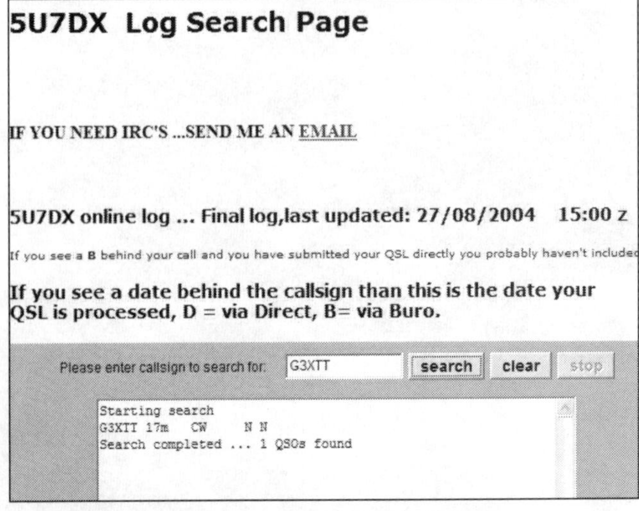

A typical DXpedition log search page on the Internet. QSL managers and individuals now have remote access to log entries, often whilst the DXpedition is actually taking place

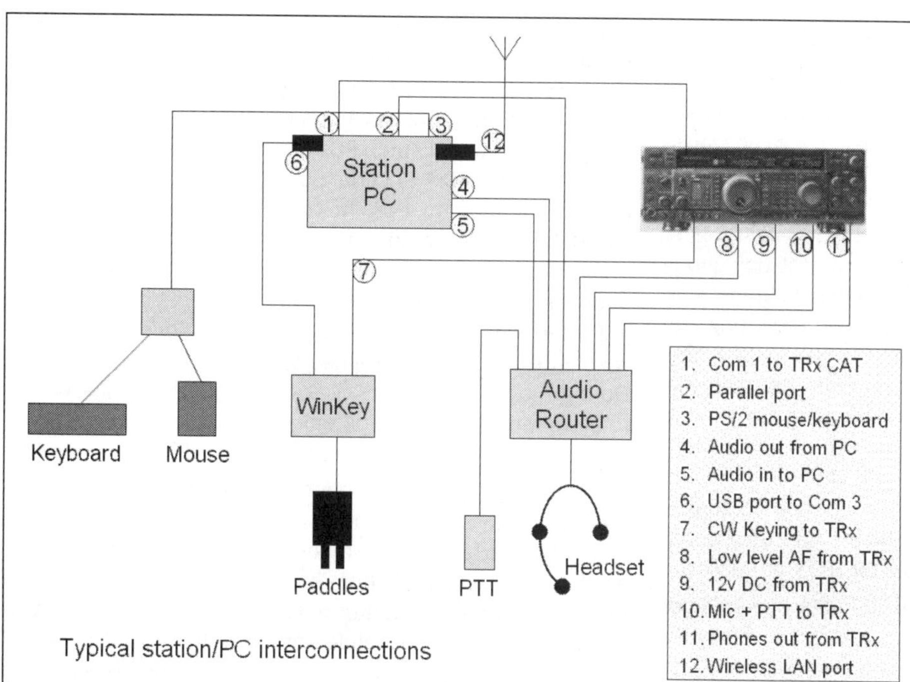

Fig 4.1: A typical station set-up, showing how PC and other equipment are linked (this is from the *Participant Manual* of the 3B9C Rodrigues Island DXpedition). In a home station, there may also be a VHF radio link for PacketCluster access and, perhaps, interfaces to antenna rotators and similar devices

pliers. There is no rule requiring this HQ station to be confined to a single site and it has become common practice to host different bands at different well-equipped contest stations around a country, and then link their logs by Internet so that each band position has access to the full HQ station log. It does not take too much of a leap of the imagination to see some contest organisers encouraging events in which all entrants are linked in some way, with running scores available in real-time. Amateur radio contesting would then become much more like other spectator sports, perhaps with non-participants logging on to see how the leaders are doing in the same way as watching a road race.

In those countries where the authorities allow linking of Internet and amateur radio, other possibilities emerge. This happened some years ago with the PacketCluster system, where European and North American Cluster networks, operating over VHF, UHF and microwave links, were linked across the Atlantic via a terrestrial data connection. Nowadays a high proportion of Cluster nodes have an Internet connection as well as VHF/UHF access, and amateurs can access the system via a Web interface or a Telnet session. More recently, the development of VoIP (Voice over Internet) has allowed VHF and UHF nodes and voice repeaters to be linked together over the Internet making it possible, for example, for an amateur in California using a 2m handheld transceiver to talk with an amateur in the UK using a similar transceiver on, say, 70cm. To the purists this isn't amateur radio in the truest sense, but it is an interesting marriage of two technologies and, of course, it relies on the amateur licensing system to permit a radio link at one or both ends of the connection.

A typical station configuration

BEFORE DISCUSSING some of the uses of the PC in more detail, it is helpful to look at what a typical modern station configuration might be. **Fig. 4.1** is illustrative only, and although complex is by no means at the limits of what might be found in, for example, a state of the art expedition or multi-multi contest station, or even a single-operator two-radio set-up as used by some of the more serious contest operators. In fact, it is the configuration used by the 2004 3B9C Rodrigues Island expedition at each of the 15 operating positions. In a home station equipped, for example, for single-operator two-radio contesting, the configuration would be rather more complex!

What is immediately apparent is the large number of interfaces to and from the PC. Indeed, this is where the bottleneck was in the early years, with limited serial and parallel ports on most early computers. Nowadays that is really no longer an issue, the bigger problem being how to avoid earth loops and other EMC-type problems with all these interconnecting cables in a high-RF environment.

Obviously the PC will have some sort of wide-area (Internet) connection, to gather information (Cluster spots, etc) and to distribute information (sending logs, Cluster spots, etc). There will be a data link (RS-232/CAT/CI-V) to the PC, for both-way sharing of frequency information, mode, maybe even data such as filters in use. There will be audio interfaces, for sending audio to the transceiver (CQ calls, etc for voice modes or tones for data modes) and for receiving audio from the transceiver (for recording voice and CW transmissions, for decoding data mode transmissions). There may be a connection to the transceiver for direct FSK keying for data modes (not shown in the diagram, where it is assumed the interface will be an audio one).

There may be interfaces to other, ancillary equipment, such as antenna rotator, antenna switches and audio router (used to switch audio sources such as microphone and sound card, and audio destinations such as sound card and transceiver microphone input, depending on the mode in use). For CW, the PC will typically be used to generate standard messages and to produce transmitted text from keyboard input. Most CW operators still prefer to copy CW by ear, but many programs exist to decode received CW although they usually fall down in the face of significant amounts of interference.

Choosing a PC for the shack

WHAT FEATURES do you need to look for in a PC for the shack? Any modern PC will run the sort of software you are likely to want to use in your day-to-day radio activities. However, the problem often comes with some of the older programs intended for amateur radio use. Several of the popular programs were written in the days of DOS-based PCs, and have not been fully migrated to the almost ubiquitous Windows operating system. The main problem is in the area of interfacing to the outside world. The earlier operating systems were able to interact directly with the hardware, which makes real-time activities such as generating CW relatively straightforward. The various Windows operating systems sit between the application and the hardware, deciding when each process can have its share of CPU time. As a result, when running multiple applications, CW can end up sounding distorted with erratic timing. Problems can also occur with other early programs, for example for RTTY or Packet.

As a result, some amateurs quite deliberately use an older PC in their shack, perhaps a previous-generation family PC that is no longer required. Others take the alternative route of using a modern PC, and discarding their earlier software, using only software that has been developed specifically for the Windows environment.

Either way, there will be certain requirements for a PC that is to be of use for the various applications described in this chapter.

Let's look firstly at interfacing to the outside world. Is a network or direct Internet connection required? If so then you will need a telephone modem, Ethernet port or Wi-Fi adaptor. Maybe, as well as Internet, you want to interface to a Packet modem, *en route* to a VHF transceiver for packet radio, including PacketCluster access, which will probably require a serial (RS232) interface. Then there is an interface to the transceiver for band data, which may also require a serial port. Many programs allow you to use either a serial port or a parallel (printer) port for CW keying. For data modes, you will need a soundcard, the transceiver interface being by way of the microphone input and sound output connections to that card. One way or another, it is easy to run out of ports, especially serial ports. There are add-in cards available for desktop PCs, to allow extra serial ports, though you will then need to consider addressing the various ports to avoid conflicts. Some of the earlier logging programs only recognised Com1 and Com2, but most can now be configured to Com3 and Com4 as well. Laptop PCs often come with only one serial port, but PCMCIA to serial port adaptors are readily available. Many modern PCs, however, have moved away from serial ports entirely, and offer only USB ports instead. All is not lost, as USB to serial adaptors are available from most PC suppliers, and some amateur radio suppliers are now offering interface boxes for data communications and logging which are specifically designed to work with a USB interface. During the next few years, it is inevitable that transceivers, rotators and other equipment in the shack will also be released with USB interfaces, reflecting this overall trend.

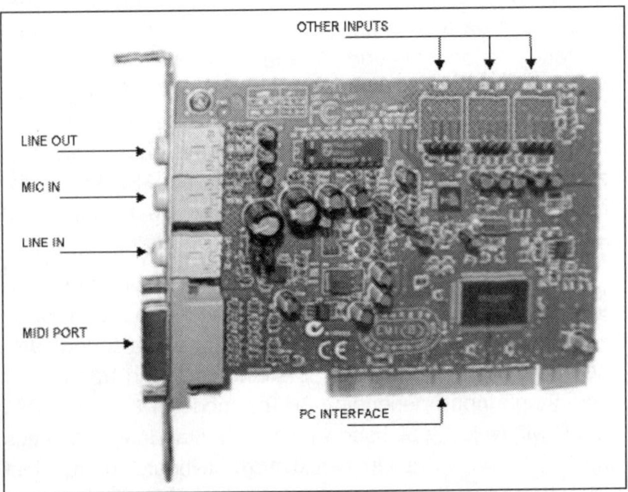

A shack computer will almost certainly have a built-in sound card that can be used for digital modes, recording QSOs etc

One of the biggest challenges you will face in interfacing the PC to your radio equipment is simply that, with so many separate interfaces to be made, there is huge potential for earth loops, resulting in hum on your transmitted audio, and for RF from your transmitter getting into the PC and causing problems. There is no simple answer to this. The use of one common station earth, decoupling of leads and installing ferrite beads on every line will help. You should also take care in the orientation of leads, keeping audio leads well clear of RF leads, for example. Network cables (twisted-pair) are notorious for RF pickup, and Wi-Fi appears to be a more reliable alternative for networking in the shack. Audio circuits (eg from PC sound card to transceiver) should usually be routed through isolating transformers or opto-couplers to permit various earthing points to be isolated from one another, avoiding earth loops. There is more on this in Chapter 8.

Many amateurs find the ideal solution is to use a laptop PC. The self-contained nature of these, and the rigorous EMC standards they must meet because they may be used in aircraft and other critical environments, means that generally they are far less likely than desktop PCs either to generate QRM or themselves be affected by RF. Most will accept a full-size keyboard and external mouse and, indeed, an external monitor, though as soon as you start adding these peripherals there is a risk of the very problems starting to re-emerge that you selected the laptop to avoid. Incidentally, some PC monitors are particularly bad at generating spurious emissions which can affect your reception of amateur signals. The modern TFT screens are a welcome step forward in this respect. Another common source of problems is the switched mode power supply and here laptops seem to be more of a problem than desktop PCs, because the power supplies are generally smaller and less well screened. Liberal use of clip-on ferrite chokes is recommended or, in the extreme, replacing the switched mode PSU with a traditional linear power supply for use in the shack.

One other benefit of a laptop, as against a desktop PC, is that it will have internal batteries, useful if the power goes down. Some amateurs solve this problem by having an uninterruptible power supply (UPS) in the shack. A good one will also provide enough capacity to keep your transceiver on the air for an hour or two as well, maybe enough to finish that midweek contest while the rest of the family sit in darkness! In contrast, the benefit of a desktop PC is that you can add additional cards, as required. For example, a terminal card

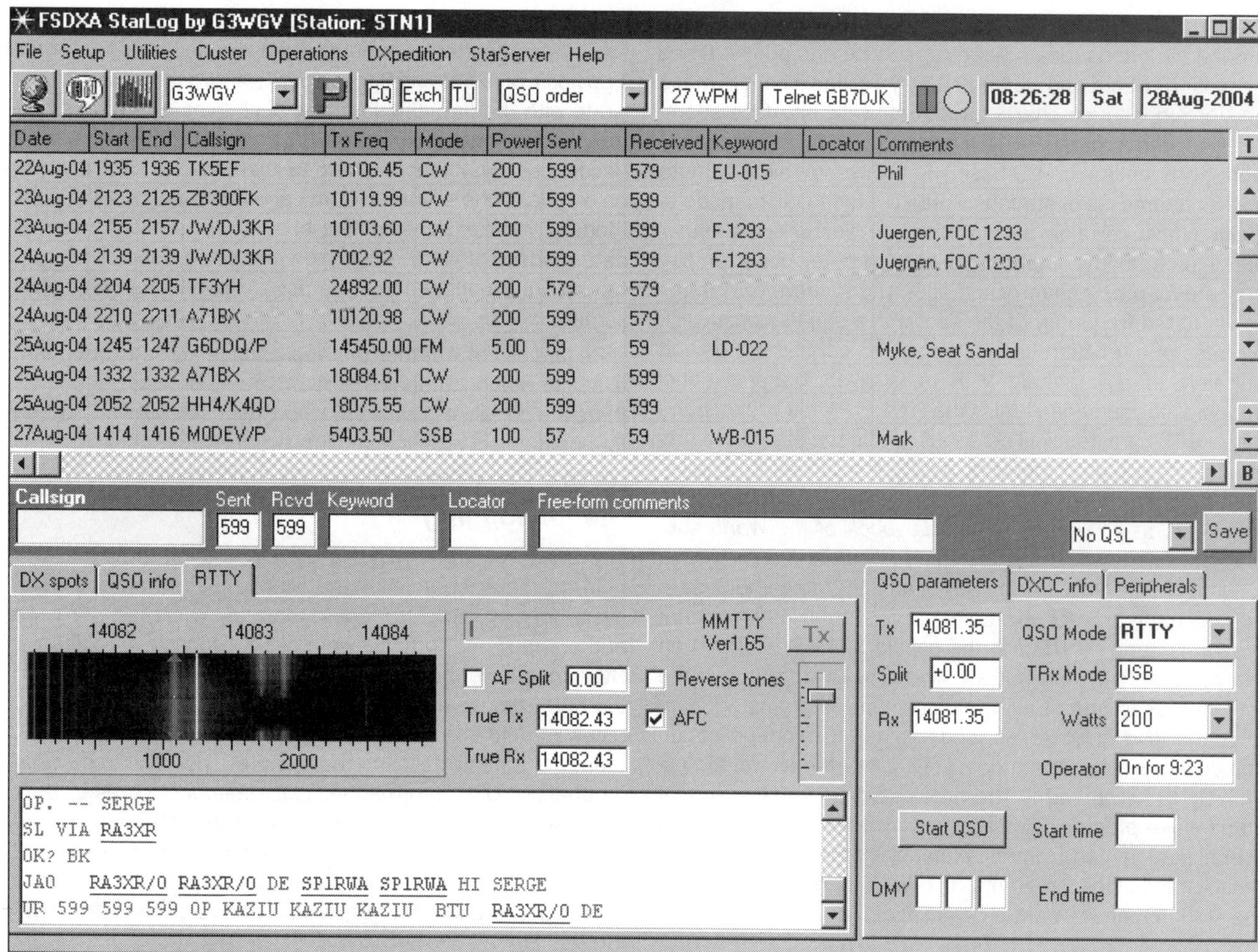

A typical logging screen from a modern station management program, in this case *StarLog*, as used on the 3B9C DXpedition. In this case, an RTTY signal is being copied (see the dual-tones in the waterfall display), with the received text appearing in the lower window. Anything recognised as a callsign is highlighted, and a mouse click will immediately put that call in the Callsign (logging) field. The various tabs and menus allow the operator to bring other data into the foreground.

for data modes or, nowadays, even a complete low-power transceiver. These do exist, with all the interfacing being done by mouse and keyboard through suitable control software. No doubt more of these 'transceivers on a board' will appear in the future, though the limitations on current supply from the PC's switched mode power supply and on power dissipation on a PCI card mean that any power amplifier will have to be external to the PC.

Station management by PC

THE TERM computer logging is really no longer appropriate, as most modern programs are better described along the lines of Station Management. While logging is the underlying function, most do very much more than this. There may be a number of underlying databases in addition to the log itself (or, more accurately, the logs themselves, as many amateurs keep several logs, perhaps for expeditions they have undertaken, or other callsigns they have held). For example, a database of IOTA islands, one for DXCC countries, several 'name' databases for club members, previously-worked stations, etc, and whatever else is appropriate to the operator's specific interests. Above these databases sits the "management" program, through which the operator can undertake a huge range of functions, of which logging QSOs is just one. Indeed, a large percentage of contacts may not be logged through the main station management program at all. For example, because most contests have unique rules, there is no universal contest logging program. The popular contest logging programs cater for the most popular events (CQWW, ARRL, IARU, etc). But specialist contest logging programs have been developed for other events, those for the European Sprint Contests and for the ARI (Italian) contest being good examples. These handle the QSO data requirements and the unique scoring system for the contests concerned. However, nowadays there is a standardisation of data formats which allows data to be exported and imported easily between programs. So, usually, logs generated by another program can be imported to your main station management program for later manipulation. That manipulation may be the generation of statistics ("how many countries have I worked on each band this year?"), the processing of QSL requests including the printing of labels or perhaps award handling (for example generating a file of recently-confirmed IOTA islands, which can then be used as a basis for the annual update).

As well as data manipulation, the logging program will almost certainly handle the interfacing to your transceiver(s), and probably most of the other interfaces described in the previous section. It will provide useful data as you tune around the bands (beam heading, sunrise and sunset times for stations heard and worked). It may well have built-in maps and/or propagation charts or, alternatively, interface seamlessly to other programs which handle these functions. It may work with online or CD-based callbooks to allow you to access addresses of stations worked or their QSL managers. It will almost certainly allow you to see Cluster spots, either off-air or from the Internet, identify whether, for example, they are for a new country and allow you to move your transceiver to the frequency of the spot with a single mouse click or press of a function key. Some can be configured to send an alert to a handheld VHF transceiver if a 'new one' appears, so you needn't miss the DX even when you're in the garden! The program will no doubt handle the other data provided by the Cluster network (WWV, Announces and Talks, etc) in both directions. It will probably allow you to generate and send off an update to your *Logbook of the World* submission. And it will almost certainly handle the data modes for you, either in itself or by way of an integrated interface to another program (for example, many station management programs hand off RTTY to the popular *MMTTY* program on the basis of "why reinvent the wheel?"). This, in fact, is the real clue as to how station management programs will continue to evolve in future. As soon as a new idea or application comes along (new data mode, *Logbook of the World*, etc.), it is likely to be served in the first instance by some sort of stand-alone program. But very quickly it will be brought into overall station management, either by integrating with one of those stand-alone programs or by writing new code within the station management program itself.

Of course, you may not choose to go the route of having everything integrated at this level. You may decide to mix and match, to find the best program for each individual requirement. This author uses a popular station management program for everyday logging, awards tracking, QSLing and analysis. However, for contest logging I use a variety of programs, according to the particular contest. My only requirement is that, after the contest, I can import the log into the main station log. With the adoption of Cabrillo as the format for most contest entries and of ADIF as an interchange format between logging programs, it is almost certain nowadays that any program will be able to export one or both of these, and any good station management program will be able to import the result, so there should be no problem. I also prefer, in a contest environment, to have a second PC running *Geoclock* or some similar program, showing a map of the world with the daylight/darkness split. I could have this running on the logging PC, but it is very easy for the screen to become so 'busy' that it is hard to keep track of what is going on. At least one amateur of my acquaintance, a keen data modes contester, runs one PC, but with two screens, with the data modes software running on one screen and other useful station management windows open on the second screen.

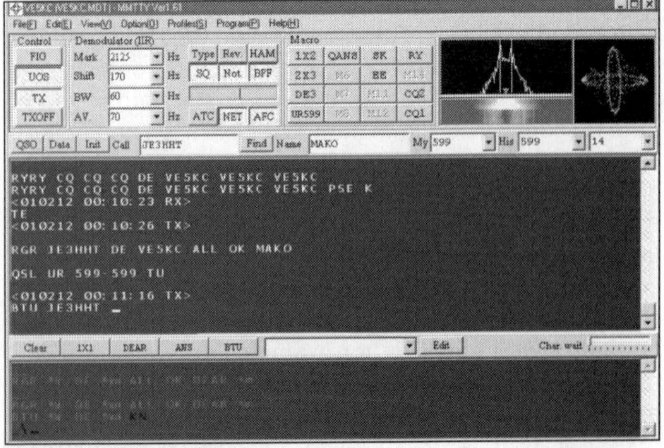

Some logging programs integrate with others for specialist functions, such as *MMTTY* for RTTY

Regardless of whether the applications are integrated into a single station management program, or quite separate, there are certain attributes that you, the user, will want to look for when selecting suitable software for your shack. The following sections look at each of the main applications in turn.

Station logging

The basic requirement for a station logging program is to hold the data required by the licence (see Chapter 2). Not every logging program does that, as overseas software authors may not be fully aware of UK licence requirements. Over and above the basics, you will no doubt want to be able to enter additional data, such as name, QTH, QSL sent and received, and so on. Then, as has already been described, there are the interfaces to radio and PC, perhaps to external databases (QSL information, club membership lists, etc), and useful additional features, either directly or by way of integration to other programs (data modes, greyline and propagation prediction, etc). And, of course, the ability to import and export data, especially via the Cabrillo and ADIF formats.

Beyond that, selection of a logging program is very much a matter of personal preference. This author prefers a logging screen that shows the last ten QSOs or thereabouts, with those and the QSO entry field looking very similar to a line in a conventional logbook. Not all logging programs take this approach. Some use pop-up windows for QSO entry, for example. I also have a particular axe to grind about callsign entry. If I am operating as G3XTT/VP9 (as was once the case), I would expect people who work me to be able to log me as such, and their logging programs recognise this as a Bermuda callsign. Some logging programs will only do so if the callsign is entered as VP9/G3XTT. This is actually inexcusable. If most programs can validly recognise the callsign either way round, why can't all of them? There are very few callsigns which are truly ambiguous - usually the shorter half of the call designates the DXCC entity.

My other *bête noire* is that some logging programs have callsign fields which are too short for some perfectly valid amateur callsigns. With hard discs having almost infinite in capacity these days, there is no excuse for cutting corners in field length. And the recent ITU decision to move to longer suffixes when existing callsign blocks run out mean that we could easily be faced with calls like VP2E/GW3AXTT/MM, some 15 characters long in all whereas some logging programs accept as few as 10 characters in the callsign field. Occasionally one hears plaintive cries on the air along the lines of "I can't log you because my logging program won't accept your callsign"; it does rather sound like a case of the tail wagging the dog!

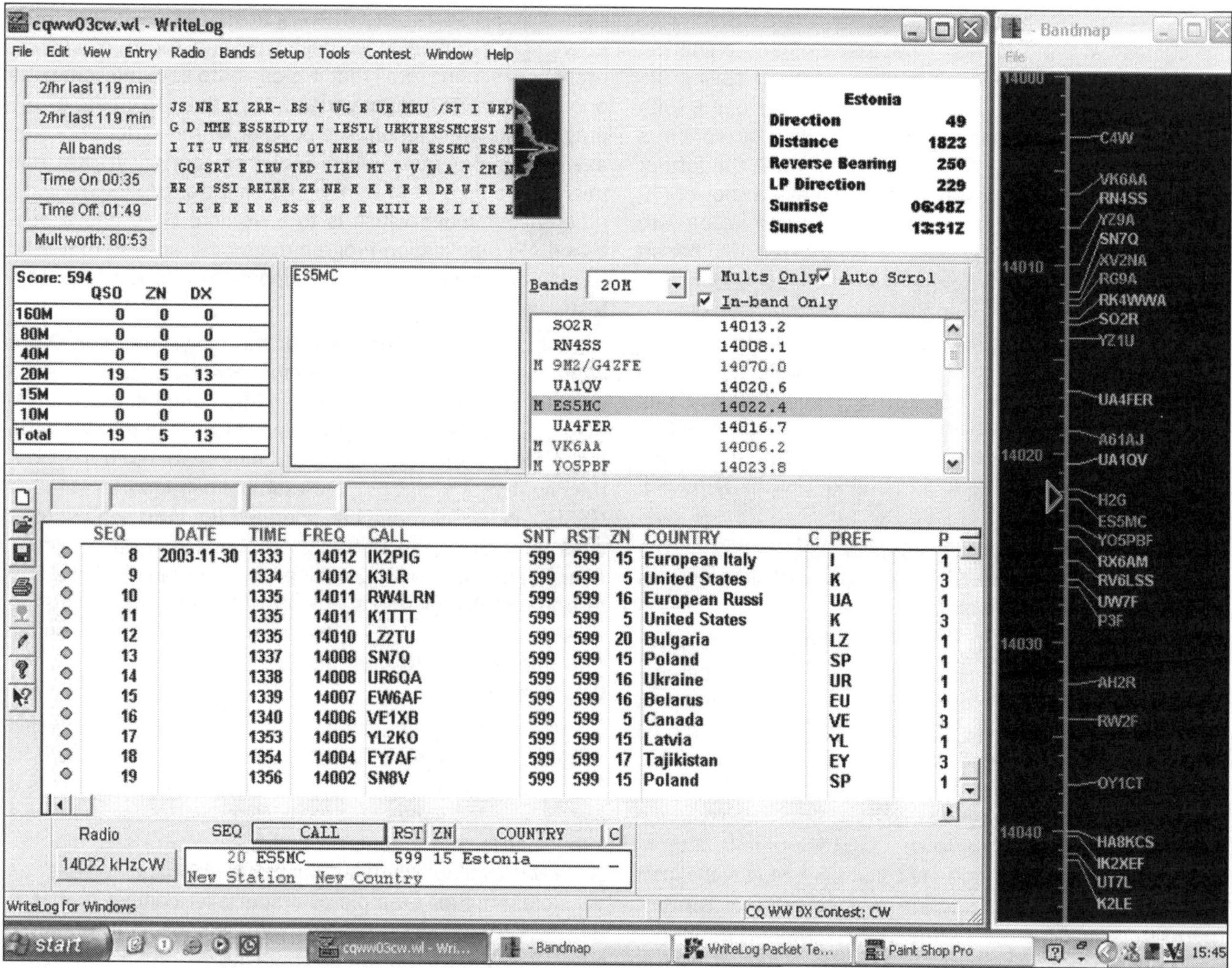

The main *Writelog* screen. *Writelog* is primarily a contest logging program. The window on the right is a 'band map', built automatically from incoming Cluster spots. The individual spots also appear in a window (centre right). By clicking on the relevant spot, the transceiver will move immediately to that frequency, and the callsign will be entered in the logging field. Other information such as beam heading, running score, etc appears in other windows. The program also works seamlessly with the *MMTTY* RTTY software for RTTY contesting.

The other aspect to bear in mind is that not all logging programs recognise all amateur bands. Some are designed primarily for HF use, some specifically for VHF use. Even those covering all bands may not, for example, recognise the 70MHz band, given that it is only available in certain countries. Neither will all programs offer the sort of facilities you may want for, say, satellite, meteor scatter or moonbounce operation, where you may need to record cross-band operation or specialist types of signal reporting.

Similarly, your choice of logging program may be influenced by specific awards you like to chase. Most logging programs will track DXCC entities, and have fields for common data such as QTH locator and IOTA reference. Others will have general purpose index fields where you can log state, county, etc.

The other requirement which is important for many operators is to be able to have several log files for different callsigns (G3XTT, GJ3XTT, G3XTT/VP9, etc.). Be aware that not all logging programs allow this, or you may need to pay an additional registration fee for each callsign.

For the reasons described above, some programs generate CW themselves but others, recognising that later versions of Windows can adversely affect CW timing, support an interface to an external keyer. Some for example, offer support for the increasingly popular *WinKey* from K1EL, others (*Writelog*, for example) for proprietary keyers.

Some station logging programs also offer contest logging facilities (see below), in some cases quite comprehensive, in others simply the ability to track serial numbers and generate a Cabrillo file but without scoring capabilities. Whether the facilities will meet your requirements will depend on how serious a contester you are, and what contests you like to enter.

It's really a case of checking out the various programs to see which best suits your particular needs. The good news is that, nowadays, most can be tried out free of charge. Usually this is done by imposing a limitation on the numbers of QSOs that can be logged. When you pay the registration fee, you are issued with a password which opens up the program to unlimited use.

Contest logging

Contest logging programs came into widespread use even before station logging programs. Contests lend themselves well to computer support. Prior to contest logging programs, contesters were faced with lots of complex tasks even while the contest was in progress, the best example being the need to keep real-time 'dupe' sheets, to avoid calling the same station a second time on any particular band. With serious contesters making maybe 3,000 QSOs or more in a weekend, this was a nightmare. Then there was the further nightmare after the contest of having to make a copy of the log, in whatever format the organisers required, along with scoring the whole thing. I well recall trying to put together an entry for a contest where several club members had operated, some of them with writing that was all but illegible! If we had been able to use computer-logging, that would not have been a problem (most people, even those inexperienced with keyboards, can keep up with the typing speeds needed to log contest QSOs). All the tasks described are absolutely run-of the-mill for a computer, and free up the operator(s) for the actual operating, thinking about strategy, and other added-value activities.

Contest logging programs normally dispense with the peripheral facilities offered by station logging programs (awards tracking, QSL management, etc.) to focus on the aspects you will need specifically for contesting.

A good place to start is the *SD* suite of contesting programs developed by EI5DI, very much with RSGB contests in mind. The programs handle logging (of course!), scoring for all RSGB events and many of the major international contests (CQWW, ARRL, etc), check partial and supercheck partial (ie checking a partial call against QSOs you have already made or checking a partial call against a database of tens of thousand of active contester callsigns), and CW keying both direct from the program itself and also via an external *WinKey*. There is an interface to the radio for capturing frequency information. The program allows editing and rescoring after the contest (sometimes it's quicker just to make paper notes during a contest if you have mistyped something, for example, and fix it later) and generation of the required files for the actual submission.

Interestingly, the *SD* approach is to have several programs for different contests or groups of contests, hence *SDV* (VHF contests), *SDI* (IOTA), etc. The argument for this is that there is enough variation in contest types (in terms of contest exchange, scoring, etc.) that it is easier to take the core code and create several slight variants than to try to create a 'one program fits all' solution. The popular *Writelog* (developed as a Windows program, unlike *SD* which started in DOS and migrated to be able to work under Windows), takes a slightly different approach which is to have core code and a published API (Application Programmers Interface) so that third parties can write add-ons to support a wide range of contests.

SD is essentially designed for the single-operator. Other contest programs have facilities for networking to allow multi-op contesting with multiple transmitters and hence multiple-PCs. In some cases the networking is via IP, so there is nothing to prevent those multiple PCs being scattered throughout the country (or the world!).For example headquarters station GB5HQ, in recent years, has operated the IARU contest from sites throughout the British Isles. Some contest programs offer full support for SO2R (single-op, two radio). And a feature that many operators look for is full integration with the Cluster network, to allow the acquisition of Cluster spots, with one-key QSY to work a multiplier that appears on the Cluster network.

Some contest programs have been developed for specific contests, an example being the program developed by DL2NBU to support the European Sprint contests. This is a case where the contest format is slightly unusual and it was important for the organisers to ensure that a suitable program was available in order to make participation as easy as possible. Another example of a specialist contest format is the Worked All Europe contest, with its concept of exchanging QTCs (data from previous contacts).

Contesters will have their favourite programs, and are generally reluctant to change as some of these programs require a fairly steep learning curve (preferably before the contest rather than during it!). In some cases the contest rules will suggest certain programs which fully support that contest, in other cases it is a matter of making enquiries, for example

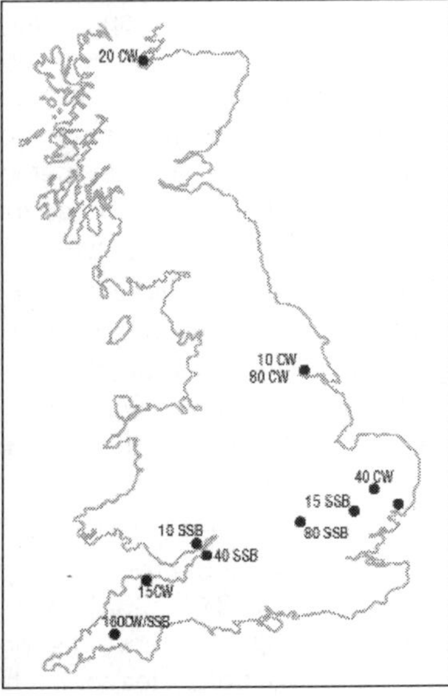

GB5HQ represents the RSGB in the annual IARU Contest, with different bands operated from locations around the British Isles, using a networked logging program linked via the Internet

via one of the contest reflectors on the Internet, to see what other contesters recommend.

Given the ability to interface some contesting programs to the Internet, it is interesting to speculate where this will lead in future. It is quite possible that serious entrants to some contests may be required to have a permanent connection open, with scores updated and published as the contest proceeds and your score at the moment the contest finishes deemed to be final. Already the fact that by far the majority of contest entries (probably around 80% across the board) are submitted in standard electronic format means that the adjudicators can themselves use a variety of software tools to aid in cross-checking and the compilation of final scores. This makes the creation of results timelier and more accurate, while relieving the adjudicators of the chore of manually checking many tens or hundreds of thousands of QSOs.

QSLing

QSLing can easily become a chore for active amateurs, with lots of incoming cards that aren't always wanted. But it is a matter of courtesy to reply, as many will be from newly-licensed amateurs who are keen for a card. After all, we were all there once upon a time. The availability of software to handle QSL management makes the whole process a lot easier. After all, the QSO details are already in your log, so it's then just a case of indicating which ones you need printed out for QSLing. Many logging programs have the facility built in. Alternatively, there are some popular stand-alone programs including *BV* by DF3CB. Most of these allow multiple QSOs to be printed to labels, for sticking on to your standard QSL card, and will usually print them ready sorted into alphabetical order so that there is no more work to do before dropping them in the mail to the QSL bureau. Typically there will be features such as printing cards separately for direct and bureau QSLing, options to print immediately or later, options to QSL other contacts with the same station and options to print to various size labels, either single or multiple QSOs.

Related to QSLing, it is worth mentioning here that files for both *eQSL* and *Logbook of the World* (see Chapter 14) can be generated from ADIF files, so most logging programs can handle these without difficulty. Expect to see logging programs go further in the near future, with full integration with *LoTW*, so that they will also track the credits you already have for your various DXCC awards, downloading this information from your *LoTW* record.

Awards tracking

As has already been mentioned, most logging programs will keep track of DXCC entity as a matter of course, along with data for other popular awards. The matter of DXCC entity isn't entirely straightforward, of course. No logging program knows automatically where a ZK1, FO or VP8 station is located, as examples, because all of these country prefixes are used for multiple DXCC entities. But once you allocate a callsign to a specific entity, the logging program will track it. It is worth noting that, for this purpose, most logging programs use a unique 'country number' as the identifier. At the moment each logging program author will use his own set of country numbers, but the ARRL now has country identifiers for *LoTW* purposes, and no doubt these will become a *de facto* standard for logging programs in the future.

There is no single way for logging programs to track other awards data. Some have general purpose index fields which you can use for various purposes. For example, *TurboLog*, popular in the UK allows you to use the same index file for several purposes: S-PA would indicate "State, Pennsylvania", while "OC-001" would be recognised as a valid IOTA reference. You can then sort and output the various data according to the relevant identifier. Some programs are specifically designed to cater for individual awards programs, US county hunting for example. If you have a favourite award that you follow, it is worth seeing which program suits it best. *TurboLog*, for example, also has the capability of generating your annual update file for the IOTA awards and tracking those island groups you already have credited.

Rig control

THERE ARE MANY transceiver control programs available and, again, most station and contest logging programs allow at least basic data (frequency, in both directions) to be exchanged with the popular transceivers. Specialist programs go much further, allowing you to control a very wide range of parameters, storing your favourite settings and memory frequencies, etc. This opens up a whole range of new opportunities to control your transceiver remotely, perhaps from the comfort of your armchair while the rig is in an outdoor shack or, more significantly, remotely across the Internet.

CW generation and decoding

Mention has already been made of the issues surrounding the generation of good-quality CW under various operating systems. The solution increasingly being adopted is the use of an external CW keyer, such as the popular and inexpensive *WinKey* by K1EL. Such keyers work as stand-alone keyers in their own right or can act on behalf of the logging program, responding to input from keyboard, stored messages associated with function keys, etc. With some programs, you can even choose to send CW with your paddle and the PC capture the callsign directly into the logging program. This only works if your CW is accurate, of course! There are many programs for receiving CW, though none has yet reached the capability of a good human operator. Most require clear, well sent CW, without interference from noise or other signals. Nevertheless, some software writers have experimented, with a degree of success, in developing programs which will run a CW contest entirely without operator intervention!

K1EL's *WinKey* can be used as a stand-alone keyer or can be integrated into a station management program

Data modes, including SSTV

Data modes software falls into various categories. On HF, the most popular modes nowadays are RTTY (emulating the mechanical teleprinters of old) and PSK31, though PacTOR, MFSK, Clover, PSK63 and others are also to be found. There are programs available to support all of these, from basic terminal emulators to full-featured data programs with waterfall displays for tuning, logging facilities and, for RTTY, contesting programs which also provide the features required by the major events. The most popular RTTY program appears to be *MMTTY* by JE3HHT. This can be used stand-alone, but the interface specification is available to allow it to be integrated into other logging packages (as several do).

Apart from packet radio, VHF data modes software tends to focus on specialist weak signal applications, such as meteor scatter and moonbounce. Best know is the *WSJT* suite of programs (Weak Signal by K1JT), including *FSK441* and *JT6M* for meteor scatter (the latter optimised for 6m use), *JT65* for EME and extreme troposcatter, and *EME* Echo for checking your own return path to the moon. Several SSTV programs are available, including *MMSSTV* from the same stable as *MMTTY*. The whole topic of data modes is covered in much more detail in Chapter 8.

Peripheral control

Nowadays there is scope for controlling a wide range of station peripherals via your PC. Examples include your antenna rotator and remote antenna switches. Satellite enthusiasts can enlist software to drive both azimuth and elevation rotators to track the satellite of choice, and EME enthusiasts can use similar software to track the moon.

Some software will control external audio switching devices to route microphone, sound card, etc to transceiver, back to sound card, etc. For example, when a CQ message is being pre-recorded you would want your microphone routed to the sound card, whereas when operating phone you would want it routed direct to the transceiver. But when you then want to use the recorded CQ, you would want the sound card output directed to the microphone input. Commercial switching devices are available to undertake this role.

DSP

Just as our transceivers are increasingly featuring DSP, so it is also possible to have software on your PC which will take audio, via the soundcard, and act on it with whatever software-defined filter characteristics you have chosen. To an extent this has been overtaken by the DSP in your transceiver, but there may be times, for example, when you want to work on some recorded QSOs, to improve their clarity. The other use for software of this kind is in decoding low-speed CW signals on the VLF bands. There are many suitable programs available.

Other applications

THE OTHER APPLICATIONS you will want to use will vary according to your interests. Antenna modelling and design, terrain modelling in respect of antenna gain and radiation patterns, circuit design and layout, and many others may be applicable. The list is endless.

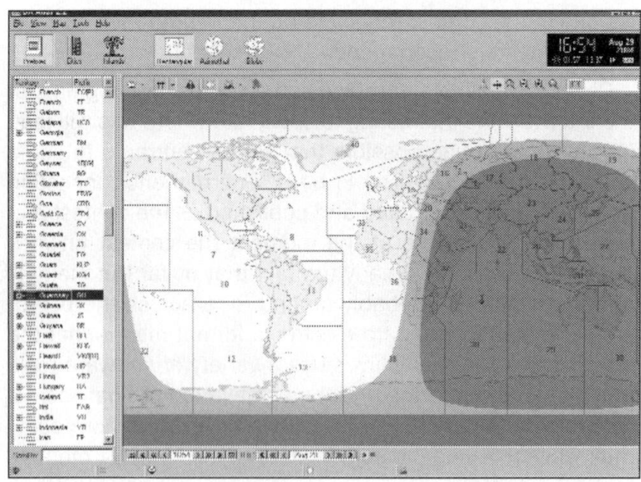

DX Atlas offers greyline, zones and much more

QSO recording

With the huge capacity of modern hard discs, it is now quite realistic to record a whole contest, particular DX QSOs of interest, or even every contact you make, especially if you then transfer them to CD. Some logging programs allow you to associate the recording with the QSO details, for easy recall at a later date. Obviously the various datacomms programs also offer recording facilities, including capturing images with the SSTV programs.

Training programs

Obviously there are plenty of programs for preparing for the various levels of amateur radio examination and also for learning Morse. Taking this a stage further, one popular genre of programs is that of QSO simulators, especially for CW. This is an ideal way of building your operating skills, especially contesting skills, away from the cut and thrust of an actual on-air event. The German *RUFZ* [1] is a popular CW contest simulator, and there are programs too from G4ZFE [2], G4FON [3], JA1DYB [4] and others.

Mapping programs

EI8IC [5] offers, free of charge for home use, a range of online maps of the world, with overlays of country prefix, IOTA reference, zone, etc. These are very handy to have available in the shack, especially if you don't have room on the shack wall for a large world map.

DX Atlas [6] is an excellent tool for propagation analysis (linked to *IonoProbe*), greyline indication and a wide range of maps with various projections. There is a charge to register the software, but a 30-day free trial is available.

Propagation prediction and greyline calculations

There is a huge selection of propagation prediction programs nowadays, though most are based on a handful of propagation prediction 'engines', ie specialist software developed for the purpose. A good example is *IONCAP*, developed initially by the US government and put into the public domain. There were two problems in using this software initially. The first was the amount of computing power it requires (it was developed to run on mainframes). This is no longer an issue, as PCs have become more powerful. The other was the user interface, which could best be described as "user unfriendly".

This has now been addressed by various software authors who have written user-friendly Windows-based front ends for the underlying engine.

Most of the propagation prediction programs available nowadays are very competent, taking into account not only the two ends of a propagation path, but also intermediate reflecting points *en route*. The amount of processing power required to do this is substantial, but modern PCs make short work of it. Nevertheless, propagation forecasting is rather like weather forecasting, anything but an exact science. As most amateurs will know, there are many anomalous events at work in the ionosphere which can enhance or adversely affect a propagation path. Most programs, for example, assume a traditional model for the launch of signals into the ionosphere and for intermediate reflections. But in practice effects such as chordal hop and ionospheric tilting at dawn and dusk can affect this traditional model, leading to unexpected propagation paths. So always use this type of software with care.

Greyline propagation and dawn/dusk enhancement on LF requires knowledge of sunrise and sunset times and the location of the terminator (the boundary between daylight and darkness). Many logging programs calculate sunrise and sunset whenever a prefix is entered. Several programs are available which show a world map, or part thereof, superimposed with the terminator.

Software is also available for beacon monitoring, for example for keeping track of the NCDXF beacon chain on HF or for monitoring beacon transmissions on the VHF bands. Whatever it is you want to do, and whichever beacons you wish to monitor, there is almost certainly software available to do the job.

Databases (prefixes, club members, QSL addresses)

Many logging programs have facilities for accessing external databases, either resident on your hard disc, on CD or via the Internet. Local examples might include a club membership list, giving a ready *aide memoire* of names and locations. Or you might have one of the popular CDs holding the international Callbook. Via the Internet you might want to access addresses or QSL information, for example via the popular qrz.com site. Some programs allow you to enter a callsign and then search a number of these resources sequentially to find the data you are looking for.

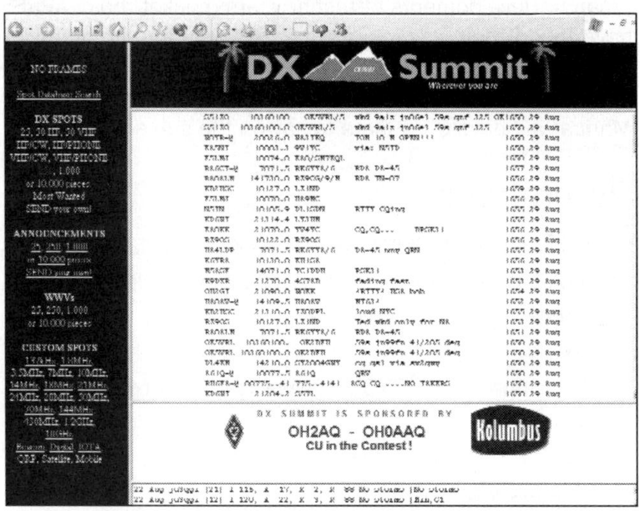

Accessing the Cluster network via the Internet using OH2AQ's *DX Summit* site

The Internet

THE PRECEDING discussion has focused on the sort of applications you may want to run locally on your shack PC. But, as has already been pointed out, this is only part of the story. The Internet takes the value of your PC to a whole new level, opening up a huge range of opportunities for data access, communication with other amateurs, posting Cluster spots, the list is endless. This section will cover some of the broad areas in which the Internet can be useful, but you will only discover the ways in which it will benefit you when you start to explore it yourself.

Cluster access

For many DXers and contesters, the great benefit of the Internet is in offering real-time access to the Cluster network (formerly, PacketCluster, but no longer, as fewer and fewer users access it via Packet radio). The Internet provides a more reliable link into the Cluster network than many users had via VHF and, with the advent of broadband, it needn't tie up your phone line.

There are two ways of seeing Cluster information. One is via one of the many Web pages which collect that information from around the world and bring it together into one place. The best-known is undoubtedly DX Summit [7], operated by OH2AQ. Anyone can access sites such as this, and if you are a licensed amateur you can input data to the system, too. The alternative, offering exactly the same interactive capabilities as if you were connecting via Packet radio, is to use Telnet access. Telnet is a communications program that comes bundled with your PC's operating system and, in this case, allows you to connect to any Cluster node throughout the world that has a suitable Internet interface. You will be asked to log on to the Cluster node with your amateur radio callsign, in the usual way.

In practice, most amateurs will access Cluster over the Internet either through a Telnet client bundled with their logging program or through a program such as *DX Telnet* which has been developed for amateur use, and can be downloaded from the Internet (there is a charge). It is designed specifically to handle the various commands and information associated with the Cluster network.

News Groups and Reflectors

There are many news groups and Reflectors on the Internet that are of interest to radio amateurs. They deal with specific manufacturer's equipment, including possible modifications, as well as contesting and DXing, popular software, operating modes, bands and specialisms (meteor scatter, moonbounce, etc.). The list is almost endless. Whatever your particular interests within the hobby, there will be a Reflector or news group that caters for it, maybe several. Some are geographically-based, for example there are times when much of the discussion on the CQ Contest Reflector is about US domestic contests, but most are of universal appeal. While some would regret that our hobby is about communication, so using the Internet to communicate with other ama-

The Internet is a mine of information about all aspects of amateur radio. This DXpedition site contained much advice on how to work the expedition even if you had only a basic station

teurs is a retrograde step, others would argue that having this extensive access to other amateurs actually stimulates the hobby. For example, if your transceiver has developed a fault, or you are having trouble configuring that weak-signal software, there will be many amateurs out there able and willing to help who, without the Internet, you might never come across.

News bulletins

Related to the above, there are many newsletters and bulletins you can subscribe to, some free and some you will have to pay for. In Chapter 9, reference is made to some of the DX bulletins which are available, but there are subscription services for Awards information, QSL information, and much more. Indeed, any subject that might have spawned a printed magazine or newsletter in the past will almost certainly have an electronic equivalent nowadays.

Web sites

For many people the Internet is synonymous with the World Wide Web, though this is just one of many facilities available. The Internet is the underlying network which carries several types of application. The web is the most popular way of accessing content in a seamless manner, and certainly is ubiquitous. Many individual amateurs have their own web pages nowadays, often reflecting their own specialist interests within the hobby. Many clubs and almost all national radio societies have web pages. Both the RSGB and the ARRL, for example, have extensive sites for public consumption, but with further information reserved for paid-up members (such as offering early access to contest results, equipment reviews, etc). Most suppliers of amateur radio equipment and software have web sites. Contest organisers, DXpeditions, special event organisers too, as you would expect. Many DXpeditions post logs and pictures even while the DXpedition is still in progress. The Internet is also your gateway to *Logbook of The World*, discussed in Chapter 14. Obviously there is a huge amount of technical information available if you are interested in home construction, antenna design, propagation studies, etc. And obviously there is a vast amount of material that you can download, from published articles, to software, manuals for equipment that you have bought second-hand, and so on. And, talking about buying second-hand, there are many sites where you can buy, sell and swap equipment. Truly, if you have a need for it, someone has probably already made it available on the web.

The TS-480, one of the first radios to come ready-equipped for control over the Internet

VoIP

Voice over Internet, already mentioned, is the means by which amateur radio voice nodes (including some repeaters) are interconnected, allowing worldwide communications from low power hand-held and mobile transceivers. VoIP is discussed in much more detail in Chapter 12.

Remote control of your station

The technology now exists to operate an amateur radio station remotely over the Internet and some amateurs are already doing so. This can be advantageous for those who, for example, have planning restraints at home but may have a weekend house where they can set up more effective antennas. At least one UK amateur has already been given an NoV to his licence to allow him to experiment with such a system, and several of the newer transceivers come ready-equipped with a suitable interface. While this has been possible for some time via traditional telephone lines, an Internet link offers greater flexibility and, because of the charging structure for Internet connections, can usually be left permanently open.

The overall conclusion, from everything that has been said in this chapter, must be that, far from taking away from amateur radio, computers and the Internet have done a huge amount to enhance our hobby, and there is still a long way to go. Amateur radio is, by its nature, a technical hobby, concerned with the advancement of communications. Many amateur developments of recent years (packet radio, APRS) have found their way into the professional and commercial sphere and we should in no way feel threatened when this becomes a two-way traffic. No doubt future editions of this *Manual* will have even more to say on the subject.

References

[1] RUFZ pile-up trainer: www.sk3bg.se/contest/rufz.htm

[2] G4ZFE pile-up trainer: www.g4zfe.com/pileup95.html

[3] G4FON Koch Morse trainer: www.qsl.net/g4fon/CW Trainer.htm

[4] Pilemania (JA1DYB): www.jg1vgx.net/etc/pilemania0.09.zip

[5] EI8IC: www.qsl.net/ei8ic

[6] DX Atlas: www.dxatlas.com

[7] DX Summit: http://oh2aq.kolumbus.com/dxs/

5 The Amateur Bands

VERY FEW AMATEUR stations are equipped for all of the allocated bands. To be so equipped would require a mountain of equipment and a rather impressive collection of antennas. Even the most experienced amateurs would probably admit to focusing their interests on specific bands or groups of bands. But one of the joys of the hobby is the sheer variety of operating experiences to be gained from exploring the many different bands and modes available to us. There is a lot to be said for spending a few years on certain bands, and then re-equipping your station to explore a completely different part of the spectrum. For example, enjoy the wide open spaces of 10m when the sunspot cycle is at its peak, then concentrate on the LF bands during sunspot minima. Or take some time away from the HF bands and try operating the VHF, UHF or microwave bands from suitable hilltop sites. One way or another, there is scope for a lifetime of interest. This chapter sets out to give a flavour of the various amateur bands, with some hints and tips about the types of propagation you might expect to find, specific issues about band planning and, where appropriate, some advice on equipment and antennas. What you will certainly find, as you spend more and more time on the air, is that each band has its own 'character' in terms of propagation and activity.

A little history is perhaps in order here. In the UK, as in most parts of the world, the first HF bands to be allocated to amateurs were 160, 80, 40, 20 and 10m. It is no coincidence that these are harmonically related. Before the days of synthesisers, many transmitters used to have crystal control or an oscillator running on one of the lower bands, and this frequency was progressively doubled to generate RF on the higher bands. 15m was a later addition, and is three times the frequency of the 40m band. Similarly, the harmonically related microwave bands were allocated to the amateur service at the 1947 World Administrative Radio Conference (WARC) in Atlantic City, USA.

One way to achieve several bands with one tower. A tribander and 6m Yagi cover the high bands. Just visible off to the right is a trapped vertical for 40/80m. And below the Yagi is a wire inverted-L for 160. This was G3XTT's antenna system a few year's back

At the 1979 WARC, amateurs were given allocations at 10, 18 and 24MHz (the 30, 17 and 12m bands). These new HF bands are relatively narrow compared with the earlier HF bands. They have the benefit of slotting neatly between the existing bands, offering some valuable propagation opportunities (for example, 12m is often open when 10m is closed). But because of their narrow bandwidth, there is international agreement that they should not be used for contest operating. The IARU also recommends restricting operation on 30m to narrow band modes (CW and data modes), though this recommendation is not universally observed. For those who like to avoid contest operation, these bands therefore offer a valuable refuge. Because of their genesis, they are often referred to collectively as the 'WARC bands'. More recently, UK amateurs gained a temporary allocation at 73kHz (now withdrawn) and an allocation at 136kHz. Most recently of all, UK amateurs have been allowed the use of several spot frequencies at 5MHz (60m) on an experimental basis, through to 2006. It will be interesting to see whether the allocation is extended beyond that time. The pattern elsewhere in the world is very much the same, though it is worth noting that some countries have yet to release the WARC bands to their amateurs, despite it being 25 years since that conference decision. It should also be noted that even the more historic bands aren't universally available. Many amateur bands are shared with other services, and in some countries this is a more significant issue than in others. Sometimes compromises are reached. For example, amateurs in Thailand do not have the use of 160 or 80m on a day-to-day basis, but are often able to get permission on an exceptional basis for contest operations or major expeditions.

Above 30MHz, the point at which the line is traditionally drawn between HF and VHF, a similar situation prevails. The Amateur Service has progressively been allocated more bands, extending into the microwave spectrum. National allocations vary, although most of the major bands are available in most geographies. For example, at the 1979 WARC mentioned above, amateurs also gained a number of new amateur Primary, Exclusive microwave bands above 24GHz. The 6m band, though, has only become available across most of Europe in recent years (and is still not allowed in some European countries). A 59MHz (5m) allocation was available back in the 1950s but was withdrawn as Band I television services were rolled out. The UK has enjoyed, along with a very few other countries, the 4m (70MHz) band, though there are hopes that this band will be more widely available within the next few years. But the 220MHz and 900MHz bands, popular in the USA, are unfortunately unavailable in Europe. Of course, there is less need for countries to co-ordinate VHF allocations on an inter-continental basis as the risk of mutual interference is very low, but for amateurs it is advantageous if their VHF and UHF allocations coincide, as this allows long-distance contacts to take place via, for example, satellites and Moonbounce. On HF this is far from the case, as propagation on most bands can be worldwide, at least at certain times of the day and certain periods of the solar cycle.

As stated in the Preface, the convention used in this chapter and elsewhere in this book is that generally used within the hobby, whereby VLF refers to the 136kHz band, LF to the 1.8, 3.5 and 7MHz bands and HF to the bands 10 through 28MHz. Similarly, the term Microwaves is used to denote all bands above 1000MHz. These terms are used in amateur radio parlance to group bands with similar propagation characteristics.

Very low frequency (VLF)

136kHz (2200m) band

The part of the spectrum between 30 and 300kHz is strictly termed LF, but VLF is used here to separate it from the lower HF bands which have been for many years called "the LF bands".

The 135.7 to 137.8 kHz band was allocated to UK amateurs in 1998 and is still considered an 'enthusiasts' band, as it requires a specialist technical approach and is unsuitable for day-to-day rag-chewing. There is no phone operation (the band is too narrow) and no contest operation. There are, however, specialist awards for DX achievement on the band, to encourage activity and experimentation.

The power limit in most countries is defined by Effective Radiated Power (ERP), limited to 1W. This may not sound much, but may actually require substantial transmitter power to generate, as antennas are inevitably going to have very low efficiency. After all, a full-size quarter wave vertical would have to be over 500m high!

Given that the band is just 2.1 kHz wide, it is clear that the use of wideband modes is out of the question, but this would also be precluded for simple technical reasons; the reduced size of the antenna means that it will inevitably have a high-Q and therefore a very narrow bandwidth. Early operations on the band were mainly using traditional CW, albeit at fairly low speeds, and it proved possible to make contacts up to ranges of 2000km or so. To achieve greater distances, amateurs have turned to very low speed CW, using tape recorders or PC software and, increasingly, to specialist data modes which take advantage of the PC's ability to integrate signals over an extended period of time and, in doing so, recover them from the noise.

Antennas for 136kHz are so small in terms of wavelength that they must use a large amount of inductive loading. This well-constructed variable inductor is shown off by ON6ND

One could consider any station in another country to be 'DX' on 136kHz but, to put a figure on it, most LF operators would feel very satisfied with an 800km+ CW QSO. Propagation on 136kHz is more stable than on 160m with very long distances, such as G to OH, being worked in broad daylight. Darkness does bring considerable signal enhancement but with it often comes a similar increase in noise. Some of the best DX QSOs have been made in the early mornings when the atmospheric noise has died down and the local noise is still low. Distances of over 6000km have been achieved during the hours of darkness using computer-assisted slow CW modes.

Almost all European countries now have a 136kHz allocation, although some are by special permit, and most have regular activity. The US has yet to open the band for general use but the FCC will issue 'part 5' experimental licences which allow tests to be carried out on fixed frequencies. Some stations have permission to engage in two-way contacts. Canada has a more liberal approach. By applying for a special permit, Canadian stations can have full access to the band and can make two-way QSOs. The first Trans-Atlantic contacts took place in 2001 between Canada and the UK. A few South American countries, including Argentina and Brazil, have the band and ZL stations can obtain permission to use 136kHz in addition to their usual 185kHz allocation. The band is an agenda item for the next WRC, possibly in 2007. The proposal is for a world wide Secondary allocation and this is likely to have the support of both CEPT and CITEL (representing the Organisation of American States).

Many HF transceivers are able to receive on 136kHz, though not necessarily very well. None of them, however, has LF transmit capability, so it will be necessary to build a dedicated transmitter or, alternatively, some sort of converter to work with your existing transceiver. Several suppliers are now offering kits for 136kHz equipment. When designing your station consider the ERP limit; a station with a large antenna may only need 100W to achieve 1W ERP but a station with a small antenna may be able to achieve the same result with a kilowatt or so. As with 160m, a good earth system is essential and earth stakes or radials should be used in conjunction with any existing underground metalwork such as water pipes. If you plan to use the low-speed modes, remember that the sent characters are much longer than on normal CW, so your transmitter needs to be designed with this in mind.

Important as radiating a good signal may be, no DX will be worked unless it can be heard. Reception is undoubtedly the most challenging aspect of LF operating. The main enemy of the LF DXer is noise - local noise from switching power supplies etc, QRM from nearby Loran or broadcast transmitters and atmospheric noise. Atmospheric noise (QRN), due to lightning, is bad during the summer months and can make the band unusable. Nothing much can be done to reduce the effect of QRN on the signal as it is propagated in the same way. This is the main reason that most DX is worked between October and April.

Other noises can usually be reduced by the use of directional receive antennas such as active loops. It must be

Table 5.1: Bandplan for the 136kHz band

No rigid bandplan is proposed for the 136kHz band, but amateurs are asked to work within the following conventions, giving long distance communications and experimentation priority.

135.7 - 136.0	Station tests and transatlantic reception window. {135.900 - 135.980 preferred transatlantic window for Europe to North America transmissions of very slow telegraphy (CW) (QRSS).}
136.0 - 137.4	Telegraphy (CW) {135.980 - 136.050 preferred transatlantic window for Europe / North America contacts.}
137.4 - 137.6	Non-Telegraphy (CW) digital modes.
137.6 - 137.8	Very slow telegraphy (CW) centered on 137.7kHz. {137.700 – 137.800 preferred transatlantic window for North America to Europe transmissions.}

borne in mind however that the transmit antenna will re-radiate the noise which it picks up. It is therefore often necessary to throw the transmit antenna off-resonance whilst receiving on a loop.

When choosing a receiver for LF, consider the following points:

It must have very good selectivity. Strong signals just a few hundred Hertz away will de-sensitise a receiver without a good narrow CW filter. DSP equipped sets can work well but there's no real substitute for a narrow filter as near to the first mixer as possible.

Stability and frequency accuracy must be of a very high order. Most modern transceivers are surprisingly good and can be relied upon to be within a few Hertz of the indicated frequency and to stay there! Remember that when using QRSS to work DX it is possible to miss the DX station altogether if you are just a few Hertz out of calibration. Any drift will make a very slow CW signal difficult to read.

Receiver sensitivity is often poor on VLF and front-end selectivity usually non-existent. Connecting the average transceiver to a large aerial and tuning to 136kHz will often yield nothing but broadcast inter-modulation and noise. A selective preamplifier will solve these problems.

If all your efforts with the receiving system have been successful, the German transmitter at 138.8kHz should be an S9+ signal, whereas the daytime band noise should be about S3 in a 250Hz filter.

Table 5.1 shows the band plan which has now been adopted by 136kHz operators. While not mandatory, it was recommended by the IARU 2002 Conference and by failing to observe it not only will you upset other band users, but you are unlike to make any contacts.

Normal CW occupies the lower part of the band, up to about 137kHz. The quite slow speeds used (about 7-20WPM) will pass through the narrow receive filters necessary to pick out weak signals. Fast CW becomes unintelligible when heard through such filters and it is best to call quite slowly in order to have the best chance of being heard far afield. The most popular CW calling frequency is 136.5kHz. Some stations are still crystal controlled so it may be necessary to tune the band after calling CQ. Tuning carefully whilst listening through a narrow filter can take a surprisingly long time, so if you are replying to a DX station's CQ call, off his frequency, give a long enough call to allow him to find you. Other modes in regular use on the band include QRSS (very slow CW, running a transmit program such as *QRS* by ON7YD, and decoding with *Argo* by I2PHD), Hell, PSK08 and Wolf. They are described in more detail in Chapter 8. Most can be downloaded from the *The World of LF* [1] downloads page.

Given the specialist nature of the band, most amateurs active on the 136kHz band are 'members' of the RSGB LF Group which operates via an e-mail Reflector. This is the place to learn about forthcoming activity and new narrow-band modes, or to ask for skeds. It is also where you can ask questions on LF matters, no matter simple or complex, with the assumption that you will get replies from experienced, knowledgeable and friendly people. To join, simply send an e-mail to: majordomo@blacksheep.org with no subject and only 'subscribe rsgb_lf_group' in the body of the message. Another good source of information is *LF Today* [2].

Low frequency (LF)

1.8MHz (160m) band

160m is often referred to as the Gentleman's Band, perhaps in the past it saw relatively little activity, and most of that was by way of local ragchewing, often on AM (amplitude modulation). Many transceivers did not include the band, as efficient transmitter operation on 160m requires a lot of inductance in the PA stages. Another reason was that the band was only available in a very small number of countries, as it was also used for commercial purposes, especially for ship-to-shore and for navigation systems.

Nowadays, almost every country has a 160m band, though allocations and power limits still vary significantly from country to country and it can be quite difficult to keep track of them. K0CKD's web page [3] makes an attempt to do so. **Table 5.2** shows some of the main ones, illustrating just what sort of variations occur. In broad terms, activity on the band divides between local ragchewing, especially during daylight hours when range is limited to no more than 80km or so, and DXing which, because of the nature of the band, takes place during the hours of darkness. In the UK, most local operation takes place above 1.9MHz, whereas DX activity stays largely within the bottom half of the band.

As far as local activity is concerned, 160m continues to be favoured for many club and special-interest group nets. While it cannot support nationwide nets during daylight hours, it is ideal for a club with members in and around a particular

Table 5.2: Some 160m allocations

USA/Canada	1800 - 2000kHz
UK	1810 - 2000kHz (Note 1)
Japan	1810 - 1825 and 1907.5 - 1912.5kHz
South Africa	1810 - 1850kHz
Australia	1800 - 1875kHz
New Zealand	1800 - 1950kHz

Note 1: 400 watts below 1850kHz, 32 watts above.

town, maybe within a circle of 35km or so diameter. This part of the band is also popular with those indulging in a little nostalgia, for example by operating AM (amplitude modulation) with restored valve equipment. Most, though by no means all, major contests include 160m, and the band is also used for a number of small local and national contests. There is increasing use of data modes, especially those such as PSK31 which cope well in high-noise conditions.

It is difficult to define 1.8MHz DX in terms of distance, but 3000 to 5000km would generally be considered to qualify. 160m propagation is not dissimilar to that experienced on the medium wave broadcast band, with little sky-wave propagation during daylight hours, but with long-distance working possible throughout the hours of darkness. In years gone by, achieving DXCC (100 countries worked) on 160m would have been considered an almost unattainable goal. However, recent years have seen a substantial increase in activity which, combined with improvements in antennas and receiver technology (and in some instances, such as in the UK, increased power limits) have led to scores of 200 countries or more becoming relatively commonplace. A few of the most dedicated 160m DXers have now exceeded the 300 country level. A well-equipped UK amateur prepared to lose sleep in the cause of 160m DXing could nowadays expect to work 100 countries or more in a season, and large contest stations have been able to work DXCC in a single weekend. Even with 10W, many stations have worked all continents.

DX propagation on 160m requires that the whole path lies in darkness, though there can be significant signal enhancement at dawn and dusk due to ionospheric tilting. For example, the path between the UK and Australia often opens for about 10-15 minutes before and after Australian sunrise. Such openings will not occur every day, and openings can be very short (just two to three minutes) with signals peaking at good strength and then falling away very rapidly indeed. To some extent, propagation will depend on ionospheric activity. In particular, signal paths through the auroral zone will be subject to strong attenuation when auroral activity is high. In the northern hemisphere, signals from the north also arrive at much lower wave angles than those from the south. To achieve these wave angles with a horizontal antenna would require antenna heights of 250ft or more, so vertical antennas are generally favoured by 160m DXers.

Many major DXpeditions nowadays include 160m. Here some of the 3B9C, Rodrigues, team walk the 87ft 160m vertical into place

On shorter paths (eg Europe to North America), the path can be open for several hours, although signals may still peak around sunset in North America and around sunrise in Europe. Having said this, peak time for paths between Europe and Central America is often around local midnight at the mid-point of the path, and therefore around 0200 or so European time. North-south paths, such as that between Europe and South Africa, frequently peak around midnight European time. In broad terms, DX working during the winter period tends to be more productive for stations in the northern hemisphere due to the longer hours of darkness and lower static levels. However, the converse is that this is the worst period for activity from the southern hemisphere and European DXers are increasingly recognising the need to be alert during the summer for activity from southern Africa, South America and even Australia.

Because of the uncertainty surrounding 1.8MHz propagation, and the way in which signal strengths can vary significantly over a short period, successful 1.8MHz DXing demands regular monitoring of the band, often at unsociable hours. For this reason it is not uncommon for 160m DXers to work together, each taking turns in monitoring, and agreeing to alert one another if a rare station becomes workable.

As mentioned above, 1.8MHz DXers typically use some sort of vertical antenna, which may be an inverted-L, a loaded vertical, or perhaps a shunt-fed tower. All such systems require an excellent earth system if reasonable efficiency is to be achieved. Details of suitable antenna systems can be found in many references, for example [4], [5]. As ground-wave communication is more effective with vertically polarised antennas, the use of a vertical antenna will also enable good daylight distances to be achieved on 160m in addition to the DX capability.

The main limitation with vertical antennas is that they are more prone to noise pick-up than horizontal antennas. Serious 160m DXers therefore use separate receiving antennas. This may be a small tuned loop or, if space is available, a Beverage antenna. Neither is suitable for transmitting purposes, but both can give significant signal to noise enhancement on received signals.

Receiver performance is important on 160m, not so much in terms of absolute sensitivity but more in respect of being able to receive weak DX signals in the presence of very strong local signals on adjacent frequencies. Good intermodulation performance is therefore crucial. Although less common than it used to be, many DX stations and DXpeditions will operate 'split frequency', and in some cases split-frequency operation is essential due to differing frequency allocations (for example, although they now have an allocation lower in the band, some Japanese stations continue to transmit between 1907.5 and 1912.5kHz, listening around 1830kHz for European stations). The ability to operate 'split' is therefore essential. Most DX operation takes place on CW, and good-quality narrow CW filters make reception of weak signals that much easier. SSB DX working is, however, becoming more common as station improvements compensate for the inherent disadvantages of the mode (wider bandwidth and lower average power, resulting in significantly poorer signal-to-noise ratio than with CW, all other factors being equal).

Over the years, increasing levels of activity and competition have taken away some of the exclusiveness previously felt by 160m enthusiasts. Activity in the major contests can be especially frenetic and, although these are an opportunity for the newcomer to increase his tally of DX, they can be somewhat intimidating. Better, perhaps, to cut your teeth on working relatively common DX, for example UK to USA, from where there is plenty of activity.

The IARU Region 1 Band Plan restricts SSB operation to frequencies above 1840kHz (which, given that LSB is used, means that the carrier frequency should be no lower than about 1842.5kHz), and the majority of CW activity takes place below 1840kHz. Because of the narrowness of the band, this split tends to be treated with flexibility in the major contests, but most Region 1 stations adhere to it at other times to the benefit of all users.

It should also be noted that, although 160m frequency allocations have been brought much more into harmony than was previously the case there are still, as mentioned earlier, differences from country to country. The one band segment which is common to most users is 1810 to 1850kHz, which is why most DX activity takes place in this part of the band.

On CW, operating speed is very much dependent on conditions. If signals are strong each way, there is no reason why normal speeds of operation should not be used. Some stations advocate slower speeds when signals are weak, though often it is better to operate at normal speeds but with several repeats in the hope that at least one transmission will be heard through the noise or fading. Remember that band openings can be of short duration so, in fairness to other operators, contacts should be completed in the shortest possible time. Equally, it is unreasonable to work a rare station several times, on consecutive nights for example, when others are trying to make a first contact.

Most rare stations and DXpeditions nowadays will make at least some effort on 160m, although some are more prepared than others to cope with the more demanding operating and lower QSO rates compared with the other HF bands. In some cases it can be productive to work a rare station on one of the higher bands and make a schedule for a 160m contact, but not all DX operators will be prepared to do this. In any case, do not waste their time unless you feel there is a good chance of making a contact at the time and on the frequency agreed.

Unfortunately there are few reliable propagation indicators for European stations on 1.8MHz, but activity is high enough nowadays for the presence and strength of DX stations to be used instead. The signal strengths of local and semi-local stations provide no guide at all to DX conditions. Careful listening can provide clues, and the occasional directional CQ at what ought to be an optimum propagation peak (for example a grey-line propagation path) can sometimes yield a call from a rare DX station.

Although significant parts of 160m are now Primary amateur allocations, UK amateurs are still restricted to lower power levels above 1850kHz and must avoid interference to other non-amateur band users. In the segment 1810-1830kHz there continue to be non-UK commercial users and, again, amateurs should exercise restraint and avoid interference to these other services.

1.8MHz has always been regarded as a specialist DX challenge. The late W1BB, the first station to gain DXCC on the band, took many years to achieve his goal. Even though DX working on the band is now much more commonplace, 1.8MHz remains the most challenging of the HF bands, requiring persistence and perseverance to achieve competitive results. K1ZM's book [6] captures something of the unique flavour of the band.

3.5MHz (80m) band

80m (or 75m as it tends to be referred to in North America) is very much a mainstream band for all aspects of the hobby. It is included in most major contests, is used for many national contests, is popular for local nets and is a magnet for those who want a real challenge in their DXing, compared with the relatively easy pickings on, say, 20m. It is increasingly used by data modes enthusiasts, too. With so much going on, the band inevitably gets rather crowded at times, so a degree of flexibility and understanding is required of its users. This is a most useful band for local and near-European working during daylight hours and for longer-distance contacts after dark. In winter, particularly during the years when solar activity is low, it is an excellent DX band, capable of providing worldwide communication. In summer, transequatorial contacts with Oceania, the Pacific and Africa are possible and there are openings to other parts of the world, but summer static can be a limiting factor. Particular attention should be paid to the use for 'grey-line' or 'shadow-line' paths (see Chapter 6).

In Europe and some other parts of the world the band is allocated to amateurs on a shared basis, with military and commercial stations and specialised point-to-point services taking many of the available frequencies. This sharing results in high levels of interference from on-frequency blanketing, and also from receiver-generated spurious signals and cross-modulation caused by high-powered non-amateur stations working off-frequency. While many countries allow their amateurs to operate between 3.5 and 4.0MHz, Europe, including the United Kingdom, uses 3.5 to 3.8MHz. Some other countries, such as Russia, Australia and Japan have restricted allocations on 80m, which DX operators need to be aware of. **Table 5.3** shows the 80 metre

On the 160 and 80m bands, it is useful to use greyline paths. Web site dx.qsl.net has an online greyline map that updates every five minutes

Table 5.3: Some important 80m band plans

US band plan for 80m	
Novice and Technician Plus classes:	
3.675 - 3.725MHz:	CW Only
General class:	
3.525 - 3.750MHz:	CW, RTTY/Data
3.850 - 4.000MHz:	CW, Phone, Image
Advanced class:	
3.525 - 3.750MHz:	CW, RTTY/Data
3.775 - 4.000MHz:	CW, Phone, Image
Amateur Extra class:	
3.500 - 3.750MHz:	CW, RTTY/Data
3.750 - 4.000MHz:	CW, Phone, Image
VK (Australia) band plan for 80m	
3.500 - 3.700MHz:	CW
3.535 - 3.620MHz:	SSB
3.620 - 3.640MHz:	digital modes
3.640 - 3.700MHz:	SSB
3.776 - 3.800MHz:	DX Window
JA (Japan) band plan for 80m	
3.500 - 3.525MHz:	CW
3.525 - 3.575MHz:	CW, Narrow Phone, Image
3.747 - 3.754MHz:	CW, Narrow Phone
3.791 - 3.805MHz:	CW, Narrow Phone, Image

band plans for some key countries, illustrating the sort of differences which occur.

As well as being a DX band, 80m is an ideal band for daytime nets and ragchews. Distances up to several hundred kilometres are typical, which is very suitable for contacts around the UK, for example. As a result, the band is very popular with clubs and other special-interest groups, as it provides reliable communications, with most participants able to hear each other comfortably. When using the band for such activity, though, it is necessary to be aware of the impact on other users who may be trying to work DX. For example, in the winter the Scandinavian countries enjoy almost round-the-clock DX opportunities as they are in almost permanent darkness, but signals from the UK can be much louder than the DX signals. So, while the DX is inaudible in the UK, UK stations may inadvertently be preventing the Scandinavians from working DX.

For CW DX working, the bottom 30kHz is used, with the lower 10kHz being most favoured in accordance with the IARU Region 1 Band Plan. As the USA restricts the use of the 3500 to 3525kHz segment to Extra Class licensees, it is necessary to monitor above this segment for contacts with American amateurs who do not hold the higher licence. Novice and Technician Plus licensees are restricted to the band segment 3675 to 3725 kHz. As with other bands, DXpeditions and 'rare' stations often use split-frequency working, listening for calls in a specified frequency or band of frequencies away from their transmit frequency.

The majority of DX working on phone is in the upper 20kHz of the European band (3780-3800kHz) although the band plan actually allows the upper 25kHz for this. When the band is open, DX contacts should always be given priority in this segment and no local QSOs should take place at all to allow faint DX signals to be heard. Local contacts in this DX 'window' should also be avoided whenever the band is capable of supporting DX traffic to/ from anywhere in Europe. In practice this means around the clock in December and January and from two hours before sunset to two hours after sunrise for the rest of the year. For contacts with countries which are not permitted to use this segment, it is the custom to operate in the upper 10kHz of the band that is allocated to the DX country.

Just as for CW working, the USA phone-band allocations are based on the class of licence held, and many of their amateurs are not allowed to work below 3775 or 3850kHz. For contacts with these stations it is necessary to work split-frequency, ie non-USA stations below 3775kHz and USA stations above this frequency. At peak times when this band is open there is always substantial interference from a large number of stations working in a relatively small segment and it is often good practice for European stations to operate below 3750kHz and nominate the frequencies where they are listening for calls.

Nowadays many DX operators are chasing the five-band DXCC, five-band Worked All Zones awards, as well as band-countries for the ARRL's DX Challenge. This means that very substantial pileups of stations occur whenever a new or rare country appears. Some of these operators work split-frequency (particularly on CW), but on telephony the trend has been to use the list system (see Chapter 9). Many 3.5MHz operators dislike the list system, but it has become an established part of the scene and there is little that can be done, other than to persuade the DX station to adopt split-frequency working.

With simple antennas at moderate heights it is possible to take advantage of midwinter conditions and work into North America and other parts of the world during the hours of darkness. For more consistent DX working, some form of low-angle antenna is required and this is often a base-fed vertical radiator operated against ground. While a quarter-wave vertical is capable of excellent performance, it can be quite inefficient unless the ground system is extensive, and being omni-directional and vertically polarised means it picks up more man-made noise and atmospheric static than a horizontal antenna.

A further disadvantage is of course that it provides no directional discrimination against interference from amateur and non-amateur signals. Many amateurs who have plenty of ground area available use a vertical antenna for transmission in conjunction with highly directional low-angle receiving antennas such as the Beverage or K9AY loop. Another popular antenna for 80m is the sloping dipole (usually called a sloper), which is basically a vertical dipole mounted from a single support and sloped at an angle of approximately 45°. To reduce the height of the support mast, the lower half of the dipole is often bent so as to run parallel with the ground in the direction of the support mast. Slopers exhibit some directivity towards the slope and radiate at the low vertical angles suitable for long-distance working. It is possible to use more than one sloper mounted from the same support mast, and to phase the feed-lines to enhance the directivity characteristics and to provide electrical rotation of the polar pattern. Vertical antennas including slopers radiate little or no high-angle signals; they do not therefore perform well under daylight conditions when high-angle radiation is required. Most serious 80m DXers are now using phased arrays of vertical antennas, including 4-squares, though these can be

By UK standards, a serious set of HF antennas. The 3-element shortened 40m Yagi sits below a KT-34A tribander. There is an array of sloping dipoles for 80m hanging below the 40m beam

complex to adjust and require a lot of real estate. The results, however, can be outstanding.

Horizontally mounted dipoles and simple wire antennas radiate at too high a vertical angle for DX working unless the support height is at least a half wavelength above ground. As few amateurs have the facilities to erect antennas in excess of 40m high, recourse is made to other configurations that work satisfactorily at lower support heights.

The pulled-out single quad and delta-loop, particularly when corner-fed for vertical polarisation, have found favour with many operators and support heights of 13-15m have been proved to be effective for DX working. Although smaller non-resonant loops have been suggested by G6XN and others in *RadCom*, it is probably easier to use the full-wavelength loop and extend the horizontal sides to make up for the shorter vertical sections of the loop. If the support height and mast structure is not a problem and there is plenty of ground area available, almost any type of horizontally polarised low-angle antenna will give good results.

For local working on 80m, including, for example, taking part in the RSGB's AFS and Club Championship contests, the aim is to generate high-angle signals, and this is usually achieved with a low dipole, quite the opposite of what has been discussed above for DX working.

It is worth a final note on antennas for 80m, which is that the band is very wide in percentage terms. Not only does this mean that propagation at the high end of the band can sometimes be noticeably different from that at the low end, but it can also present challenges for antenna design. Even full-size antennas may not cover the whole band, and antennas that are reduced in size through, for example, inductive loading, are likely to have a bandwidth which limits them to one very specific area of the band. A number of solutions have been proposed over the years, but the best advice is to consider where your main interests lie, whether CW or SSB, and install an antenna optimised for that end of the band. With luck, you will be able to use it throughout the rest of the band via a suitable antenna tuning unit.

Earlier in this summary, mention was made of receiver-generated spurious signals and cross-modulation problems. Unfortunately, many of the older solid-state transceivers and receivers suffer from these defects as a result of non-linearity and insufficient dynamic range in the RF and mixer stages. Often the user may be unaware of the problem, as strong off-frequency and out-of-band commercial signals appear in-band, perhaps on a completely different frequency, due to the nonlinear mixing process in the receiver. As most receivers have more gain than is required at 3.5MHz, passive preselectors comprising several loosely coupled ganged tuned circuits will usually provide some improvement. Front-end attenuators are also helpful in reducing cross-modulation, but they are not usually as effective as the passive preselector in clearing up the spurious signals.

The number of countries that could be contacted on the band was once relatively small in comparison with those available on the higher frequency bands. The Five-Band DXCC Award and Worked All Zones dramatically changed the situation and it is now much easier to achieve quite high country scores. A substantial number of operators have been able to contact in excess of 200 countries and there are some who have more than 300 countries confirmed for 3.5MHz CW and SSB working. A low-angle antenna system, a good receiver and an amount of single-minded persistence are needed, but for the newcomer to amateur radio and the operator who wishes to try a new band, DXing on the 3.5MHz band can be most rewarding.

5MHz (60m)

It is no mistake that this section is headed simply 5MHz, rather than 5MHz Band. This allocation is actually a series of spot frequencies, rather than a continuous band of frequencies, and is currently allocated to UK amateurs on an experimental basis, through to 2006 [7,8]. The status of 5MHz varies from country to country, with US amateurs also having five discrete frequencies allocated on a secondary basis, only one of which corresponds to one of the UK channels. The channels are shown in **Table 5.4**.

The 5MHz allocation is available to UK amateurs only through a Notice of Variation (NoV) to their normal licences.

Its use has been agreed with the MoD (who are the primary user) on the basis that it will be used for experimental purposes, rather than for the more conventional type of amateur communications.

Because the channels are also used by cadet forces, with whom amateur users are allowed to communicate, it helps to introduce the cadets to amateur radio. The experimental use envisaged by those who negotiated the agreements regarding the 5MHz allocation was NVIS (Near Vertical Incidence Skywave) propagation. For the purpose of gathering useful and consistent data, which can be used by the RSGB for analysis of propagation on 5MHz, the SINPO signal-reporting system is preferred to the more traditional RST. SINPO will be familiar to anyone who has been a broadcast band SWL, though the RSGB's Spectrum Committee, which oversees the 5MHz experiment has modified the definitions slightly for this specific purpose.

Most amateurs who operate on 5MHz do so with their normal SSB transceivers, many of which can be modified for coverage outside the usual amateur bands. Modification details can often be found on the Internet or, if you are uncomfortable with modifying your transceiver, you should ask the original dealer to make the modification on your behalf.

Antennas should be designed to take advantage of NVIS propagation, so something like a low dipole would appear to be appropriate.

Transatlantic contacts now take place quite regularly, propagation being, as one would expect, somewhere between what would be experienced on 80m and what would be expected on 40m. In other words, 5MHz lends itself well to intra-UK contacts during the hours of daylight, but offers scope for effective long-distance working at night, even with simple antennas and low power.

Anyone intending to operate on 5MHz should acquaint themselves with the guidelines laid down on the RSGB Spectrum Forum Web site [9], as the situation changes from time to time. The guidelines cover all you will want to know, from how to apply for an NoV, to the sort of experiments you might wish to conduct, the type of reporting required, and how to conduct contacts with non-amateur (Cadet Force) stations.

7MHz (40m) band

The widely differing propagation conditions that exist on 7MHz during a 24-hour period, and the differences between winter and summer conditions, make this a very useful band for both local and DX working. In many ways there is a marked similarity to 3.5MHz, with signal attenuation through ionospheric absorption being the main limiting factor for DX working. Other common factors are the 'grey line', dusk-dawn openings and the band's shared nature, resulting in high levels of interference from non-amateur stations, although this situation has improved due to IARU/ITU action to remove 'intruders'. During daylight hours, ionospheric absorption is high and the skip zone is very short or non-existent, thus limiting communication to local contacts up to a few hundred kilometres. The band is ideal for contacts around the British Isles and the nearer countries in mainland Europe, and daytime activity includes regular nets, special event stations and general ragchewing.

Table 5.4: Channel identifiers & frequencies on 5MHz

Channel Name	Centre Frequency KHz	USB[1] carrier frequency
FA	5260	5258.5
FB	5280	5278.5
FC	5290	5288.5
FE	5400	5398.5
FM	5405	5403.5

Note 1: USB is preferred over LSB for this experiment

Table 5.5: US Band Plan for 40m

Novice and Technician Plus classes:	
7.100 - 7.150MHz:	CW Only
General class:	
7.025 - 7.150MHz:	CW, RTTY/Data
7.225 - 7.300MHz:	CW, Phone, Image
Advanced class:	
7.025 - 7.150MHz:	CW, RTTY/Data
7.150 - 7.300MHz:	CW, Phone, Image
Amateur Extra class:	
7.000 - 7.150MHz:	CW, RTTY/Data
7.150 - 7.300MHz:	CW, Phone, Image

Around sunset, there are long-haul grey-line openings and, because attenuation is less than on 3.5MHz, these are longer in duration and signals are usually stronger than on the lower frequency. After dark, the skip zone lengthens and good medium-distance contacts are possible with North and South America, Asia and Africa. Because of the varied conditions that are found on the band, many operators regard 7MHz as the key to making a winning score in the RSGB Commonwealth Contest and other multi-band CW events.

In every respect, therefore, 40m is very much a mainstream band, with a high level of participation in all aspects of the hobby. This is especially true during the years of low solar activity, when the higher bands are closed and 40m comes into its own as a band for all purposes. The limiting factor has always been its width. The full band of 7.0-7.3MHz has not been available to amateurs in ITU Region 1 who are generally restricted to the 7.0-7.1MHz segment. The band is shared with broadcasting and at night, particularly during the winter months, the level of direct interference is high. This, together with cross-modulation problems and the likelihood of receiver-generated spurious signals from off-frequency broadcast stations, limits the frequencies available for amateur use. This situation is set to change as a result of decisions made at the 2003 World Radio Conference. The use of 7.1 to 7.2MHz by broadcast stations will gradually decline, and eventually that part of the band will become available to amateurs on a worldwide basis. Already, some Region 1 administrations have allowed their amateurs access, though the full changeover will not take place until 29 March 2009 and, at the time of writing, it looks possible that UK amateurs may gain access to the additional 100kHz even before this Manual is published. However, until the majority of IARU Region 1 countries gain access to the extended band it is recommended that only phone and CW modes with a maximum bandwidth of 2.7 kHz use the segment 7.1 to 7.2 MHz.

For daylight intra-UK SSB contacts the newly extended band will, in the first instance, offer the opportunity of contacts free from continental interference. Operating in this segment will also help ease the current congestion in the lower part of the band.

Under the present crowded conditions of 40m, receiver performance is critical and the parameters outlined for 3.5MHz equally apply to this band. The use of front-end attenuators and/or passive preselectors will help to alleviate the problem. The use of rotary directional antennas and phased vertical arrays is becoming commonplace as, apart from providing extra gain, the semi-unidirectional pattern helps to reduce interference. While low-angle radiation is desirable, dipoles, loops and other horizontal antennas are very popular and are capable of providing good DX performance. Ground planes, base-fed verticals and 'slopers' are also widely used. For local working with Europe, a simple dipole is more than adequate. At the sort of heights typically possible in a suburban location (30 to 40ft), it will generate mainly high-angle radiation, perfect for working across distances up to a several hundred kilometres.

The IARU Region 1 Band Plan currently recommends that 7.0-7.04MHz is used for CW and that 7.04-7.1MHz is shared between phone and CW with a small segment for data (this will undoubtedly change when the extended band becomes available). As a result of the high interference levels, most CW DX operators use the bottom 10 kHz during the peak broadcasting hours up to midnight UTC. Later in the night and in the early morning hours, the interference is less and more of the band can be used for CW DX operation. For phone working the situation is worse and it is often a case of finding a gap between the broadcast stations. The segment between 7.07 and 7.09MHz is popular, and often intercontinental telephony contacts are possible on these frequencies during the peak broadcasting periods. US phone operation commences at 7.15MHz, so that working US stations on phone requires split-frequency operation. Finding a clear listening frequency in what, in Europe, is a broadcast band, can be difficult at times, though matters improve around dawn as the UK starts to lose propagation to Europe and the US can be heard more easily. US phone operation commences on 7.15MHz for Advanced and Extra Class licensees and 7.225MHz for General Class. US Novices and Technician Plus licensees may use 7.1-7.15MHz for CW. The full US band plan appears as **Table 5.5**.

High frequency (HF)

10MHz (30m) band

The 30m band is actually an interesting transition band, exhibiting both LF and HF characteristics. Allocated for amateur use at the 1979 World Administrative Conference, almost all countries now permit their amateurs to use 10.100-10.150MHz on a shared basis, though some administrations have yet to release the band for amateur use and some allow only spot frequencies. In the US, the band is open to General, Advanced and Extra Class licensees. Most operation is on CW. IARU Region 1 has recommended that phone operation and contests be excluded. Data modes operation, especially RTTY and PSK31, has increased noticeably in recent years and will no doubt be even more in evidence during the solar minimum as activity decreases on the higher frequency bands. Contacts on the band do count for a number of awards such as IOTA, DXCC, Commonwealth CC, WAB and IARU Region 1. Propagation reflects the characteristics of the adjacent 7 and 14MHz bands. In daytime the skip shortens as MUF rises but a skip zone generally persists all day except under exceptional sunspot maximum conditions. Absorption is lower than 7MHz. Under night-time conditions propagation can become worldwide as absorption falls, being best towards the dark sector and being enhanced at the onset of sunset or sunrise. Grey-line effects are very noticeable, offering worldwide propagation between, for example, the UK and the Far East or South Africa. During periods of sunspot minima, long-range propagation can persist all day. During the last sunspot mimimum, there was propagation between the Far East and the UK in the mid-afternoon (UK time). Under very low sunspot conditions the MUF may not rise much above 10MHz at any time of day.

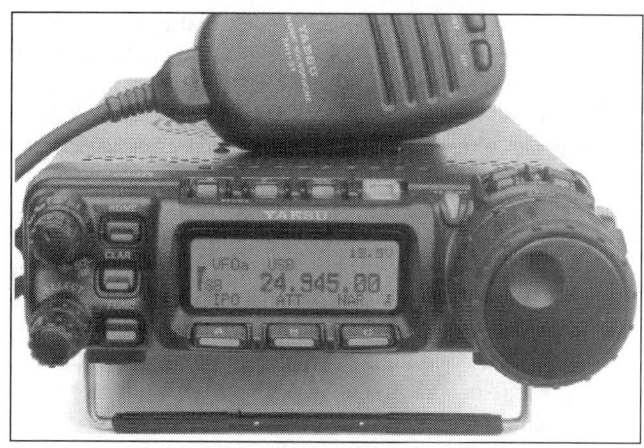

Modern radios all cover the so-called WARC bands at 10, 18 and 24MHz

Long-path propagation, especially to VK/ZL, occurs most mornings under undisturbed conditions. This path starts around UK sunrise and can extend for up to two hours afterwards. The closure of this long path is often signalled by a short enhancement of Central American signals, followed by rapid closure of both paths. In order to exploit 10MHz propagation some form of grey-line calculator is useful.

A major problem on 10MHz is commercial activity. This confines most amateur activity to a series of narrow 'slots' centred on 10.102, 10.104 and 10.110MHz, for example. These 'slots' tend to move under the pressure of commercial stations. These commercial operations tend to limit the development of amateur activity since stations operate on the band for a limited period and little regular usage occurs, despite the favourable propagation characteristics of the band. Fortunately, most DXpeditions now make an effort to operate on 30m, and it is remarkable to note the long hours the band is open to many parts of the world. The characteristics of the 10MHz band mean that it is suited to antenna and propagation experimentation, Compact directional antennas for reception and a better understanding of the many propagation modes will allow good DX results to be achieved by the average CW operator. Given the excellent propagation characteristics and other virtues of the band, it really does offer a strong motivation to become proficient in CW.

All modern transceivers incorporate 10MHz, though older ones (pre-1979) may not. The band is also popular with low power (QRP) operators, and many designs have been published for self-build QRP transceivers for the band. It took some years after the 1979 WARC before manufacturers started to incorporate 10, 18 and 24MHz into linear amplifier designs. However, many earlier valve linear amplifiers will work effectively on those bands, adjusting the tune and load controls accordingly. Most use a low-pass filter as the input circuit, so always set the linear band switch to the band above (14MHz for 10MHz operation, 21MHz for 18MHz operation, etc). The main thing to check before running substantial power is to ensure that there is no unexpected resonance in the anode choke. Such a resonance would result in excess heat and possible damage. As far as antennas are concerned, because a half-wavelength is just 45ft or so, many operators will be able to erect at dipole at or near this height and enjoy good low-angle propagation. Vertical and loop antennas can also be very effective. Some amateurs also press their 80m dipoles into service (10.1MHz is the third harmonic of 3.35MHz, so an extended 80m dipole can work as a one-and-a-half wavelength antenna).

14MHz (20m) band

This is the band which carries the main load of intercontinental communication throughout the whole of the sunspot cycle. There are very few days even at the time of sunspot minimum and in the middle of winter when propagation is not available for at least some time into each continent. A result of this is that for much of the time the band is very congested, and this situation is made worse by the ITU regulation which permits stations of the fixed service in the CIS and other countries to use the 14,250-14,350kHz segment on a shared basis with amateurs. The IARU Region 1 Band Plan recommends that 14,000-14,099 kHz be reserved for CW use - with the area 14,070-14,099kHz being used for data communications. There are several RTTY, PacTOR and other mailboxes in the data modes area of the band, which can occasionally lead to problems with real-time data modes activity. In the USA only stations with Extra Class licences are allowed to use 14,000-14,025kHz. Particular care should be taken to avoid causing interference to the beacon chain on 14,100kHz. Packet operation should take place in the data sub-band, preferably in the upper half. DXpedition stations often tend to use CW frequencies which are multiples of 5kHz above the lower band limit but rarely go above 14,050kHz, and 14,025kHz is perhaps the most widely used. Most listen for replies a few kilohertz above their transmitting frequency and usually announce their tuning procedure.

The part of the band below 14,150kHz is not available to phone stations in the USA and is therefore often used by non-USA stations working each other or by non-USA stations working 'split-frequency' and listening in the US band for callers (this is often helpful when interference is heavy). At the lower end of the segment there are very often nets of French speaking stations - including those from all over the world as well as France itself. The most used DXpedition frequency is 14,195kHz, with 14,145kHz as second choice, usually listening above 14,200kHz. 14,150kHz to 14,175kHz is reserved in the USA for those who have Extra Class licences. The Advanced Class phone section commences at 14,175kHz and the General Class at 14,225kHz. SSTV signals from all over the world will be found around 14,230kHz (see Chapter 8). 14,260kHz is the most popular Islands on the Air (IOTA) expedition frequency. The area above 14,300kHz is very often used by USA stations running 'phone patches' with servicemen overseas in those countries with which FCC regulations permit third-party communication. This area is also favoured by a number of special interest group nets. Even in the major contests, activity tends to stay below 14,300kHz, allowing room for non-contest activities. **Table 5.6** shows the full US band plan for 20m.

Table 5.6: US Band Plan for 20m

General class:	
14.025 - 14.150MHz:	CW, RTTY/Data
14.225 - 14.350MHz:	CW, Phone, Image
Advanced class:	
14.025 - 14.150MHz:	CW, RTTY/Data
14.175 - 14.350MHz:	CW, Phone, Image
Amateur Extra class:	
14.000 - 14.150MHz:	CW, RTTY/Data
14.150 - 14.350MHz:	CW, Phone, Image

There are no special equipment issues on 20m. However, it is probably true to say that there is a higher percentage use of gain antennas (Yagis, quads, etc.) on this band than on any other, because it is the primary band for reliable DX working. This can be intimidating if you are struggling with a vertical antenna or a simple dipole. In this respect, the 17m band (see below) may be a better choice for day-to-day activity and occasional DXing, as far fewer stations have gain antennas for that band or for 12m. By far the most popular gain antenna on HF is the tri-band trapped Yagi for 20, 15 and 10m.

18MHz (17m) band

Allocated for amateur use at the 1979 World Administrative Radio Conference but only released for service some years later, this band is now very popular with some excellent DX around; most DXpeditions provide some operation on it. However, although commercial multiband beams are available for the band, many stations still use dipoles, especially if they have already put up, say, a triband Yagi for 14/21/28MHz, and this does limit the number of strong signals around. As already mentioned, propagation is similar to the 14 and 21MHz bands, and the band is a useful 'half-way' house. The IARU Region 1 Band Plan recommends that the segment 18.068-18.100 is reserved for CW use only, with the area 18.101-18.108 for data modes and CW. Phone operation is allowed from 18.111-18.168MHz. Data mode activity is increasing quite rapidly on the band, especially as the data modes sub-band on 20m tends to get rather busy. In the US, the band is available to General, Advanced and Extra Class Licensees.

The main limitation of 17m is its narrow width. If a DXpedition is operating on, say, 18145 kHz and listening on 18150 kHz, that takes out a significant part of the allocation. Nevertheless, many amateurs find this an extremely reliable band for keeping long-distance schedules with friends or relatives in the US, Southern Africa or even Australia/New

Zealand. Modern equipment incorporates 18MHz as a matter of course. For older, pre-WARC equipment, see the remarks under 10MHz (above). As far as antennas are concerned, a full-sized dipole at a half-wave high is very achievable for most amateurs and will work well. There is also a wide range of commercial antennas available which cover this band.

21MHz (15m) band

This is a favourite band with many HF operators, with more space than the crowded 14MHz band, but significantly more reliable than 28MHz, except perhaps near sunspot maxima. The IARU Region 1 Band Plan recommends that the segment 21,000-21,149kHz be reserved for CW use with the area 21,080-21,120kHz for data operation. DX on CW, although fairly evenly distributed in the first 75kHz or so, tends to be heaviest around 21,025kHz, this being a popular frequency for DXpeditions. It is also the upper limit of the CW frequency allocation exclusive to the Extra Class licensees of the USA. Contest stations usually operate in the first 50kHz of this segment although in the bigger contests they may spread up to and even above 21,100kHz. The rest of the Region 1 CW sub-band falls within the USA Novice and Technician Plus allocation (21,100-21,200kHz) and is mainly used for working the USA. When conditions are good this part of 15m is very crowded and is therefore one of the simplest indicators of propagation into North America.

Moving up the band, SSB signals commence around 21,151kHz with German, French and Spanish language stations showing a preference for DX work around the lower end. When conditions are good SSB signals may be heard from the low-power Australian Novice stations in the segment 21,151-21,200kHz. As it is outside the USA phone allocation, 21,151 to21,200kHz is often used by DX stations particularly wishing to work Europe, including Canadians, and Central and South Americans. When DX propagation is poor but short skip is possible, this part of the band is used for inter-European working. The USA phone segment commences at 21,200kHz and, when conditions are good, very strong signals are heard from USA Extra Class licensees who have the exclusive use of the first 25kHz in their country. The segment 21,250 to21,350kHz is usually very crowded at weekends and tends to attract high-powered stations. Those with more modest means are therefore advised to operate in the 21,350 to21,450kHz segment when working into the USA. The Advanced Class phone section starts at 21,225kHz and the General Class at 21,300kHz. IOTA activity is centred on 21,260kHz. SSTV operators centre their activities on 21,340kHz and some 'phone patching' takes place in the area above 21,400kHz, the top 50kHz often being used by Americans living abroad to work stations back home. **Table 5.7** shows the full US band plan for 15m.

Table 5.7: US Band Plan for 15m

Novice and Technician Plus classes:	
21.100 - 21.200MHz:	CW Only
General class:	
21.025 - 21.200MHz:	CW, RTTY/Data
21.300 - 21.450MHz:	CW, Phone, Image
Advanced class:	
21.025 - 21.200MHz:	CW, RTTY/Data
21.225 - 21.450MHz:	CW, Phone, Image
Amateur Extra class:	
21.000 - 21.200MHz:	CW, RTTY/Data
21.200 - 21.450MHz:	CW, Phone, Image

Over the years, both US and non-US DXpedition stations have tended to use 21,295-21,300kHz for their operations, but some DXpeditions operating from areas other than those controlled by the USA seem to favour frequencies around 21,195kHz and 21,245kHz for this purpose, announcing their listening frequencies for various areas from time to time.

As with 20m, there are no special equipment issues for this band. Some amateurs take advantage of the benefit that 15m is the third harmonic of 40m, so antennas designed for 40m (half-wave dipole, quarter-wave vertical) can easily be pressed into service, often with good results. Of course, many 15m operators will be using tri-band Yagis or even high-gain monoband antennas. While a full-size Yagi for 20m is beyond the scope of many suburban plots, a three-element Yagi (for example) for 15m is no bigger than a typical tri-band trapped Yagi, and has less weight and wind resistance by virtue of having no bulky traps. The difference in performance between a trapped antenna and a no-compromise monoband antenna is one that can only be fully appreciated when you have experienced it first hand.

24MHz (12m) band

Allocated for amateur use at the 1979 World Administrative Radio Conference, this band can be quiet during periods of low solar activity. However, it is well worth checking the various beacons as there can often be propagation but no activity. At such times a CQ call can be a very good idea. Like the 18MHz band, it also suffers from a lack of beam antennas in use but, again as with 18MHz, this can be beneficial when you are chasing DX, as you will find it easier to compete. 12m can frequently provide communication on days when the 28MHz band is quiet, and should not be overlooked. The author recalls two cases, separated by several years, but both DXpeditions by G3SXW and G3TXF to the Pacific, where they were workable for hours at a time on 24MHz from the UK, whereas 28MHz opened only briefly and, on some days, not at all. The first of these was from H4 (Solomon Islands) and the second from FW (Wallis and Futuna). 12m also benefits from Sporadic E propagation in the June/July time period each year, with loud short-skip signals from around Europe.

The IARU Region 1 Band Plan reserves 24.890 - 24.919MHz for CW operation, with data operation from 24.920-24.928MHz. Phone operation takes place from 24.931-24.990MHz. In the US, the band is available to General, Advanced and Extra Class Licensees.

Modern equipment incorporates 24MHz as a matter of course. For older, pre-WARC equipment, see the remarks under 10MHz (above). Because antennas for 12m are relatively small in size, it is well worth thinking about some sort of gain antenna, perhaps a two-element Yagi or a quad. It is conceivable that one of the mass-produced 27MHz Yagis, popular with CB operators, could be modified to achieve a low-cost, lightweight but effective antenna for 24MHz. For a time, the author used a two-band quad for 10 and 12m, made from garden canes for just a few pounds.

A 10/12m cubical quad used for a while by the author, with great results. This was built with garden canes and some wire from a club junk sale. Total cost, about £2.50!

28MHz (10m) band

The 28MHz band is on the borderline between HF and VHF. Of course the delineation between HF and VHF, specified by definition at 30MHz, is man-made and Nature draws no such firm division. It is this location in the spectrum which gives the band, sometimes described as "the band of surprises", the variability which is one of its attractions. As at VHF, high power is by no means necessary to operate long ranges. It is generally accepted that if a path exists at all then 10W, say, of CW and little (if any) more of SSB will achieve satisfactory communication. Indeed, contact with almost all the USA call areas has been made with 200mW. Even a simple ground-plane antenna performs well, especially for sporadic-E (Es) or short-skip conditions which can produce good coverage of Europe from the UK during the summer (May-September). It will be seen that these features, coupled with the wide frequency range available, make it a very good band for relatively simple and inexpensive stations. It should be noted, though, that the band is unavailable to UK Foundation Class licensees.

The band is much more dependent on solar activity than the 14 and 21MHz bands, but it is to be regretted that the majority of operators desert it during the years around sunspot minimum. Those who continue to use it through these periods are often surprised at the paths which appear from time to time. To work 100 countries during the lean years can be a stimulating challenge. Whilst, as in the lower HF allocations, propagation from the UK tends to swing from the east in the morning to the west in the afternoon, paths to many parts of the world will often exist simultaneously and WAC (Worked All Continents) in five minutes working is by no means a rare feat.

Although, again speaking generally, propagation requires daylight over most if not all of the path, DX contacts may still be made during the hours of darkness. Stations operating from close to the Equator regard this as commonplace. For example, from West Africa there is often a long-path opening to Japan which extends through much of the night. It may well be that the few contacts recorded from the UK under these conditions would be increased in numbers if operators did not take such a dogmatic view of 28MHz propagation possibilities, but checked the band at times when experts say there will be no signals and then transmitted a 'CQ'. The same suggestion holds good also for the years around sunspot minimum. As an aside, evening propagation to the southern states of the USA can sometimes happen when the operators at both ends point beams to the South Atlantic. Frustration occurs when the distant station does not realise this is necessary and turns to the direct bearing, and then considers the contact lost. Apart from E and F propagation, the band performs in a similar manner to that of 50 and 144MHz and signals can be ducted over quite long distances under 'lift' conditions. Extended ground-wave contacts over distances of several hundred miles are commonplace via ducting.

The IARU Region 1 Band Plan for the 28MHz band follows a similar pattern to those for the other HF bands. That is to say, the lower frequencies from 28.0-28.05 and 28.15-28.20MHz are reserved for CW, with a band of 100kHz centred on 28.10MHz allocated for CW and data shared use. The remainder of the band, 28.20-29.70MHz, is available for both CW and phone, though, as might be expected, CW operation centres on the portion below 28.20MHz. A small 10kHz band centred on 28.68MHz is recommended for SSTV working. The band plan recommends that beacons use the 28.190-28.225MHz segment. This segment should never be used for two-way communication. The FCC permits Novice

The Marquesas Islands are tough to work from Europe, but this expedition at the peak of the sunspot cycle in 2001 went into many logs, even on 10m

and Technician licensees to use 28.1-28.3MHz for CW and data, and 28.3- 28.5MHz for CW/SSB, and restricts other USA phone stations to above 28.30MHz. During years of high solar flux this last division causes non-American phone operators to spread either below 28.30MHz or well up the band, eg 28.90MHz and upwards, to avoid USA interference. Towards sunspot minimum, random phone operation tends to be conducted between 28.50-28.80MHz. **Table 5.8** shows the full US Band Plan for 10m.

Stations using low-power AM and FM may be heard above 28.80MHz. The RSGB recommends that FM activity should take place between 29.60-29.69MHz, with 29.6MHz as the calling frequency. 29.6MHz is also the FM simplex calling frequency in the USA, and there are 29MHz FM repeaters with outputs at 29.620, 29.640, 29.660 and 29.680MHz (inputs are 100kHz lower in each case). Increasing numbers of DXpeditions are including some activity on 10m FM, and it is remarkable how well the mode can work when the band is open. But the existence of repeaters means that there is scope for working over extended ranges even when propagation is at an ebb.

A specialist aspect of the 28MHz band is concerned with amateur space service communication and the sub-band 29.30-29.50MHz has been recommended for amateur satellite downlink use (see Chapter 13).

The availability of synthesised FM CB equipment that can be easily converted for 29MHz operation has encouraged many mobile operators to use the band both for DX and local working. Many early SSB transceivers did not include FM, but nowadays it is a normal feature. It should be noted that linear amplifiers in the USA cannot be sold with 10m activated, except to someone who can prove that he is a licensed amateur, so you may occasionally see imported amplifiers which do not appear to cover the band. In any case, some early valve amplifiers had much lower efficiency on 10m than on the lower bands. Fortunately, given the nature of the band, maximum licensed power is rarely required. However, it is worth noting that at these frequencies, losses can be high if you have a long run of co-axial cable. The difference in loss between 50m of, say, the popular UR67 and the more expensive H100 or H103 is probably 1dB or so; not huge but worth having. Using UR43 cable would result in a further 2dB or so of loss, which is starting to be significant. If you have longer feeder runs, it is even more important to invest in low-loss cable.

The smaller size of antenna elements for this band allows the construction of compact, efficient installations. Gain antennas are also very easy to construct, perhaps by modifying a CB antenna or building a lightweight quad. Those who do have high-gain antennas on 10m, perhaps a 5 or 6 element monoband Yagi, find the band full of surprises at sunspot maximum, for example being able to work long-path to the Pacific during the evening or to the US West Coast around dawn.

Table 5.8: US Band Plan for 10m

Novice and Technician Plus classes:	
28.100 - 28.300MHz:	CW, RTTY/Data–Max power 200W PEP
28.300 - 28.500 MHz:	CW, Phone–Max power 200W PEP
General, Advanced, Amateur Extra classes:	
28.000 - 28.300MHz:	CW, RTTY/Data
28.300 - 29.700MHz:	CW, Phone, Image

Very high frequency (VHF)

THE TERM 'VHF' applies to frequencies between 30 and 300MHz, and 'UHF' generally means 300MHz to 3GHz, but in amateur practice frequencies above 1GHz are normally termed 'microwaves'.

The ITU VHF/UHF allocations for Region 1 are 144-146MHz and 430-440MHz. Most Region 1 countries permit 144-146MHz operation but there are several with restricted 430-440MHz Amateur Service allocations (see RSGB Yearbook). Notwithstanding ITU allocations, national administrations may permit amateur service operation in additional bands. Starting with the UK in the early 'eighties, amateurs in the majority of Region 1 countries have been granted permits to operate in the 50-52MHz band. In some countries, such as the UK, normal licensing conditions apply but in others there are restrictions on the width of the band, transmitter power, modes, antennas and times of operating.

Amateur allocations in Regions 2 and 3 (see Chapter 2 for an explanation and map of ITU Regions) are broadly similar to those in Region 1, with the addition of an ITU allocation between 50 and 54MHz. In Region 2 the bands 220-225MHz and 902-928MHz may also be allocated for amateur use. It should be noted that many of the amateur bands above 30MHz are shared with other services. The four VHF/UHF bands of particular interest to UK amateurs are those at 50, 70, 144 and 430MHz, commonly referred to as 'Six', 'Four', 'Two' and 'Seventy' respectively. The 70MHz band is a special allocation granted by the UK administration in the 'fifties. The initial allocation was only 200kHz wide, but nowadays is 70.0-70.5MHz. Because of the wide variety of activities taking place on VHF and UHF, the band plans are necessarily much more complex than those for the HF bands. The main aim of the band plans is to separate incompatible transmission modes, and so let everyone get on with the business of communicating by his or her chosen method. The outlines of the 144 and 430MHz band plans are laid down by international agreement in the IARU after much debate and discussion. The 50 and 70MHz band plans were devised by the RSGB, and follow a similar outline to those for the higher bands.

Although the band plans are, as on HF, purely voluntary arrangements (in the UK, at least), there are good reasons for observing them at all times. Calling CQ on CW on 145.7MHz is quite legal within the terms of the amateur licence, but is very unlikely to result in a contact, and certainly will not make any friends. Similarly, the beacon sub-band may seem completely empty and an ideal spot for a contact, but even a short transmission there could well cause serious annoyance to somebody many miles away who is intently listening in the noise for a distant beacon. There is room on the bands for all of the many activities, provided operators show a little care, consideration and respect for the interests of others. The band plans act as a guide in this. For example, packet operators have specific calling frequencies for data communications, so they can concentrate their listening and call-

Voluntary Operating Code of Practice for Six Metre Operators

(as issued by the UKSMG in conjunction with JAROC, HARDXA, SixItaly, DRAA, LABRE-SP and SSA, and reproduced with kind permission of UKSMG).

6m AS A DX BAND: Six metres is a DX band just like any other of the amateur radio high frequency DX bands and it, along with other 6m operators, should be treated with respect and tolerance.

LOCAL BAND PLAN: Always respect your local band plan. In Europe this is issued by the IARU and is shown below.

LOCAL QSOs: Do not cause nuisance and disturbance to other dedicated 6m local and overseas DX operators with local QSOs within the 50.100MHz to 50.130MHz DX Window. If you do wish to locally rag-chew, it is recommended that you do this above 50.250MHz where interference will be minimised. Note: Please remember in Europe that French operators are not allowed below 50.200 so local QSOs held just above 50.200 could affect their ability to work DX.

LEARN TO LISTEN: True 6m DXers spend about 5% of their time transmitting while 95% of time is spent listening, and observing changing band conditions and propagation modes. Learn to recognize propagation mode characteristics and when the band is likely to be showing signs of an opening. This will be far more effective than just calling CQ DX at random and ad infinitum.

50.100 - 50.130 DX WINDOW: The DX Window is a widely accepted concept and should, in principle, be used for *inter-regional DX QSOs* only, especially the 50.110 calling frequency as discussed below. The definition of what constitutes a 'DX' station naturally lies with an individual operator, especially when a particular station within your own Region constitutes a new country! The 50.100 - 50.130 DX window is only to be used for QSOs between stations in different regions, where the same region is anywhere within a range of single-hop Es propagation ie roughly 2400km or 1500 miles. We would ask you to think carefully before having any intra-European short distance QSOs in the DX window. For those of us in Europe, this is especially important in periods of multiple-hop Es or F2 propagation to avoid burying inter-regional QSO opportunities under a layer of European QRM.

PLEASE BE SENSIBLE and avoid local QSOs in the DX window if at all possible!

As the DX Window is heavily used, always listen before you call and always ask if the frequency is being used before you transmit (should be done on any frequency anyway). Just because *you* can't hear anything, it does not mean that the frequency is not occupied or some rare DX is using it. Remember that operating etiquette calls for you to ask if the frequency is occupied *before* calling CQ.

50.110 INTER-REGIONAL CALLING FREQUENCY: The international DX calling channel is 50.110MHz. This should be used for long range DX contacts and such contacts should be inter-regional in nature (please note that a "region" is not necessarily a "Continent" the use of the term "Region" provides more freedom in particular circumstances to make QSOs within your own Continent on 50.110. eg in the USA: east-to-west coast QSOs, or in Europe, JW to ZB2 which was technically prohibited using the old term of Inter-Continental calling frequency). If a local station returns to your CQ, move quickly to an unused frequency above 50.130MHz. Do not use the DX calling channel for testing or for tuning up your radio/antenna.

Do not encourage pile-ups on 110. If you have a successful CQ ensure that you QSY elsewhere in the band.

50.110 CQING: *Listening* is the first rule of working rare DX on 6m. So think twice before calling CQ on 110. It would be stupid to say that you shouldn't call CQ but please remember that this is a shared frequency so your reputation will be on line if you insist on calling CQ unceasingly every minute of the day or throughout an opening - even if you do say "CQ DX only" or "CQ outside of my region only". The occasional CQ is good as it can discover an unrecognised opening.

If you are a 6m DXer and have been intensely listening for weak exotica for hours on 110 and up pops a CQ caller, rather than ask him rudely to clear off, ask them *politely* to QSY and *tell them why or what you are hearing listening for*, and *please give your callsign*. Of course, this applies equally well to any frequency on 6m. Most operators are sensible and will do so - probably because they would like to work the DX themselves! Conversely, if you call CQ or are occupying 110 and someone asks you politely to QSY and *gives you a reason*, do so without arguing about the rights of doing so - remember that that you share this resource with thousands of other operators.

If you really must call CQ on 110, think twice, listen for five minutes, cross your legs, count to 100, and if the overwhelming desire is still there go ahead and *call* - but keep it short! At the end of the day the choice is yours and yours alone. Don't forget to QSY when successful unless it is inter-regional DX!

QSO TECHNIQUES: Many operators do not take the time to learn how to DX, develop QSO skills and techniques, and jump right in. This is not to be recommended as typical 6m propagation does not allow wasting of time during DX QSOs due to the nature of propagation of the band (borderline HF/VHF). Openings could be very short in time duration and DX stations wants to work as many callers as they can during an opening.

Basically, follow the style and take the lead of the DX operator in providing information. Otherwise keep it simple and to the point as there are other stations who are also waiting in line for a QSO with the DX station. Do not waste times in exchanging unnecessary information such as locator codes, names, QTH, equipment, weather and so on. Just exchange your call signs and confirm your signal reports and move on to allow other DXers to have their QSOs. Leave out all the extra information (such as Maidenhead squares) unless it is requested. Many opportunities to work a DX station are extremely short and if your operating practices prevent others from working the station it will be remembered by those who missed out for a long time. Next time it may be you who misses out.

FREQUENCY CONFLICTS: With the quickly shifting propagation as regularly encountered on 6m, it is quite possible that two stations who have been occupying a frequency for several hours running pile-ups without hearing each other, to suddenly find themselves in a clash. In these circumstances, operators should mutually resolve the situation as quickly as possible to avoid conflict. It should always be remembered that no individual operator 'owns a frequency', even if you have occupied a frequency for several hours.

DX PILE- UP OPERATING: Working and breaking DX pile-ups can be a frustrating experience on 6m as it is on HF. Manners and good operating are very important. You should listen to the DX stations carefully and not continue to call if they request a particular country or prefix to go back to them if that is not you. You should always go back with your complete callsign, give it quickly and give it only once. There is nothing more frustrating and aggravating for others in a pile-up to you to double with the DX station and miss who they going back to. Of course, you should *not* call if you cannot hear the DX station!

If a QSO is uncompleted due to QSB or QRM, don't continue to try and complete the QSO to an excessive degree, use your judgment and call back later. It is likely that others are hearing them OK and can complete a QSO. Take the lead from the DX station and don't call back immediately if they are working someone else. The message is simple, try to avoid calling over the top of the DX station - it does you no good and just upsets your fellow DXers.

SPLIT FREQUENCY OPERATION: When a DX station creates a large pile-up of stations all calling him on their own operating frequency (simplex operating) it creates tremendous QRM problems for those calling and the DX station. Under these circumstances, it is recommended that the DX station uses split operating; that is transmitting on one frequency but listening over a range of frequencies above the frequency being used by the DX station. This mode of operating will significantly increase the QSO rate of the DX station.

However, split operating on 6m can cause *tremendous* interference with other DX operators who, through no fault of their own, are running a simplex pile-up in the same split-frequency section of the band. To minimise this interference, it is recommend that a maximum split of 10kHz (definitely *not* 100kHz) is used.

DUPLICATE QSOs: It is always tempting to call a rare DX station every time you hear it. This should be avoided as it means that you taking away the opportunity for the DX station to work a new station and give them their first QSO with the DX country. Use your judgment if the DX station is known to be rare! Conversely, a quick call can sometimes be useful if no one else is going back to the DX station to show that there is propagation.

CW OPERATION: CW is probably the major mode of operation on 6-meters due to the usually weak nature of many real DX openings. Do not call a CW DX station using SSB as they will not be able to hear you and you will be causing severe interference to other CW DXers trying to work the station. The contrary is true as well, if you cannot break a SSB pile-up using SSB then do not call using CW!

FM QSOs: All FM transmissions should be made above 50.500MHz for the obvious reason that FM is wide band and could wipe out weak DX signals. There is no acceptable reason to transmit FM below 50.500MHz, as there is plenty of spectrum allocated for this purpose.

Notes: This Code of Practice may be amended by UKSMG, JAROC & HARDXA from time to time to reflect current licensing conditions and operating practices.

ing on known frequencies, and avoid interference both to and from other modes. All VHF/ UHF users are recommended to keep a copy of the band plans to hand near the rig.

50MHz (6m) band

The Six Metre band sits at a very interesting point in the radio spectrum, behaving for much of the time as any other VHF band but, for short periods during each sunspot cycle, enjoying the benefits of E and F layer propagation, enabling worldwide DX contacts to take place. It is probably true to say that 6m is the only band where every type of propagation is observable and usable. Meteor scatter propagation is reliable on an almost daily basis for those with the right equipment and software, sporadic E propagation, especially during the summer months, brings the band to live with contacts throughout Europe and beyond, and some well-equipped stations even achieve EME (Moonbounce - Earth Moon Earth) contacts on the band.

In the UK, 6m is effectively divided into two halves. 50 to 51 MHz is allocated on a Primary basis and 51 to 52MHz is a Secondary allocation, with a lower power limit. Many operators never stray outside the lower 250kHz of the band, where the majority of SSB and CW operation takes place. Beacons are located in the bottom 80kHz of the band, giving an early warning of a rising MUF, though many 6m enthusiasts also monitor commercial frequencies (eg TV transmitters) below 50MHz for the first indication of possible band openings. The band segment 50.1MHz to 50.3MHz is the DX window, with an inter-regional calling frequency at 50.110MHz, and 6m DXers tend to be very protective of these arrangements, getting upset if intra-continental contacts take place within this segment or if any QSOs at all take place on the calling channel (as with all calling channels, the intention is that stations move away as soon as communication has been established). Day to day SSB activity in Region 1 should centre around 50.150MHz. The problem, is that the band can get very busy indeed when there is a good sporadic E opening, and stations inevitably start to spread themselves further and further from that frequency.

Almost all European countries now have access to 6m (Hungary being the notable exception at the time of writing), as do most other DXCC countries around the world. In some cases access is by way of a special permit, rather than as a basic part of the licence, so that the authorities can withdraw permission at short notice if problems occur with other services. In years gone by, crossband working to 28MHz was quite common, to enable contacts with countries that had no 6m access. Now that 6m is almost ubiquitous, that is no longer the case, but 28.885MHz remains a focal point for 6m DXers to exchange information and pass the time until 6m band openings occur. Even this is becoming less important as more and more stations rely on the Cluster network for information about 6m activity. The excellent UK Six Metre Group web page [10] is also a focal point, bringing together announcements, a calendar of 6m events, 6m spots from the Cluster network and other related information all into one window. It should be noted that frequency allocations in some countries are more restricted than in the UK. French stations, for example, can be found on SSB only about 50.2MHz.

Higher in the band, there is a certain amount of FM activity, simplex and via repeaters, and there are allocated Packet channels. The Region 1 Meteor Scatter reference frequency is 50.2MHz, but JT6M meteor scatter operation typically takes place on or around 50.230MHz.

The 6m DXer lives a rather different life to either an HF DXer or 2m/70cm DXer. Unless he ventures into the specialist areas of meteor scatter or EME, there will be long periods when there is nothing much to chase. But during those periods of the year when propagation is enhanced and there are DXpeditions to be worked (most 6m DXpeditions are timed to coincide with the Sporadic E season), he cannot afford to be away from the radio, because band openings can be fleeting. It's no good working even ten minutes from home and being able to drop everything to rush back to the radio if a DX spot appears. By the time you get there the opening could well have disappeared. So 6m DXers either organise their lives to work from home, or schedule their annual holidays for June and July, getting those painting and gardening jobs done, but being ready to drop everything the moment the band opens. It is different again, of course, when F2 propagation is expected. This is likely to be optimum in the autumn and early spring during sunspot peaks but, again, there will only be certain days when the MUF goes above 50MHz, so there are long periods when nothing much happens, then all hell breaks loose when the band opens. Of course, this is both the joy and the frustration of the band.

The various propagation modes are discussed in detail in Chapter 6, but it is worth mentioning that, from the UK, double-hop, and even triple-hop, Sporadic E is a remarkably consistent phenomenon around early July each year, and allows contacts into the Middle East and to North America. It is not unusual to work North American stations in the early hours of the morning when the higher HF bands are completely

Table 5.9: Consolidated 50MHz Bandplan

50.000 - 50.100	CW only
50.020 - 50.080	Beacons
50.090	CW calling frequency
50.100 - 50.500	SSB and CW only
50.100 - 50.130	DX window
50.110	Inter-Region calling frequency
50.150	SSB centre of activity
50.185	Cross-band activity centre
50.200	MS reference frequency (CW and SSB)
50.500 - 51.000	All modes
50.500 - 50.700	Digital communications
50.510	SSTV
50.550	Fax
50.600	RTTY
50.710 - 50.910	FM repeater outputs (UK)
51.000 - 51.410	All modes
51.210	Emergency communications priority
51.210 - 51.410	FM repeater inputs (UK)
51.410 - 51.830	All modes
51.430 - 51.590	FM, 20kHz channel spacing
51.510	FM calling
51.830 - 52.000	All modes
51.940 - 52.000	Emergency communications priority

EA5AD made a trip to Algeria during the 2004 Sporadic E season to give out a nice one to 6m DXers

dead. Stations closer to the equator are well served with trans-equatorial propagation (TEP), the level of ionisation at equatorial latitudes remaining high almost constantly. UK stations are often frustrated to see Cluster spots for DX being worked by Italian and Greek stations that is totally out of the question at more northern latitudes. TEP sometimes extends as far north as the southern half of the UK, usually around March and October. What we do benefit from in the UK, though, is auroral propagation, which can provide some useful openings to other countries in northern Europe.

The good news is that, with so many countries now active on 6m, achieving DXCC (100 countries worked and confirmed) is realistic for anyone with a reasonable location and antenna and 100 watts or so to play with. Even in years of low solar activity, a European station who is alert to what is happening on the band could expect to work perhaps 60 or 70 countries in a year, and have DXCC within 5 years or less. The more serious and better-equipped operators do somewhat better. But, of course, the leading scores (at least three UK DXers now have over 200 countries on the band) are achieved only by being active through at least a couple of solar maxima.

As far as equipment for 6m is concerned, many amateurs nowadays choose to buy one of the many HF transceivers which has 6m as standard. The IC-756 from Icom is popular because not only does it have good 6m performance, but the spectral display is an excellent way of monitoring the band for openings. The alternative approach is to use a dedicated 6m transceiver, though fewer of these are now available, or to transvert from another band (a modern example is the FTV-1000 transverter from Yaesu, designed to work with the popular FT-1000MP MkV HF transceiver). All of these will offer you adequate power levels, around the 100 watt mark. There are also several linear amplifiers marketed for 6m, and some HF amplifiers also cover the band. In addition, modification details are available for several older HF amplifiers, now available at low prices, for converting them to 6m use. The good news, though, is that when Sporadic E propagation is in evidence, signal strengths are usually high and 100 watts is more than adequate.

A number of contests take place on 6m each year, sponsored particularly by the RSGB and by the UK Six Metre Group (a body well worth belonging to, if you start to take 6m operating seriously). Even if you don't consider yourself a contester, these events generate activity on what might otherwise be a dead band and, unlike HF contesting, QSO rates are usually low enough that there is time for a brief chat with other stations worked, should you so wish.

Antenna systems vary enormously, from a dipole in the loft (fine when Sporadic E signals are loud) to long-boom Yagis and, for the really serious players, stacked Yagi arrays. There is no doubt that, at times, every last decibel of performance can be critical and at these times those amateurs with a hilltop location, high power, a first-rate receiver, the lowest-loss feeder and a stack of Yagis will be able to work DX that others simply won't hear. But the varying nature of 6m propagation means there are other times when that very same amateur, with his top-of-the-range station will sit in frustration listening to band noise while it is you, just 20 miles away and with your modest set-up, who is working the DX.

70MHz (4m) band

It is unfortunate that because the 70MHz band is available in only a very few countries, its full potential cannot be recognised, though this is gradually changing, with Denmark (including Faroes and Greenland), Croatia and Slovenia being some of the recent arrivals. Other countries including Greece, Poland, Sweden and Finland, are hoping to gain access, even if only via some sort of limited "special licence". Several beacons are now active from Sweden, Faroes and elsewhere. The situation is fluid, and it is always a good idea to check the latest information, for example via the 70MHz Web page [11]. At the time of writing, for example, the Danish allocation is: 70.0125-70.0625MHz, 70.0875-70.1125MHz, 70.3125-70.3875MHz and 70.4125-70.4875MHz. Danish stations are limited to 25 watts but individual permits are no longer required.

In addition, there are several operators in other countries who have suitable receiving equipment and are interested in cross-band working. Most commonly, frequencies around 28.885MHz are used for talkback, but other bands have also been employed, with 6m/4m working becoming quite popular (propagation often being similar). There have been a few 70 to 144MHz crossband contacts made from the UK to 'the Continent' by meteor scatter, where the more modest power and antenna gains in use on the lower band are compensated by the greater propagation efficiency. Meteor scatter contacts also take place, with skeds usually co-ordinated nowadays via the Cluster network. The ultimate cross-band achievement is to complete a 50 to 70MHz contact with a station on the other side of the Atlantic, and very few such contacts have been made.

When arranging cross-band skeds, care should be taken over the choice of the 70MHz frequency as this band is used for broadcasting and other purposes in various parts of the world. The advice of the distant station should be sought on this point.

In 1995 the European Radiocommunications Committee concluded (as reported in June 1995 *RadCom*): "It would therefore seem possible to agree a limited amateur transmitting facility of at least 100kHz centred on 70.2MHz. It is also hoped that the existing beacon network between 70.0 and 70.15MHz can be maintained and extended". It is clear that only limited progress has been made in subsequent years but, as indicated above, the pace could quicken, with further countries making the band available on a limited basis. It is anticipated that widespread availability may finally come about by 2008.

One of the brakes on 4m activity in the UK has been the availability of suitable equipment. FM transceivers are available commercially and many surplus PMR sets can easily be converted for the band. This has led to an increase in FM activity in some parts of the country, especially where local clubs have run a project to modify such equipment for members, in order that the club net can run on 4m. The band is also used for PacketCluster access and other data modes activity. But SSB and CW operation has relied largely on home-built transverters operating in conjunction with an HF or 2m transceiver. This situation is slowly changing. The popular FT847 transceiver is available in the UK with limited 4m capabilities and, as more countries gain access to the band, it is to be expected that the manufacturers will begin to take 70MHz more seriously. As far as antennas are concerned, FM activity takes place with vertical polarisation and most users have a quarter-wave or other vertical antenna. SSB and CW operation is usually best accomplished, especially if you are chasing DX, with a rotatable Yagi, four or five elements being a convenient size for most locations.

144MHz (2m) band

This has long been the most popular of the amateur VHF bands, enjoying a boost in the sixties with the launch of the early OSCAR satellites, again in the seventies as VHF-only licensees gained access (having previously been limited to 70cm and above) and on into the eighties, boosted by voice repeaters and the development of the packet network. More recently, as licensing rules have changed further and perhaps for other reasons too, day-to-day activity has declined. However, under good conditions it is possible to make contacts from the UK deep into Europe, to North Africa and down to the Canary Islands in the North Atlantic.

When an opening of one sort or another occurs the high level of activity ensures there will usually be someone on the other end of the path keen to make a contact. As well as the normal CW, SSB and FM, many specialist communication techniques and propagation modes are in regular use, and this is reflected in the complexity of the usage part of the band plan.

The bottom 35kHz is devoted to moonbounce and it is important that this region be kept clear unless the Moon is well below any European horizon. It is in regular use by stations using high-gain antennas and sensitive receivers to copy weak signals which may be inaudible on most normal equipment. The CW-only segment extends up to 144.150MHz, with a calling frequency at 144.050MHz. Most CW activity takes place between 144.035 and 144.075MHz, and during openings, especially of the auroral type, there are usually many good DX contacts to be made in this part of the band. In particularly intense auroras the entire CW exclusive section can become quite congested. There is a CW activity period from 2000 local time every Monday evening.

The most popular DX mode is SSB for which the calling frequency is 144.300MHz. To avoid overcrowding a substantial change of frequency is recommended once contact has been established on 144.300MHz. When activity is high, such as during openings and contests, the concept of a calling frequency tends to be dropped and stations may be heard calling CQ anywhere from 144.15 up to 144.35MHz or higher. In these circumstances contacts are made in a similar manner to those on the HF bands. Cross-mode CW/SSB working is rare but can prove useful in getting through interference. The SSB and CW exclusive segment continues up to 144.4MHz, the higher frequencies being more popular for local SSB working and nets, such as those involving Worked All Britain enthusiasts. The bottom 500kHz of the band includes several meteor scatter and field-aligned irregularity calling frequencies and working segments, which should be avoided by stations not participating in such activities.

The beacon band falls between 144.400-144.490MHz, and most European countries have one or more beacons in this region, as shown in the *RSGB Yearbook*. These beacons are used by keen DXers to help evaluate propagation conditions, and by careful monitoring may often give a valuable forewarning of an impending opening. This section should be regarded as strictly 'out of bounds' for transmitting.

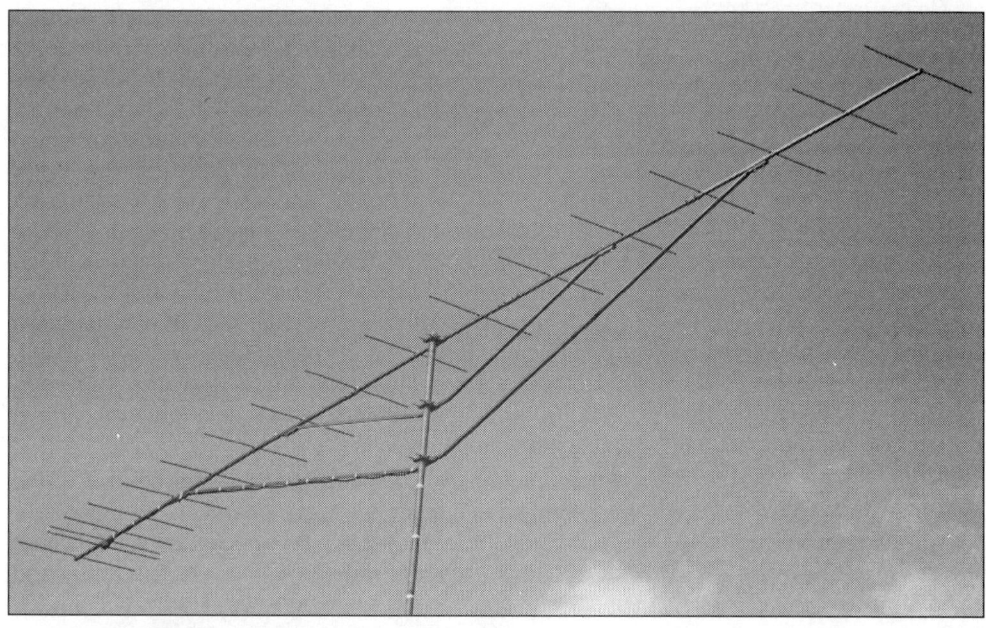

A long-Yagi is suitable for working DX on the 144MHz band

The non-channelised all-mode segment runs from 144.5 to 144.800MHz and it is here that the specialist communication modes, including RTTY, fax and SSTV, are to be found. Each of these modes has a specific calling frequency which should be avoided by other operators.

The sub-segment 144.800 to 144.990MHz is designated for data modes, mostly the DX Cluster network and packet radio.

The top megahertz of the band contains allocations for FM simplex, repeaters, satellite and ISS communications, which are dealt with in Chapters 12 and 13.

Equipment considerations for the 2m band have been discussed in Chapter 3. For FM operation, a wide range of transceivers is available, from small handhelds, through sets designed for car installation to fully-fledged base stations. SSB and CW DX operators will be more demanding in terms of RF performance.

For receiving, a masthead pre-amplifier may prove valuable if a long cable run is involved. On the transmit side, many serious DXers use linear amplifiers, in which case it is especially important to check that the transceiver is properly adjusted, to avoid causing problems to other band users. Antenna systems for FM operation usually consist of a vertical antenna, probably 5/8 wave, mounted well in the clear. For DXing, a Yagi of probably eight elements or more is typical, with some stations opting for large, stacked arrays.

430MHz (70cm) band

This used to be very much an enthusiasts' band, most of the equipment being home-built, but now there is a wide selection of excellent commercial equipment available, from all-mode transceivers through high-power amplifiers to antennas. Although path loss, which is frequency dependent, is greater than on the lower bands, this is compensated for by the higher antenna gains in common use.

Most terrestrial contacts are made by tropospheric propagation, although the better-equipped stations complete auroral and meteor scatter contacts. Sporadic-E mode does not exist at 430MHz, the highest reported sporadic-E frequency being in the 220MHz region in the USA. The anatomy of the DX section, 432.00-432.99MHz, is very similar to that of 144MHz, with CW, SSB, all-mode and beacon sub-bands, as well as special allocations for moonbounce and data modes. Many of the comments in the preceding section apply equally to 430MHz. Operating practice is also similar to that on 144MHz.

A common practice during lifts is for operators who are interested in 144MHz, 430MHz and perhaps 1.3GHz to call on the lower band and announce that they are "QRV on 70cm" or "23cm", or both. If the other station is interested, a frequency on the higher band is agreed. This procedure has the advantage of allowing beam headings to be accurately determined, which is particularly useful when the narrow beamwidths in common use on the higher bands are considered. More and more new technology is appearing on the market place these days with DSP (digital signal processing) being just one new addition - DSP is extremely useful for weak-signal working on any VHF/UHF band.

The FM segment of the band is used for simplex contacts, repeater contacts and data modes. There are many 70cm FM repeaters in the UK, and the data modes section is busy

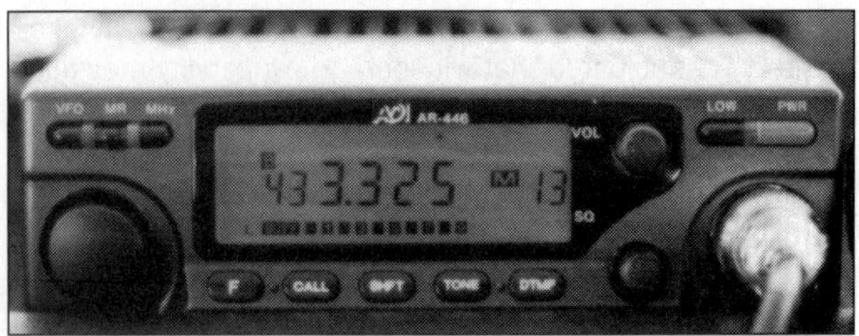

Modern mobile transceivers set the frequency split automatically when a repeater channel is selected

with packet mailboxes. Some amateur television activity also takes place on the band, though most is now on 23cm or higher frequencies.

In the UK the Primary user of this band is the Ministry of Defence (MoD) and as Secondary users the amateur service and amateur satellite service generally enjoys a peaceful co-existence. There are however increasing pressures on this band and users should be aware of local restrictions that may exist. These can be found in the current band plan.

The equipment issues are much the same as for 2m, except that frequency stability is even more important and, of course, feeder losses are significantly higher on both transmit and receive. This latter may necessitate, for example, siting a receive pre-amplifier and remote power amplifier close to the antenna.

FM antennas usually consist of some sort of phased vertical, suitably weatherproofed. Many suitable antennas are commercially available. DX operation uses horizontally-polarised Yagi antennas, typically of 18 elements or more. As on 2m, serious DXers use stacking to achieve greater gain. For moonbounce or satellite operation, it will be necessary to be able to adjust antenna elevation as well as azimuth.

The microwave bands

1.3GHz (23cm) band

The 1.3GHz band is the lowest-frequency 'microwave' band but exhibits some of the characteristics of both the VHF/UHF bands and the higher bands. Propagation losses are higher than on 430MHz, and unless efficient equipment is used results can be rather disappointing. Nevertheless, many dedicated 1.3GHz operators have made contacts of well over 1500km and some have worked over 100 locator squares. However, with the exception of over-water super-refraction paths (West Coast USA to Hawaii, or across the Great Australian Bight), longer paths are easier via the half-million mile Earth-Moon-Earth path! Uses include amateur satellite Mode L operation where the Earth to-space uplink is in the 23cm band and the space-to-Earth downlink is in the 70cm (433MHz) band. The band is popular for ATV and there are growing numbers of ATV and speech repeaters in this band. There are also many propagation beacons (between 1296.800 and 1297.000MHz) which help to indicate when tropospheric propagation is good.

Some commercially-available transceivers cover 1.3GHz, more than adequate for day-to-day operating but not always considered suitable for serious DX working. Such equipment that is sold is usually of rather low power (a few watts) and usually with poor receive characteristics in terms of noise figure. For serious DX work some form of power amplifier (PA) is essential and raising the power output to 20-30W will effect a useful improvement in transmitter range in average conditions.

Such power levels are easily obtained from the 2C39 family of planar triodes, although nowadays most serious DX operators have moved to solid-state amplifiers, located close to the antenna. On the receive side, commercial transverters usually incorporate some form of RF preamplifier. Most stations employ masthead preamplifiers and these are always of great benefit regardless of the feeder losses involved.

As with the lower bands, a good antenna system is of great benefit. Corner reflectors, and small Yagis and dishes, are unlikely to give very good results under any conditions, they are too low-gain and too broad beamwidth for anything except strong signal conditions, such as working to ATV repeaters. The more serious operators use multiple, stacked Yagi arrays or dishes (greater than 2m diameter).

Since coaxial cables are considerably more lossy at 1.3GHz than on lower frequencies, the best quality cable you can afford should be used. For example, an 11m run of RG214 cable will have a loss of 0.78dB at 144MHz, 1.52dB at 432MHz but almost 3dB at 1.3GHz. This means that only one-half the power generated by the PA will reach the antenna and that your receiver noise figure will be degraded by 3dB, too. So-called 'low-loss' UHF TV cable should not even be considered at 1.3GHz, and Andrew Heliax ® feeder is a good choice for this or any other microwave band below 10GHz, although mounting the receive preamplifier(s) and PA stage(s) at masthead will allow the use of less expensive coaxial cable eg Pope H100.

In the past it was common to set up contacts initially on 432MHz and then move to 1.3GHz, but nowadays most contacts are established directly on the higher band.

The IARU Region 1 band plan is quite detailed. As far as DX activity is concerned, most operation is around 1,296.200MHz, referred to as the 'narrow-band centre of activity'. Two points are important, however. The segment 1,296.000 to 1,296.025MHz should be left clear for moonbounce operating, and no transmissions should be made in the beacon segment (1,296.800 to 1,296.990MHz). Contrary to the practice on the lower bands, all activity, local or DX, SSB, CW or FM, is horizontally polarised.

The 2.3GHz (13cm), 3.4GHz (9cm) and 5.7GHz (6cm) bands

These three 'intermediate bands' are considered together since comparatively little use has been made of any of them. Transmitter power output levels drop with increasing frequency, either because solid-state power devices become progressively more expensive for a given power output, or because conventional disc-seal valves become less efficient and are definitely 'running out of steam' above 3.4GHz. Receiver noise levels are below 1dB.

At 2.3GHz, distances up to around 860 to 900km for terrestrial contacts are possible, beyond which the EME path is easier! The corresponding terrestrial distance for the 3.4GHz band is a little less, between about 820 and 840km: at 5.7GHz it is about 800 to 820km.

At one of the regular UK microwave round table events, G7OCD and G3LYP test horns made for the 13cm band

Loop-Yagi antennas are practical up to about the 3.4GHz band. Beyond this, dimensions and constructional tolerance become too critical to make them worthwhile. Consequently, above 3.4GHz, parabolic dish antennas predominate. Present uses are limited, although the 13cm band is now used by a number of ATV repeaters. The higher bands are increasingly being used in amateur satellite communications, as described in Chapter 13, as well as for other experimental work including EME. Highest activity is probably during contests, when amateurs equipped for these various bands set up on hilltop sites to achieve maximum range and, hence, number of contacts.

The 10GHz band

10GHz (3cm) has, for many years, remained a very popular microwave band. This is mainly because very simple, low-powered, wideband FM (speech) transceivers are very easy and inexpensive to construct. These have been based on surplus intruder-alarm Doppler units used as both the receiver local oscillator/mixer and the transmitter at power levels in the range 1mW to 30 or 40mW. The techniques are simple and serve as an admirable introduction to microwave operation over short distances from fixed locations, or longer line-of-sight paths when operated portable.

A small dish antenna, typically 600mm diameter, may have a gain of 35dB or more and a beamwidth of one or two degrees. This makes accurate antenna pointing important: at the same time, the antenna gain on both receive and transmit is such that a 10mW station 'sounds' like a 10W station.

Since the advent of satellite TV broadcasting (at 11 to 13GHz), much surplus equipment has appeared on the amateur market. This has proved to be very easily modified for

G3PHO/P at Alport Height, near Matlock, Derbyshire operating on 10GHz narrow band

ATV use at 10GHz and so the band is much used for this mode. Normally distances of up to 150km, line-of-sight, with either WBFM speech or ATV, are possible.

At the same time as satellite TV broadcasting started to expand, amateur-designed narrow-band (linear) transverter designs, suitable for all-mode transmission and reception, appeared. In the UK, the local oscillator designs of G4DDK, the transmit and receive converters and power amplifiers of G3WDG and the transverter control circuits of G3SEK or G4JNT have enabled the home construction of very effective equipment for this band. Transmit powers up to 20W, solid-state, or up to the permitted maximum using travelling wave tube amplifiers (TWTAs) are within the grasp of many home-based stations. Receiver noise figures are below or around 1dB. Coupled with enough antenna gain (say a 4 or 5m dish), EME contacts are possible.

Under good tropospheric propagation conditions, even a modestly powered home station with, say, 1W output power, a 2dB receiver noise figure and a small (600mm) dish antenna can work distances up to around 1000km using narrow-band modes. The world record for terrestrial tropospheric DX is almost 2000km.

The 24GHz band and higher

These bands lie in a region of the spectrum where atmospheric water/water vapour absorption is very high. However, relatively long-distance terrestrial communications is possible from time to time on the 24 and 47GHz bands by either super-refraction (over the North Sea) or by forward rain scatter, and world-wide by EME and worldwide ranges, via amateur satellites, will be possible. Although the technology exists, most amateurs are several years away from being able to afford the devices or learn the skills necessary to exploit the 'millimetre' bands. Work has started, with low powers (currently approaching 10W), high antenna gain and narrow-band (CW) techniques, and is yielding promising results.

References

[1] *The World of LF* (G3YXM): http://www.wireless.org.uk/index.htm

[2] *LF Today*, Mike Dennison, G3XDV, RSGB

[3] Topband Frequency Allocations (K0CKD): http://www.machlink.com/~k0ckdennis/topbandfrequencyallocations.txt

[4] *Low-Band DXing*, John Devoldere ON4UN, ARRL

[5] *ARRL Antenna Book*, ARRL (available from RSGB)

[6] *DXing on the Edge - The Thrill of 160 Meters*, Jeff Briggs, K1ZM, ARRL 1997

[7] The 'Fivemegs Experiment', *RadCom*, September 2002, p.44, RSGB

[8] 5MHz Experiment: http://www.rsgb-spectrumforum.org.uk/5MHz.htm

[9] RSGB Spectrum Forum: http://www.rsgb-spectrumforum.org.uk/

[10] UK Six Metre Group: http://www.uksmg.org/

[11] 4m band: http://www.70Mhz.org/theband.htm

6 Propagation

A MAJOR PART of the fascination of amateur radio as a hobby lies in the tremendous variety of communication paths provided by the amateur bands. This caters for a wide range of interests, from regular schedules across town or across the world to the search for contacts with rare and exotic DX stations, and a variety of competitive activities and contests. In all these aspects, satisfaction and competitive success benefit from a thorough knowledge of the possibilities presented by the various propagation modes which will be encountered on the bands.

This chapter discusses the propagation mechanisms of most interest to amateurs, but is by no means intended to be a technical treatise on propagation. Rather, its focus is on how our operating is affected by, and needs to take account of the various propagation mechanisms. There are many excellent textbooks dealing with propagation at a more detailed level, though it is certainly worth bearing in mind that propagation mechanisms which are of little interest to the professional world, because of their unpredictability and sporadic nature, may be of huge interest to amateurs. One of the great pleasures of amateur radio is finding an unexpected propagation path, and making contacts over that path, whereas such anomalies are anathema to professional communicators because, often as not, they actually serve to disrupt normal communications. A good example is Sporadic E, of great interest to amateurs on 6m and, occasionally, 2m, but extremely disruptive of VHF band television (where that still exists) and FM radio broadcasting, as well as other services using those frequency bands.

The historical divide between HF and VHF, at 30MHz, is a recognition that this is normally the highest frequency at which ionospheric propagation can take place, allowing long-distance communications. Frequencies above 30MHz were considered line-of-sight (or a little beyond that). In practice, of course, nature is never so simple. The 11-year solar cycle, onto which are superimposed both annual and daily cycles, determines that the maximum usable frequency for ionospheric propagation varies widely and, at times, can rise to well above 30MHz. In addition, over the years both amateurs and professionals have discovered, explored and learned to use a wide variety of other propagation mechanisms which were little known, if at all, when that early divide was set in place.

What follows, therefore, is a discussion of the main propagation mechanisms that you will encounter in day to day amateur radio operating, with hints and tips on how to exploit them to advantage. The discussion inevitably refers to the frequency bands on which these propagation mechanisms are likely to be encountered. For further information on each band, refer back to the previous chapter. It should also be mentioned that, on occasion, more than one propagation mechanism may be at work at the same time, for example a combination of ionospheric propagation and Sporadic E. In some cases, it may not even be possible to determine what mechanism is at work to make a particular contact possible. Often it is only possible to do so after combining information about a large number of contacts taking place during a specific period. There is much still to be understood and bodies such as the RSGB's Propagation Studies Committee set out to gather data and add to the fund of knowledge which exists. A world-wide network of amateur frequency marker and propagation beacons exists in most of the bands - LF to high microwave - in order to provide enhanced data for propagation studies in addition to alerting amateurs to propagation opportunities.

Ground wave propagation

THE STARTING POINT with radio propagation is that radio waves are just one component of the electromagnetic spectrum. Like other elements of that spectrum (visible light, X-rays), radio waves will travel in straight lines unless something acts to divert them from that path. That something could be a change in density of the medium (think of light waves being refracted as they enter or leave water), or a strong magnetic or electric field when in the presence of free electrons. Even when travelling in a straight line, although the waves will theoretically go on for ever, they will be attenuated by the medium they are travelling through. However high the gain of the antenna they are propagated from, they will diverge with distance, reducing in strength according to the inverse square law. Although a coherent beam of light from a laser, for example, can remain concentrated over extended distances, there is no straightforward way of achieving this with the wavelengths involved in radio frequencies except in the microwave bands where parabolic reflectors can be used to focus the radiated energy into a 'beam', much like light, that may only be a few fractions of a degree wide. But however high the gain of an antenna, the radiation will gradually spread out.

Which brings us back to line of sight propagation. All frequencies, from VLF through to the highest microwave frequencies will propagate from the transmitting antenna just as light does (which, after all, is what 'line of sight' actually means). Some very impressive distance records have been set on the microwave bands by stations on mountaintops with no intervening obstructions. Without going to those extremes, the distance achievable by ground-wave propagation will vary according to the terrain and conductivity of the ground and the nature of any obstacles (such as buildings, vegetation and hills). The distance will also vary with frequency. The higher the frequency, the greater the attenuation as signals travel close to the earth. All other factors being equal, a 160m signal, for example, will travel farther than an 80m signal before attenuation renders it inaudible at the receiver. Other factors can come into play, for example in the microwave region where some bands are more affected by water absorption with the result that a rain storm can severely affect ground wave communications. However, in practice, radio waves will usually travel about one third farther than a geometric line-of-sight, mainly as a result of variations of refractive index with height causing bending around the earth. More locally, mechanisms such as diffraction over the tops of hills, or reflections from hills and large metal objects (gasometers and the like), may come into play. To put a figure on something which is difficult to quantify, ground wave contacts on the low frequency bands are likely to be over distances up to 30 or 40 miles (50 - 65km) , this figure reducing for the higher frequency bands. However, this can be countered to an extent by using high gain antennas. On 2m, for example, it is easy to achieve 10dB gain over a dipole so, while ground wave communications with an omnidirectional antenna (such as a mobile whip) might be only 10 to 15 miles (16 - 25km), from a good home station with a Yagi well in the clear, and the same at the other end of the path, reliable contacts might be achieved over 100 miles (160km) or more. By the use of active repeater stations, much greater distances can be achieved, especially if they are on high spots. Hence the networks of hilltop repeater station on the VHF and UHF bands in most countries but, even more so, the various amateur satellites which, of course, achieve exactly the same result but from a much greater elevation.

Diffraction

IT IS WORTH A brief mention here of the way in which radio waves can travel beyond line of sight through diffraction over hilltops and other objects. **Fig.6.1** shows what happens. In practice, the effect depends upon the size of the object concerned. Waves with wavelengths much shorter than the size of the object will be reflected from the object (in this case a hill). Waves with wavelengths much larger than the size of the obstacle will pass virtually unaffected and hence continue in a straight line. However, waves with intermediate wavelengths curve around the edges of the obstacles by a process called diffraction, allowing the radio signals to propagate behind obstacles. This will typically happen in the VHF region of the spectrum, on the 70MHz band and above.

Ionospheric propagation at LF & HF

PEOPLE FIRST STARTED to get really excited about the potential for radio communications when it was realised that radio waves could propagate over much greater distances than could be accounted for by ground wave. It didn't take long before the mechanisms for this were explained. It was clear that signals were being reflected or, more accurately, refracted within the higher atmosphere in a region which became known as the ionosphere. The ionosphere has been studied extensively over time and we now know a lot more about the mechanisms involved and have identified several layers of ionisation, discussed in detail in any propagation textbook.

Ionospheric propagation became the backbone of international communications and international broadcasting for many decades, and amateurs were lucky to hold on to their HF allocations over this time. Nowadays the situation has changed. International communications is almost exclusively by undersea cable and by satellite, and international broadcasting is achieved through satellites and, increasingly, via the Internet. But for amateurs, the joy of making long-distance contacts via the ionosphere remains as great as ever.

Ionospheric propagation due to direct solar activity is useful on all amateur bands up to 50MHz, though 50MHz openings are infrequent and occur only when solar activity is at a maximum. However, from the UK it is easy to get only a partial impression. Stations nearer the equator often continue to benefit from ionospheric propagation on the high bands when they are closed at higher latitudes. The corollary of this, though, is that absorption on the lower frequency bands can be much higher close to the equator whereas stations at very high latitudes, for example in Scandinavia, can often be heard working the Pacific on the LF bands at times when this is out of the question for stations closer to the equator. These thoughts should be borne in when reading the remainder of this section, which describes the ionospheric propagation very much from the perspective of the UK, although other parts of the world at similar latitudes will experience similar propagation. Even within the UK there can be significant differences in propagation. It is not unusual for stations in the Channel Islands and southern UK to be working DX on 28MHz which is inaudible in the north of England and Scotland, as the MUF at those higher latitudes is somewhat lower. Conversely, in the winter months sunrise in the Orkney islands, for example, is significantly later than in London, with stations in that northern location being able to work Pacific DX on the low bands that would be impossible from the more southerly latitude. There are also some sporadic (occasional and short-lived) ionospheric effects, discussed later in this chapter, which can lead to ionospheric propagation on some of the higher VHF bands.

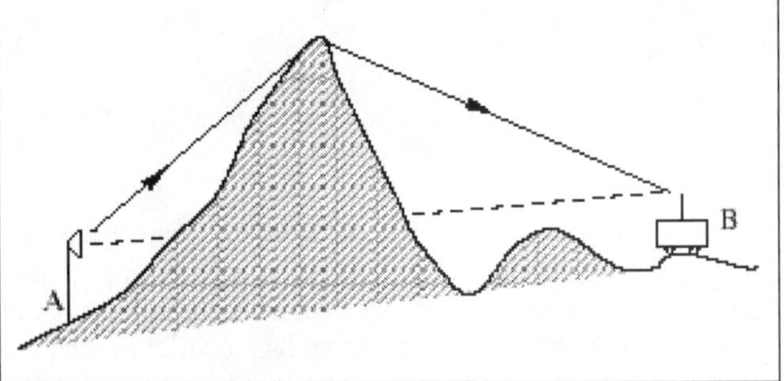

Fig.6.1: Diffraction over a hilltop

Ionospheric propagation depends on the build-up of charged particles high in the rarefied upper fringes of the atmosphere where wave and particle emissions from the Sun arrive with sufficient intensity to ionise the air (what little there is of it), in other words to split the molecules into positive ions and negatively charged electrons. This layer of ionised air then behaves almost like a semi-silvered mirror as far as radio waves are concerned, causing some of them to be returned to earth. However, the higher the frequency of those radio waves, the higher their energy, and at any given time there will be a frequency above which all radio waves will pass through the ionosphere into space. That frequency (the 'critical frequency', when applied to waves travelling perpendicular to the earth's surface) will vary according to the level of ionisation. And the level of ionisation will vary according to the amount of energy being received from the Sun. And the energy received from the Sun varies constantly. There are several superimposed cycles involved here:

Diurnal: variations within the day due to the varying altitude of the Sun in relation to a particular path as the Earth rotates.

Seasonal: variations from month to month, again due to alterations in mean solar altitude and the duration of daylight. This effect is very similar to the seasons we experience due to the incidence of sunlight. Higher latitudes will receive less energy from the sun than latitudes close to the equator.

Solar: changes from day to day in the intensity and mix of the solar radiations responsible for ionisation in the upper atmosphere. These changes can be considerable over quite short periods of time as well as showing longer-term trends, of which the 11-year cycle is the best known (more strictly a 22-year cycle, but this is not relevant to the present discussion).

Geomagnetic: variations in ionospheric behaviour caused by alterations in the intensity and shape of the Earth's magnetic field. The magnetic variations are themselves caused by certain solar emissions.

It is important in the context of radio propagation to note that ionisation takes place at different levels within the ionosphere, corresponding to the D, E and F layers. Long-distance radio propagation relies mainly on the higher, F layer (which, at certain times of the day, itself splits into two layers, the F1 and F2 layers). But to reach the F layer, the radio waves have to travel through the lower D layer, which absorbs but does not reflect the radiation. At times the E layer also absorbs energy, although at other times it can reflect signals (Sporadic E, 80m during daylight, etc). So solar energy affects two characteristics of the ionosphere:

(a) its ability to reflect HF waves of a particular frequency at a given time and angle of incidence; and

(b) the absorption (attenuation) suffered by the waves passing through the lower regions of the atmosphere on the way to and from the reflecting regions.

Both of these vary but not by any means always in step. Both reduce as frequency is increased, the absorption decreasing roughly with the square of frequency. In general, communication is possible over a given path at a given time if the frequency is low enough to be reflected and high enough not to be attenuated below the noise level at the receiver.

This leads to the concepts of Maximum Usable Frequency (MUF) and Lowest Usable Frequency (LUF). The MUF is higher than the critical frequency, mentioned above, as we are now concerned with radio waves impinging on the ionosphere at an oblique angle rather than straight up. For long-distance communications the ideal is to launch your signals at an angle low to the horizon, so that they will reflect over the maximum distance before returning to earth (**Fig 6.2**.). Because it is impossible to predict the MUF in advance for a given path, for all the reasons explained above regarding hourly, daily and other variations, broadcast and commercial users generally plan to use a frequency safely below the MUF for their communications, the so-called Optimum Frequency, and compensate for any additional absorption by using higher power than they might otherwise. Amateurs can often work very close to the MUF, as we are not looking for highly reliable communications but for the fleeting propagation opportunities where we can achieve long-distance communications with minimal power. The 10m band is well-known for providing worldwide communications with modest power and antennas at the right point in the solar cycle when the MUF often sits around the 30MHz mark. The one limitation we do have as amateurs is that we are restricted to discrete frequency bands rather than being able to use any frequency in the radio spectrum. But our bands are close enough together that this is rarely a problem.

The hour by hour change in MUF can be observed at work, especially in contests where there is a high level of amateur activity. Around dawn, the higher bands will start to support propagation and signals can be worked from the east, firstly on 20m, then on 15m and finally on 10m (depending on the point in the solar cycle). Similarly, later in the day, the path to the west, to North America, will start on 20m as sunrise reaches the East Coast, then 15m and 10m will open later. Typically, the majority of the contesters will follow this upward move in MUF and then, later in the day as darkness sweeps across Europe, the MUF will start to drop at the European end of the path and the contesters will follow it down through 15m and 20m, before working through the night on the LF bands. The same effects are taking place on other days, but it is not always so obvious if activity levels are low. Variations, such as long-path propagation, are discussed below.

As far as LUF is concerned, as has been mentioned this is not so clear cut as MUF. It is very much a matter of absorption. Even when 10m is open in a major contest, you will still hear plenty of contest activity on 20m, with DX being worked.

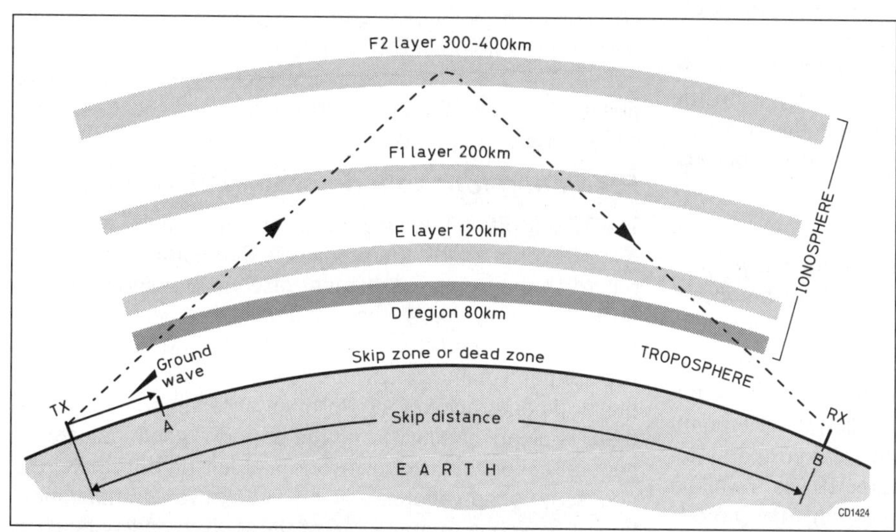

Fig 6.2: Signals launched close to the ground reach the ionosphere at an angle where refraction occurs

But the serious 20m contester, perhaps undertaking a single-band entry, will need a high-gain antenna and reasonable levels of power, probably up to the legal limit, to overcome absorption and achieve a high score. Absorption on the lower bands is usually sufficient to prevent long-distance communications during much of the day but, again, with the right equipment and enough activity it is surprising what can be achieved. This author recalls being part of a multi-multi contest team in the *CQWW CW* contest one November, when the 40m station was able to work Japan over the long-path almost to midday and again by short-path from early afternoon onwards. But we did have a full-size 40m quad antenna on a high location. The combination of high gain and low take-off angle, along with plenty of activity from well-equipped stations at the Japanese end meant that the band openings could be 'stretched' at both ends of the day.

As far as day-to-day operations on the HF bands is concerned, the general rule of thumb is that the bands 14MHz and above are daytime DX bands, with the MUF typically falling below 14MHz at night, leaving the band dead. This may not be true at times of high solar activity or in mid summer or near the equator, when 14MHz can be open throughout the night. In contrast, the bands 7MHz and below are effectively night-time bands, day-time absorption being too high to allow long-distance propagation. This leaves the 10MHz band which, during years of high solar activity, behaves much as an LF band and, during years of low solar activity, more as an HF band.

Seasonal variations

Even with unchanging solar activity F2 layer MUFs are much higher in local winter than in the summer, being highest in the Northern Hemisphere in January/February and October/November with something of a dip in December. Around the equinoxes in March and September the distribution of MUFs in the two hemispheres is similar, and these periods tend to be excellent for worldwide propagation on all bands. Many major DXpeditions quite deliberately time their operations around the equinoxes to achieve best results.

Solar variations

The various ionising radiations from the Sun are not constant in their effect. Since the sources of radiation are not evenly distributed over the Sun's surface there is usually a 27-day cycle of variation, due to the Sun's rotation relative to the Earth. The daily count of sunspots (R) has been the traditional measure of solar activity, a more modern and somewhat more objective one being the power received on the Earth at 2800MHz (solar flux). On average the two vary together and are nearly linearly related. For practical purposes the relation:

$$R = 1.1\,(SF - 60)$$

gives an answer sufficiently accurate for amateur purposes, enabling the WWV 18 minutes-after-the-hour broadcast of the daily solar flux value (SFU) to be converted to an approximate sunspot number if so desired (see below).

The most well-known aspect of solar variation is the approximately 11-year cycle of rise and fall in the 12-month mean of the daily sunspot numbers and solar flux; 'approximately' since Cycles 15-19 were all nearer 10 years while a recent one lasted nearly 12 years. The average rise time is about four years. Since the cause of this cyclic behaviour is not yet fully understood (there is even evidence that it is not always present, the last absence being in the 75 years from 1650AD), prediction of future trends is based on extrapolation from the past. For the amateur communicator it is important to remember that professional propagation predictions are based on forecasts of solar activity and that these are based on heavily smoothed data. While the ionosphere does not respond instantly to solar variations its smoothing effect spreads over days rather than months, and generally the higher the mean solar activity, the greater the short-term fluctuations. For example, during the peak months from November 1957 to March 1958 the highest daily sunspot number was 342 and the lowest 90. Since forecasts have to be prepared well ahead of events one should always be on the look out for conditions which are outside the limits predicted. There are also from time to time shorter periodicities within the 11-year cycle. On its down slope one recent cycle had distinct subsidiary peaks at intervals of rather more than two years, and over the years 1975-77 there was a fairly regular rise and fall with a period of approximately 120 days. Professional forecasts smooth out these variations and, since they perforce are based on data which is many months old by the time the prediction appears in print, they can even get 180° out of phase with them. The amateur, on the other hand, would like to know what band conditions will be like the next day, or for the following weekend's contest. As with weather forecasting there can be no certainty but a surprising amount can be done with relatively little effort.

Only those who have lived through a complete 11-year cycle can fully appreciate the impact it has on HF propagation. At the peak of the cycle, MUFs can climb above 50MHz, so that even the 6m band can enjoy worldwide propagation, with UK stations working into the Far East and the Pacific at times. Yet during the solar minimum 10m, 12m and even 15m can be dead for weeks at a time, enlivened only by summer Sporadic E or other anomalous propagation. Amateurs may still enjoy a certain amount of local activity on those bands, or perhaps use the FM repeaters on 10m or one of the satellites which has a transponder on those bands, but global propagation will have to wait until the next sunspot peak. It is not all bad news, of course, as absorption on the lower bands tends to be lower, again due to the lower levels of solar activity, so there are great opportunities to increase DX scores on those bands. 40m in particular comes into its own during sunspot minima, with excellent worldwide propagation. The most recent sunspot cycle is thought to have peaked in late-2000/early-2001, and the next peak is expected around 2011.

Predicting ionospheric propagation

The 27-day (28 in the early stages of a cycle) solar rotation is a key factor in short-term prediction. Some amateurs keep a record of their own assessment of band conditions on this basis and know that similar conditions, both good and bad, can often be predicted 27 days ahead. The criteria to be used depend on individual interests. A useful one is the duration and penetration of the North American opening because there is plenty of activity and the path is a good indicator of general conditions. Not everyone has the time to make the necessary observations, and an alternative or supplementary approach is to make use of the WWV broadcasts at 18

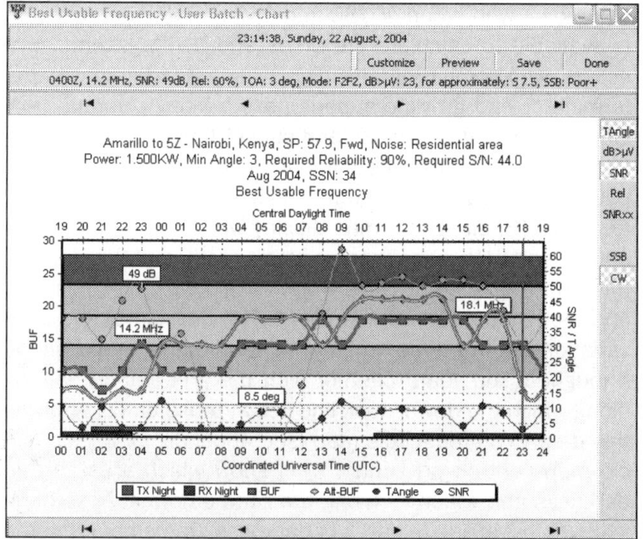

Software can be used to predict ionospheric propagation. This is a screen from *WinCap* that suggests the best usable frequency for a particular path

minutes past each hour. These give the most recent value of 2800MHz flux which is recorded at 1700UTC each day, ie WWV broadcasts from 1818 UTC usually contain the current day's value. The broadcast also gives a daily geomagnetic index (A-index), mentioning events such as solar flares, and gives a 24-hour projection of solar and geomagnetic trends. Reliable copy of WWV needs a good antenna, preferably with a good null to the east to reduce interference from other standard transmissions and intruders, but if the flux and 'A' values can be copied on most days and the gaps filled by a friendly North American contact, a really up-to-date picture of solar activity and trends is available. If you have difficulty in receiving WWV, remember that propagation data is available on the packet network, the web and the *GB2RS* news bulletins. The web pages of the NOAA (National Oceanographic and Atmospheric Association [1]) are an excellent source. However, there is a good summary of data, collated from a number of sources, maintained by N6RT on the *qsl.net* web site [2], which is well worth bookmarking.

The A-index is a measure of worldwide geomagnetic activity. In itself, a low value (15 or less) means a stable magnetic field and stable radio conditions, usually with low absorption. A low A-index with a high flux value means excellent conditions, particularly on the high bands (it was around 10 during the early February and March flux peaks in **Fig.6.3**). For good LF band conditions, look out for low flux values together with very low 'A'.

A 27-day plot of the A-index shows recurrent peaks due to persistent sources of particle emission from the Sun and coronal holes. High peaks mean disturbed conditions, magnetic storms and possibly auroral effects, and if recurrent these can be predicted from the 'A' plots. However, an SID (sudden ionospheric disturbance) caused by a flare cannot be so predicted since it is a 'new' event, and the rise in the A-index follows a day or two later when the effects of the flare disturb the magnetic field. All that can be said is that such events are more likely to appear near a peak in the solar flux plot. 27-day calendars are also of importance in VHF auroral communication.

The above should serve to show that with not too much effort an amateur can form quite a reliable view of the likely trend of radio conditions a month or more ahead, and with the help of current solar data be aware of what is happening more or less currently.

For those interested in the trend of the solar cycle a three month running mean plot of the provisional sunspot number gives a good idea how things are going.

Since the geomagnetic field is affected by emissions from the Sun it also shows cyclic behaviour although this is not so clearly defined. Geomagnetic activity, ie the incidence and intensity of disturbances, ionospheric storms and auroral activity, certainly increases as the sunspot peak approaches but may continue to rise before reaching its own peak.

Nowadays there are many propagation prediction programs available for traditional ionospheric propagation, and these are dealt with in some detail in Chapter 4. These make life a lot easier than in the past, when it was common to use quite complex sets of tables to determine possible propagation paths. For those without computers, propagation predictions covering some of the main areas of the world appear monthly in the RSGB's *RadCom* and other similar publications. It should, of course, be borne in mind that propagation predictions are, at best, statistical in nature, giving some idea of the probability of propagation on a certain day and time, and on a certain frequency, along with a prediction of likely signal strengths. There is no guarantee, as there are so many variables which affect a propagation path, particularly one that travels great distances around the earth. This is especially true if the path concerned passes through the auroral zone, where significant absorption can take place.

Remember that antenna gain, power and exact location at both ends of the path will have a significant bearing on whether the path is usable for long-distance communications. Clearly, if the MUF is too low at any point on the path then, whatever the power levels, no communication will be possible. But where some sort of propagation exists, weak signals may be unworkable because they are below the ambient noise level, but the path may be perfectly usable where signals are stronger. DXpeditions, for example, often choose locations right on the sea shore, which results in much more effective take-off of their signals than from an inland location.

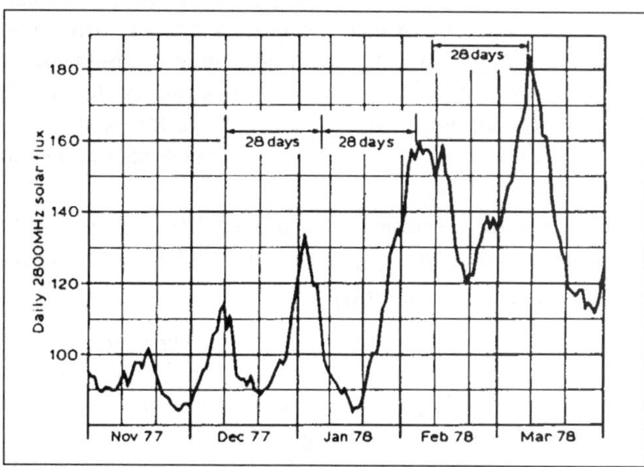

Fig 6.3: Daily 2800MHz solar flux from November 1977 to March 1978

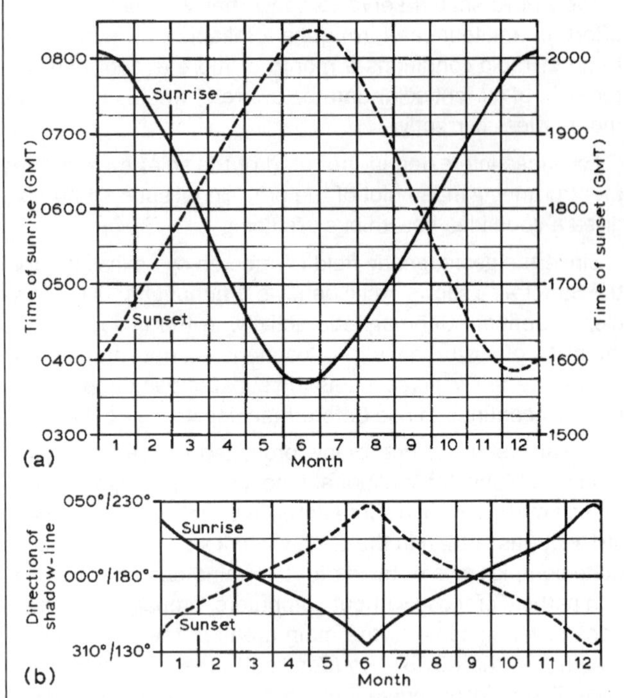

Fig 6.4: (a) Time of sunrise and sunset in London. (b) Approximate great-circle direction of shadow-line at local sunrise and sunset in UK

The last point to mention is that, when looking at the possibilities for ionospheric propagation, it is often worth considering possible long-path propagation as well as short-path. A word of explanation is perhaps required. It is assumed that radio signals follow a great circle path (the shortest possible distance) between any two locations (though there are occasions when some skewing of the path takes place). But there will also be a possible path 180 degrees opposed to that, ie going round the world the opposite way. In the case of working New Zealand or Australia from the UK, there is very little difference between the two distances and, as an example, the 20m long-path around UK dawn is a very reliable path. At that time, absorption on the short-path (which will be in daylight) is likely to be too high for propagation to take place. At time of higher solar activity, it is not unusual to experience simultaneous long- and short-path openings to Japan on 15m shortly after UK dawn. This can lead to flutter on the received signals, as the two paths arrive slightly out of phase with each other. There are many other long-path openings which UK DXers look out for. To the US West Coast during the afternoon on 20m, for example, to Australia and New Zealand in the evening on 15m and even 10m at times of high solar activity.

Many books are available on propagation, its relation to solar activity, and how to go about making forecasts [3, 4].

Grey-line propagation

Low band DXers are very familiar with grey line propagation, whereby long-distance DX is possible where signals can travel along the terminator, the division between daylight and darkness. At the equator, the greyline exists only for a very short period each day, as the sun rises and sets very quickly, whereas at high latitudes twilight can exist for long periods during the winter months, allowing a wide range of DX locations to be worked on 40, 80 and 160m. Computer software is available to calculate the times and bearings when this occurs, with some programs displaying a world map with the terminator and greyline superimposed. Many computer logging programs give sunrise and sunset times, but the visual display on a map has more impact in showing likely greyline paths at a glance. Programs such as DX Atlas [5] and Geoclock [6] all have a map display which shows the terminator clearly. However, there is also a method of determining this involving a great circle map, an aid which no keen DX operator should be without. **Figs 6.4(a)** and **6.4(b)** show the variation in the time of sunrise and sunset at London throughout the year, together with the great circle bearing along which the dawn/dusk line lies at those times. Applying this data to a great-circle map (see Appendix for a great circle map centred on London) will show which areas are in darkness and which lie along the zone of lowest absorption which is just inside the area of darkness. Remember that the dawn/dusk line is only a straight line on a great-circle map at sunrise and sunset.

Sunrise and sunset times are different elsewhere in the UK - typically 10 minutes later in Birmingham and as much as 40min later in Glasgow and Belfast in summer - and the differences are not the same for sunrise and sunset. To make a table for your own location, borrow a copy of Whitaker's Almanac from the local library. The bearing of the dawn/dusk line in Fig 6.4(b) is accurate within a few degrees for any location in the UK at local sunrise and sunset. **Fig.6.5** shows this information incorporated into a great-circle map by Ray Flavell, G3LTP [7].

In this connection it should be remembered that the standard great-circle map centred on London, while applying with sufficient accuracy to the whole of the UK in most cases, can be misleading with paths to the antipodes. While the bearing of ZL4 from London is 060°/240°, it is 030°/210° from Belfast. The corresponding values for ZL1/2 are 010°/190° and 350°/170° respectively. While these differences may seem small they mean a completely different path for the two locations. The difference in sunrise and sunset times and the difference in bearings (which can impact whether the signals have to travel through the auroral zone) mean that a station in, say, the Orkney Islands, will experience very different low band propagation to a station in the Home Counties.

The importance of the twilight zone can be seen from the following example. At sunset in mid-April and mid-August the sunset line lies along the great circle path from the UK to Ascension Is and absorption goes through a minimum about an hour later. During this period, contact between these two places has been made successfully on 21, 14, 7 and 3.5MHz, with a return to 21MHz to complete the contact. However, as G3LTP points out in reference [7], it must be remembered that it is not the ground-based shadow that determines the state of the ionosphere because the Earth's shadow is shaped like a cone; the area of darkness at F2 heights is appreciably less than that at ground level. Sunrise comes earlier than on the ground, sunset later. In fact, in mid-summer the F2 layer is in sunlight for all 24 hours of the day over the whole of the UK. So the ionospheric grey line (as opposed to the ground-based grey line) cannot be considered as a great

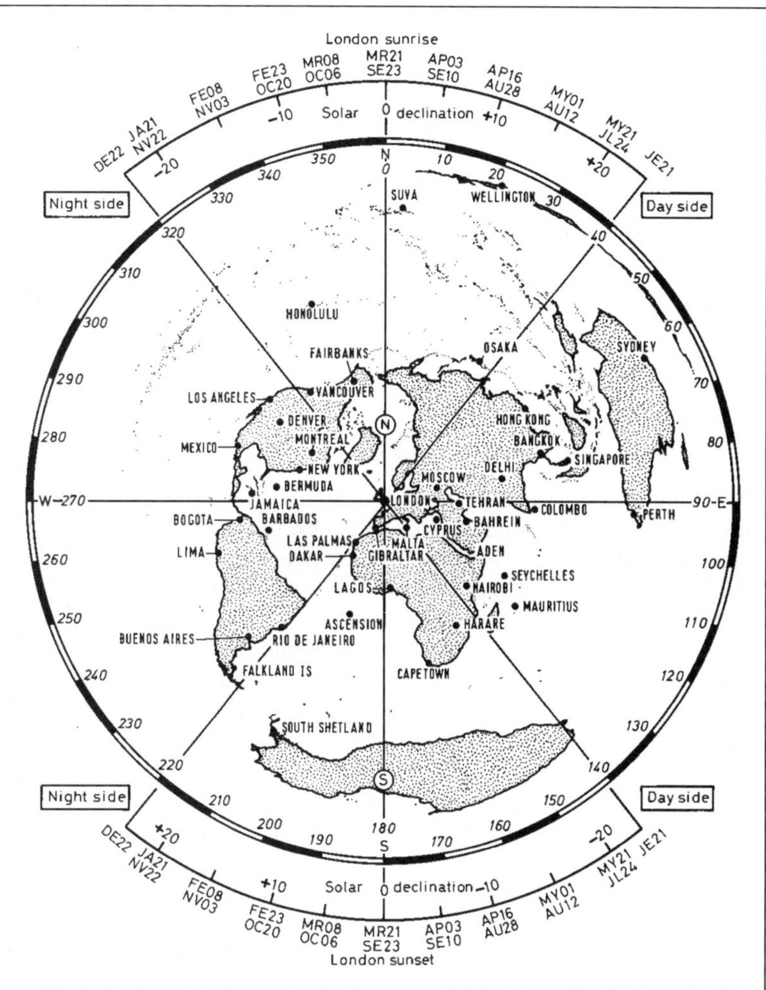

Fig 6.5: Grey line propagation map

circle and, therefore, cannot be represented by the straight line on the map. This should not stop you from trying your luck, however! But there is no point in trying to calculate the true outline of the Earth's shadow, because your signals are going to take the great-circle route no matter what you come up with on your computer. You may as well make all your plans using ground-based data, because it is easy to come by, and make up for its likely deficiencies by being generous with your timing. At the sort of frequency you are using, the beam width of the antenna will be wide enough to take care of direction.

To summarise, DX can be worked throughout the year on the LF bands although interference and noise level may make life difficult in the summer months. Basically the rules are simple. Most or all of the path must be in darkness and the best times, particularly for long hauls, are when much or all of the path lies just inside the area of darkness, a situation which occurs if it is near sunrise or sunset at both ends of the path. The latter condition cannot of course always be met, in which case there are two optimum times - around sunset at the western end of the path and near sunrise at the eastern end. With the shorter paths, eg to North America, the path is open between these times but with long hauls, eg to the Far East and Australasia, the openings can only be expected at these times.

Anomalous propagation, disturbances and blackouts

THERE ARE VARIOUS ways in which band characteristics depart from the general pattern, as described in the preceding paragraphs, and the effect of those of most concern to the amateur are briefly described below.

Extended ('chordal') hops

When transmitting in a direction in which there is a 'valley' in the MUF contours the F2 ionisation gradient, though not steep enough to return your signal to earth, may bend it sufficiently for it to follow the curvature of the Earth until it encounters rising MUF on the far side of the 'valley' when it will be deflected downwards. This mode of propagation is most common between antipodes (points diametrically opposite to each other on the earth's surface), where it is dawn at one end and dusk at the other, as there is a tilting of the ionosphere at these times (the charged layer rises in daylight, and falls after dusk). Such hops have low attenuation and can be very much longer than 4000km.

Ground scatter

At certain times of the day and in certain directions the path attenuation may be low enough for quite strong signals to be scattered from the point of ground reflection both sideways and back along the transmitting path. This is useful to the amateur in three ways:

1. If a beam antenna is used to determine the direction from which the back scatter from other UK or Continental stations is arriving, this is evidence of a good DX path in that direction.

2. It can be used to contact stations who are in the skip zone if both beam towards the scatter source.

3. When there is no normal path to, say, the USA it may still be possible to communicate if both stations beam towards West Africa or South America.

An interesting example of this can be seen in the evenings on 14 and sometimes 21MHz when there is no direct path to Australasia but a good path to South Africa. Good communication is then possible with the Australasian and UK stations both beaming on Cape Town. Whether the scatter occurs in Africa or in the South Polar Region is an open question. In fact, both the long and short paths to stations near the antipode sometimes show significant deviations from the great circle route from 'over the pole' before the opening is fully developed to north of (LP) or south of (SP) the true direction as the path closes. Side scatter, ionospheric tilts and polar Es may all contribute to these effects.

Skip and antipodal focusing

When operating well below the MUF the various vertical rays from and to your antenna follow different vertical paths with different hop lengths When, however, the operating frequency is close to the MUF for the path, these rays tend to converge and this 'skip focusing' can provide significant signal enhancement, equivalent to the difference between a typical dipole and a good beam antenna (6-9dB). This accounts for the signal peak which often occurs soon after an MUF-limited path has opened and shortly before it closes, and is the best time for the operator with low power. Antipodal focusing is also an important mechanism. To the antipodes (in the case of the UK, this is somewhere near New Zealand) all directions are great circle paths (no need for a beam!) and therefore all signals arriving there (not all directions will necessarily be open, of course) will be cumulative in the distant receiver. This is one of the reasons the path from the UK to Australia/New Zealand is so reliable.

Disturbances and blackouts

Events taking place in the Sun can cause major and minor upsets to HF communication in basically two ways. As already mentioned, a rise in certain emissions can cause daytime absorption to rise to high levels. On such occasions paths in a generally westerly direction which are normally open at a given time may show signals for a short time after opening, but they will then fade to return after dark if the path MUF is still high enough. In extreme cases, usually associated with solar flares, the absorption rises suddenly to a high value and all daylight paths are 'blacked out'. Such a 'sudden ionospheric disturbance' (SID) may last minutes or hours. Sometimes solar noise is high on 21and 28MHz before the blackout and MUFs may be abnormally high both before and after the disturbance. Particle radiation from flares or through 'coronal holes' affects the intensity and shape of the Earth's magnetic field and therefore the shape of the MUF contours. These magnetic disturbances or 'storms' generally result in lower MUFs and higher absorption in high latitudes, particularly in the auroral zones. Under such conditions paths in northerly directions, notably to North America, may be badly affected while conditions to the south may even be improved. Disturbances resulting from persistent solar anomalies are predictable since they recur at 27-day intervals.

Ionospheric propagation at VHF

AS MENTIONED IN the introduction to this chapter, as well as the more conventional forms of ionospheric propagation, due to the various daily, seasonal and 11-year solar variations, there are other ways in which the ionosphere can be energised so as to reflect radio waves and therefore enable long-distance propagation. This section discusses the main mechanisms involved.

Trans Equatorial Propagation

Trans Equatorial Propagation or TEP, is peculiar to six and two metres only. This mode allows contacts to be made over paths several thousand miles in length between stations on either side of the equator. The mode is much more common for those stations located in a band around the tropics; however, 50MHz will produce TEP propagation, particularly around the months of March and October, as far north as the UK. To date no TEP contacts have been made on two metres from the UK.

Sporadic-E (Es) propagation

This is the name given to intense ionisation of the E-layer which happens sporadically. Patches of high ionisation can appear without warning and disappear as suddenly. In the UK area they are most likely in the daytime and from March to September, peaking in June and July, and can result in communication over ranges of 500-2000km at frequencies very much above the F2 MUF. For the HF operator their effect is most noticeable on 21 and 28MHz where, as already mentioned, they not only give good contact with Europe but may 'help' a DX signal into a region of higher F2 MUF. Es elsewhere in the world can also help the DX operator. It is common throughout the year in daytime in equatorial regions and mainly at night in the auroral zones. The so-called 'M' reflection, involving a signal on its way down from the F2 region being 'bounced' back off the *top* of an Es cloud, can help your signal cross an area of low F2 MUF and has low attenuation because the signal still only passes twice through the absorbing regions.

The mechanism of Sporadic E has been studied for many years and the general conclusion seems to be that there is no single cause of this phenomenon though upper atmosphere wind shear effects and the geomagnetic field play a role. Es gives rise to propagation over distances from a few hundred to over 2000km at frequencies up to about 200MHz, so that it affects the 24, 28, 50, 70 and 144MHz bands. However, the ionisation has to be very intense for 144MHz propagation to occur such that on occasions when Es may be observed continuously on 28MHz for several days, it may reach 144MHz for only a few minutes during this time. Particularly in June and July, the 50MHz band is often full of Es signals on a daily basis, sometimes supporting multi-hop propagation from the British Isles to the Eastern Mediterranean, the Middle East and across the Atlantic to North America. For example, there was a superb multi-hop Es opening to North America in June 1994 when JY7SIX (Jordan) made a multi-hop contact with W4 at 9600km. This event occurred within about a year of sunspot minimum so F-layer propagation can be discounted. Several other major openings have occurred on 'six' in recent years during June and July between Sweden and Japan, Greece and Japan. Several rare DX stations located in the Caribbean were reported as being worked in the UK during the summer months. The 70MHz band is often open for lesser periods in these months but still provides a stepping stone and MUF monitor to 144MHz openings, particularly now that more countries have access to the band. Typically, as the intensity of Es increases and higher bands start to be affected, propagation distances on the lower bands start to shorten because higher-angle radiation is reflected. So, for example, when UK amateurs are able to work Italy on 2m, they will probably find themselves working near-in DX such as Germany and Luxembourg on 6m.

The most interesting Es band is 144MHz and since openings can be very short, from a few seconds to at most a few hours, it is desirable to know when Es is likely. This involves careful monitoring of signals in the approximate range 28-118MHz and a general-coverage receiver, preferably able to receive both AM and FM, is desirable. Most modern amateur transceivers with VHF capability allow scanning of frequencies over a wide range, perhaps aided by a panoramic display. Do, however, bear in mind that it is illegal to listen to certain types of transmission which can be found in the 30-144MHz range.

28MHz band. European signals will always be audible when Es is around. When ionisation is intense, signals are extremely strong and the shorter the distance, the more likely it is that higher frequencies such as 50MHz are affected.

Band I TV video signals (48-68MHz) can be useful but are often difficult to identify, especially the vision on air due to multiple signals being received. This can be overcome by using a receiver with SSB reception - the offset frequency can clearly be monitored and recognised because all the European TV Band 1 frequencies are now listed in various locations on the Internet. Small portable TV sets are useful monitors if you can get one but most modern British sets are UHF only so they are useless for 50MHz MUF monitoring. It is now possible to buy multi-standard portable TV receivers in the UK and even surplus spectrum analysers are becoming so realistically priced that their use can be put to other situations.

Band II (88-108MHz) is used by most European countries for VHF FM broadcasting. The sudden appearance of DX stations from Italy or Spain indicates that 144MHz may well open in those directions. In some cities in the British Isles several dozen UK FM stations are always audible and the appearance of a DX station may pass unnoticed. There can be some confusion since there may be local stations serving ethnic communities broadcasting in foreign languages (eg London Greek Radio on 103.3MHz).

Auroral propagation

The natural phenomenon known in Europe as the 'northern lights' has been studied and used as a propagation medium by amateurs for more than 50 years. Radio auroral events cause great excitement among VHF operators, who are able to work DX stations at distances far exceeding their normal tropospheric range. During strong events, stations located in southern England are often able to make contacts with Finland and Estonia by beaming their signals towards the auroral reflecting zones. All auroral openings occur after a solar flare has released energy from the Sun. The *GB2RS* news bulletins in the UK and Internet news pages often give details of sunspot activity and flares that are usually associated with these eruption holes on the disc of the Sun. A solar flare releases tremendous amounts of energy across the entire electromagnetic spectrum from X-rays to radio waves. The Sun emits ionised gas continuously and this is termed the 'solar wind'. During flares, bursts of energetic charged particles stream outwards from the Sun and spiral towards the Earth via the solar wind. These particles are divided by the Earth's magnetic field and then follow the field lines to regions known as the 'auroral zones'. These zones are oval shaped and typically (depending on particle energy) extend outwards from the poles to a radius of 23° on the night side of the Earth and to 15° on the daylight side. Visual auroral sightings indicate where the charged particles impinge on the Earth's upper atmosphere, ionising the E layer at a height of 110km. The number of auroral openings in any year is dependent on the solar activity. Some areas of the Sun can remain active for several weeks, causing repeats of events 26 to 28 days after the initial aurora. This is due to the period of rotation of the Sun and events like these are known as 'solar repeats'.

Auroras are accompanied by spectacular visual displays - the Northern Lights - which are sometimes visible in the UK. This one was photographed by GM0CLN, in West Lothian, in October 2003

Warning signs of impending auroral events

Large increases in the solar noise levels on 95, 136 and 225MHz can be measured during flares. These sudden ionospheric disturbances are often followed by short-wave fade-outs on the 14-28MHz bands, causing disruption of amateur and commercial HF communication. This is caused by cosmic particles and X-rays ionising the D-layer which absorbs rather than reflects radio signals. These particles complete the 150 million kilometre journey from the flare region on the Sun in less than 15 minutes. It should be noted that short-wave fadeouts occur which are not accompanied by auroral events, but fade-outs followed by large magnetic disturbances almost always signal an impending aurora.

A good and reliable indication of a forthcoming auroral event is known as 'pre-auroral enhancement' and is familiar to HF band operators. This effect is particularly obvious during periods of poor propagation such as in the summer months at sunspot minimum. A typical example occurred on 6 April 1995 when, during a sustained period of mediocre conditions on 14MHz, the band became full of very strong signals from Australia and New Zealand with the propagation akin to that during sunspot cycle peaks. The following day HF band conditions had collapsed and there was a very intense aurora enjoyed by VHF operators on the 50, 144 and even 430MHz bands.

Changes in the Earth's magnetic activity are measured in three directions - horizontal, vertical and declination. All three change prior to and during auroral events but amateur observers have noticed that the angle of declination measurements give the first geomagnetic auroral warning signs. Declination is the angle measured between geographic and magnetic north. **Fig.6.6** shows the magnetic disturbance recorded on 1 May 1978 on a chart recorder connected to a magnetometer set up in the garden of the home of Dr Gadsen of Aberdeen University. The chart shows a fairly quiet initial period with small normal daily changes in magnetic

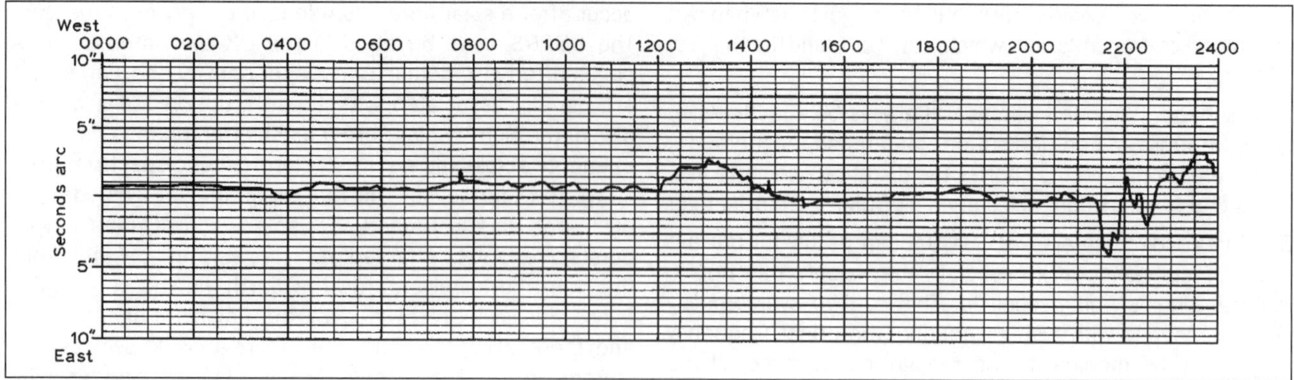

Fig 6.6: Magnetometer recording taken on 1 May 1978

activity, and then at midday it shows the start of a 'sudden commencement geomagnetic disturbance'.

These magnetic effects are measured in professional observatories and a daily equivalent planetary amplitude figure (Ap) is issued which gives the average level at several different locations. These changes in magnetic activity which take place on a worldwide basis are caused by the slower-moving particles which take one or two days to complete the journey from the Sun to the Earth's magnetosphere. Large-scale radio auroral events took place on 1 May 1978 in three distinct phases - in the afternoon, late evening and again after midnight - the chart in Fig.6.6 shows the changes in magnetic activity preceding and accompanying the aurora.

It is quite easy to make a simple magnetometer to monitor deviations in the Earth's magnetic field using readily available components and several such designs can be found on the Internet [8].

Shortly after the commencement of a magnetic storm the comparatively slow-moving particles ionise the E layers and align along the Earth's field lines. VHF radio signals beamed towards the auroral regions are reflected and refracted by the moving area of auroral ionisation. This moving reflector causes frequency shift and spreading, making all auroral signals sound distorted and difficult to copy. Morse signals are transformed into a rough hissing note and SSB voice transmissions vary from a growl to a whisper. The amount of frequency change on signals varies proportionately to the frequency band used - this effect is known as 'Doppler shift' and can be as much as 1.5-2kHz HF or LF of the actual transmit frequency on 144MHz. Because the frequency change is less on 6m, making Auroral contacts on that band is somewhat easier. If the aurora is strong enough, a form of Sporadic E develops, known as Auroral Es.

Many operators keep special 27-day auroral calendars on which they record both the visual and radio events which are reported in *RadCom* and on the *GB2RS* news bulletins (and elsewhere). The auroral calendar in **Fig.6.7** which started on 1 January 1977 and records auroral events until 1 August 1978 shows the correlation between the visual and radio events, and demonstrates the fact that auroras often repeat 27 days later. A study of Fig.6.7 shows that in the period 1 August 1977 to 1 August 1978 UK observers recorded 70 visual aurora and 100 radio events. These numbers are con-

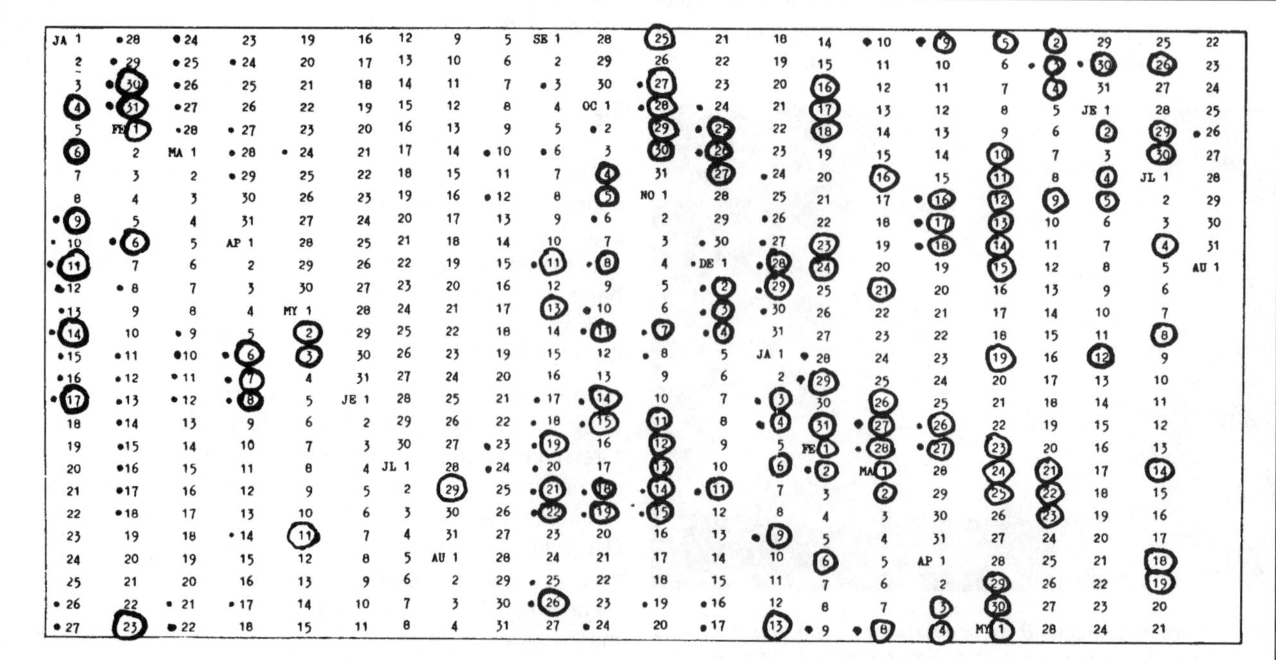

Fig 6.7: Example of a 7-day auroral calendar

siderably higher than during the same period for the previous two years, thus reflecting the increase in solar activity as Cycle 21 got under way.

The auroral warning calendar is very easy to use - simply circle any radio events and dot any visual auroras. An operator who was on for the 21 September 1977 event would have been prepared for the events which occurred on 18 October, 14 November and 11 December 1977. As the calendar shows, many events repeat in 26 to 28 days, often three or four times, proving that this method can be used successfully.

Meteor-scatter propagation

Meteor scatter (MS) is a DX propagation mode which relies on reflecting signals off the brief ionised trail left by a falling meteor. These can last for up to a minute or more on rare occasions, but more usually for fractions of a second. This requires specialist operating techniques (see Chapter 9), relying nowadays mainly on signal-processing software. Meteor scatter is open to exploitation by most serious VHF operators; it should not be regarded as the province of a few specialists. However, it does require a higher level of station organisation and operational competence than random tropo DX chasing.

What are meteors? Meteors are particles of rocky and metallic matter ranging in mass from about 10^{-10} kg to larger than 10kg. About 10^{12} are swept up by the Earth each day. At an altitude of about 120km they meet sufficient atmospheric resistance to cause significant heating. At 80km all but the largest are totally ionised (and generating trails of ionised gas), and this ionisation can be used to scatter radio signals in the range 10MHz to 1GHz. The level of ionisation required for 2m meteor scatter usually means that contacts can only take place during well-known meteor showers (which recur annually as the earth orbits the sun and passes through the same areas of cosmic particles). However, on 6m, meteor scatter propagation is possible most days, as there is a constant stream of cosmic debris entering the earth's atmosphere.

Signal strengths associated with meteor scatter propagation, especially on 6m, can be quite high, and distances are comparable to those achievable with Sporadic E propagation.

Non-ionospheric propagation

THE REMAINDER OF this chapter is devoted to long-distance propagation through means other than reflection off the ionosphere. Some of these occur naturally, some make use of more artificial mechanisms.

Tropospheric propagation

In the early days of VHF it was thought that propagation was only possible over line-of-sight paths and at distances beyond this attenuation was rapid; however, experience in the early 'thirties showed that this was not always so and sometimes much longer distances could be covered. These effects were soon related to atmospheric conditions and it was realised that radio waves were being bent back to Earth by the troposphere, the lowest layer of the atmosphere, characterized by clouds and weather, and in which temperature generally decreases with increasing altitude. Hence the term tropospheric propagation.

The relation between weather and tropospheric propagation is complex but in general it may be said that the main requirement is a temperature or a humidity inversion. Normally the temperature of the atmosphere decreases with increasing height above Earth, but in abnormal circumstances it may increase over part of the distance so that VHF waves which are normally lost in space are bent back to Earth, sometimes at a range of hundreds of kilometres.

Since first published in the early 'seventies *DUBUS* magazine has included 'Top Lists' which now include the bands from 50MHz up. Examination of the 144MHz list for mid-1994 shows the average best distance claimed (usually known as 'ODX') by the top 80 stations to be just over 1500km, with four operators claiming contacts in excess of 2000km. Clearly the DX enthusiast will wish to forecast the good conditions. Two essential aids are:

Weather map (synoptic chart). This may be found on television or in a newspaper. The former is preferred as it is more likely to be up-to-date. Be careful to distinguish between actual maps showing the situation a few hours before and forecast maps, which are not necessarily accurate, as the weather is notoriously difficult to predict.

Barometer/barograph. Some means of observing changes in atmospheric pressure is required. A barometer, or better still a barograph, is suitable, though a surplus aircraft altimeter will be satisfactory, providing this is of the correct type (ie not a radio altimeter).

What to look for

Good conditions are usually associated with stable weather patterns and this means areas of high pressure (anticyclones). Therefore, look for anticyclones on the map and a barometer reading high. It will soon be found that the appearance of a high pressure system does not produce good conditions, but when it starts to decline things may start to happen, especially if the anticyclone is short-lived. However, good conditions can occur when the atmospheric pressure is steady or even increasing. It must be added that anticyclones may form over the British Isles and decline without any significant effect on conditions. Conversely DX can appear when the weather map appears to be a series of depressions, though an opening under these conditions is usually short lived. A complete understanding would require a study of the atmosphere in great detail.

How to identify enhanced conditions

The simplest method is to monitor known distant signals and the most useful of these are the beacons. A comprehensive beacon list is published in the annual *RSGB Yearbook*. A quick check of signal strengths of the beacons on the bands of interest will usually give a clue to the state of conditions. This is especially useful on 144MHz where many beacons are operating. It should be added that the beacons may be observed at enhanced strength when no other signals can be heard, either because there is no activity or because stations which are operating are beaming in other directions.

Other distant stations, eg television transmissions from Europe, may give a clue to conditions. These used to be difficult to identify but a detailed study has taken place during the last 10 years and now the 48 and 49MHz TV video signals can be identified by their own personal offset frequency. Sometimes unusual patterning on the screen of the domestic UHF TV set or an announcement from the broadcasting organisation concerning 'Continental interference' may indicate that an opening is taking place.

Some points to observe:

1. All bands are not necessarily affected equally. It is possible for propagation to be enhanced at 144MHz but not at 432MHz and vice versa.

2. Propagation does not vary uniformly. It can be good to, say, the south but poor to the north simultaneously.

3. Skip effects are noticeable at times. It can be possible for a station 300km to the west to be working DX several hundred kilometres to the east which is quite inaudible to a station in between. This is very frustrating and the only thing to do is to monitor carefully and hope for a change.

Moonbounce

NOT STRICTLY propagation in the conventional sense, but amateurs have, for many years now, been using the moon as a passive reflector of VHF signals. In theory, any frequency which is not reflected by the ionosphere but passes out into space can be used for moonbounce (also known as EME - earth-moon-earth) communication. In practice, the lowest frequency in use is 6m, where moonbounce is possible only when Sporadic E and other enhanced propagation is absent. The 2m, 70cm and 23cm bands are also in regular use for moonbounce contacts. Path losses can be calculated with a reasonable degree of accuracy, allowing the station to be designed with sufficient antenna gain, transmit power and receive sensitivity to achieve two-way communications (depending on the station at the other end of the QSO, of course). Modern software-based systems, discussed in Chapter 8, have made EME accessible to many more amateurs.

Artificial satellites

AGAIN, NOT STRICTLY propagation in the conventional sense, the use of active amateur satellites has been growing over a number of years, and extends from the upper HF bands into several of the higher microwave bands. Amateur satellites are, in effect, extremely well sited 'repeaters in the sky'. Unlike the static terrestrial repeaters which are mainly in-band transponders, most of the artificial satellite-borne transponders are cross-band, for example VHF to UHF, UHF to microwave, and so-on. Many are LEO (Low Earth Orbit) satellites and, as such, move relatively fast relative to the earth's surface. Thus, amateur stations operating through such satellites must be capable of predicting accessible satellite 'pass' orbits to allow for antenna steering (if high gain beams are used) and correction for Doppler shift on the satellite signals.

Not strictly propagation, but amateur satellites provide a useful way of working DX [picture: AMSAT-ZL]

More recent amateur satellites have been placed in highly elliptical orbits which minimise Doppler shift and antenna tracking problems when the satellite is at its most distant point from earth (apogee). Modern software systems, like those mentioned in the EME section above, have made satellite predictions, Doppler correction and antenna steering available to many more amateurs.

Microwave propagation

IONOSPHERIC PROPAGATION rarely if ever occurs above 1GHz. Indeed, the upper limit appears to be somewhere around the amateur 70cm band (432MHz). There are a few isolated reports claiming to have observed ionospheric propagation at 1.3GHz but these are largely unconfirmed and therefore doubtful.

Free-space transmission losses, measured in decibels, increase with the square of the frequency (in megahertz) as well as with the square of the transmission path distance (in kilometres). In addition, above about 23GHz, atmospheric absorption by water, water vapour and oxygen peak in certain frequency bands, adding greatly to the free-space losses. As a consequence, some microwave bands are useable for contacts over very limited distances.

All the tropospheric propagation modes observed at VHF and UHF occur at microwave frequencies. It is becoming apparent, as more regular fixed-station activity takes place, that 'lifts' or 'openings' may occur more frequently than at VHF or UHF because the vertical extent of the tropospheric anomaly can be smaller to have the same effect. That is, the ability of a 'duct' of a particular thickness to propagate radio waves with low-loss (attenuation) is related to frequency - amongst other things! DX of 1000km or more has been worked quite frequently.

Another propagation mode, allied to tropospheric ducts, is the formation of a low-level 'super-refraction' layer over large stretches of water, for instance across the North Sea. **Fig.6.8** illustrates some of the trans-horizon atmospheric propagation mechanisms, briefly discussed in the paragraphs above, and in the earlier section on VHF/UHF propagation modes. The principal difference between VHF/UHF propagation and microwave propagation is one of scale: the effectiveness of an atmospheric 'duct', or the forward scatter properties of the atmosphere itself and of hydrometeors (rain, hail, snow), are all functions of frequency. A shallow duct (such as a super-refraction duct over calm water in settled weather) which will not support VHF or UHF propagation may well act as a near-perfect 'waveguide' for microwave signals. Similarly, large raindrops, hail or snow, such as those typically associated with thunder cells, can provide a very effective, if short-term, scattering medium particularly in the 10 or 24GHz bands.

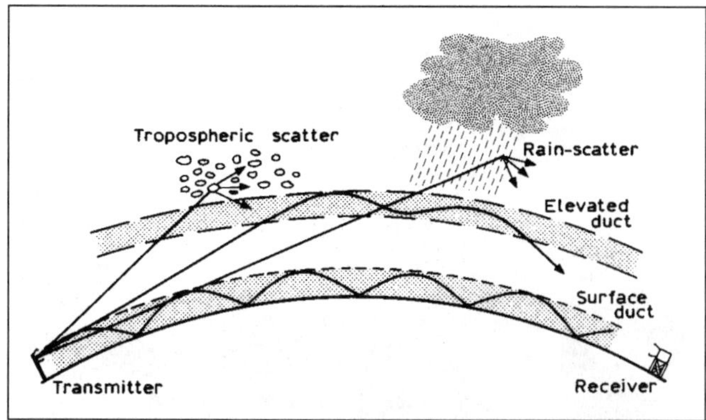

Fig 6.8: Trans-horizon propagation mechanism in the lower atmosphere

Microwave Scatter propagation

Quite a lot has already been said about the various scatter propagation modes (such as ionospheric, tropospheric, meteor and auroral scatter) as observed and used at HF, VHF and UHF.

All scatter propagation, regardless of the frequency in use, depends upon irregularities, for instance changes in the level of ionisation of the ionosphere in the case of HF and the lower VHF bands or changes in the temperature, humidity and therefore 'radio refractive index' of the atmosphere in the case of the VHF, UHF and microwave bands.

Scatter propagation is always a 'dispersive' mode, in that *only a tiny proportion of the radio wave incident on the irregularities is scattered in the desired direction*, depending on the angle of incidence of the radio wave. At an acute angle, back-scatter and absorption tend to predominate, whilst at an oblique angle forward scatter (or side-scatter, or both) tend to predominate. Scattering is *always* a mixture of reflection and refraction.

Forward troposcatter which results from atmospheric irregularities, for example temperature, pressure and humidity 'cells', is a reliable, ever-present mode in the microwave bands and is much used professionally for 'beyond-the-horizon' communications.

To be reliable and cover the maximum link range (in commercial or professional terms) requires that a number of factors need to be satisfied. First, high transmit power, high antenna gain and low receiver noise. Second, the antennas of both stations need to be pointed accurately along the Great Circle path and radiate at as low an angle to the horizon as possible. This is in order that both stations can 'see' a common scattering volume of the atmosphere, the height of which largely determines the ultimate range of the link. It is also essential that both stations have 'good horizons' - that is, an *unobstructed* horizon, as the path loss in a scatter link is so high (eg >300dB at 10GHz over a 1000km path) that additional losses caused by obstructions at either end of the path may shorten the link length by hundreds of kilometres.

Reliable forward troposcatter over long distances is not really practicable with amateur power levels, although signals showing the characteristics of forward troposcatter have been exchanged, for example on the 10GHz band, over distances of up to about 100 - 150km, using low power (less than 10W) and small dish antennas.

What may be more practical to amateurs is the use of *reflection from solid objects* which are line-of-sight to both stations, but off the direct path. Such reflection is also a dispersive mode, since such solid objects are seldom either perfect reflectors or perfectly smooth as is a mirror to light. Similar considerations to troposcatter apply, although for minimum path loss, the reflecting object should be close to one end of the path. This is because the path loss is proportional to $1/(d_1 \times d_2)^2$, where d_1 and d_2 are the distances of station 1 and station 2 from the reflecting object. It can be seen that minimising either d_1 or d_2 will minimise the path loss. Incidentally, this is the principle on which 'periscope' or 'fly-swatter' antennas work.

Ephemeral scatter occurs in the microwave bands due to a number of temporary, short-term, small-scale phenomena, such as rain, hail and snow (collectively known as 'hydrometeors'), aircraft, passing ships etc.

Aircraft scatter plainly requires the presence of a passing aircraft close to one end or other of the path to be covered and is a phenomenon which may last only a few seconds. Using this mode may be similar to meteor scatter on the lower (VHF) bands - that is, short signal enhancements necessitating a quick exchange of signals - so it may be advantageous to be close to an airport takeoff path to be able to use aircraft scatter effectively!

Passing ships are a rare phenomenon unless the amateur stations are using the super-refraction layer which forms low over extensive stretches of water (eg the North Sea, the Great Australian Bight, the Mediterranean, UK - Canaries, and California - Hawaii) under settled weather conditions. Large passing ships might conceivably aid (or possibly hinder!) such propagation by acting as slow-moving reflectors. Most if not all of the extreme microwave DX has resulted from a mixture of tropospheric propagation modes - super-refraction, combined with other forms of ducting and possibly refraction and reflection - across such stretches of water.

Rain scatter requires, preferably, very heavy, localised precipitation such as that associated with thunder cells close to one end of the path or the other (see above). There is really no difference between rain scatter on the higher microwave bands (eg10GHz/24GHz) and any other form of (normal) tropospheric forward scatter on any microwave band (or UHF band, come to that) - the only difference is one of scale and the fact that, with increasing frequency, atmospheric water and water vapour absorb microwave signals (as does oxygen in the millimetre bands).

Thus it is largely a matter of balance between forward scattering and water droplet absorption, when the droplets are comparable to something like $\lambda/10$ in size (say of the order of 3mm or more at 10GHz or above). As a rule of thumb:

- droplets too small [fine drizzle + high water vapour pressure (humidity)] = absorption, and
- oversized droplets [thunderstorm, usually with low water vapour pressure, or at least a sharply defined precipitation (water or ice) boundary] = forward scatter.

In the millimetre bands (above 24GHz) forward scatter DX is more likely with heavy snow than heavy rain because, at sub-zero temperatures, the loss due to water vapour absorption is minimised ie the relative humidity is very low.

Microwave forward scatter signals due to any of these short term phenomena may sound like auroral signals on the VHF bands, more so with rain scatter than aircraft or ship scatter, because of the Doppler shift caused by the relative velocity of the scattering object.

It can be seen, therefore, that there are several apparently conflicting factors affecting microwave propagation. On the one hand, settled weather conditions can lead to the formation of ducts and, on the other, turbulent, unsettled weather can enhance scatter modes. Again, at higher microwave frequencies, atmospheric water vapour absorption can increase attenuation and yet super-refraction layers over water (where the humidity is obviously high) can enhance propagation! It is these apparent contradictions which perhaps add to the fascination and challenge of microwave operation.

The beacon network

PROPAGATION PREDICTIONS are all very well but if you have just switched on your radio and want to work DX, it's obviously better to know what is happening right now, rather than what has been forecast. This is where beacons can help. On each HF and VHF band there are many beacons situated in strategic locations all over the world which can provide an excellent clue to band conditions, and these are proving valuable in both amateur and professional propagation research. A list of these beacons appears annually in the *RSGB yearbook*.

Of particular interest are the beacons operated by the Northern California DX Foundation (NCDXF) in cooperation with the IARU. These beacons operate on 14.100, 18.110, 21.150, 24.930, and 28.200MHz. At the time of writing, 18 beacons are active. Each beacon transmits in turn at various power levels from 100 watts down to 100mW, with each transmission repeated every three minutes. A full transmission schedule can be found on the NCDXF web site [9] from which it is also possible to download software for automated monitoring of the beacons.

The beacons on 28MHz all have their own frequencies in the 28.190-28.225MHz sub-band, and run continuously.

VHF beacons have already been mentioned and, as with the HF beacons, are an invaluable indication of propagation.

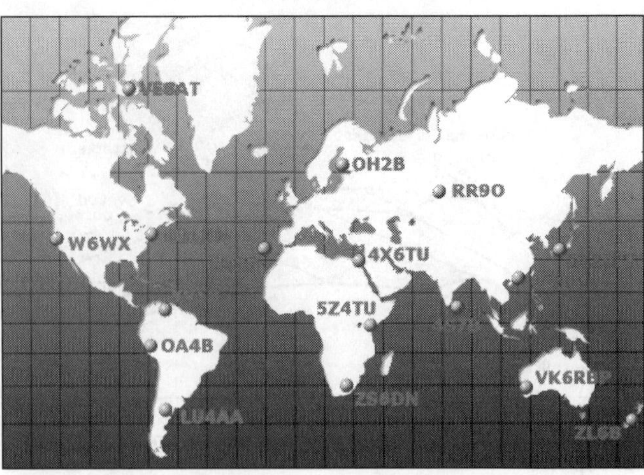

The DXNCF HF beacon chain is a good resource for checking propagation in real time on the HF bands

Many DXpedition and DX stations also run interruptable beacons. This saves having to monitor a band continuously, but if you hear the beacon you can break the transmission and, hopefully, alert an operator at the DX end. However, *never* transmit on, or very close to, a normal beacon frequency or in a beacon sub-band, even if you can't hear anything - your signals will cause severe interference to others straining to catch the faint signals.

References

[1] NOAA Solar Data: http://www.noaa.gov/solar.html

[2] N6RT propagation data: http://dx.qsl.net/propagation/

[3] The Shortwave Propagation Handbook, George Jacob, W3ASK, and Theodore J Cohen, N4XX, CQ Magazine.

[4] Radio Propagation - Principles & Practice, Ian Poole G3YWX, RSGB 2004.

[5] DX Atlas: http://www.dxatlas.com/

[6] Geoclock: http://home.att.net/~geoclock/

[7] Radio Communication Handbook, 7th edn, ed Dick Biddulph, M0CGN, RSGB, 1999, Chapter 12.

[8] Build a magnetometer: http://www.payton.cps.k12.il.us /magnet/magnet_welcome.htm

[9] NCDXF Beacons: http://www.ncdxf.org/beacons.html

7 An Operating Primer

CHAPTER ONE COVERED some of the basics of amateur radio operation, and explained why a manual of this sort is necessary. This chapter covers operating in a greater level of detail, from making your first QSO to the point where you have achieved a high degree of proficiency. From that point onwards your operating interests are likely to migrate to one of the more specialist aspects, which are covered in subsequent chapters.

Listening

IN DAYS GONE BY, short-wave listening was by far the commonest route into amateur radio. Most licensed amateurs would have started by spending time listening on the bands. This is less common nowadays, but there is no doubt that time spent listening is time well spent. However detailed and comprehensive an operating manual such as this, it's no substitute for actually observing what happens on the bands and, in the fullness of time, making contacts yourself. By listening to the amateur bands, you start to get a feel for propagation, begin to recognise callsign prefixes, start to get used to some of the abbreviations in common use and, of course, get used to using your own equipment in a live environment. You will hear good operating and bad operating and, hopefully, will learn to distinguish between the two. There is no specific requirement to keep a log of what you hear, though you may wish to make notes for future reference.

Listening also gets you used to what you will find where on each of the bands, a practical exercise to complement the theoretical knowledge of bandplans which you will need to have before you start operating and, potentially, operate in an illegal or inappropriate part of the band. Listening also helps you to become familiar with amateur callsigns, a topic which confuses many newcomers and even many experienced operators. To help matters along, both bandplans and callsign structures are covered in the following sections, before the discussion turns to making your first contact.

There's no substitute for listening to get to know what to do on a band, and where, and what conditions are like

Even when you are ready to start transmitting, it is always helpful to have a listen around the band first. It will give you an idea of what propagation is like at that specific time. It will also show you how busy the band is and whether, for example, there is a contest taking place or maybe some special event stations active. You may well also hear one or two stations calling CQ, and decide to call one of them. And if you decide to call CQ yourself, you will be better able to make a decision about what frequency to choose. This advice applies to all bands, though is more applicable to HF operating, or to the VHF bands when they are 'open'. On the VHF (and higher) bands under normal circumstances, you will probably need to do no more than check the calling channel or local repeater, to ensure it is not already in use before making your CQ call.

Band Plans

AT THE OUTSET, it is important that you are aware of the bandplans applicable to the band(s) you intend to operate. Bandplans come in two forms, mandatory and recommended. Mandatory bandplans are those imposed by the licensing authority. In the USA, for example, the SSB section of each band is delineated by the FCC (US licensing body) whereas in the UK our licence doesn't specify which modes we use where in each band. Instead, we follow the recommendations made by the IARU, amateur radio's own international body (see Chapter 2). However, that isn't to say that there is no mandatory bandplanning in the UK. Although Full and Intermediate licence holders can use all of the UK allocation in each amateur band, the power limits differ, while Foundation Licence holders have limitations regarding both frequencies and power limits. And even for Full licence holders, it is important to be aware of specific notes in the licence schedule, for example the differing power levels permitted in different parts of the 160m band or the geographic restrictions applicable to the 431-432MHz section of the 70cm band.

There continues to be talk about whether the UK licensing authority should lay down bandplans by mode, but this has potential pitfalls, particularly in respect of the data modes, whose use is increasing quite rapidly. The expected release of a further 100kHz, in the UK and elsewhere, on 40m will also, inevitably require some modification of existing IARU bandplans in due course.

There is also an issue about recommended frequencies for contest operating, which is discussed in Chapter 10 (Contesting).

Callsigns

MOST UK AMATEURS will be familiar with the callsign series used in the UK and will know immediately whether a station they work is in England or Wales, for example, and the class of licence, Foundation, Intermediate or Full. But would you be able to do the same for callsigns that you hear from outside

The DXCC enitity of Timor Leste came into being when this former province of Indonesia was recognised in its own right as a nation state. The 4W prefix had previously been used by Yemen

the UK? This is an area that causes a huge amount of confusion, not helped by the daily appearance of new prefixes or unusual callsigns on the bands. Over the years, DXers and contesters develop a knowledge of callsigns that goes way beyond what you might find in a prefix list. This section aims to help you make a modest start, but because this area is a moving feast, you will need to be observant to snippets which might appear in magazines or newsletters which add to your knowledge.

All callsigns are structured with a prefix and suffix, in addition to which they may include other designators, showing portable operation from another country, for example. It is actually easier to describe a suffix, rather than a prefix. A callsign suffix consists entirely of letters. The prefix is what precedes that. In the case of the two callsigns VP2EZZ and VP2MZZ, for example, the suffixes are EZZ and MZZ respectively. Both have the same prefix, VP2, although most amateurs would tell you that the prefixes are VP2E and VP2M, for Anguilla and Montserrat. Yes, there is a local agreement that suffixes starting with E are issued in Anguilla and those with M in Montserrat, but as far as the ITU is concerned the prefix VP2 is allocated to the British West Indies, and any subdivision of this is by local arrangement. Equally, a callsign with prefix VP8 could be in one of several DXCC entities, but the authorities in Port Stanley, who issue VP8 callsigns, don't make any local arrangements to distinguish between the Falklands, South Georgia, South Sandwich, etc. so it is impossible to tell from the call which of these DXCC countries a station is operating from.

In Greece, many amateurs erroneously assume that the prefix SY is allocated to Mt.Athos, but the only amateur currently active from Mt.Athos uses an SV (normal Greece) prefix, whereas the SY prefix is often used by Greek special event stations.

The simple fact is that ITU-recognised countries do not map onto amateur radio 'entities'. In some countries the national licensing authority will play ball with the amateur community and set aside certain callsign blocks for specific DX entities. In other countries the licensing authority will see absolutely no need to go down that route, and amateurs have to use other methods to keep track of who is operating from which DXCC entity. ZK1 is the prefix for the Cook Islands, for example, but the North and South Cook Islands count separately for DXCC purposes. Experienced amateurs will know that there is rather more activity from the South Cooks than from the North Cooks and that ZK1CG who lives in the South Cooks is quite active and also runs a guest house from which regular DXpedition operations take place. So if a ZK1 station appears on the bands, there is a high probability that it is from South Cook. An expedition to North Cook is such a rare event that it will almost certainly have been well publicised in advance and you will be alert to the fact.

Even when you are able to determine the DXCC entity, there is then a matter of call areas within that entity. The best-known example is the USA. US callsigns used to be allocated by state. An amateur with a callsign starting W2, K2, AA2, etc. would be in New York or New Jersey. An amateur with a W6, K6, AA6, etc. callsign would be in California. If he operated from elsewhere in the US, he would have to sign an appropriate designator. NK1G, operating from Montana, would become NK1G/7 or, from Hawaii, NK1G/KH6. This is no longer the case. Callsigns can be allocated to US amateurs irrespective of their location, and no portable designators are required. This applies even to US possessions offshore. So KH6XYZ may be operating, not from Hawaii, but from mainland USA or, perhaps, even from somewhere like the US Virgin Islands. He may never have lived in Hawaii, even when the licence was issued. Similarly, NK1G could actually be operating from Hawaii or Alaska. In practice, most amateurs will use some designator, on a voluntary basis, to indicate their DXCC entity, but nowadays generally won't bother to indicate which part of the mainland USA they are in. Apropos of which, experienced DXers will know that a station signing with a KG4 prefix and a two-letter suffix is in Guantanamo Bay, whereas a station signing with a KG4 prefix and a three-letter suffix is in mainland USA, probably in the "4" call area. Most stations with KG6 callsigns are in the California area, but some KG6 stations are in Guam, with callsigns preceding the allocation of the KH2 prefix to Guam. Confusing, isn't it?

In contrast, in Japan the number in the callsign indicates in which part of Japan an amateur is located, and Japanese amateurs will always sign a portable designator if they are operating away from the address where the callsign was issued; all nice and clear! The same is true in certain other countries with discrete call areas, such as Sweden.

Generally, none of this is too important, other than in those contests where the call area is a multiplier, but it does make life confusing. Contesters, probably more than other amateurs, get to be quite good at knowing whether a callsign is or isn't possible. In the UK, if we logged the callsign G2XTT, we would quickly realise when looking at the log afterwards that this was an error, as G2 callsigns never got as far as the second part of the alphabet - they were issued before WWII, and after the war any new callsigns were issued from the new G3 series. Similar local knowledge applies to specific prefixes and suffix blocks in many other countries of the world, and gradually you will come to know what is and isn't possible. Contest and expedition operations often use a so-called Super-Check Partial (SCP) facility as an add-on to their computer logging. This is a database of active callsigns, built up from previous contest or DXpedition logs. If the operator hears a callsign that doesn't appear in the SCP database, it may simply be a newly-issued licence or newly-active amateur, but it may also be that the operator has miscopied the call.

By far the best source of detailed information on callsign prefixes is the RSGB's Amateur Radio Prefix Guide [1].

Your first transmission

BEFORE MAKING your first transmission, you will want to ensure that your station is working correctly (transceiver and antenna) and that you know how to operate it, at least at the basic level. You should check the antenna SWR using an antenna analyser of some sort, or running very low power and ensuring that you find a clear frequency on which to make your checks. If you do not use a resonant antenna, you will want to be sure that you are familiar with how to use your antenna tuning unit (ATU). Some can give false indications, so do carefully follow the tuning instructions in the manual.

As far as the transceiver is concerned, the first step is probably to run it into a dummy load and determine whether everything appears to be working correctly. Remember that most dummy loads are not rated for continuous power, but for 10 or 15 seconds at a time, the sort of time it should take to tune up a transmitter. When the transceiver is correctly tuned into the dummy load (not necessary with solid state transceivers) you are ready to connect it to the antenna. If you are using an ATU, it should be adjusted for minimum SWR and maximum forward power with the transceiver's drive at a low level. Power can then be increased to the desired level and the adjustments repeated. It is most important that any tune-up signal radiated by the antenna should not cause interference to stations already using the band, and a careful check of the chosen frequency should first be made. In particular, any temptation to tune up on the frequency of a DX station before calling should be very firmly resisted for obvious reasons.

When near a band-edge, great care must be taken to ensure that the transmission does not accidentally occur outside the amateur band. Allowance should be made for drift, calibration accuracy and sidebands, particularly those of FM signals (NBFM carriers should be at least 10kHz within the limits of the band in use).

When you are ready to go on the air, do bear in mind that older transmitters and receivers with a free-running VFO can exhibit appreciable drift within the first 15 minutes or so of operation and should therefore be switched on and allowed a reasonable period to warm up before they are actually used, particularly if a narrow-band mode such as CW is going to be employed. There is nothing more irritating than 'following' a CW station down the band, and of course it may drift onto another station's frequency and be lost altogether. Part of this warm-up period can usefully be employed by searching the band for interesting stations. Each time one is heard, its callsign and frequency can be noted on a scrap pad or in the callsign buffers in your online log. In this way a short list of frequencies to be monitored is built up, which will be useful during the operating session. This process can be further automated if a transceiver with memories is used although such transceivers should not require a warm-up, they will drift very little from switch-on.

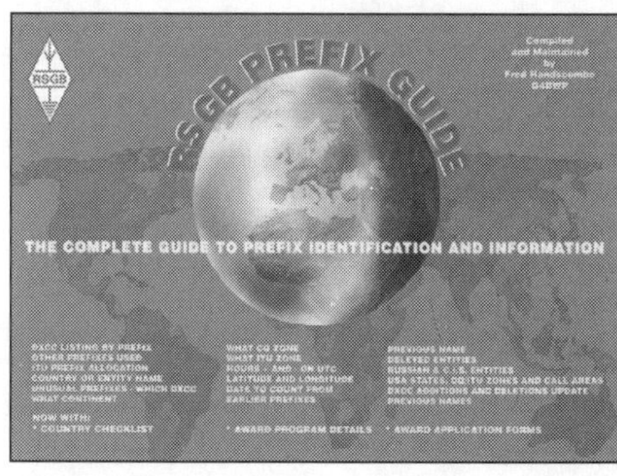

The *RSGB Prefix Guide* is invaluable for the HF operator

Establishing contact

THE BASIC PRINCIPLES behind establishing and conducting a contact have already been discussed in the opening chapter. There are two accepted ways of establishing contact with another amateur station. The first method is to put out a general call or broadcast to all stations, known as a CQ call, and to hope that another station responds. The second is to call another specific station by prior arrangement (known as keeping a schedule or 'sked') or after the other station has just finished a contact or made a CQ call.

Calling a specific station which has just finished a contact or made a CQ call has the advantage that you know who is likely to reply, and the signal strength of that reply. This is important on the HF bands because likely fading can be taken into account to determine whether a contact can be sustained. Another factor is that any rare or distant (DX) station on the band is probably already having a contact and would not reply to a CQ call.

When calling a specific station it is good practice to keep calls short and to use the callsign of the station called once or twice only, followed by your own repeated several times and pronounced or keyed carefully and clearly (particularly when signal strengths are not good or in the presence of interference). The calling procedure should be repeated as required until a reply is obtained or it is clear that someone else is in contact. VOX operation (or break-in on CW) is very useful, because if it is properly adjusted it will be possible to listen between words and know what is happening at all times.

This basic procedure may be summarised as follows:

1. Listen - to find out just what is happening on the frequency.
2. Be patient - wait until any other station already in contact has finished.
3. Make calls short - give the other station's callsign once or at the most twice, but your own two or three times.
4. Listen carefully - between words if possible.
5. Be ready to stop transmitting if the station being called replies to someone else.
6. If unlucky, be patient! Wait for another chance and call again.

If activity on the band is low and a reasonable amount of power is available, a CQ call may be useful. When this is transmitted just as 'CQ' it can be answered by any other station. If the call is 'CQ DX' this limits replies to calls from distant (DX) stations. The definition of DX varies from band to band, and also on conditions (see Chapter 9). Make sure this

Table 7.1: International Q-code (extract)

QRA	What is the name of your station? The name of my station is . . .
QRB	How far approximately are you from my station? The approximate distance between our stations is . . . kilometres.
QRG	Will you tell me my exact frequency (or that of . . .)? Your exact frequency (or that of . . .) is . . . kHz (or MHz).
QRH	Does my frequency vary? Your frequency varies.
QRI	How is the tone of my transmission? The tone of your transmission is . . . (amateur T1-T9).
QRK	What is the intelligibility of my signals (or those of . . .)? The intelligibility of your signals (or those of . . .) is . . .(amateur R1-R5).
QRL	Are you busy? I am busy (or I am busy with . . .). Please do not interfere.
QRM	Are you being interfered with? I am being interfered with.
QRN	Are you troubled by static? I am troubled by static.
QRO	Shall I increase transmitter power? Increase transmitter power.
QRP	Shall I decrease transmitter power? Decrease transmitter power.
QRQ	Shall I send faster? Send faster (. . . words per minute).
QRR	Are you ready for automatic operation? I am ready for automatic operation. Send at . . . words per minute.
QRS	Shall I send more slowly? Send more slowly (. . . words per minute).
QRT	Shall I stop sending? Stop sending.
QRU	Have you anything for me? I have nothing for you.
QRV	Are you ready? I am ready.
QRW	Shall I inform . . . that you are calling him on . . . kHz (or MHz)? Please inform . . . that I am calling him on . . . kHz (or MHz).
QRX	When will you call me again? I will call you again at . . .hours (on . . . kHz (or MHz)).
QRY	What is my turn? (Relates to communication). Your turn is Number . . . (or according to any other indication). (Relates to communication.)
QRZ	Who is calling me? You are being called by . . . (on . . . kHz (or MHz)).
QSA	What is the strength of my signals (or those of . . .)? The strength of your signals (or those of . . .) is . . . (amateur S1-S9).
QSB	Are my signals fading? Your signals are fading.
QSD	Is my keying defective? Your keying is defective.
QSI	I have been unable to break in on your transmission or Will you inform . . . (callsign) that I have been unable to break in on his transmission (on . . . kHz (or MHz)).
QSK	Can you hear me between your signals and if so can I break in on your transmission? I can hear you between my signals, break in on my transmission.
QSL	Can you acknowledge receipt? I am acknowledging receipt.
QSN	Did you hear me (or . . . (callsign)) on . . . kHz (or MHz)? I did hear you (or . . . (callsign)) on . . . kHz (or MHz).
QSO	Can you communicate with . . . direct (or by relay)? I can communicate with . . . direct (or by relay through . . .)
QSP	Will you relay to . . .? I will relay to . . .
QSR	Shall I repeat the call on the calling frequency? Repeat your call on the calling frequency; did not hear you (or have interference).
QSS	What working frequency will you use? I will use the working frequency . . . kHz (Normally only the last three figures of the frequency need be given).
QSU	Shall I send or reply on this frequency (or on . . . kHz (or MHz)) (with emissions of class . . .)? Send or reply on this frequency (or on . . . kHz (or MHz)) (with emissions of class . . .).
QSV	Shall I send a series of V's on this frequency (or . . . kHz (or MHz))? Send a series of V's on this frequency (or . . . kHz (or MHz)).
QSW	Will you send on this frequency (or on . . . kHz (or . . .MHz)) (with emissions of class . . .)? I am going to send on this frequency (or on . . . kHz (or MHz)) (with emissions of class . . .).
QSX	Will you listen to . . . (callsign(s)) on . . . kHz (or MHz)? I am listening to . . . (callsign(s)) on . . . kHz (or MHz).
QSY	Shall I change to transmission on another frequency? Change to transmission on another frequency (or on . . . kHz (or MHz)).
QSZ	Shall I send each word or group more than once? Send each word or group twice (or . . . times).
QTC	How many messages have you to send? I have . . . messages for you (or for . . .).
QTH	What is your position in latitude and longitude (or according to any other indication)? My position is . . .latitude . . . longitude (or according to any other indication).
QTQ	Can you communicate with my station by means of the International Code of Signals? I am going to communicate with your station by means of the International Code of Signals.
QTR	What is the correct time? The correct time is . . . hours.
QTS	Will you send your callsign for tuning purposes or so that your frequency can by measured now (or at . . . hours) on . . . kHz (or MHz)? I will send my callsign for tuning purposes or so that my frequency may be measured now (or at . . . hours) on . . . kHz (or MHz).
QTV	Shall I stand guard for you on the frequency of . . . kHz (or MHz) (from . . . to . . . hours)? Stand guard for me on the frequency of . . . kHz (or MHz) (from . . . to . . . hours).
QTX	Will you keep your station open for further communication with me until further notice (or until . . . hours)? I will keep my station open for further communication with you until further notice (or until . . . hours)
QUA	Have you news of . . . (callsign)? Here is news of . . .(callsign).
QUM	May I resume normal working? Normal working may be resumed.

is understood before making (or answering) a CQ DX call. If it is desired to make contact with a particular country a directional CQ call can be made, such as 'CQ VK', which means that only replies from Australia will be answered.

Before making a CQ call it is important to find a frequency which appears unoccupied by any other station. This may not be easy, particularly in crowded band conditions. Listen carefully - perhaps a DX station is on the frequency which is difficult to hear. If you are using a beam antenna, rotate it to make sure.

If after a reasonable time the frequency still seems clear, ask if the frequency is in use before transmitting the CQ call (On CW this can be done by transmitting 'QRL?' or just '?'). If two or three CQ calls produce no answer it may be that interference is present on that frequency for distant stations and a new frequency should be sought.

Each CQ call should be short with a break to listen for replies. It may then be repeated as often as required. Long calls without breaks denote poor operating technique - inter-

Papua New Guinea is a nice catch for any band, but the German group who activated P29VXX made a special effort on the low bands

ference may be unwittingly caused to stations which were already on the frequency but which the caller did not hear in the initial check, and moreover stations intending to reply to the call may become impatient and move on to another frequency.

CQ calls on VHF should include details of your location so that those stations using a beam antenna can work out the rough bearing and swing their antenna round before answering your call.

Summarising, the important points in making a CQ call are:

1. Find a clear frequency - check that this is so.
2. Keep calls short as possible and listen frequently.
3. Do not answer directional calls unless in the category of station being called.

Conducting the contact

IF CONTACT HAS been established on a special calling channel, the frequency should be vacated as soon as possible, and the contact completed elsewhere. After the usual greetings it is customary to exchange details of signal strength, name, location and information on the equipment being used, the latter often consisting only of the model number of the transceiver, the antenna and, if not immediately obvious, the power in use. Often on the VHF bands the height above sea level (ASL) of the location is also given, along with the QTH locator, while HF operators usually mention the local weather and radio conditions. A contact limited to exchanging such information (quite common on the HF bands) is often known, somewhat disparagingly, as a 'rubber stamp' contact. Yet many overseas amateurs deserve great credit for learning enough of a foreign language (such as English) to enable them to do this. They may not be familiar with other words and expressions, certainly not colloquialisms, and if a contact goes beyond the basic details with a foreign-language amateur it is always wise to use the simplest words possible (even to the extent of using international Q-codes on telephony). A further point is that in poor conditions it may be necessary to keep the whole contact short in case fading or interference occur. The good operator takes both these factors into account when expanding on a basic contact.

On VHF, contacts tend to be much less formal due to the usual absence of language difficulty, and 'rubber stamp' contacts are rare except under good conditions when DX contacts are possible.

On both HF and VHF it is good operating practice to use the minimum amount of RF power output consistent with 100% copy at the other station. Any reports of better than S9 received, eg "S9 + 20dB", indicate too much power is in use and this should be reduced if possible to avoid interference to other band users.

Concluding the contact

IT IS CUSTOMARY in a final transmission for an operator to express some gratitude for the contact, and to convey best wishes to the other person, with often a hope that another contact may be made at a later date.

After concluding the contact, both stations will listen carefully for callers, and what happens next depends on which station was using the frequency or channel prior to the contact. This station has some claim to the frequency, and it is usual and polite for the other station to move off elsewhere after the contact. However, this convention may be modified to suit the circumstances. Good operators move off a frequency where they have been fortunate enough to be called by a rare or DX station, to enable others to contact it. No band is so crowded that it is not possible to find another frequency (though occasionally it may seem that way!).

Abbreviations and Procedure Signals

FOR THE NEWCOMER, some of the terminology and abbreviations used on the air can be confusing. Not only will you hear other amateurs using technical terms to describe their equipment and antennas, but you will run across both abbreviations and codes. Both originate in the world of CW (Morse) operation, where it speeds things up. The Q-codes, which you will also hear used on telephony, come from commercial radio activity, and have very specific meanings. Incidentally, it is because these Q codes are so widely used, that no UK callsign suffix starts with the letter Q, in order to avoid confusion.

If you look in any commercial list of Q codes or on the relevant web sites, you will see that the full list is very extensive. Each Q code can be used in two ways, either to give information or to ask a question. Thus the code QTH, for example, is defined officially as meaning "My position is", which would normally be followed by latitude and longitude or some other recognised method of giving a location. Sent as "QTH?" it would obviously mean, "What is your position?" In amateur usage, it also refers to location, either in the context of QTH locators, commonly used on the VHF bands, or simply to say, "My QTH is Reading" or whatever. An extract from the list, showing the codes most commonly used in amateur operation, appears at **Table 7.1**, and a list of the more informal meanings attributed by amateurs appears at **Table 7.2**. Obviously, Q codes specific to the world of flying, or other specialist activities don't find application in amateur radio. Neither do the "Z" codes used in military communications. There is no need for you to learn all the Q codes, but you will

Table 7.2: Informal use of the most common Q-codes

Code	Meaning
QRG	Frequency.
QRM	Interference from other stations.
QRN	Interference from atmospheric noise or from nearby electrical apparatus.
QRO	High-power.
QRP	Low-power.
QRT	Close(d) down.
QRV	Ready.
QRX	Stand by.
QSB	Fading.
QSL	Verification card; confirm contact.
QSO	Radio contact.
QSY	Change frequency.
QTC	Message.
QTH	Location.
QTR	Time.

Note also:

QSLL	(card sent in receipt of yours) and QTHR (address is correct in the current *RSGB Yearbook*)

Table 7.3: Abbreviations and procedure signals commonly used in CW & data modes contacts

Abbreviation	Meaning
AA	All after . . . (used after a question mark or RPT to request a repetition)
AB	All before . . . (see AA)
$\overline{\text{AR}}$	End of transmission
$\overline{\text{AS}}$	Wait a moment
BK	Signal used to interrupt a transmission in progress
BN	All between . . . and . . . (see AA)
$\overline{\text{BT}}$	Signal to mark the separation between different parts of the same transmission
CFM	Confirm (or I confirm)
CL	I am closing my station
CQ	General call to all stations
DE	"from . . ." (precedes the callsign of the station transmitting)
K	Invitation to transmit
$\overline{\text{KA}}$	Starting signal
$\overline{\text{KN}}$	Invitation to transmit (named station only)
NW	Now
OK	We agree (or It is correct)
PSE	Please
R	Received
RPT	Repeat (or I repeat or Repeat . . .)
SK	End of work
TFC	Traffic
TU	Thank you
WA	Word after . . . (see AA)
WB	Word before . . . (see AA)
WX	Weather report (or Weather report follows)
HRD	heard
HV	have

Informal amateur CW abbreviations

Abbreviation	Meaning
ABT	about
ADR	address
AGN	again
ANI	any
ANT	antenna
BCNU	be seeing you
BD	bad
BLV	believe
B4	before
CK	check
CLD	called
CNT	cannot
CNDX	conditions
CPSE	counterpoise
CRD	card
CUD	could
CUAGN	see you again
CUL	see you later
DR	dear
DX	long distance
ELBUG	electronic key
ENUF	enough
ES	and
FB	fine business
FER	for
FONE	telephony
FQ	frequency
FREQ	frequency
GA	good afternoon (or go ahead)
GB	goodbye
GD	good day
GE	good evening
GLD	glad
GM	good morning
GN	good night
GND	ground (earth)
GUD	good
HI	laughter
HPE	hope
HR	here
HV	have
HVY	heavy
HW	how
INPT	input
LID	poor operator
LOC	locator
LSN	listen
MNI	many
MSG	message
ND	nothing doing
NR	number
OM	old man
OP	operator
OT	old-timer
PA	power amplifier
PP	push-pull
PSE	please
PWR	power
RCVR	receiver
RPRT	report
RX	receiver
SA	say
SED	said
SIGS	signals
SKED	schedule (prearranged transmission)
SN	soon
SRI	sorry
STN	station
SUM	some
SWL	short-wave listener
TDA	today
TKS	thanks
TMW	tomorrow
TNX	thanks
TRX	transceiver
TT	that
TU	thank you
TX	transmitter
U	you
UR	your
VY	very
WID	with
WKD	worked
WKG	working
WL	will
WUD	would
XYL	wife
YDA	yesterday
YF	wife
YL	young lady
55	best success
73	best regards
88	love and kisses

certainly come across the abbreviated list in Table 2 on a daily basis as you operate on the amateur bands.

Abbreviations and procedure signals are found mainly on CW and, to an extent, in RTTY operation. Abbreviations are exactly that in most cases, "HR" for "here" or "TU" for "Thank you" for example. Some are slightly more obscure, but obvious when you think about it, "BCNU" for "be seeing you" and "XYL" for wife ("ex-young lady"!). If you are familiar with the sort of the abbreviations in common usage on text messaging with mobile phones, you will probably take to most amateur abbreviations very quickly! Although most of the abbreviations are obvious derivations of English words, they are well understood throughout the amateur community and even used by overseas amateurs who may well not be aware of the English word(s) from which they derive.

Procedure signals are used to facilitate contacts, for example by indicating that you are listening for calls, passing the transmission to a specific station or closing down your station. "CQ" (Seek You) is, of course, also widely used in voice transmissions.

Table 7.3 lists the most commonly used abbreviations and procedure signals.

Signal reports

THE OTHER ELEMENT of a contact which you will come across from the very start is the exchange of signal reports. It is very rare for a contact to take place without this, though there are many amateurs nowadays who would question why we even bother.

Signal reports date from the earliest days of amateur radio, when every contact was a major achievement, and many contacts were made under some degree of difficulty, with poor copy at one or both ends, either because of weak signals, badly-adjusted or drifting transmitters, or any one of many other possibilities. Nowadays most of those problems are consigned to the past, with most signals of good quality and readable even when they are quite weak.

Signal reports are based on the RST code, shown in **Table 7.4**. Due originally to W2BSR, it covers readability of the signal (on a 1-5 scale), strength (on a 1-9 scale) and tone (1-9). The latter applies to CW and data modes transmissions, but not to voice. Nowadays it is rare that a tone report of anything other than "9" would be given, as modern transceivers should, unless something is badly wrong, generate a pure CW tone. The exception is under auroral conditions, when tones will sound raspy. In this situation, the number is usually replaced by the letter A to indicate Auroral flutter (so a signal report might be 59A).

It is rare to hear anyone give a readability report of less than 3. Anything less than that and you probably wouldn't be attempting to make the contact. In any case, at least one of the major awards programmes used to require a signal report of 33 or 339 as a minimum for a valid contact, though this is no longer the case.

As far as signal strength is concerned, this can be quite a controversial area, mainly because there doesn't seem to be any standard set of definitions, other than the rather qualitative ones that appear in the table. Although most transceivers have a signal strength meter, usually calibrated from S1 to S9, and then in decibels above S9, the reading is generally meaningless other than on a comparative basis. Even if you knew exactly what voltage you were measuring at the antenna terminals (which is, strictly, what signal strength is about), the reading probably tells you more about the gain (or otherwise) of your antenna system than it does about the absolute strength of the other station's signal. So what you are actually telling him is not how loud his signal is in absolute terms, but how loudly you are hearing him at your particular station, with the receiver settings in use at the time, and in the light of noise and interference on the frequency. There is also dispute about whether an "S point" is 3dB or 6dB to which there cannot really be an answer.

After the preceding discussion you might well be wondering why amateurs do continue exchanging signal reports. It isn't required by the licence or for awards and it's fairly meaningless most of the time! But, provided you aren't looking for scientific measurement, signal reports do give some idea of how well the other station is hearing you and therefore, for example, whether you should repeat information when you give it. As an example, a 59 signal report (599 on CW) would indicate that you are receiving at good strength and with good readability. A 579 report indicates that signals are moderately strong and perfectly readable (so there probably isn't much in the way of interference) whereas a 479 report would indicate that there is a problem, perhaps due to interference from adjacent channels, so the distant station should take this into account, perhaps slowing his sending speed on CW or using phonetics on phone.

Just to confuse things even further, most DXpeditions and contest operators nowadays pay only lip service to signal

Table 7.4: RST code

Readability	
R1	Unreadable.
R2	Barely readable, occasional words distinguishable.
R3	Readable with considerable difficulty.
R4	Readable with practically no difficulty.
R5	Perfectly readable.
Signal strength	
S1	Faint, signals barely perceptible.
S2	Very weak signals.
S3	Weak signals.
S4	Fair signals.
S5	Fairly good signals.
S6	Good signals.
S7	Moderately strong signals.
S8	Strong signals.
S9	Extremely strong signals.
Tone	
T1	Extremely rough hissing note.
T2	Very rough AC note, no trace of musicality.
T3	Rough, low-pitched AC note, slightly musical.
T4	Rather rough AC note, moderately musical.
T5	Musically modulated note.
T6	Modulated note, slight trace of whistle.
T7	Near DC note, smooth ripple.
T8	Good DC note, just a trace of ripple.
T9	Purest DC note.

reports, always giving 59 or 599. It saves them having to slow down to record an alternative report, but is therefore meaningless, other than as a 'token' of information to give the contact a degree of validity. The main piece of information exchanged in such contacts is the callsign and, in the case of many contests, other data as required by the contest rules. More of this in the relevant chapters, though it is worth noting that some contest organisers have bowed to the inevitable and removed the need for exchanging signal reports altogether, instead replacing them with some alternative type of data, for example a serial number or QTH locator.

Finally, it is worth noting that other signal reporting systems are used in specialised instances, 136kHz, 5MHz, SSTV and specialist VHF modes (including meteor scatter) being the main examples. This is dealt with in the relevant sections.

Modes

JUST A WORD HERE about operating modes, although they are covered more fully in the chapter on Modes. On SSB, the convention is to use USB (upper sideband) above 10MHz and LSB (lower sideband) below. This should quickly be obvious when listening on the bands, but can be slightly confusing at first. On CW, most modern transceivers allow you to operate through either the USB or LSB filters in the transceiver. Normally you would always use the default setting, but sometimes switching to the alternative can help to minimise adjacent channel interference.

A typical CW contact

ALL THE CODES and abbreviations discussed earlier may seem rather daunting to the newcomer - it is difficult enough to learn the Morse code without having a whole new set of codes superimposed. Yet after a few CW contacts have been heard and understood the usage begins to become clear and the value of the codes and abbreviations can be appreciated. To assist this learning process, an imaginary CW contact and its literal equivalent is reproduced below as an example.

CQ CQ CQ CQ DE G3XTT G3XTT K

"General call to all stations from G3XTT. Over"

This is known as a 'four by two' CQ call, meaning that 'CQ' is sent four times and the callsign twice. A much longer call is not recommended, as noted earlier.

G3XTT G3XTT DE NK1G NK1G KN

"G3XTT from NK1G. Over"

Note that the call is short, only 'two by two'. Quite often it is possible to hear a station still calling when the station called has replied to another station. Ending with KN indicates that a reply is expected from the specific station indicated (as against K, which invites calls from anyone).

NK1G DE G3XTT GA OM ES MNI TNX FER CALL = UR RST 579 = NAME DON ES QTH READING = SO HW CPY? AR NK1G DE G3XTT KN

"NK1G from G3XTT. Good afternoon old man and many thanks for the call. Your signals are fully readable and moderately strong, with pure DC note. My name is Don and my location is Reading. So how do you copy me? NK1G from G3XTT. Over"

Nigel, G3TXF, and Roger, G3SXW, activate yet another rare one; this time the island of Yap in Micronesia

Each station has the other's callsign correct, so there is now no need to give callsigns more than once.

G3XTT DE NK1G R FB DON ES GM OM = UR RST 559 = QTH SR [ERROR] SPRINGFIELD, ILL = NAME IS ED = SO HW? AR G3XTT DE NK1G KN

"G3XTT from NK1G. Roger. Fine business Don and good morning old man. Your signals are fully readable, fairly good strength, and pure DC note. My location is Springfield, Illinois. My name is Ed. So how do you copy me? G3XTT from NK1G. Over."

'R' denotes all received correct and should not be sent if there was any part of the message which was not copied or understood. Some operators send it before the callsigns. Note the error made in giving the location and correction; '[error]' means the eight-dot error signal was sent

NK1G DE G3XTT SRI OM QRM5 = PSE RPT UR NAME?? BK

"NK1G from G3XTT. Sorry old man, extreme interference here. Please repeat your name. Break."

BK NAME IS ED ED ED BK

"My name is Ed. Break."

BK R R TNX ED = QRM GONE = RIG IS HOMEBREW WID 75W INPT = ANT IS DIPOLE = MNI TNX FER QSO ES CUAGN = 73 ES GB AR NK1G DE G3XTT SK

"Roger. Thanks (for the repeat) Ed. The interference has gone now. My rig is homebrew with an input power of 75W. My antenna is a dipole. Many thanks for the contact and I hope to see you again some time. Best wishes to you and goodbye now. NK1G from G3XTT. Over."

G3XTT DE NK1G R UR RIG T9X ES FB = RIG HR IS FT-897 = ANT IS 2EL QUAD = WL QSL VIA BURO = SO 73 ES GUD DX = GB G3XTT DE NK1G SK

"G3XTT from NK1G. Roger. Your rig sounds crystal controlled, and very nice. The rig here is an FT897. The antenna is a two-element quad. I will send my QSL card via the bureau (and I hope to receive one in return). So best wishes and good DX. Goodbye. G3XTT from NK1G."

With both stations having sent 'SK', the contact is at an end and either station may be called by a third station for another contact.

Table 7.5: The Morse code and sound equivalents

Alphabet and numerals

A	di-dah
B	dah-di-di-dit
C	dah-di-dah-dit
D	dah-di-dit
E	dit
F	di-di-dah-dit
G	dah-dah-dit
H	di-di-di-dit
I	di-dit
J	di-dah-dah-dah
K	dah-di-dah
L	di-dah-di-dit
M	dah-dah
N	dah-dit
O	dah-dah-dah
P	di-dah-dah-dit
Q	dah-dah-di-dah
R	di-dah-dit
S	di-di-dit
T	dah
U	di-di-dah
V	di-di-di-dah
W	di-dah-dah
X	dah-di-di-dah
Y	dah-di-dah-dah
Z	dah-dah-di-dit
1	di-dah-dah-dah-dah
2	di-di-dah-dah-dah
3	di-di-di-dah-dah
4	di-di-di-di-dah
5	di-di-di-di-di
6	dah-di-di-di-dit
7	dah-dah-di-di-dit
8	dah-dah-dah-di-dit
9	dah-dah-dah-dah-dit
0	dah-dah-dah-dah-dah

Accented letters

à, á, â	di-dah-dah-di-dah
ä	di-dah-di-dah
ç	dah-di-dah-di-dit
ch	dah-dah-dah-dah
è, é	di-di-dah-di-dit
ê	dah-di-di-dah-dit
ñ	dah-dah-di-dah-dah
ö, ó, ô	dah-dah-dah-dit
ü, û	di-di-dah-dah

Abbreviated numerals

1	di-dah 6 dah-di-di-di-dit
2	di-di-dah 7 dah-di-di-dit
3	di-di-di-dah 8 dah-di-dit
4	di-di-di-di-dah 9 dah-dit
5	di-di-di-di-dit 0 daaah (long dash)

Punctuation

Full stop (.)	di-dah-di-dah-di-dah
Comma (,)	dah-dah-di-di-dah-dah
Colon (:)	dah-dah-dah-di-di-dit
Question mark (?)	di-di-dah-dah-di-dit
Apostrophe (')	di-dah-dah-dah-dah-dit
Hyphen or dash (-)	dah-di-di-di-di-dah
Fraction bar or solidus (/)	dah-di-di-dah-dit
Brackets - open [(]	dah-di-dah-dah-dit
- close [)]	dah-di-dah-dah-di-dah
Double hyphen (=)	dah-di-di-di-dah
Quotation marks (")	di-dah-di-di-dah-dit
Error	di-di-di-di-di-di-di-dit

Spacing and length of signals

1. A dash is equal to three dots.
2. The space between the signals which form the same letter is equal to one dot.
3. The space between two letters is equal to three dots.
4. The space between two words is equal to seven dots.

The reader will appreciate that this is a basic contact with only the essential details exchanged between the stations. Nevertheless this type of contact can still give much pleasure. There is of course nothing to prevent much more information being transmitted in such favourable circumstances, although the individual transmissions should be kept reasonably short. Strictly speaking, such details as name, location and signal report should be sent only once as shown here and if the other operator does not copy the details he or she should ask for a repeat. However most amateurs find it easier to repeat these basic details the first time round, rather than risking time-wasting queries, especially if conditions are poor. The established CW operator may also like to bear this point in mind when contacting stations obviously new to CW operating.

This also brings us to the question of the speed of sending. Most day-to-day CW contacts take place at speeds in the 22-28WPM range, though you will certainly hear both slower and faster contacts taking place. Experienced amateurs will normally be comfortable at these speeds, sending on an electronic key (keying with a hand key becomes uncomfortable above about 25WPM) and receiving by ear except to make a note of specific information for the log (Name, location, signal report, for example). But don't feel intimidated. When answering a CQ call, answer at a speed you are comfortable with and a good operator will respond in kind, reducing his speed to match yours. When calling CQ, do so at the speed you would like others to respond but, again, if someone responds more slowly then be courteous and slow down for him. Contest operations often take place at higher speeds, usually around the 28-32WPM range. This need not be as intimidating as it sounds, as much of the contest exchange will be standard, so you do not have to copy as much information as during a ragchew type of QSO.

For convenience, an extensive list of CW characters appears in **Table 7.5**, including accented characters used in other languages. You will rarely run across characters other than the standard ones, but may do so if you decide to try working foreign amateurs in their own language (see later section).

Semi- and Full- break-in operation

One of the operating decisions you will make in respect of CW operation is whether to use manual, semi-automatic or full break-in operation. Manual operation is self-evident; you switch to transmit using the MOX button on your transceiver or maybe a footswitch. In practice, very few CW operators do so. Instead, the majority use semi-automatic break-in, whereby your transceiver goes to transmit when you first hit the key, and drops back to receive when there is a pause in sending. Usually you can adjust this pause. In contest or slick day-to-day operating, for example, you may want to keep the break short, but if you are ragchewing, perhaps at low speed, this could result in the transceiver reverting to receive between words or even characters, which can be distracting.

Full break-in operation is rather different. The transceiver will revert to receive between every dot and dash so that, to all intents and purposes, you are listening continuously. This allows very interactive contacts, and is invaluable if the other station needs to interject, for example to say that he is having trouble copying you, or maybe has to leave for a moment

Crozet Island has more penguins than human inhabitants, so any amateur radio activity is much in demand

to take a phone call. Break-in operation takes a little time to get used to, but can be extremely satisfying. In contesting it is particularly valuable, because you can hear immediately if, for example, interference appears on the frequency. However, not all transceivers are capable of break-in operation and even some of those which claim to be are actually rather limited in their break-in capabilities. It's not too difficult to understand why. If break-in is to be possible without adversely affecting the CW (for example, by shortening the dots and dashes), the switching between transmit and receive must be very fast indeed. This is usually only possible with PIN diode switching; relays simply aren't fast enough. This capability must also apply to your linear amplifier, if you are using one. But very fast switching can lead to other problems, especially if you are operating split-frequency (for example when calling a DXpedition station), because the frequency synthesiser cannot always change frequencies fast enough, so your transmitted signal will be affected. It is really a case of experimenting, and getting to know the limitations of your equipment, perhaps by getting another station to listen while you try sending at different speeds, both co-channel and split-frequency.

Telephony operation

ON THE HF BANDS, telephony operation is roughly equal with CW in terms of overall use, though most amateurs heavily favour one over the other. Most day-to-day operation on VHF is on telephony (especially FM), but CW is popular for DX working. Though telephony does not require knowledge of codes and abbreviations, correct operation is more difficult than it may appear at first sight, as is only too apparent after a listen to any amateur band. Part of the problem is that many operators will have acquired some bad habits in their pronunciation, intonation and phraseology even before entering amateur radio. To these are then added a whole new set of clichés and mannerisms derived from listening to bad operators. Some of these can be extremely difficult to remove once learnt, even if a conscious effort is made.

Microphone technique

Unless there is very little external noise and room echo, it is best to hold the microphone fairly near the mouth, between 70 and 140mm away. Some microphones are unduly sensitive to letters like 'S' and 'P', and better audio quality may then be obtained by speaking across the microphone.

Audio quality should be tested by running the transmitter into a dummy load and monitoring the output on a receiver with headphones. In this way the characteristics of the microphone and the optimum speaking distance will be apparent. If a separate receiver is not available, the opinion of a local amateur should be sought on the air. Speech processing is often a mixed blessing. If too much is used, the modulation quality suffers greatly and the PA transistors or valves could overheat due to the increased duty cycle if SSB is used. Tests should be made to determine the maximum level which can effectively be used, and this noted or marked on the control. Be ready to turn it down if it is not really required during a contact. Nowadays, some transceivers allow extensive tailoring of the audio via a series of menu options, so it may be worth experimenting while getting feedback from another amateur listening to your signals.

Conversation

It is important to speak clearly and not too quickly, not just when talking to someone who does not fully understand the language, but at all times as this is excellent practice.

Plain language should be used when you are having a conversation with the other person - radio clichés should be kept to a minimum. In particular, avoid the use of 'we' when 'I' is meant and 'handle' when 'name' is meant. Of course, use of phrases like *"That's a roger"* has to be a matter of personal taste but don't feel you have to talk in slang like this to have an amateur radio contact.

The use of CW abbreviations (including 'HI') should also normally be avoided and the Q-code should really only be used when there is a language difficulty or where it has become accepted practice, eg *"QRZ?"* or *"Please QSL via the bureau."*

Phonetic alphabets should only be employed when they are necessary to clarify the spelling of a word or callsign. If they are to be effective the listener should know them, and it follows that only the internationally recommended phonetic alphabet should be used (see **Table 7.6**). It is confusing to the listener to use other phonetic alphabets and especially to generate new letter words. An exception is when it is found that a letter is being consistently miscopied. Although the recommended alphabet was selected to avoid ambiguity, it can happen in very poor reception conditions that, for example, 'Oscar' sounds like 'Alpha'. In this case, the use of an alternative like 'Ontario' might be the solution.

Unlike CW operation, it is very easy to forget that the conversation is not taking place down a telephone line. The listening station cannot interject a query if something is not understood and cannot give an answer until the transmitting station has finished. The result, especially on VHF, is often a long monologue in which the listening station has to take notes of all the points raised and questions asked if a useful reply is to be given. This should not be necessary if these points are dealt with one at a time.

Voice-operated changeover (VOX) operation should be used where possible as it enables a more normal two-way conversation to be carried on, which tends to avoid long monologues. However, it must be remembered that relays are supposed to be changing over frequently and prolonged "aaahs" spoken to prevent this happening are bad practice. Remember to give callsigns as often as required by the licensing authority in this type of contact. If VOX is not available, nimble use of the push-to-talk (PTT) switch is an acceptable substitute, but of course this requires more effort.

Both PTT and VOX operation are simplex systems, ie communication can take place in only one direction at any given time. The capability of instant and spontaneous response typical of an ordinary telephone conversation is only possible if duplex operation is used, ie simultaneous communication in both directions. This requires two communication channels which must be well spaced to avoid the transmitter desensitising the receiver, they may be located in the same band (inband duplex) or in two separate bands (cross-band duplex).

Generally in-band duplex is not practical on the narrow HF phone bands due to receiver desensitisation and not too popular even at VHF and UHF because separate transmitters and receivers for those frequencies are unusual items these days, and many amateurs cannot afford two transceivers for the same band! Most duplex work therefore takes place cross-band (for example, 144-432MHz). If harmonically related bands are chosen, the receiver frequency needs to be well clear of any transmitter harmonics. Care should also be taken to comply with the relevant band plan(s) which may be difficult with in-band duplex. It is best to avoid the usual simplex channels for what will appear to others as a one-sided conversation. In any case, it is wise to check that the transmit channel is clear at, say, five-minute intervals. As with VOX operation, remember to give callsigns as frequently as required by the licence authority, in this case also stating the other station's transmit frequency. Generally headphones should be used at least at one end of a duplex contact to avoid 'howl-round' but a carefully adjusted loudspeaker output does allow the other operator to hear how his transmissions sound and may even give a more natural quality to the contact; after all, this is what duplex operation 'is all about'!

Table 7.6: International phonetic alphabet

Letter	Word	Pronounced
A	Alfa	AL FAH
B	Bravo	BRAH VOH
C	Charlie	CHAR LEE or SHAR LEE
D	Delta	DELL TAH
E	Echo	ECK OH
F	Foxtrot	FOKS TROT
G	Golf	GOLF
H	Hotel	HOH TELL
I	India	IN DEE AH
J	Juliett	JEW LEE ETT
K	Kilo	KEY LOH
L	Lima	LEE MAH
M	Mike	MIKE
N	November	NO VEM BER
O	Oscar	OSS CAH
P	Papa	PAH PAH
Q	Quebec	KEH BECK
R	Romeo	ROW ME OH
S	Sierra	SEE AIR RA
T	Tango	TANG GO
U	Uniform	YOU NEE FORM or OO NEE FORM
V	Victor	VIK TAH
W	Whiskey	WISS KEY
X	X-Ray	ECKS RAY
Y	Yankee	YANG KEY
Z	Zulu	ZOO LOO

Procedure

As noted earlier, when calling a specific station on phone it is good practice to keep calls short and to use the callsign of the station called once or twice only, followed by your own callsign pronounced carefully and clearly at least twice using a phonetic alphabet, for example:

"NK1G. This is Mike Zero Alpha India Mike calling, and Mike Zero Alpha India Mike standing by."

Emphasis should be placed on the caller's own callsign and not on that of the station called. If there is no response, the caller's callsign may be repeated once more after a brief listen. Some stations send very long calls because operators think that when everybody else has finished calling they will still be heard. The reader is advised to forget this 'trick of the trade'. It rarely seems to work, it irritates others on the frequency and it causes severe interference to the station called if he has already replied to another station. As in CW operation CQ calls should also be kept short and repeated as often as desired. An example would *"CQ, CQ, CQ, CQ. This is Golf Three X-ray Tango Tango calling, Golf Three X-ray Tango Tango calling CQ and standing by."* There is no need to say what band is being used, and certainly no need to add *"for any possible calls, dah-di-dah!"* or *"K someone please"* etc!

When replying to a call both callsigns should be given clearly, usually in the phonetic alphabet, so that the calling station can check his callsign has been received correctly. From then on it is not necessary to use the phonetic alphabet for callsigns until the final transmissions. An example would be: *"November Kilo One Golf. This is Golf Three X-ray Tango Tango."*

Once contact is established it is only necessary to give your own callsign at the intervals required by the licensing authority. A normal two-way conversation can thus be enjoyed, without the need for continual identification. If necessary the words 'break' or 'over' may be added at the end of a transmission to signal a reply from the other station. In good conditions this will not normally be found necessary. When FM is in use it is self-evident when the other station has stopped transmitting and is listening, because the carrier drops. There was a time when many amateurs adopted an end-of-transmission beep, perhaps copying what they had heard when watching NASA transmissions from space. While it can be helpful under weak signal conditions on the VHF bands, it is usually more irritating than helpful.

Operating procedures become more complex where three or more stations are involved, and it is a good idea to give your own callsign briefly before each transmission, for example:

"From G3XTT . . ."

At the end of the transmission the callsign should again be given together with an indication of whose turn to speak it is next, for example:

". . . NK1G to transmit. G3XTT and the group."

It is not necessary to run through a list of who is in the group, who has just signed off (and who may possibly be listening) after each transmission, although it may be useful for one person in the group to do this occasionally.

Signal reports on telephony are usually given using the RST code although in this case an indication of tone (T) is not required. The report is given as a single two-digit number, in a similar fashion to the three-digit CW RST code. When the time comes to end the contact, end it. Thank the other operator (once) for the pleasure of the contact and say goodbye. This is all that is required. Unless the operator is a good friend there is no need to start sending best wishes to everyone in the household including the family dog! Nor is this the time to start digging up extra comments on the contact which will require a 'final final' from the other station to answer - there may be other stations patiently waiting to call. It is recommended that both callsigns be given in the final transmission using the phonetic alphabet so that listening stations can check that they have them correct before calling, for example: *". . . This is Golf Three X-ray Tango Tango signing clear with November Kilo One Golf and Golf Three X-ray Tango Tango is now standing by for a call."*

Note that some indication to listening stations is useful to indicate what is planned next. Such an indication is also appropriate if an immediate change to another frequency is intended, for example:

". . . This is Golf Three X-ray Tango Tango signing clear with Golf Two X-Ray Yankee Zulu Mobile. Golf Three X-ray Tango Tango now monitoring V40 for a call."

Data modes operation

IN THE CONTEXT of two-way datamodes contacts, mainly RTTY and PSK, the previous advice applies. It is often recommended that you actually give your callsign three times so that, if the other station suffers any interference and gets corrupted text, he can use a 'best of three' approach to figure out what your callsign actually is.

In days gone by, most RTTY transmissions started with a sequence of RYs ("RYRYRYRYRY ..") to enable the other station's teleprinter to synchronise to your transmission. This is no longer necessary, but it is certainly a good idea to start each transmission with a carriage return, so that your transmission will start on a new line on the other station's screen.

One of the commonest problems with RTTY reception is when a SHIFT character is lost in interference, so that you end up copying letters rather than numbers or vice versa. In actual fact, it is usually quite obvious when this has happened, and you can probably work out what has actually been sent. The simple key is that the number characters correspond to the row of letters below them on a normal QWERTY keyboard. So it you were to receive a contest exchange of "G3XTT TOO-ERW BK", rather than ask for a repeat you would immediately be able to log the incoming report and serial number as "599342". When operating RTTY, you should also ensure you have AFC and NET set to OFF when calling CQ, as two stations with both these set to ON will drift all over the band!

Perhaps the most irritating aspect of RTTY operation is the way in which some RTTY operators fill their buffers with detailed information about their station, the weather, their medical ailments, or whatever, and insist on sending the whole lot to anyone they contact. It's easy to do so, as it's just a case with most RTTY programs of hitting a few function keys, but that doesn't make it good operating. By all means use your buffers to store information that you want to transmit on a regular basis, but don't over-egg the cake.

Perhaps the other main point to remember with data modes is that they really do rely on the PC to do the work, and PCs are not as clever as the human ear in picking one signal out from a crowd (the 'cocktail party' effect which works well on SSB and even better on CW). Copy will only be good when just one station is calling at a time. This leads some operators to call at great length in the hope that they will be the last one transmitting and will therefore be the first to be copied by the distant station. This is just bad manners and usually counter-productive. For DX working, of course, the DX station will almost always use split-frequency operation (see Chapter 9) to avoid this problem, and your best way of being copied is to find a clear channel on which to call.

Of course, it's not possible here to describe the detailed operation of your RTTY program, as every one is different, so you will need to learn the user interface. But that doesn't absolve you from following the normal courtesies of a QSO, just as on the other modes.

SSTV operation

SLOW SCAN TELEVISION (SSTV) operation is different again. Because there is limited interest in this specialist mode, most operation congregates around well-known meeting frequencies (14230kHz on 20m, for example). It is common to start by establishing an SSB contact, and then moving to the image mode when both stations are ready to do so. Of course, there is nothing to stop you sending CQ by way of transmitting an image, or of replying to someone else's CQ sent in the same way (but remember that the licence requires you to identify on SSB or CW at regular intervals).

Again, SSTV operation is very dependent on the actual software you are using. Read the manual and practice receiving images before you think about transmitting. The main issue to overcome is the problem of sloping images, which are the result of not being properly synchronised (because all PC clocks tend to run at slightly different speeds). Once you have everything set up to go, making two-way image contacts should be quite straightforward. But rather than exchange details of weather, antennas, etc, it is more normal to exchange pictures, maybe of your shack, your house or your local town.

ATV operation

FAST-SCAN TV has changed significantly in recent years. Whereas much of the activity used to be on 70cm, most operation nowadays is on 23cm and above, largely through the chain of ATV repeaters (see Chapter 12). This simplifies matters considerably, as both sound and video are transmitted together and contacts can be established directly through the repeater. Of course, there is nothing to prevent direct contacts when signals strengths are sufficient, but it has to be remembered that TV requires much more bandwidth than, say, FM voice, and therefore requires much higher signal strengths for adequate signal-to-noise ratio (in a similar manner to voice transmission compared with CW). Sometimes a separate

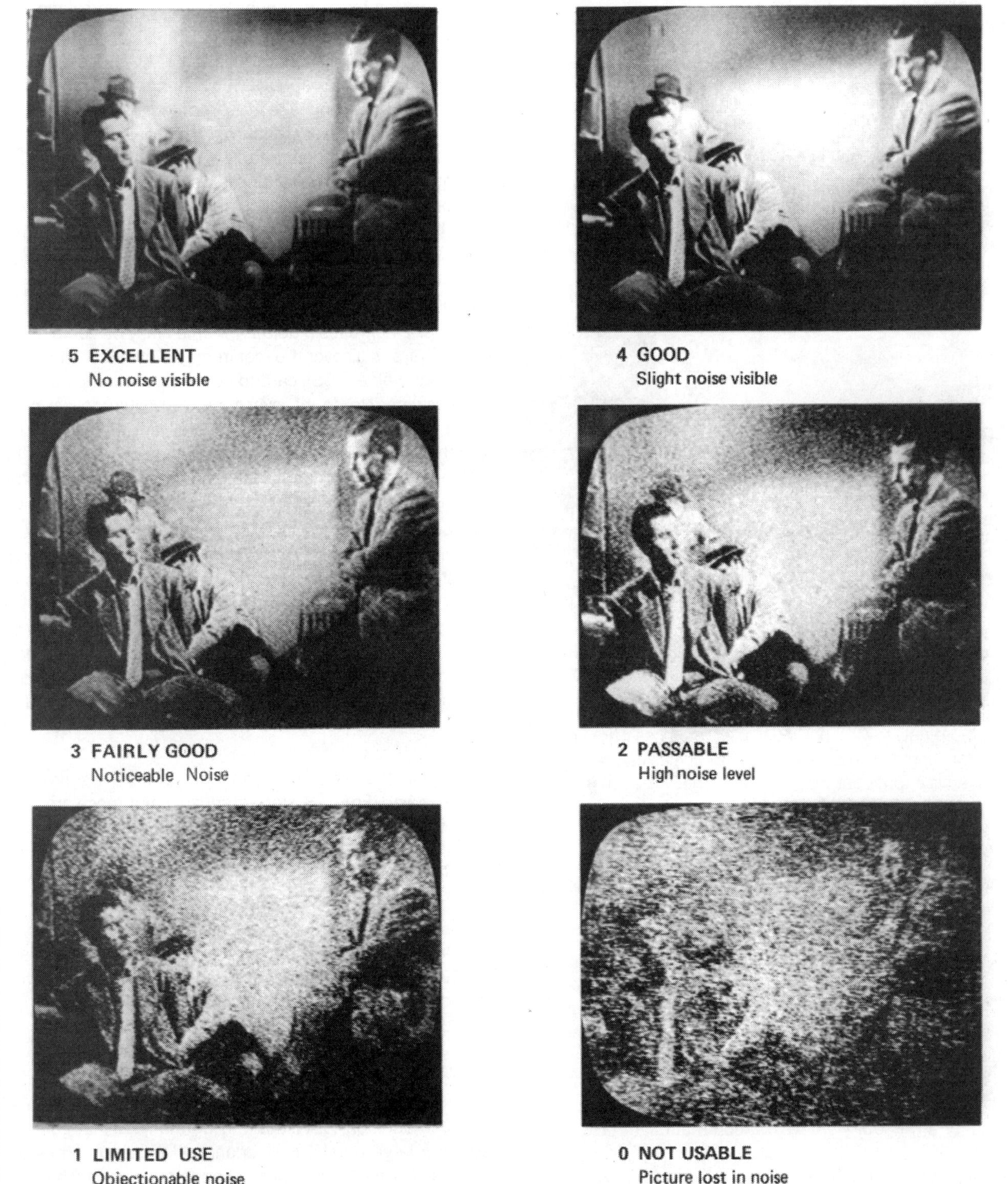

Fig 71: The British Amateur Television Club ATV reporting chart for P0 - p5 [Reproduced with acknowledgment to the BATC]

voice channel will be opened on, say, 2m or 70cm to allow full-duplex contacts to take place, allowing both operators to stay in constant contact as they exchange video. It is worth remembering that ATV repeaters operate in "beacon mode" when not otherwise in use, so they are always available as a set-up aid and a guide to propagation conditions.

Signal reports on ATV are given using the P code - PO representing no picture, to P5 representing a perfect, noise-free, broadcast-quality one. As with RST reports, the exact P report is very much in the eye of the beholder - what one person would call 'P4' another would call 'P5'. The chart reproduced in **Fig 7.1** will, however, act as a guide.

Emergency communications

UK AMATEURS, thankfully, are rarely involved in emergency communications. RAYNET, The Radio Amateurs' Emergency Network, co-ordinates those UK amateurs who want to be

Raynet operation enables amateurs to become involved in helping the community

involved in emergency preparedness. It runs training exercises, co-ordinates with potential user services (fire, police, ambulance, etc), takes care of issues such as insurance, and gives advice on operating matters specifically relating to emergency communications. It is not the aim of this *Manual* to second-guess the excellent work that RAYNET does in this regard.

Of course, there may be times when you are on the air and have to give assistance in some way, at short notice, for example an amateur on board a sailing vessel that is experiencing difficulties. Provided you are a competent operator, this shouldn't present any special problems. Perhaps the main concern is, unlike in your day-to-day operating, the necessity of keeping an accurate transcript of all communications, not only so that you can pass details to any parties you need to bring in (Coastguard, Police, etc), but also so that you can retrace the sequence of communications after the event, for any enquiry or investigation that might take place.

Operation in a foreign language

IT IS SOMETIMES claimed that CW operation consists entirely of code groups and thus amateurs who do not possess a common language can communicate with each other. This is only partly true. A typical reply by a Russian amateur to a call would be

```
GM OM TNX FR QSO UR RST 589 QTH MOSCOW OP VLAD HW?
```

Apart from the two Q-code groups, every word is an English abbreviation. The Russian amateur does not necessarily see it like this - unless he is a linguist, he will probably have a list of phrases with the Russian equivalents and he will treat these phrases as code groups and not as abbreviations of English words.

Given a similar list of phrases in other languages, there is nothing to prevent a monoglot English speaker from having contacts in those languages. No knowledge of the language concerned is necessary, and on CW there is no problem of pronunciation or understanding the accent of the foreign amateur. For generations, English speakers have expected everyone else to learn English in order to communicate with them but this attitude is not universally popular! Amateurs, with a minimum of effort, can make a real contribution to international goodwill by greeting fellow amateurs in their mother tongues.

A list of 24 phrases (**Table 7.7**), which may be combined in various ways, will cover the requirements of most simple contacts and enable a QSL card to be made out in the appropriate language. No doubt, over time, you could collect other useful ones, too. Of course, there is always the danger that the other amateur may assume that one's knowledge of his language is greater than it really is. A combination of phrases 17 and 18 will meet this situation without giving offence.

The words in roman type are for general use in almost all contacts. Those in italic type are for occasional use or for use on QSL cards. It is desirable to write the month in words on QSL cards to avoid the confusion which may arise from different conventions when figures only are used. After each list will be found information regarding accented letters for easy reference. It should, however, be noted that in French and Spanish working, the accents are often omitted and in German 'Ä' is sometimes sent as 'AE', 'Ö' as 'OE' and 'Ü' as 'UE'.

In English, the use of endearments between persons of the same sex would be regarded as unusual, but these are quite common in some languages - "lieber Hans", "cher Marcel", "amigo Juan", etc. To avoid complications, feminine forms have not been given and so care should be taken when working YLs!

Phrase 8 can be easily adapted; if the rig is an internationally known one, the type number can be inserted in place of '100 WATTS'. As to antennas, those known by the inventor's callsign present no difficulty and the expressions '3 EL', 'YAGI' and 'QUAD' are used in all languages.

It is suggested that German should be the first language to be attempted because it is already used extensively in CW operation and the procedure and abbreviations are well known. In addition to Austria and Germany, the language is used in a large part of Switzerland. All these countries are easy to contact on a number of bands and it is much better for one's first contacts in a foreign language to be with nearby countries when readability is usually good.

French is not so easily abbreviated but it is used over the air quite extensively. The language is still spoken in parts of Africa and it is the first language in Quebec Province (VE2). French-speaking Canadians particularly value contacts in their own language.

Spanish is used throughout South America (except in Brazil) and it is for that reason that it has been selected as one of the languages for inclusion here. It will be noticed that in some cases, the English abbreviations are retained (or given as alternatives) when the equivalent wording in the for-

Table 7.7: CW phrases in English, French, German and Spanish

ENGLISH

1. GM/GA/GE/GN OM
2. TNX FR CALL (ES FIRST QSO)
3. *Nice to meet u agn*
4. *We have met B4*
5. UR RST . . . QTH . . . NAME . . .
6. HW?
7. TNX . . . FR (FB) REPORT
8. HR RIG [100 WATTS] ANT [DIPOLE]
9. WX (1) FINE (2) CLEAR (3) CLOUDY (4) RAINY (5) WINDY (6) FOGGY (7) WARM (8) COLD (9) SNOW TEMP . . . C
10. TNX . . . FR INFO ON UR RIG (ES WX)
11. *Only partly OK*
12. *All OK except ur QTH*
13. *Some/much/too much QSB, QRM (etc)*
14. *Pse rpt my report/ur name/ur QTH*
15. *Pse QSY up/down . . . kHz*
16. *Band vy noisy*
17. *Sri but I do not understand completely*
18. *I speak only a little English*
19. QSL OK VIA BURO
20. *I have recd ur crd*
21. *Have u recd my crd?*
22. *I am QRU nw*
23. *Best 73 es DX*
24. TNX . . . FR QSO NW QRU 73 DX ES GB

January	*April*	*July*	*October*
February	*May*	*August*	*November*
March	*June*	*September*	*December*

FRENCH

1. BJR/-/BSR/BN MON VIEUX
2. MCI BCP POUR VOTRE APPEL (ET POUR PREMIER QSO)
3. *Je suis enchanté de vous rencontrer de nouveau*
4. *Nous avons déjà fait QSO*
5. VOTRE RST . . . QTH . . . NOM . . .
6. HW? (Quel est mon contrôle?)
7. MCI BCP . . . POUR RPRT *(contrôle) (Bien aimable)*
8. ICI RIG *(appareil)* [100 WATTS] ANT [DIPOLE]
9. WX (1) MERVEILLEUX (2) CLAIR (3) NUAGEUX (4) PLUVIEUX (5) IL Y A DU VENT (6) IL Y A BROUILLARD (7) CHAUD (8) FROID (9) IL NEIGE TEMP . . . C
10. MCI BCP . . . POUR L'INFO SUR VOTRE RIG *(appareil)* (ET WX)
11. *OK seulement en partie*
12. *Complètement OK excepté votre QTH*
13. *Peu/bcp/trop de QSB, de QRM (etc)*
14. *Repetez mon rprt (contrôle)/votre nom/votre QTH svp*
15. *QSY plus haut/plus bas . . . kHz svp*
16. *Il y a bcp de bruit sur la bande*
17. *Je regrette bcp mais je ne vous ai pas complètement compris*
18. *Je parle un peu le français*
19. QSL OK PAR BUREAU
20. *J'ai reçu votre carte mci bcp*
21. *Avez vous reçu ma carte?*
22. *Je suis maintenant QRU*
23. *Mes meilleurs amitiés et bonne chance pour le DX*
24. MCI BCP . . . POUR QSO ICI QRU 73 DX ET AU REVOIR

janvier	*avril*	*juillet*	*octobre*
février	*mai*	*août*	*novembre*
mars	*juin*	*septembre*	*décembre*

À = di-dah-dah-di-dah È and É = di-di-dah-di-dit
Ô = dah-dah-dah-dit Ç = dah-di-dah-di-dit
Ê = dah-di-di-dah-dit Û = di-di-dah-dah

GERMAN

1. GM/GT/GA/GN LBR FRD
2. VLN DK . . . FR DEN ANRUF (UND ERSTES QSO)
3. *Es freut mich sehr Sie wiederzutreffen*
4. *Wir haben uns schon mal getroffen*
5. IHR RST . . . QTH . . . NAME . . .
6. WIE?
7. VLN DK FR DEN (NETTEN) RPRT
8. RIG (Gerät) HR IST [100 WATT] UND ANT IST [EIN DIPOL]
9. DAS WX IST (1) SCHÖN (2) KLAR (3) BEWÖLKT (4) REGNERISCH (5) WINDIG (6) NEBELIG (7) WARM (8) KALT (9) ES SCHNEIT TEMP . . . C
10. DKE . . . FR BRT ÜBER IHR RIG (Gerät) (UND WX)
11. *Nur teilweise OK*
12. *Alles OK ausser Ihrem QTH*
13. *Etwas/vl/zu vl QSB, QRM (etc)*
14. *Bte wiederholen Sie meinen Rprt/Ihren Namen/Ihr QTH*
15. *Bte QSY/höher/tiefer . . . kHz*
16. *Auf dem Bande ist vl Lärm*
17. *Leider habe ich nicht alles verstanden*
18. *Ich spreche nur wenig Deutsch*
19. QSL OK VIA BÜRO
20. *Ich habe Ihre Karte bekommen*
21. *Haben Sie meine Karte bekommen?*
22. *Ich bin nun QRU*
23. *Die besten Grüsse und DX*
24. DKE SEHR . . . FR QSO NUN QRU 73 GUTES DX UND AWDH (auf wiederhören)

Januar	*April*	*Juli*	*Oktober*
Februar	*Mai*	*August*	*November*
März	*Juni*	*September*	*Dezember*

Ä = di-dah-di-dah Ö = dah-dah-dah-dit
Ü = di-di-dah-dah

SPANISH

1. GM/GA/GE/GN OM
2. MUCHAS GRACIAS POR TU LLAMADA (Y POR ESTE PRIMER QSO)
3. *Tengo un gran placer en encontrarle*
4. *Nos hemos encontrado ya antes*
5. TU RST . . . QTH . . . NOMBRE . . .
6. HW?
7. MUY TNX *(muchas gracias)* . . . POR RPRT
8. MI TX TIENE [100 VATIOS] MI ANT ES [UN DIPOLO]
9. EL WX AQUÍ ES (1) MUY BUENO (2) CLARO (3) NUBLADO (4) LLUVOSO (5) VENTOSO (6) NEBULOSO (7) ACALORADO (8) FRIO (9) ESTA NEVANDO TEMP. . . C
10. TNX FR INFO
11. *OK sólo en parte*
12. *Completamente OK con excepción de tu QTH*
13. *Poco/mucho/demasiado QSB, QRM (etc)*
14. *Pse repetirme mi RST/tu nombre/tu QTH*
15. *Pse QSY más alto/más bajo cerca . . . kHz*
16. *La banda está muy turbulenta*
17. *Sri pero no he comprendido completamente*
18. *Hablo solamente un poco español*
19. QSL OK VIA BURO
20. *He recibido tu QSL tnx*
21. *Has recibido mi QSL?*
22. *Tengo ahora QRU*
23. *73 y buenos DX*
24. MUCHAS GRACIAS . . . POR QSO QRU 73 DX Y ADIOS

Enero	*Abril*	*Julio*	*Octobre*
Febrero	*Mayo*	*Agosto Novembre*	
Marzo	*Junio*	*Septembre*	*Dicembre*

Á = di-dah-dah-di-dah Ñ = dah-dah-di-dah-dah
Ó = dah-dah-dah-dit

Table 7.8: 'Goodbye' in 15 languages

Language	Goodbye
Danish:	FARVEL
Dutch:	TOT WERKENS
English:	GB (CHEERS)
Esperanto:	G̅IS
Finnish	HEI
French:	AU REVOIR
German:	AWDH
Italian:	CIAO
Norwegian:	HEI
Polish:	CZESC
Portuguese:	ATÉ BREVE
Russian:	DSW
Spanish:	ADIOS (HLV)
Swedish:	HEJ
Welsh:	POB HWYL

G̅ = dah-dah-di-dah-dit É = di-di-dah-di-dit

eign language is rather long. In contacts between (say) two Italian amateurs, one will often hear a number of English expressions.

In recent years, it has become popular to say 'Goodbye' in the appropriate language, and a list is given in **Table 7.8**.

The effort involved in using a foreign language is well repaid by the thanks which will be expressed in almost every contact, and the final courtesy should be to include a few remarks in the language on the outgoing QSL card. It is necessary to remember that, in some countries, language is an explosive political matter. This usually occurs in a country where only a very small minority of the people speak a particular language. In these circumstances, it is wise to make sure that use of the language concerned will be welcome before using it over the air.

Phone operation in a foreign language

The ability to conduct a straightforward contact in, say, French or Spanish is most useful for the DXer. Unlike the method of CW operation described earlier this does require an elementary knowledge of the language, but it can still be broadly based on a few stock phrases committed to memory such as those given in the Appendix. The best way of learning them is to listen to contacts in the target language, recording them on tape if possible. If the two speakers are fluent a good deal of the conversation will not be understood but this is not important. The main thing is to discover how contacts are initiated, how details like name, QTH and signal report are exchanged, and how contacts are completed. If a few other useful phrases can be acquired at the same time, so much the better but be sure to learn the appropriate responses.

The process should be completed before any attempt is made to use this new-found knowledge, otherwise the results could be a little embarrassing. However, most foreign amateurs do appreciate the effort being made and assist where possible, so perfection is certainly not required. Many of the comments made in the foreign CW section are just as relevant to phone operation and should be noted. Contest operators often make a special effort to make contacts in another language. It isn't too difficult as the contest exchange will be quite specific, so you may only need to learn how to say numbers plus a few other words and phrases to

AMATEUR RADIO STATION LOG

DATE	TIME (UTC) start	TIME (UTC) finish	FREQUENCY (MHz)	MODE	POWER (dBW)	STATION called/worked	REPORT sent	REPORT received	QSL sent	QSL rcvd	REMARKS
2 Nov '88	0800	0810	3	J3E	20	GMSABC	59+10	59+5			Bert
"	0811	0820	145	F3E	16	G7XYZ	57	56			Terry first G7
"	0825	0830	14	J3E	20	CQ					No reply
"	1725	1735	145	F2D	16	GB7XYZ					Local packet mailbox
"	1740		Station closed down								
4 Nov '88	1030	/P	from 73 Antenna Lane, Squelch-on-Sea								
"	1031	1036	50	J3E	10	G1ØXYZ	55	56			Jim, Bridgetown
"	1036	1045	50	J3E	10	G7XYL	58	58			Anne, Nr Squelch-on-Sea. QRM
"	1205	1215	433	F3E	13	G2XYZ	46	47			
"	1220	Station closed down									
5 Nov '88	0945	/P	from 73 Antenna Lane, Squelch-on-Sea								
"	0950	1005	144	J3E	16	GB2GUY	56	56	✓		Catherine Fawkesville
"	1010	1015	144	A1A	16	GD5ZZZ	542	541	✓		QSB! QSL via WF9XYZ
"	1526	1530	144	A1A	16	G7CW	579	589			Good keying!
"	1535	Station closed down and dismantled									
7 Nov '88	1810	1902	435	C3F	10	G7ZZZ	P3	P3			Ted, first ATV contact!
"	1930	1945	21	J2B	16	VK2ABC	559	569	✓		RTTY, Sid at Bandedge
"	1946	2005	21	J2B	16	ZL3ZZZ	569	559	✓		1st ZL on RTTY
"	2010	Test for TVI/Harmonic Radiation - Nothing noted									
"	2020	Station closed down									
8 Nov '88	1735	1737	7	J3E	20	CQ					
	1738	1805	7	J3E	20	GIØZZZ	58	58			Nobby - chatted about G5RV ant
	1930	1945	51	F3E	10	GØSIX	55	55			Allen, wanted WAB ref.
	1950	Station closed down.									
NOTES											

Fig 7.2: Typical logbook entries

help the contacts along. It can significantly increase your contest score and perhaps give you the confidence to take the whole matter further so that before long you are holding lengthy QSOs in another language.

Logging

THE LICENCE requirements as they apply to log-keeping have been discussed in Chapter 2. But that is just the legal requirement. You will almost certainly want to log more information than the licence requires.

When operating from your home station or portable, you will want to maintain a reasonably detailed log. Mobile operation is rather different, in that it is dangerous to try and write into a logbook while on the move, so the requirements are rather less stringent.

Fig.7.2 shows a page from a typical traditional logbook. No log entry need be made if the station is only used for a period of reception. Only the frequency band (not the exact frequency) is required, although the keen operator may find it useful to record the exact frequency (especially of DX or rare stations). The 'Mode' column should be filled in with the international emission code (see Chapter 2), and not 'CW' or 'FM'. Calls to specific stations which went unanswered should be logged, as should both successful and unsuccessful CQ calls. 'No contact' may be written in the 'Remarks' column to differentiate any unsuccessful attempts.

Any further information added to the log naturally depends on your specific interests. The casual operator may perhaps record only the names and locations of stations worked for the first time. Those interested in propagation may find it useful to record details of the equipment and antennas at the other stations so that their ERP can be roughly ascertained, or even make a note of the solar indices for the date concerned. Award chasers may note when a new station, country, prefix, locator square etc is worked for the first time. QSL information can likewise be recorded, and a 'D' or 'B' written in the 'QSL' columns to indicate 'direct' or 'via bureau'.

There is, however, a limit to how much information can be entered in a standard printed log. No matter how carefully this is designed it has to cater for all interests and is bound to be a compromise. If found inadequate there is nothing to prevent the operator from designing one more suited to his or her needs, provided of course that it complies with the licence regulations.

Another possibility is to use a standard log in conjunction with a scrap pad or notebook. A small reporter's notebook is ideal for this purpose because it can be folded back on itself to take minimal space on the shack table. The date may be entered at the top of each page for future reference, and then rough notes made from each contact. This will be found useful for slow CW contacts or the long monologues often heard on VHF FM.

Many amateurs go one step further, by keeping a card index, in alphabetical order, of all stations worked, so that it becomes easy to find details of previous contacts if you work that station again. The author used to do exactly that, but by the time it ran to several shoe boxes of cards it was becoming a serious chore to maintain. Thank goodness computer-logging came along at that time, to ease the burden!

Logkeeping using a computer

The UK licence allows you to maintain a log on your personal computer, and this has many benefits. A detailed discussion appears in Chapter 4. There are many advantages, not least of which is that you can instantly recall details of any previous contacts with a particular station, along with any information you may have recorded, such as his name and location. To be able to respond to a caller with "Hello Fritz, nice to see you again. Are you still using that FT-747 and G5RV antenna?" helps to make the contact more personal.

References

[1] *RSGB Prefix Guide,* Fred Handscombe G4BWP, RSGB.

8 Operating Modes

THE EARLIEST AMATEUR radio transmissions were sent using Morse code as the mode of communication, keying a spark gap transmitter. It is perhaps astonishing that Morse remains so popular a century later, but the fact is that it has many benefits. Morse transmitters are easier to construct than those catering for other modes, the various codes and abbreviations used in Morse mean that two amateurs who have little knowledge of each other's language can hold at least a basic QSO. And Morse, because of the low bandwidth it occupies, is an efficient mode of transmission, with potentially much better signal to noise ratio than voice transmissions. This is because voice transmissions occupy more bandwidth for the same amount of power, whereas the total noise power in that wider bandwidth will be that much higher. And last but by no means least, many amateurs get a lot of satisfaction from using their skill in Morse operating, a skill which takes time to develop but which eventually becomes second-nature.

Notwithstanding what has been said in the previous paragraph, amateurs were quick to adopt voice transmission as soon as it became feasible. Voice is our natural mode of communication, learned from our earliest years, and it is relaxing to sit back in the operating chair and take part in a two-way or round-table voice QSO, with everyone's signals booming out of a good loudspeaker. The earliest form of voice communication was Amplitude Modulation (AM), still used a little on the amateur bands, particularly by those who enjoy restoring and using earlier generations of equipment, but otherwise largely obsolete. AM sounds good on the bands when there is little interference and remains in daily use on the long, medium and short wave broadcast bands.

When single-sideband first started to be heard on the amateur bands in the 1950s, there was huge resistance from many members of the amateur community. On most of the receivers of that time it was tricky to demodulate, and often sounded dreadful. But the benefits were too great to ignore. Half the bandwidth of AM, with all the power going into one sideband, rather than being shared between two sidebands and a carrier, so the signal-to-noise performance was substantially better than AM. Perhaps more importantly, as the amateur bands became more crowded, twice as many stations could be accommodated in the bandwidth available. What's more, when two or more AM signals were close together in frequency, there would always be a nasty heterodyne (whistle) as the carrier signals beat with each other. As single-sideband signals have no carrier, this problem disappeared. AM was still in fairly widespread use in the late-60s and early 70s, but the increasing availability of affordable SSB transceivers (mainly from the Far East, it has to be said, although the pioneer manufacturers were American and there were a few models produced in the UK) meant that by the late-70s AM was all but dead, at least on the HF bands. Although SSB signals still have to be tuned carefully for best results, modern transceivers have demodulation circuits and filters designed specifically for the mode, and are dramatically more stable than valve equipment of old which, mainly because of the amount of heat generated from the valves, tended to drift significantly after switch on. All this means that the early problems of signal fidelity are very much a thing of the past.

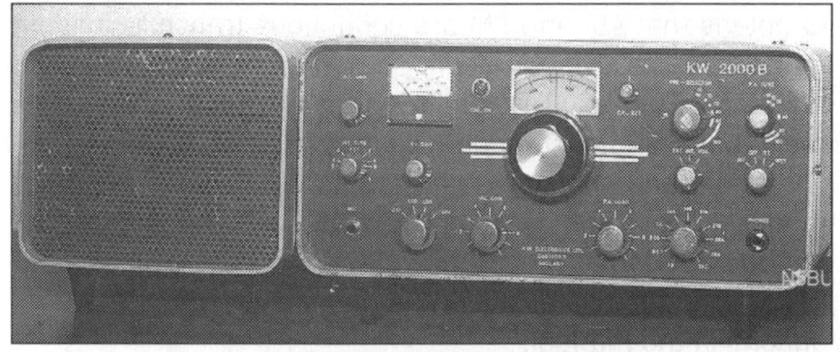

The British-made KW-2000 series of SSB transceivers were popular in the late 1960s and 70s ***[Photo N5KU's web site]***

Through to the early-60s, Amplitude Modulation (AM) was the mode of choice on the VHF bands, gradually being replaced by Frequency Modulation (FM) which is in common use today. An advantage of FM is that it doesn't require a high-power modulator, so that a modulated signal can be put through a frequency multiplier to generate a signal on the higher bands (70cm signals, for example, used be generated as 2m signals, and then put through a tripler, and a similar approach was used right through to the microwave bands). This said, even AM signals could be and were multiplied in this way at one time, the carrier frequency being multiplied up, and the final amplifier then amplitude modulated. Even a narrowband FM signal is at least as wide as an AM signal. The usual channel spacing in the FM segments of the VHF and UHF bands nowadays is 12.5kHz (previously it was 25kHz). This is much narrower than the wideband FM used in VHF broadcasting, but still much wider than the 2.5kHz or thereabouts required for an SSB signal. On the VHF and UHF bands this is not a problem, and FM remains the mode of choice for day to day ragchewing, particularly through repeaters. For DXing on the VHF and UHF bands, SSB is preferred for the reasons given above - while not having the fidelity of FM, it has better signal-to-noise benefits or more 'talk power', which is what you need when signals are weak or propagation is varying. FM is also used in the top half of the 10m HF band, the only HF band wide enough to accommodate it. A number of recent DXpeditions have operated in the FM part of 10m and generated a lot of interest. Earlier HF transceivers did not cater for FM operation, but most modern ones do, not only for 10m use but also so they can be used with transverters for VHF/UHF.

At the time of writing, a number of amateurs around the world are conducting experiments with digital voice on the amateur bands. This is a logical step, given that the necessary coding and decoding devices are becoming affordable and are already in widespread use for commercial voice transmission, both on landlines and over radio links. This said, there are many problems with using such equipment in the crowded environment of the HF bands, but it is certainly

RTTY became popular when the Creed 7B machine became available in quantity

conceivable that digital voice may start to replace FM as the mode of choice in the VHF/UHF spectrum, perhaps when one of the manufacturers brings out a transceiver with the facility built in and at a price not much different to existing VHF/UHF transceivers. But whether for HF or VHF, digital voice is unlikely to replace SSB for weak signal (DX) voice communications. Like FM, digital voice tends to have a threshold above which the signal is 100% copy and below which it is more or less unusable. DXers require a mode in which copy deteriorates gradually so that contacts can still be made under marginal conditions, albeit requiring some perseverance on the part of the operators.

Modes other than Morse and voice were a little slower to catch on, but not dramatically so. Radio Teletype (RTTY) started to become popular with the release onto the surplus market of large numbers of mechanical teleprinters, around the 1960s. These could be used on the amateur bands through a suitable terminal unit, which converted the DC signals (used for operating over a landline) to tones which could modulate an SSB transceiver. Similarly, early Slow Scan Television (SSTV) systems used mechanical scanners to send and receive pictures. But the real explosion in the use of data modes, both text and picture, came about with the advent of the ubiquitous personal computer. The first generation of systems required a terminal unit to interface between the computer and transceiver, taking signals from the computer's RS232 serial port, and converting them to tones which could modulate the transceiver. Most of the earliest terminal units were actually developed for VHF Packet Radio (AX25), which took off in a big way in the late-80s, especially when the licensing authority started licensing packet mailboxes. But several of those terminals units, for example the popular AEA PK232, could generate and decode RTTY, FAX and other modes as well, and were pressed into service on those modes on the HF bands, not always with ideal results as the filters with which they were fitted were wide enough for VHF packet, so rather too broad for HF use. Later models put this right. But the revolution came when PCs with sound cards became universal (and somewhat more highly featured), so that terminal units were no longer required. Nowadays, the PC's sound card can generate the tones required, whether for RTTY, PSK31, SSTV or whatever mode comes along, and these tones can then go directly to the transceiver's microphone input or, if it has one, auxiliary audio input. Received audio can be demodulated by the PC, with the software offering digital signal processing (DSP), to emulate the optimum filter(s) according to the mode in use.

An early multimode terminal unit, capable of running Packet Radio on VHF and HF, as well as several other data modes

The other major mode in use by amateurs is Fast Scan TV, equivalent to the day-to-day broadcast TV that we are all familiar with. Although digital techniques are increasingly used, for example for captioning pictures or pre-processing the video, the transmission method is usually still analogue, though no doubt this will change over time. Right now, amateur TV can be received on standard TV receivers preceded by a suitable frequency converter.

Nowadays, new digital modes are appearing almost daily. Most significantly, perhaps, a revolution is underway in weak signal communications, especially on the VHF/UHF bands. The WSJT suite of software, developed by K1JT, offers reliable communications via meteor scatter, EME and other extremely weak signal modes, such as extreme tropospheric propagation, to amateurs whose stations would have been considered totally inadequate for those paths. One result is that a debate has started over whether contacts conducted by such means are 'valid' and in the spirit of amateur radio, as the PC is doing most of the work. This isn't the place to debate such philosophical questions. No-one is obliged to use those modes but, for many who do, the WSJT software has brought new excitement to their hobby, which surely has been the story of amateur radio's progress over the decades.

Voice modes

THERE IS LITTLE more to be said about the voice modes than what has been covered in the introduction. SSB and narrow band FM are the two voice modes in widespread use in amateur radio, with a small amount of AM. Wideband FM has been used in the past on the microwave bands, though even on those bands it is more common nowadays to use the narrow band modes because they are more effective for good communications, and the technology to generate them is now within reach of the home constructor. What is important to note is that AM and FM are continuous transmissions, in that a carrier is always present even when no speaking is taking place. The result is that they have a much higher duty cycle than SSB. Most modern transceivers are rated for SSB operation, and should be derated accordingly for the other modes. For example, a 100 watt transceiver should probably not be operated at more than 50 watts carrier power on FM or AM but, to be safe, check the manufacturer's recommendations in the manual.

Some amateurs go to a great deal of trouble to improve the readability of their voice transmissions, and there are endless debates over microphone types and the need for tailoring of voice response. For some years now, the Heil range of headsets has been available with two alternative microphone inserts, one designed for high-fidelity voice transmission and the other for DX working. Some hand and desk microphones come with a switch to change the frequency response. It is also increasingly common for modern transceivers to offer a range of audio tailoring, to suit.

In practice, the only way to set up your transmitter to sound the way you want it is to listen to the transmitted output, or have a friend do so. There are two factors to take into account, the nature of your own voice and the effect you want to create. Everyone's voice is different, so there certainly can be benefits from making fine adjustments. And there really is a difference between the sort of 'armchair quality' audio that you might want for a ragchew with a friend across town and the high impact audio that you might prefer when trying to break a DX pile-up.

What is crucial is that you don't over-drive your transmitter by simply turning up the audio gain. The other common fault is to use too much speech processing. Again, although the meters on your transceiver will tell you a certain amount of the story, only by looking at your transmitted signal on an oscilloscope / monitor scope or listening to it on the air will you know whether your transmitted speech is distorted, or whether you are over-driving the transmitter and generating spurious signals outside your immediate passband. But do remember that the microphone gain control is there to be used, and sometimes more gain is desirable. Many amateurs feel the need to shout loudly into the microphone, especially when they are chasing rare DX. Experienced contesters quickly learn that this is counter-productive - you will lose your voice long before the end of the contest! Instead, let the transceiver do the work for you. Speak at normal levels, and adjust the microphone gain and speech processor controls accordingly. For the cross-town ragchew, you won't want to use the speech processor anyway, as it reduces the fidelity of your signals.

If you do make regular use of speech processing, or like to keep your voice at a moderate level, do ensure that there aren't any extraneous noises in your shack which are being picked up by the microphone and transmitted on-air. Fans, in particular, can form a very irritating background noise when heard at the far end. And your voice may echo if your shack has many hard surfaces. Again, the best way is to get someone to listen to your transmissions. And be aware if there are others talking in the background in your shack, as their voices can easily be picked up and transmitted.

If you choose to record various exchanges, for example CQ calls to save your voice in a contest, it is again important to check levels and ensure that the recorded audio drives your transmitter to the same level as your normal speech. It is not uncommon to hear some very distorted CQ calls in contests, where the transmitter is being overdriven by a pre-recorded message. It is also not uncommon to hear the CQ in a very different voice to the one that comes back when you answer! The better contesting programs allow each operator to record a personalised CQ call (and other messages) for use in a multi-operator contest environment.

When operating with any form of voice transmission, do bear in mind the person at the far end. If you are in contact with someone for whom English is not their native language, or if there is heavy interference, then always speak slowly and clearly, using phonetics to pass any critical information.

The ARD9800 from AOR is the first commercially available digital speech modem

Finally, many regular phone operators like to use VOX (voice-operated break-in), to come as close as possible to having a natural conversation, given that, unlike a telephone, amateur radio is inherently a one-way form of communication. All transceivers with VOX offer the ability to adjust several parameters, mainly the time it takes to activate and to trip out, and the level at which it activates and then drops out. These adjustments are quite critical to being able to use VOX successfully. Again, any background noise (from having a window open, for example) can cause the transmitter to activate even if you weren't actually saying anything. So by all means use VOX, but set it up with care.

Digital voice transmission

It's not entirely clear whether this section should appear here or under data modes, which is very much a sign of the times. A number of amateurs have been experimenting with digital transmission of voice for the past few years and, at the time of writing, a commercial digital voice modem has recently appeared on the market [1]. This employs a digital vocoder using DQPSK modulation with 36 tone carriers within an overall bandwidth of 312.5Hz to 2500Hz, allowing transmissions to take place using a standard SSB transceiver. This is absolutely not a weak signal (DX) mode, requiring about 25dB signal-to-noise ratio to work effectively but, when that is the case, apparently produces good telephone quality, considerably better than the average SSB quality.

The modem is currently quite expensive. However, as with other digital modes, expect prices to drop and, in due course, for the mode to be supported via a sound card or even offered within the transceiver itself. As a modem of this sort is unaware of what is being fed into it, the system can equally well carry data or images.

Any new mode of this sort is like the first telephone, of little use until someone else has one. And obviously it is unsuited to the cut and thrust of a DX pile-up. But it may well find a niche among certain groups within our hobby.

Telegraphy

THERE HAS BEEN considerable opposition in some parts of the amateur radio community to the abolition of mandatory Morse testing for access to the HF bands. It seems to be forgotten that no test of operating skills has ever been required for voice or data modes. The reason for the Morse requirement was not to create some artificial hurdle to prove some sort of 'worthiness' to operate on HF. Historically, it was because many of our HF bands were shared with other services who continued to use Morse. It was essential that, in the event of interference to their activities by an amateur station,

Morse was originally sent using a 'straight' key, often made of brass and hard wood, like this recent model beautifully constructed by Denis Lewis, M3BIA

they could call on Morse and ask the amateur to move. Since the discontinuation of Morse usage by those services, the requirement no longer applies. But Morse telegraphy continues to be, and almost certainly will continue to be, one of the most popular modes in use by radio amateurs. There is a certain satisfaction in being able to send and receive Morse competently, and Morse is still one of the most effective modes for working through heavy QRM or with low signals (though, it has to be said, some of the data modes are proving even better than Morse in this respect). Morse abbreviations and Q-codes make it a more suitable mode than telephony for overcoming language barriers. And it is still easier to build a telegraphy transmitter than a phone one.

Just a word of explanation here, as the previous paragraph mixed the terms Morse and telegraphy. We are talking here about using a method of transmission requiring keying the transmitter on and off or, in the case of MCW (Modulated Continuous Wave), keying a tone on and off which is then used to modulate the transmitter. In practice, when we use that method of transmission, we usually adopt the international Morse code for the purpose, as it is well established after more than a century of use. Actually, the Morse code as we now know it is rather different to the code that Samuel Morse first proposed for those long-distance telegraph links across the USA, following the lines of the newly-created railways. Time and experience have meant that the code has evolved and, indeed, continues to do so. Only recently there has been debate about the newly-announced Morse character to designate the @ symbol, so crucial to transmitting e-mail addresses. What has perhaps been most surprising is that the new Morse character was announced by a committee of the ITU, despite the fact that, to all intents and purposes, Morse is no longer used in the professional world. There are also many Morse characters that we in the UK don't come across too often, but which are used elsewhere because they represent alphabetical and grammatical characters that simply don't occur in English. In practice, they are rarely used on the air either, except perhaps by two stations of the same nationality.

Sending and receiving Morse can be done in many ways. Most beginners start with a conventional straight key, with its up-down mechanism. Many are available, both new and old (many of us who became licensed in the 50s and 60s started with ex-military Morse keys). A number of straight key events are held each year (not contests in the strict sense of the word as they are for fun rather than competitive), to encourage amateurs to retain and practice their skills with straight keys. The very need for such events suggests that the world has moved on, just as it has from AM transmission. After the straight key came the semi-automatic bug key, where dashes are created manually by holding the key to one side, but holding the key to the other side creates a series of dots, as a result of the vibration of a weighted arm. It takes a particular skill to send well with a semi-automatic key, but the advantage is that it is difficult to send at speeds much more than about 25WPM on a straight key, certainly for extended periods. I finally made the change from a staight key after a 48-hour contest which resulted in a severe case of wrist-ache!

Automatic keys, like semi-automatic keys, have a paddle which can be pressed to the left or the right. An electronic circuit generates dashes when the key is pressed one way and dots when it is pressed the other. Iambic keying goes one stage further - a twin-paddle which, when squeezed, will produce alternate dots and dashes. With automatic keys, the number of movements to send a sentence in Morse is considerably less than with a straight or semi-automatic key, with the result that it is possible to send at very much higher speeds and with less fatigue. Competent CW operators, using an automatic key, tend to ragchew or contest as speeds in the 30-35WPM range. Some can operate very much faster than this, but you then need someone else with an equal level of competence at the other end, or you are wasting your time!

Finally, CW can also be generated nowadays from your PC keyboard. Most logging programs cater for this, and it is easy to store not only CQ calls but also regularly-sent messages (such as name, QTH and equipment details) associated with a function key. Free text can be keyed into the keyboard itself. Or you may choose to have a traditional keyer in parallel with the keyboard as many contesters do. They send the standardised contest exchanges from the PC, but can immediately resort to the keyer if there is a need to send anything other than the stored messages.

Most operators choose to receive CW by ear. Although there are programs for decoding CW, they tend not to work effectively in the presence of fading of heavy interference. Many newly-licensed amateurs are unsure whether to copy everything down by hand, or try to copy in their heads. It is very much a matter of experience. If you are engaging in a

A semi-automatic 'bug-key' makes automatic dots by mechanical means

For comfortable and high speed operating, the 'paddle' can be used in conjunction with an electronic keyer, either external or one built into the rig

typical 'rubber stamp' QSO with, perhaps, an overseas amateur with little English, the exchange is likely to be fairly predictable. RST, name, QTH, perhaps his equipment and/or the weather at his location. So you don't need to write everything down, just the salient details. When you hear "QTH" get ready to make a note of his location in your log. Generally it will be sent twice in any case. Experienced CW operators, engaging in a lengthy ragchew on Morse, tend not to write down anything unless they specifically want to note something for later. Instead the whole exchange is copied by ear in exactly the same way as if the conversation were taking place using voice.

If you are new to CW, it can be daunting to call someone who is obviously an experienced CW operator, sending at high speeds. You may feel competent to copy a contest exchange (RST, serial number, for example) at reasonably high speeds, but not to engage in a lengthy conversation. The trick is, quite simply, to ask the other station to slow down (`"QRS PSE"`). Most will be only too happy to do so. If they don't, it is their loss. But every CW operator had to start somewhere, and probably enjoyed a similar courtesy from other amateurs at that time, so will almost certainly be prepared to do the same for you. Incidentally, don't assume that, just because you hear fast CW, you are listening to a competent operator. There are far too many CW operators on the bands who send somewhat faster than they really should, and end up spending much of their transmission correcting errors!

Finally a word about your transmitted signal. Depending on the rise and fall time of your transmitted characters, it is possible for your transmitter to generate so-called key clicks, which can be heard some way from your carrier frequency. Some commercial transceivers are well-known for generating key clicks though, in most cases, there are modifications readily available which go at least some way to curing the problem. There can also be an issue when using break-in, either semi- or full-break-in (in the former you hit the key and your transmitter is activated, but only goes back to receive after a pause of more than dot's length, the pause being adjustable; in the latter your transceiver does back to receive quite literally at every gap in the CW, giving the effect that you are actually listening continuously to the band). Any transmitter will take a finite time to go into transmit, even longer if it is activating a linear amplifier, perhaps via a relay. So your first CW character can be foreshortened, leading to problems in copying at the far end. With full break-in, every character may be affected in this way. It is difficult to avoid. It takes a finite time for a transceiver to switch between transmit and receive, even if it uses solid state (usually PIN diode) switching, especially if you are operating split-frequency, as the synthesiser also needs to change frequency every time you do so. So it is quite impossible to follow high-speed CW exactly. There will probably be a comfortable CW speed for break-in operation, above which your transceiver starts to struggle. Again, the best way to check for this and key clicks is to get a nearby amateur to listen to your transmission and maybe record it for you to hear.

High speed CW

High speed CW was used for many years for meteor scatter (MS) operation, though it has now largely been superseded by WSJT (see below). Messages would be sent at perhaps 1000 characters per minute, recorded at the far end and replayed at lower speed. This was done on tape recorders which could be run at various speeds (the old reel-to-reel recorders were ideal) and, latterly, by recording to hard disc. A random MS QSO could take several hours to complete, depending on the number of meteor 'pings'.

Very low speed CW

At the other end of the scale, very low speed CW (each character taking several seconds or even minutes) has been used on 73 and 136kHz, using software to record and integrate the signals over a long period. Using a very low speed means that very narrow bandwidths can be employed. As noise, which is usually the limiting factor in achieving a contact, is directly proportional to bandwidth, this approach enables weaker signals to be received, thereby increasing the distances that could be worked. Because the QSO takes a long time to complete, and because it is necessary to create a very narrow filter, the mode is carried out with suitable DSP software and your transceiver needs to be very stable. The mode became known as QRSS (QRS being the Q code for "Please send more slowly" in CW). It was originally implemented by a hardware DSP unit and software developed by G3PLX, but a program called Spectrogram became popular with 136 kHz operators. Whilst not as sophisticated as the G3PLX system, it was easier to implement. More recently, other programs have become more popular, including *Argo*, *EasyGram*, *Spectran* and *SpecLab*.

These are capable of displaying Morse with dot lengths from less than one second to over 100 seconds. All work in conjunction with the PC's soundcard. In practice a dot length of three seconds is the default QRSS mode. This allows a meaningful two-way contact to take place in less than an hour. Slower speeds are used, but usually only for intercontinental DX. The centre of activity for QRSS3 (three second dot length) is 137.700kHz, and the screen will display stations within 30-40Hz of this frequency.

Because of the time taken to send QRSS signals, a simplified QSO format has been devised. The 'de' between callsigns is not used, and reports are in the form 'O' for perfectly readable, 'M' for readable with difficulty and 'T' for visible but not readable. Callsigns are rarely repeated and are abbreviated after the first full call. However, in common with standard amateur radio practice, a contact is only valid after a successful exchange of full callsigns and reports, and the final 'rogers'. A typical contact, lasting about 40 minutes in QRSS3, is shown below (the locator is optional and would be omitted if it is already known or in marginal contacts):

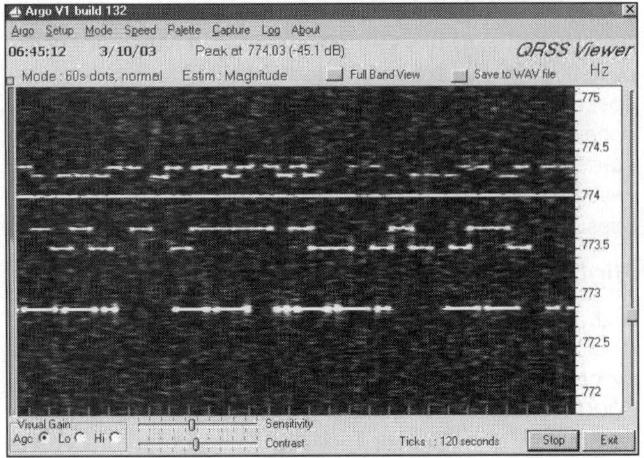

An *Argo* display showing both DFCW and normal QRSS CW signals. The callsigns are G3AQC at the top, CT1DRP and Canadian beacon MP

```
CQ ON7YD K
ON7YD G3XDV K
XDV YD O O JO20IX K
YD XDV R M M IO91VT K
YD R TU SK
```

Because this is still rather time consuming a method has been devised to speed up the information transfer whilst still retaining the same bandwidth (and hence signal to noise ratio). DFCW (dual frequency CW) uses two closely spaced frequencies, one for dots, the other for dashes, and can be received using exactly the same software and settings as QRSS. The time savings are made by making the dots and dashes the same length, and having only a very short gap between each dot or dash, resulting in up to 50% time improvement. In all other respects it is used in exactly the same way as QRSS, and cross-mode contacts are common.

A popular program for sending QRSS or DFCW is '*QRS*' (by ON7YD), used in conjuction with a simple interface..

Data modes

ARGUABLY, WITH THE preceding discussion of QRSS, the chapter has already moved to data modes. QRSS is a good example of how previous distinctions between traditional modes (voice and CW), data modes and image modes, have now become blurred.

The modes which will be considered here fall into several distinct categories. There are data modes for sending text in routine situations on the VHF and HF bands, modes specifically designed for low-signal applications (meteor scatter, troposcatter, EME) and those specifically designed for image transmission. In the future we may find ourselves dealing increasingly with data modes for transmitting voice and ultimately data modes whereby we can send absolutely anything, as is pretty much already the case for transmitting data over the Internet.

The difference between radio communication and the Internet for data transmission is primarily that a radio circuit tends to much less reliable than a wired network. Usually it has less bandwidth, and it is also subject to propagation issues , such as some stations not hearing other stations on the same frequency, interference, fading and the like. It is to deal with these issues that so many new data modes have come into being in recent years. Generally, what has happened to make each successive data mode possible, and better than its predecessors, is the increasing power of PCs. The early data modes used very little processing power, later ones may use quite substantial amounts. Given that most PCs now are very powerful indeed, the question might be asked as to why older modes like RTTY are still around. The reason is largely because it is a well-established standard, which many amateurs are equipped for. Meanwhile, some other data modes have come and gone, never having reached a high enough level of acceptance to survive when newer, more effective modes took their place.

Much on-air data activity has been through the use of VHF/UHF packet mailbox systems, ie message boards, where amateurs don't communicate directly with each other on a one-to-one basis, or indeed in a net. Also, the error-resistant protocols used in the TOR handshaking modes described later don't invite quick-fire break-in type communication over the airwaves, nor roundtable nets between a group of amateurs. RTTY allows others to 'listen in', to have quick one-line overs and is especially suitable (and widely used) in HF contests, yet it's based on technology invented many, many years ago. Like Morse, its usefulness and simplicity have kept it going in the face of other more advanced data modes which, technically, are far superior in getting through when all else fails.

Handshaking

In contrast to RTTY, some other modes like AMTOR, Packet, GTOR, PacTOR etc, are 'handshaking modes'. Here, when in QSO, the Information Sending Station (ISS) sends a small group, or 'packet', of characters at a time, and the Information Receiving Station (IRS) receives these and performs a parity check to make sure the information adds up, ie that the characters were received correctly. If so, the IRS sends a brief "OK" and the ISS then sends the next packet, and so on. When the time comes for the partner station to have its over, a changeover occurs (your TNC or software handles all this for you) and the ISS and IRS change between the two stations. This is ideal if you are sending data to, or receiving data from, a mailbox, as there is no human operator at the far end to alert you if the message has been corrupted in any way. It can also work for some day-to-day two-way contacts but, as described above, is less suited than old-fashioned RTTY for quick, snappy operating.

Connecting PC and transceiver

The first task in using any data mode is to connect your PC to the transceiver, unless yours is one of the modern transceivers that allow you to connect a keyboard directly. You may be using one of the popular terminal units (data mode usage really exploded with the availability of multimode terminal units such as the popular AEA PK232), in which case the PC connects to the terminal unit via an RS232 link, and the terminal unit to the transceiver according to the manufacturer's instructions.

More likely, though, you will be connecting your PC's sound card to the transceiver. This has been covered in publications [2] and on many Web sites [3, 4]. Some suitable interface circuits are also shown in **Figs.8.1 and 8.2**. To describe the process in the simplest terms, the received audio signal (taken, perhaps, from an auxiliary headphone output on your transceiver, as you will want to listen to the incoming tones at the same time) goes to the microphone input on your PC sound card. Usually there is a facility within the data modes program you are using to enable you to adjust the levels. Alternatively, it is also possible to do so from within the Windows operating system.

The transmitted signal is taken from the sound card's output to an auxiliary (data) input on your transceiver or, if necessary, to the microphone input. In either case, ensure the microphone is disconnected when using data modes. The output from the sound card will almost certainly be too high for the microphone input of your transceiver and although some adjustment will be possible in the software, it is often advisable to use a simple resistive potential divider circuit to reduce the level by 10dB or so. Many of the commercial interfaces which you can buy for this purpose not only have a suitable potential divider, but also have an audio transformer or opto-coupler so there is no direct connection between sound card and transceiver. This minimises the risk of hum on the transmitted signal.

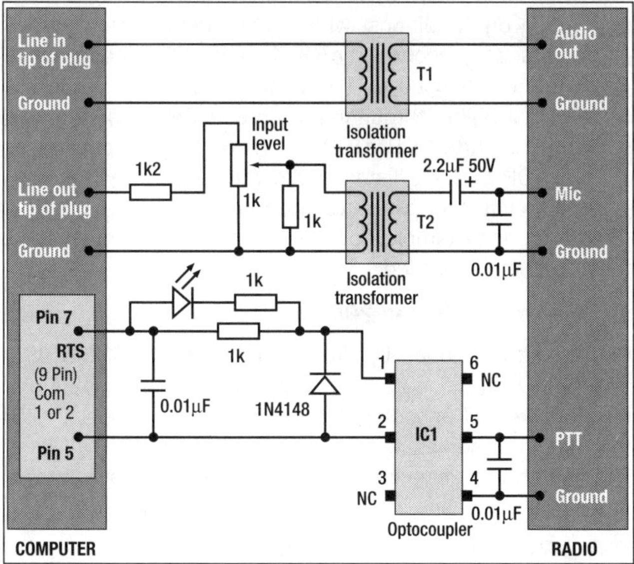

Fig 8.1: Interfacing a sound card to a transceiver. The transformers are 600-ohm type 9000 (RS part no: 208-822). IC1 is a 4N25 optocoupler (RS 579-289). The LED is a high sensitivity type. Leads should be screened and the interface mounted in a screened box

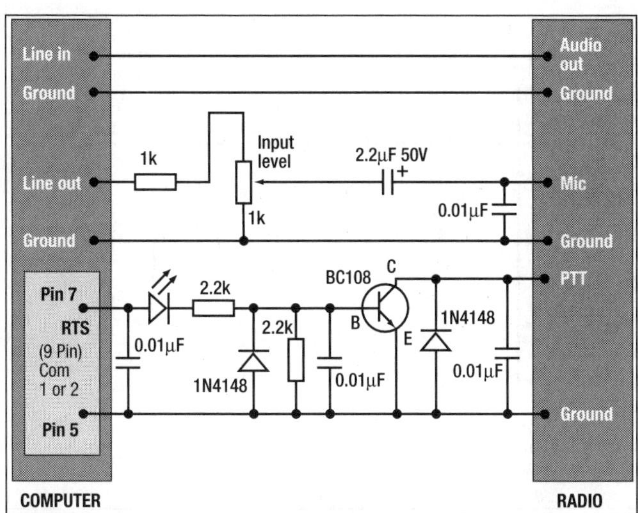

Fig 8.2: Interfacing having the same electrical performance as in Fig 1, but without isolating transformers and optocoupler

To check that all is well, load some suitable software for one of the more popular data modes (probably RTTY, as there are almost always RTTY signals to be heard on 40, 20 and 15m) and see what you can copy. If you can copy RTTY signals correctly, you will almost certainly be able to copy other data modes without trouble, once you have suitable software installed. Depending on whether your equipment and software is set for low tones or high tones (see next section) you may need to switch your transceiver to USB or LSB respectively. Similarly, once you are happy with the receive side, check the transmit side. You are checking to ensure that you are not overdriving the transmitter (if, on turning up the audio level from your sound card, the transmit power stays the same, you already have the output set too high) and, ultimately, that other stations are able to copy your transmitted signal. The most common mistake is to transmit inverted, ie the two RTTY tones are reversed. Normally, if you are receiving correctly, then you should also be transmitting correctly. It is assumed here that you are sending audio tones, rather than using the FSK input of your transceiver. The latter is fine for RTTY (check the wiring carefully and be aware that you may need to reverse the tones), but won't help you with the other data modes.

A word of warning. Like FM and AM, most of the data modes described in the following paragraphs have a 100% duty cycle, so it is important to ensure that your transceiver is able to handle this, usually by turning down the power level to about 50% of the SSB/CW power rating.

RTTY

RTTY is the oldest and by far the most popular of the data modes. It is unsophisticated in modern terms, with no error detection or correction, and it only handles upper case characters. But it is well suited to rapid-fire QSOs such as in contest operation. And there are plenty of competent software packages available free of charge, which offer a wide range of RTTY facilities, probably the most popular being *MMTTY* [5].

RTTY operation is covered in Chapter 7. There are just a few points worth making here about the use of this mode. Firstly, RTTY uses two tones, spaced 170Hz apart. It can be copied on most transceivers through a 500Hz or even a 250Hz filter, giving good receive performance. Alternatively, with suitable software, you can leave the filter open at full SSB bandwidth so that you can see a number of RTTY signals on the waterfall display on your PC screen, and then select the one you want to receive. The software has its own internal audio-filtering capabilities (using the sound card) to extract the tones you are looking for and reject any interfering signals (provided they are not co-channel with either of those tones). This is a substantial improvement on many earlier systems. For example, the PK232, already mentioned, actually used 200Hz tone spacing, simply because this was needed for one of its other modes of operation. Furthermore, its internal filters were much wider than ideal for RTTY oper-

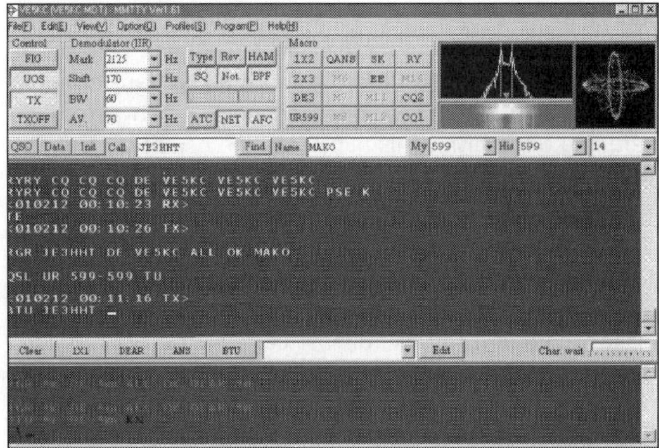

A screen shot from JE3HHT's popular MMTTY program for RTTY. The windows at the top right are tuning aids. The top text window shows received text while the bottom text window is for transmitted text

ation, as they also had to cater for 300 baud VHF packet. The design was a reasonable compromise for the many functions the unit was being asked to perform, but was far from ideal for HF RTTY operation.

Because RTTY uses two audio tones, there can easily be confusion when RTTY frequencies are cited, as there are really two frequencies we might be interested in. One is the carrier frequency, but this is almost irrelevant, as what matters is not the exact audio tone used for modulation but the separation between the two. In any case, in many parts of the world RTTY operators use so-called 'low' tones of 1275Hz and 1445Hz (a 170Hz difference), whereas most amateurs outside Europe, and an increasing number of European operators too, favour 'high' tones of 2125Hz and 2295Hz (again a 170Hz difference). The advantage of high tones is that any harmonics are likely to be outside the audio passband. The other, more useful frequency to quote, therefore is the Mark frequency, which is the one that is transmitted when no data is being sent, but even this will be designated differently according to whether high or low tones are being used, high-tone USB signals being 1.46kHz higher than LSB low-tone ones (**Fig 8.3** shows the relationships when using USB). In general tuning around there's no difference, but when arranging a sked or chasing a spot from the Cluster system, it's important to define which you're using!

AmTOR

AmTOR is a derivation of SITOR, used in the commercial world, and was developed for amateur radio use by Peter Martinez, G3PLX. Unlike RTTY, it allows direct linking between two stations with data acknowledgement and error checking. Because of the two-way to-ing and fro-ing which this requires, it is not ideal for contest QSOs, but is useful for ragchewing via the keyboard . It is also suitable for working with mailboxes (RTTY, AmTOR and Packet mailboxes exist on the HF bands), as you can be more confident, compared with RTTY, that any message you leave is uncorrupted and ready for the downloading by the intended recipient.

Communication with AmTOR makes use of a 'selcal', which is a four-letter combination. This is typically the first letter and the final three letters of your callsign, ie the selcal for G3XTT would be 'GXTT', and when you're transmitting a CQ you should include your selcal in your CQ text as well as your callsign. Once in QSO, normal callsigns are exchanged as usual within the QSO text. For listening, all AmTOR terminal units and software also have a 'listen' mode where, provided signals levels are satisfactory, you can 'listen into' existing contacts just like on RTTY, so you can call one of the stations at the end of a QSO if you wish.

Like traditional RTTY, one limitation of AmTOR is that it uses a five-bit code, so cannot handle both upper and lower case character sets. Many terminal units were developed especially for AmTOR use, but the mode is waning, having largely been replaced by Pactor for mailbox use (see below).

PacTOR

PacTOR and the later PacTOR II and PacTOR III were developed in Germany as an amalgam of the best in AMTOR and Packet, specifically to provide reliable file transfers to and from HF mailboxes. Pactor operates at 100 or 200 baud depending on conditions, with net throughput of up to 18 characters per second. PacTOR-1 is an FSK mode, while PacTOR II (introduced in 1995) moved to PSK. It has the potential for higher throughput than PacTOR. PacTOR III is a software upgrade to PacTOR II, offering higher data rates still. PacTOR allows a 'listen' mode where, provided the path is good-quality, you can eavesdrop on PacTOR communications prior, for example, to calling one of the parties when their contact has ended.

Clover and Clover 2000

Clover was developed by HAL communications of the USA, specifically for HF data communications. It uses multiple-tone phase-shift encoding. Effective throughputs are similar to Pactor-II. It serves a similar purpose to PacTOR, allowing error-free transmissions. It can be used for two-way contacts but is generally used for links with mailboxes.

G-TOR

G-TOR (Golay-TOR) is a proprietary FSK mode developed by Kantronics Inc of the USA. It is claimed to have better throughput than PacTOR, and better immunity to interference, multipath and other effects encountered over radio links.

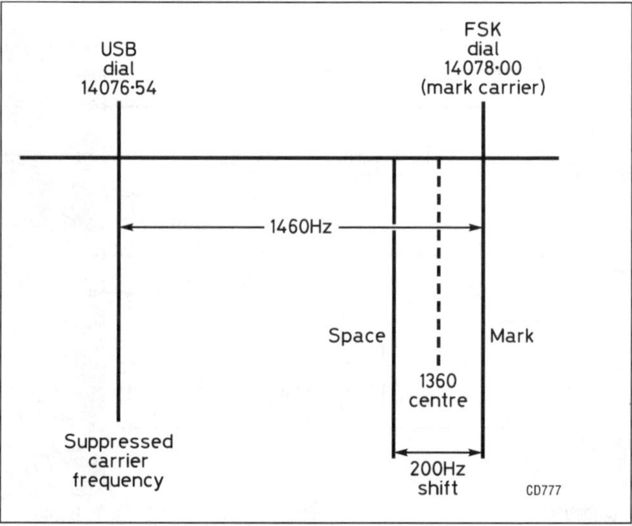

Fig 8.3: Relationship of transceiver dial readings to Mark carrier frequency for USB and FSK operation

PSK

PSK31 [6] was developed by Peter Martinez, G3PLX (creator of AmTOR), specifically as a replacement for traditional RTTY for real-time contacts. Peter's argument was that modes using error correction were inherently unsuited for real-time contacts, not for technical reasons, but because the users tended to be uncomfortable with the time delays inherent in hand-shaking between the two ends of the contact.

BPSK is an abbreviation for binary phase shift keying, although Peter himself refers to the modulation used in PSK31 as polarity reversal keying. The 31 refers to the number of characters sent per second. The character set is based on a number of 'varicodes', ie variable length codes, devised in a similar way to Morse code, whereby the more common letters can be sent more quickly than the less common ones.

Without going into any more detail, the benefits to the user of BPSK31 (usually referred to as PSK31) compared with traditional RTTY are that it tends to work better in weak signal conditions and uses less bandwidth (a single carrier, as against the two of RTTY, with a theoretical bandwidth of 31Hz).

PSK31 requires a stable transmitter and receiver, but this should not be a problem with modern transceivers. In any case, most of the software available for PSK31 uses a waterfall display and incorporates DSP filtering. Therefore operating the mode is simple. You can leave your transceiver's filters on a wide (SSB) setting and watch something like 2.5kHz of the band. This is room aplenty for many PSK31 signals. You can then click on an individual signal to decode it and start a QSO. Unlike RTTY, it doesn't matter whether you transmit and receive in USB or LSB mode, as there is only one tone, so there are no issues about tones being reversed. And if you invoke automatic frequency control (AFC) it will stay locked to the signal, even if there is some subsequent drifting in frequency.

PSK63 [7] is a variant of PSK31 operating, as the name suggests, at a higher speed. It has been developed very much with contesting in mind, with the intention that contacts can be conducted that much more quickly. As you would expect, it takes up roughly twice the bandwidth of PSK31. Most of the popular software available for PSK31 also supports PSK63 nowadays. Programs include *Digipan*, WinPSK, Winwarbler, Multipsk, PSK31 Deluxe, QuickPSK and *RCKRTTY*. As well as text, PSK63 is capable of sending thumbnail pictures, with a transmission time around two minutes.

PSK08 is a low-speed variant of PSK 31, aimed primarily at 136kHz operators. Its narrow bandwidth requirement is ideally suited to 136kHz operation, permitting the use of very narrow DSP filtering for receive, to enhance overall signal-to-noise performance.

MFSK

MFSK (multi-frequency shift keying) is not widely used on the amateur bands, but is supported by many of the popular data modes packages. It takes the two-tone concept of RTTY and extends this to several tones, which makes for a system that is more robust than PSK31 in the face of interference and when signals are weak. It is therefore more suited to DX working in a data modes environment. The tones are close-spaced and a stable transmitter and receiver are required. MFSK was first used commercially in systems such as Piccolo (used by Britain's Diplomatic Wireless Service) and has proved resilient in adverse conditions.

THROB

THROB, by G3PPT, develops MFSK still further, using a 9-tone signal. The throughput is slower that other text modes, but the system is reported to be more resilient in the face of low signals or propagation difficulties.

MT63

MT63 is a DSP-based mode for sending text over paths that experience fading and interference from other signals. It uses a matrix system whereby 64 different tones are combined across both time and frequency. This 'overkill' is intended to help protect against errors while maintaining a data rate of 100WPM. However, this requires a bandwidth around 1kHz which, while narrower than voice transmissions, is unacceptably wide for data modes on the crowded HF bands such as 20m. Most MT63 activity takes place around 14110kHz.

Hellschreiber

Strictly speaking, the various Hellschreiber [8] modes are not digital modes, but nevertheless are conveniently covered in this section. They are actually based on a very old landline method for transmitting facsimile traffic (invented by Dr Rudolf Hell of Germany in 1929), but have been adapted for use with modern software in the amateur radio environment. Text is not sent as discrete characters, but rather in the way of a facsimile transmission where a page builds up from a series of dots, each containing black and white, such that they gradually build up an image which can be text or even

A Feld Hell contact on !4.0635MHz [from IZ8BLY]

graphics of some sort. The benefit over modes like PSK31 is that, in the face of interference or fading, the human eye may still be able to discern the transmitted characters whereas once they are lost with PSK31 or similar modes, they are lost forever. The overall bandwidth of Hellschreiber transmissions is about 75Hz, similar to PSK63, though there are several versions including concurrent multi-tone Hell (C/MT Hell) and sequential multi-tone Hell (S/MT Hell).

WOLF

WOLF (Weak-signal Operation on Low Frequency), by Stewart Nelson KK7KA, is a new signal format and protocol designed specifically for the LF bands. It can be used for beacons and for two way communication. Unlike existing formats, which are optimised for a particular S/N (and corresponding speed), WOLF can operate over a wide range of signal levels. For example, a WOLF beacon transmits a 15-character message repeatedly. If the received signal would be adequate for conventional CW, copy will be displayed in 24 seconds. At a level barely enough for 0.4WPM QRSS, copy will appear within two minutes. Even if the signal is another 10dB weaker, the message can still be received. It will take from 20 minutes to several hours, depending on the stability of the transmitter and receiver. It is also necessary that the propagation path remain open over the required interval. WOLF is still very much at the experimental stage, and the software can be downloaded from the web site [9].

WSJT

Developed for weak signal working on the VHF bands by K1JT, the description in the manual says: "WSJT is a computer program for VHF/UHF communication using state of the art digital techniques. It can decode signals propagated by fraction-of-a-second reflections from meteor trails, as well as steady signals more than 10 dB weaker than those needed for conventional CW or SSB". WSJT is Windows-based, and will run on any modern PC.

WSJT offers the following operating modes:

- FSK441. Developed for VHF meteor scatter operation on 6m and 2m, FSK441 effectively replaced high-speed CW as the preferred option for meteor scatter work. It remains popular but for 6m work is being replaced by JT6M (see below).
- JT65 really is a weak signal mode, designed for EME and extreme troposcatter, and replacing the previous JT44.
- JT6M, as mentioned above, is for meteor scatter, optimised for 50MHz. It is no surprise that 6m is the focus for this mode, as this is by far the most reliable band for meteor scatter communications, open more or less round the clock, 365 days of the year, not only when major meteor storms occur. During the major storms, signals can be quite strong, but JT6M has opened up new horizons, allowing meteor scatter contacts to take place on a much more regular basis than previously.
- EME Echo for measuring your own echoes from the Moon.

In addition to these communication modes, WSJT offers a Measure mode for testing Sun noise, etc, and an EME Calculator to help you predict the maximum strength of your own and other stations' echoes from the moon.

A detailed description of the program is provided in the online WSJT User's Guide. The manual may be downloaded and printed from the web site [10]. The WA5UFH [11] and K6SIX [12] web sites are also a valuable resource for would-be WSJT operators.

Packet Radio

Packet radio arrived with a bang in the mid-80s, mostly using a protocol known as AX.25, an amateur derivation of the X.25 protocol in use on commercial data networks. The main differences were in the addressing structure (AX.25 needed to recognise and work with amateur callsigns) and in error detection and correction, given that radio links are less reliable than wired networks. Although AX.25 can be used for real-time QSOs (and was, quite extensively, on 2m and 70cm in the early days), its main application has been with unattended mailboxes for sending and receiving text around the country and, in due course, the world. Many such mailboxes still exist, along with the PacketCluster network for DX spotting purposes, which also uses the AX.25 protocols. In the early days the backbone system, linking the mailboxes together, was largely run on the UHF and microwave bands, especially on 70cm and 23cm. This was typically at speeds of 9600 baud (most local links were at 1200 baud, as this can be accommodated easily in a typical NBFM channel). Nowadays, most of the backbone links are via the Internet. However, not only has the Internet offered a solution for these backbone links, it has also largely wiped out the packet mailbox network, as it provides an effective alternative for communicating not only with other amateurs but with absolutely anyone who has access to an Internet connection. It has been argued that amateurs missed an opportunity with packet radio to develop it for higher speeds and a wider variety of applications, which could certainly have happened on the higher microwave bands where almost unlimited bandwidth is available. Some groups did experiment with web-based interfaces and graphics, but the rise of the Internet was too rapid and too all-embracing to compete with. One popular use for packet radio is APRS (Automatic Position Reporting System). This is discussed in more detail in Chapter 12.

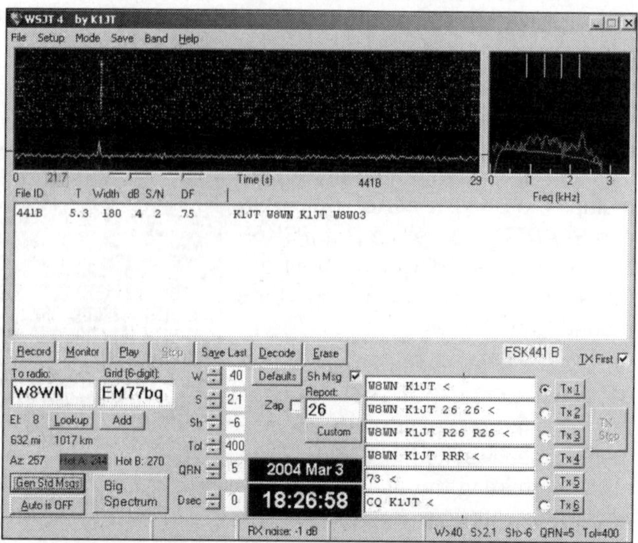

A screen shot from the *WSJT FSK441* meteor scatter program

As well as AX.25, some amateurs experimented with TCP/IP protocols for data transmission on the VHF and UHF bands. There were some advantages for wide area networking, via intermediate stations but, again, the Internet has made development of these networks irrelevant.

Finally, it should be noted that some AX.25 activity took place on the HF bands, both two-way QSOs and packet mailboxes. These were at 300 baud. Nevertheless, AX.25 is not well suited to the vagaries of HF propagation, and more recent data modes have taken its place.

Although many packet radio users continue to employ an external TNC, there are many programs available which emulate all TNC functions on the PC, as with the other data modes described in this chapter.

Packet Radio and satellites

One of the more exciting applications for packet radio in recent years has been its use with amateur satellites. This topic is covered in more detail in Chapter 13.

PacketCluster, Bulletin boards (BBS), & APRS

The PacketCluster (and Cluster) network and its use are described in detail in Chapter 9. Bulletin Board operation and the APRS Network are covered in Chapter 12.

FAX/SSTV

In the previous edition of this book, image communications were dealt with in a separate chapter, but that is really no longer appropriate. The software used for Slow Scan TV (SSTV) and Facsimile (FAX) is little different from that used for the data modes described earlier in this chapter, and also works through the PC's sound card.

SSTV has been popular for many years with a select group of amateurs who have enjoyed the challenge of sending pictures over the HF bands. While Fast Scan TV (moving pictures) requires considerable bandwidth, SSTV is similar to FAX, whereby one image is sent at a time, over a normal voice channel. In the early days, pictures would probably have been created by mechanically scanning a photograph and images were in black and white. Nowadays, colour pictures are sent as the norm, either generated from one of the popular graphics or paint programs, or captured from a digital camera.

SSTV picture received off-air from IT9MRW

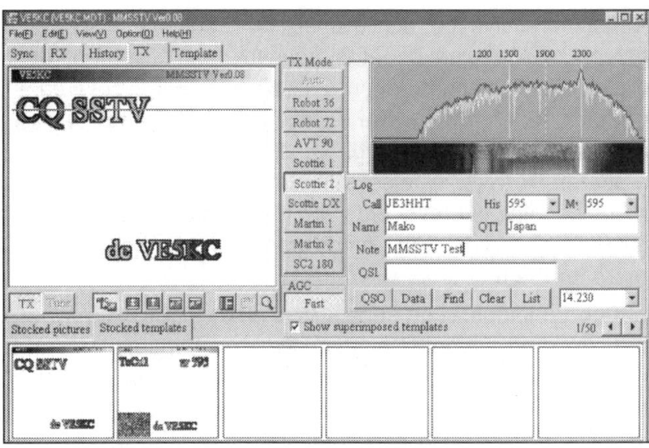

A screen shot from the *MSSTV* program

As with all the data modes described so far, the best way to get set up on SSTV is to download one of the popular programs (for example, *MMSSTV* by JE3JHHT [13]), read the accompanying manual or help file, connect up to your transceiver via your sound card, and start decoding signals. The main difference between this and other data modes is that the signals will be images rather than text. Some useful hints and tips on getting started with SSTV appeared in a 2004 *RadCom* article [14].

Nowadays, most amateur interest in FAX operation is in receiving the various weather and news FAX services from around the world, as well as images from dedicated weather satellites. For amateur band service, images are now exchanged using SSTV systems as described above.

Fast Scan TV

FAST SCAN TELEVISION is a special-interest activity limited by its need for substantial amounts of bandwidth to 70cm and higher frequency bands. Nowadays, mainly due to the adoption of full-bandwidth colour transmission, and the increased use of 70cm for other activities, ATV operation takes place on 23cm and the other microwave bands.

Getting going on ATV has become very easy. Whereas ATV equipment always used to be home-constructed (from kits or published designs), now there are inexpensive

An attractive SSTV identification picture

transmit/receive modules available for 23cm and 13cm. The growth of ATV also benefits from the establishment of a chain of ATV repeaters on 23, 13 and 3cm, covered in Chapter 12. Many of these include innovative features such as Teletext, remote controlled VCRs, interlinking between repeaters, etc. They also operate continuously in beacon mode sending out test cards and text pages, which is helpful for the newcomer to the mode who is setting up his equipment for the first time.

If portable operation appeals to you, try 10GHz ATV, where by converting a simple Doppler microwave burglar alarm unit, or a commercial satellite TV receiver, a simple but very effective, FM ATV station can be built. On this band, even a small satellite TV-type dish can give very high gain, so you can achieve surprising DX contacts with the sort of power (a few tens of milliwatts) generated by a burglar alarm unit.

Digital amateur television (D-ATV)

Amateur TV, as described in the previous section, is an analogue system, in that the image is modulated as a continuously varying voltage and frequency onto a carrier. The main drawback with analogue image systems is the bandwidth required to represent the image with full dynamic range, equating to the full spectrum of colour. An amateur FM ATV signal on the microwave bands occupies a bandwidth of about 14MHz.

Straightforward digitising of a colour signal initially provides a data stream that requires considerably more bandwidth than the comparable analogue signal, so there is no advantage here. However, due to modern digital compression and reduction techniques it is possible to reduce this data stream by such an amount that the required transmission bandwidth is far narrower than the comparable analogue one, while maintaining an acceptable level of quality. One benefit is that the resulting signal can be fitted into the available part of the 70cm band, allowing users to take advantage of the more favourable propagation conditions which are often to be found on that band compared with the microwave bands. In any case, narrower bandwidth equates to improved signal-to-noise ratio for a given signal strength.

D-ATV is rapidly standardising on MPEG2 as used for terrestrial and satellite broadcast digital TV. The bit rate can be changed to suit the purpose so, for example, a high bit rate (and hence wide bandwidth) mode could be used to give very high quality pictures for local contacts, or for DX contacts the bit rate can be reduced, giving much lower resolution pictures but, because of the smaller bandwidth, the range is increased. There are several different types of modulation used for broadcast digital TV transmission; the two most popular being QPSK as used on digital satellite TV and OFDM, used for terrestrial digital TV. Both these schemes have been used in D-ATV tests and both have pros and cons. QPSK is relatively easy to implement and there is a large choice of satellite TV set-top boxes available that can be used for receiving, but it is very susceptible to multipath interference (it was, of course, designed for satellite TV where there is nothing to cause reflections!). OFDM is much harder to implement and requires extremely linear power amplifiers in the transmitter but, being designed for terrestrial digital TV it copes well with multipath distortion. As yet there is no standard for D-ATV but, as tests continue, no doubt one will emerge. D-ATV repeaters are just starting to appear.

D-ATV is still very much at the experimental stage. PE1JOK's web pages [15] are a useful resource for finding out the latest developments.

References

[1] 'Digital Voice Transmission: the AOR ARD9800 Fast Data Modem', *RadCom*, July 2004, p.18

[2] 'Simple sound-card-to-radio interface circuits', *RadCom* April 2004, p.38

[3] AA5AU RTTY Pages: http://www.aa5au.com/rtty/

[4] Sound Card Interfacing: http://www.w5bbr.com/soundbd.html

[5] *MMTTY* Download: http://mmhamsoft.ham-radio.ch/mmtty/index.html

[6] PSK31 Homepage: http://bipt106.bi.ehu.es/psk31.html

[7] PSK63: http://www.qsl.net/kh6ty/psk63/

[8] NB6Z Hellschreiber page: http://home.teleport.com/~nb6z/hell.htm

[9] WOLF download: http://www.scgroup.com/ham/wolf.html

[10] WSJT: http://pulsar.princeton.edu/~joe/K1JT

[11] WA5UFH WSJT site: http://www.qsl.net/wa5ufh/

[12] K6SIX WSJT site: http://personalpages.mcttelecom.com/~b_mobile/6Mweak.htm

[13] MMSSTV download: http://mmhamsoft.ham-radio.ch/#MMSSTV

[14] 'An SSTV "how-to"', *RadCom*, May 2004, p.24

[15] Digital Amateur TV (PE1JOK): http://www.xs4all.nl/~pe1jok/dvbsvsdatv.html

9 DX Operating

CHASING DX CONTINUES to hold great fascination for many amateurs. It appeals to our competitive instincts, and even in these days of the Internet and mobile phones there can be a real thrill from using your modest station to speak with someone on a remote Pacific atoll or in the mountains of Bhutan. And there are many accepted ways of measuring your achievement and giving you goals to aim for.

The term DX has never been closely defined, but is generally taken to mean a station which, either through distance or rarity, you wouldn't be able to work in the normal course of events. This leaves the field pretty wide open, so a few guidelines might be in order. On the HF bands, a US or even an Australian contact wouldn't necessarily qualify as rare DX, as propagation allows such contacts to take place on an almost daily basis. Distance as such really isn't an issue. But if the target was a station on an uninhabited Australian island group, or a country such as North Korea which rarely allows amateur radio activities, then that would certainly qualify. On the LF bands the definition can be extended somewhat. On 160m, for example, anything outside Europe can be quite tough to work, so might reasonably be considered DX. By the time we look at the VHF and UHF bands, then DX takes on another meaning again. Because there is a limited number of countries workable on the VHF and UHF bands from any given location, those operators seek other challenges, the most popular of which is chasing Locator squares. In this context, DX may be a rare square, even though its distance may not be especially great. Locator squares are explained in more detail later in this chapter.

As far as DXCC entities are concerned, several surveys are run each year to determine which are the 'most wanted'. **Table 9.1** shows the highest-ranked from the *DX Magazine's* [1] 2003 survey. Although this will change from year to year (you can see how the same entities were ranked the previous year), some factors remain constant. DXCC entities are rare for one of two reasons. Peter 1st Island (ranked 5th) is rare because it lies deep in the southern ocean, and any expedition is hugely expensive to mount. The Andaman Islands, ranked 2nd, are easy to reach and have excellent hotels, but licensing is well-nigh impossible, for political reasons.

Table 9.1: The ten most Wanted DXCC Entities (*DX Magazine* 2003 survey)

2003 Rank	PREFIX	COUNTRY	2002 Rank
1	BS7	SCARBOROUGH	2
2	VU4	ANDAMAN	1
3	P5	NORTH KOREA	4
4	VU7	LAKSHADWEEP	3
5	3Y/P	PETER 1	7
6	7O	YEMEN	5
7	FR/J	JUAN DE NOVA	6
8	KP1	NAVASSA	9
9	KP5	DESECHEO	8
10	YVØ	AVES ISLAND	10

Nepal used to be quite an easy one, but is becoming rarer because of political instabilities in the mountain kingdom

Whatever the band you use, successful DXing comes down to the same set of elements. Firstly, a competitive station, both in terms of the equipment in the shack but also, and more importantly in most cases, the antenna system. You may choose to restrict yourself in some way to increase the challenge, for example by chasing DX with QRP (low power, usually 5 watts or less). Having a competitive station is not enough of itself, any more than it would be possible to take someone off the street, sit them in a Grand Prix racing car and expect them to be able to compete in races. More important than the station is you, the operator. As in any competitive activity, DXing requires commitment and skill. In this case, the skill covers many areas, from a thorough technical understanding of your station in order to get the best out of it, through knowledge of propagation, to actual operating skills. It is also extremely helpful to have access to sources of information about what DX might be expected to be active on the bands, and when. All these aspects are covered in this chapter.

It is worth pausing to consider what drives DXing. In the early days of amateur radio, every contact was an achievement. Human beings are competitive creatures, though, and demand soon started to appear to be able to measure and recognise achievement. Various awards programmes were born, most notably the ARRL's DXCC Awards and *CQ Magazine's* Worked All Zones award. Details of both appear in Chapter 14. Amateurs started to chase countries and zones, but were happy to work each country or zone just the once, regardless of band or mode. After all, building a high score was tough enough, without trying to repeat the exercise on additional bands and modes.

Over the years the situation started to change, especially as amateur radio activity started to develop again after World War II. With lots more activity on the bands, and the world returning to peace, high country scores became easier to achieve and amateurs started looking to new goals. New awards programmes came into being, and DXCC was extended to have a separate CW award. The real explosion came with the introduction of the 5-band DXCC award and (in 1979) of the 5-band Worked All Zones awards (at this stage there were no 30, 17 or 12m bands, and 160m was excluded on the basis that many countries had no 160m allocation and, as a consequence, very few commercial transceivers included 160m capability). Amateurs who had high scores on, perhaps, 20 and 15m, started seriously to chase countries and zones on 80 and 40m. This was actually a real boost to technical development, leading over the years to much greater understanding of antenna designs (phased vertical arrays, low noise receiving antennas, etc) and improved receiver designs, able to cope with the wide range of signal strengths and high noise levels more common to the LF bands than to the HF bands. DX stations and DXpeditions were also under pressure to ensure that they covered all bands during their operations, not just the 'backbone' bands of 40, 20 and 15 metres.

In recent years, DXers have found even more to chase. The IOTA Award, now managed by the RSGB, has grown hugely in popularity, and offers plenty to chase even during the years of sunspot minima when big DXpeditions may be few and far between. Details appear in Chapter 14, and it is worth noting that the IOTA Programme has been extended to include 6m. The ARRL has introduced individual DXCC awards for the nine regular HF bands as well as for 6m and 2m, and a DX Challenge programme which includes the 10 bands from 160 to 6m. Many DXers look for contacts with any given DXCC entity on all ten of these bands, and on three modes (CW, SSB and RTTY), as the data modes have also ceased to be the preserve of a specialist few and become accessible to anyone with a home PC. While demand has increased, so has supply. The availability of lightweight transceivers, the ubiquity and relatively low cost of international air travel, easing of amateur licensing between countries (see Chapter 11) and other factors have made it much easier to mount modest DXpeditions. The result is that every day there is plenty of DX activity on the bands, with anything up to 280 or so entities from the DXCC list and hundreds of islands active in any given year. Some DXpedition organisers have risen to the challenge by putting together mammoth operations, with large teams of operators and huge amounts of equipment in order to satisfy the demand for multiple band and mode contacts from around the world. Several expeditions in recent years have achieved close to 100,000 contacts while two (D68C from the Comoros and 3B9C from Rodrigues) have exceeded 150,000 contacts each.

If you are a beginner to DXing, the thought of trying to contact each of 335 DXCC entities on 9 bands and three modes, which would require a minimum of 3015 contacts

Who says you need Yagis? This impressive array of wire antennas belongs to Jim, 5U7JB, in Niger

Major DXpeditions often include one or more VHF bands. Here the team from 3B9C, the 2004 Rodrigues operation assemble a 6-over-6 stack for the 6m band

(not all DX, but many of them would be) might be enough to put you off before you even start. Or maybe you are embarking on chasing islands for IOTA, hoping to achieve that coveted award for 100 island groups and then seeing the annual IOTA Honour Roll, with its leaders at over one thousand groups worked and confirmed. Perhaps you have looked at the countries and squares totals amassed by some of the more active VHF DXers. But the nice thing about DXing is that it is what you make it, and with luck it will maintain your interest for a lifetime. If you worked them all in the first year, what would there be left to achieve?

The trick is maybe to set specific goals. Perhaps focus on just one or two bands for a while, where you have a good capability, then when you feel you have achieved a reasonable score change your focus to a couple of other bands. Maybe set out to achieve RTTY DXCC. I have had a rough rule of thumb of trying to work 10% of missing band and mode slots in any given year. This has proved rather easier to achieve in high sunspot years than at the solar minimum! When a DXpedition is expected on the bands, think about what you want to achieve. Is it a country you need for an all-time new one? In which case, think about which band is likely to be easiest to work it on. For example, 20m may offer the best chance of good propagation, but 30m might suit you better because fewer stations on 30m have high gain antennas, and therefore you may be able to compete on a more equal playing field. There again, it may be a country you have already on 20m, but you would like to catch it on at least a couple of other bands. If it is near the sunspot peak your best bet might be to focus the chase on 10m and 12m. Then when there is another expedition to that same country in a few years time you can think about filling in those missing slots on the lower bands. If you had chased the lower bands the first time round, you would have lost out as, by the time of the later DXpedition, there would have been no chance of those high band contacts. At the end of the day, it comes down to your personal goals and practical factors such as location, station capability and personal restrictions.

If you work long hours and are frequently tied up at weekends, you may decide to focus on LF DXing, as you can do most of that during those darkness hours when you are at home. On the other hand, if you work from home, it might well suit you to chase high band DX, catching those tough ones when everyone else is at their office desk. On VHF, the fleeting nature of some of the propagation mechanisms such as Sporadic E is no respecter of office hours or weekends, but might happen at any time, so the most successful 6m DXers tend to be those who either work from home or can, at least, arrange to be at home at those times of the year when such propagation is most likely to occur.

Given that the VHF, UHF and microwave bands offer much smaller ranges than the HF bands, DXCC countries are less important as a measure of achievement. It is interesting to note that the ARRL held back from offering a 6m DXCC for quite some time as those concerned felt that it would be unachievable, and therefore frustrating to 6m DXers. How times have changed! Even 2m DXCC has now been achieved, though only by those with EME capability. But, again, the human psyche requires goals, and the most widely used on VHF is the Locator square (see later). Thus the commonest measure of achievement, and the basis of most VHF operating awards, is the number of squares worked. On the microwave bands even this is tough, so the most usual measure is distance, with awards available for achieving specified distances on each of the microwave bands. Whatever bands, modes or specialisms you follow, there is no virtue in becoming so paranoid about DX chasing that it takes over your life. Those at the top of the tables are probably very old, never take holidays, or perhaps confined to their homes for domestic or health reasons. Don't expect to catch them up overnight! But set your own goals and enjoy making them happen. At the end of the day this is a hobby, not a matter of life and death.

Historically, most books of this kind would have dealt separately with HF and VHF DXing, but the approach taken in this chapter is slightly different. The distinction is drawn, instead, between what might be described as 'traditional' DXing and what VHF DXers tend to refer to as 'weak signal' DXing. In some ways the latter term is a misnomer. All DXers wrestle with weak signals, whether through ionospheric absorption, the fact that the distant station is running QRP, or various other reasons. It's true that HF DXing often involves chasing quite a loud DX station, the challenge being to get through in the face of competition from lots of other callers. The same happens on 6m, 2m and 70cm, too, when the band is 'open' and perhaps a rare square is active. There are times, though, when HF DXers struggle to pull weak signals from the air waves, hence their interest in specialist receiving antennas, stacked Yagis (used from time to time on the higher HF bands) and other techniques to pull that weak one through. And 136kHz DXers revert to specialist software-based techniques to integrate signals over extended periods, a QSO sometimes taking several hours to complete.

The German-run ST0RY expedition to Sudan in 2003 was the biggest ever amateur radio operation from that country

When VHF DXers talk about weak signal DXing, they really have something a little different in mind. Because the VHF bands experience enhanced propagation only occasionally, VHF DXers have found ways of exploiting other opportunities to make long-distance contacts, for example by reflecting their signals off the moon or off the ionised trails of meteors. The signals are indeed weak (most of the time - some meteor reflections can be quite strong during the big meteor showers), but this is not the only challenge. The bigger issue with meteor reflections, for example, is that the return signals are very brief, just short 'pings' with large gaps in between. So specialist operating procedures have been adopted, and strict rules as to what constitutes a completed QSO. A contact can take anything up to an hour or so to complete. There is little doubt that specialist approaches like these, along with software equivalent to the WSJT suite of programs used on VHF, could permit DX QSOs to be made on the HF bands at times when the traditional modes fail to allow a QSO to take place. The fact that this hasn't happened probably owes more to the nature of HF operating than to the potential of the technology. HF operators simply wouldn't have the patience to wait maybe an hour or so for each QSO to be completed. There are simply too many HF DXers waiting for a contact for this to be acceptable!

This chapter therefore talks about the sort of traditional DXing that most of us are familiar with, regardless of band. It then goes on to discuss what I would probably prefer to describe as 'specialist' techniques designed to allow contacts to take place at times when the traditional methods simply won't do the job.

Sources of DX information

WHETHER YOU ARE chasing countries, islands, US counties, or Japanese prefectures, just to give a few examples, the underlying principles of DX chasing are common to all. The aim is to secure a contact (essentially, a two-way exchange of callsigns and, usually, signal report) with the DX station. This requires that the DX station hears and answers your call or, less likely, he calls you. The first task is to find the DX station you are interested in contacting. Many amateurs still enjoy doing so by tuning the bands, ready to be surprised at what they run across. Others will use every means at their disposal to find out about possible DX activity, through magazines, newsletters and the Internet. Nowadays any major DXpedition is likely to work very hard at publicity beforehand. After all, any individual or group making a big effort to set up from a rare location is going to be keen to ensure as many contacts as possible, to make the whole exercise worthwhile.

Sources of information are many and varied. Taking the long-term first, most of the monthly magazines carry information about forthcoming DX activity, provided it has been notified in time for their publishing deadlines. In the UK, the obvious examples are the monthly HF and VHF columns in *RadCom*. There used to be several weekly DX newsletters available, but interest declined dramatically when the Internet became widely available, principally because the Internet delivers the information much more quickly. Not, as some have suggested, a case of the Internet taking over from amateur radio but, rather, taking over from the postal service. At the time of writing, there are several sources of regular DX information on the Internet. *425 DX News* [2] and the *OPDX Bulletin* [3] are both published weekly and are free to anyone who signs up for them. *QRZ DX* [1] and *The Weekly DX* [4] again are published weekly, but are on subscription. The *Daily DX* [4] is, as it name suggests, published daily (on weekdays), again on subscription. All these bulletins contain information about forthcoming and current DX activity, after-the-event information on many operations, QSL information and lots of other information of interest to DX operators. Unless you really do prefer to cut yourself off from outside information, it is well worth ensuring that you are in receipt of one or more of these electronic publications. Incidentally, all but *425 DX News* are US-based, but most of the information is of global interest. In addition, there are several Internet-based Reflectors and News Groups devoted to DX and DXing, which carry similar information as well as comments, controversies and speculation.

In real-time, DX information is available from the PacketCluster network (referred to hereafter as the Cluster network, as it is no longer exclusive to packet radio). This system was developed initially by AK1A to help major contest groups keep track of contest activity, including possible contest multipliers. It has developed into a global network of Cluster nodes linked nowadays primarily by the Internet, although many end users still access their local

DX information is freely available on the Internet

The Good Clustering guide

As the Cluster network is at present restricted to, generally, 1200Bd operation, there are some things, which can affect the network performance if common sense does not prevail. The following guide outlines the preferred operating practices.

PACKETCLUSTER - Do's and Don'ts

DON'T use ANNOUNCE/FULL unless the information is perishable (ie time-sensitive) and REALLY needs to go to ALL users immediately.

DO ask yourself before you do an ANNOUNCE/FULL whether the info wouldn't be better in a message to ALL where a lot more people than those logged on at the time will see it.

DO try to keep ANNOUNCEments and mail to DX related matters. If you want to send out general mail, please use the BBS network.

DO send replies/comments to an ANNOUNCE back to the originator using TALK, NOT ANNOUNCE.

DO try the GOLIST QSL database before putting out a Mail message to find a QSL manager.

DO update QSLNEW when you find a new QSL manager - then it would be available to the rest of the folks using the Cluster.

DON'T rise to the bait if someone is obviously abusing the Cluster facilities.

DO hit 'carriage return' or 'enter' after 68 characters or so when you are sending mail on the Cluster.

DON'T fill your mail messages with lines of spaces - they all take airtime to transmit - the object of the exercise is to convey information, not to make a message look pretty!

DO use your nearest PacketCluster. Don't DX through the node network, as this will probably slow the inter-cluster links down considerably.

DO use L4 connects to your cluster; if it appears in the node list on your local access node, use C (Cluster callsign). Don't try to tailor a route through the network by connecting to intermediate nodes if it isn't necessary.

DO pick a Cluster and stay with it and don't flit from one-to-another. Any mail for you will follow from cluster-to-cluster and this congests the network unnecessarily.

DO kill your mail when you've read it - PLEASE!

DO use the UPLOAD/USERCMD utility to tailor your own configuration, and especially the filters.

DON'T complain about VHF spots if you are an HF DXer, or HF spots if you are a VHF DXer. Use the SET/FILTER command inside a USERCMD file to tailor what you get to your own tastes.

DO - if you have any problems, please send your SysOp a mail message or ring him up. Please don't use the ANN/FULL facility to ask for advice, which might well be in the User Manual.

DO ENJOY the facilities and if you have any suggestions for us that you think will improve the system, please let us know.

DO consider the effects of your actions on other users of the network - remember there is a rush hour and if possible, avoid heavy usage at that time.

DO SH/CLUS in preference to SH/CON whenever possible. Then, if you see a whole load of clusters connected you can just do a SH/CON GB7xxx for whichever Cluster you want, rather than getting the whole lot.

DO send B or Q to disconnect rather than a hard disconnect which leaves the network cluttered with packets that have nowhere to go.

Issued by the UK Cluster Working Group in the interests of better Clustering for all.

node via a VHF packet radio link. The Cluster network carries real-time spots of DX activity, announcements, WWV solar data and weather information. Some local Cluster nodes also have other data available, such as QSL information and online callbooks. If you are logged on to the Cluster network, you can send DX spots, WWV information and 'Announces', as well as 'Talk' messages to others who are logged on. In addition to accessing the network via a VHF/UHF link, you can readily access it via the Internet. There are several ways to do so. To log on in a way which allows you to post information, you need to use Telnet (a terminal emulation program available as part of your PC's operating system) to log on to a suitable node. Many such nodes are available to choose from, though you will normally connect to one in your own country. You will need to use your legitimate amateur callsign to connect; the system is only available to licensed amateurs as it does have links to on-air channels. There is more information on DX Cluster access in Chapter 4.

If you are going to make regular use of this sort of access, you might want to consider the use of DXTelnet, a piece of software developed specifically for use with the Cluster network. It offers Telnet facilities, but with a user-interface specifically developed to handle the information which comes off the Cluster, separating DX spots from WWV and other information. DXTelnet can be obtained from a number of locations, including the WD4NGB web page [5]. Many modern logging programs also incorporate facilities for connection to the Cluster network, both via a radio interface and via the Internet. The better logging programs then allow you to filter the incoming information, for example only to display Cluster spots for bands or modes you are interested in, or for countries you still need to work.

If you don't need a direct connection to the Cluster network, then there are several ways of watching Cluster information via the Internet in a passive fashion. The most popular web page is DX Summit [6] run by OH2AQ in Finland, which collects Cluster spots from around the world and displays them in various ways according to which menu option you select. Several other popular web pages also show Cluster spots. For example, the UK Six Metre Group's web site, not surprisingly, takes only the 6m spots from the Cluster network, and makes them available to users. At the end of the day, though, if you are a regular user of spots from the Cluster network, there is a moral duty to input information in return. This is very much a self-help network, relying on everyone to play a part by spotting interesting DX. This begs the question of what it is legitimate to post on the Cluster system. The sidebar, issued by the UK Cluster Working Group, gives some guidelines on what is acceptable.

Finding DX on the bands

IT WILL BE APPARENT from the foregoing that a budding DXer could simply sit in the shack with his rig turned on, and wait for a DX station to be 'spotted' on the Cluster network. Then simply tune the radio to that frequency, turn the antenna to the correct beam heading (some logging programs will do both these things at the press of a function key) and, hey presto, one call and the DX station is in the log. A modicum

3A2MW operates from the tiny principality of Monaco, and is much sought after on HF and 6m

of satisfaction, perhaps, but some would liken it to the proverbial shooting of fish in a barrel. Where is the skill? What have you learned about propagation?

In practice, it's rarely quite that simple. One of the disadvantages of the Cluster network is that, when a rare station is 'spotted' all hell tends to break loose, with many stations calling at once. Unless you have full legal power and a huge antenna array, you might as well take time out for a cup of tea while the 'big guns' battle it out to make a contact. Better to use the Cluster and other information sources to learn about the DX station's operating patterns and, next time, be there before the masses.

This is where the real art of DX operating is developed, a skill which will be equally applicable if and when your interest turns to, for example, contest operating.

Let's start with the HF bands. You may know from a newsletter that a DXpedition is taking place to a Pacific island, maybe somewhere quite rare like the Cook Islands (ZK1). Or maybe you don't gather such information but, nevertheless, are interested in finding DX in the Pacific. The first aspect is to think about propagation. Which bands are likely to support propagation to that part of the world, and at what times? Propagation forecasts, such as those in *RadCom*, can be a good starting point, as can propagation prediction programs (see Chapter 6). Feed in the relevant solar data, and the location you are interested in, and see what comes out. By the time you have been active on the HF bands for several years you will have a pretty good idea, simply on the basis of past experience. Even if you have never heard or worked the Cook Islands, you will be aware that they are not too far from New Zealand. The path to New Zealand is actually quite reliable on several bands, especially 40, 30 and 20m, and the Cook Islands are rare from the UK not so much because of difficulties with propagation but simply because there is very little activity. Just a handful of local amateurs, most of whom use amateur radio for chatting back to friends and relatives in New Zealand or other Pacific Islands and may even go out of their way to avoid DX pile-ups. Occasionally there will be a DXpedition, either a one- or two-person effort or something rather more substantial.

When you've worked out what times propagation is likely to be favourable, it's not a bad idea to check what that means in terms of local time at the distant end. Let's suppose, depending on the time of year, that you feel there's a good chance of a contact around 0600 UTC. The good news is that that's 1730 local in the Cook Islands. Not a bad time for someone to be on the bands. If it's a DXpedition you are after, they will probably be around on the main bands whenever propagation is likely, but if we are talking about a local amateur, remember that on weekdays he will probably be at work and at night (his time) he will probably be asleep! Remember also, by the way, that weekdays vary. In Muslim countries, weekends are Friday and Saturday, so Friday can often be a good time to catch their local amateurs on the bands. French overseas territories observe French public holidays, so if you know it's a French holiday, it might be a good time to look for amateur radio activity from Tahiti or Reunion. To go back to our Pacific example, many of the islanders are Seventh Day Adventists and will be at church most of Sunday. The moral of the story is to understand your quarry, whether local amateur or DXpedition. Try to put yourself in their shoes.

So you have some idea of when and on which bands you may find the station or country you are looking for. The next aspect is to think about what frequency the station will be on. Many DXpeditions publish their operating frequencies beforehand. Or you may already know, from the Cluster network, that the station you are looking for prefers a particular part of the band or a particular mode. He may be exclusively a CW operator, for example, or perhaps prefer RTTY. It is also worth checking whether there are any frequency restrictions that apply to the station or country concerned. Maybe the most regular operator has some sort of Intermediate licence class, which limits him to certain parts of the band or maybe the country concerned has country-specific bandplans. Australia and its offshore islands, for example, have only limited allocations on the 80m band. Some Middle Eastern countries have yet to release 30m to their amateurs or only allow operation on designated spot frequencies. As always, information is invaluable, and can be garnered from many sources, including those described earlier.

There are no hard and fast rules about where to find rare stations on the bands. From the UK, Pacific stations are often identifiable by having some flutter on their signals, resulting from passing through the auroral zone. A local amateur, trying to avoid major pile-ups, might make a point of operating away from the more popular areas of the band, so

QSL card from the 2003 Takabonerate Island (IOTA OC-242) expediton

This operation from Fiji was put on by a group of German DXers who enjoy activating rare spots around the world

may, for example, operate above 14050kHz on CW or above 14300kHz on SSB. He may also take refuge in one of the popular DX nets (dealt with later in this chapter). Accents are also important in alerting to you to a possible DX station. An Australian or Japanese accent is usually distinctive, while an American accent heard when the band is closed to the continental USA could be from somewhere like Hawaii.

DXpeditions, who very much do want to get noticed, tend to stick close to certain well-known frequencies. On CW, look 5kHz up from the bottom of the band or thereabouts on 80, 40, 30, 17 and 12m, and 25kHz up or thereabouts on 20, 15 and 10m. On SSB, 3795, 7045, 14195, 18145, 21295, 24945 and 28495kHz are perhaps the most popular DXpedition frequencies. On RTTY, around .070 on 20, 15 and 10m, but RTTY activity is increasing on the other bands too, for example around 10120kHz. Again, there is no hard and fast rule. Many expeditions will assume nowadays that most DXers have Cluster access and will therefore find them on the bands wherever they choose to operate. If you are chasing some sort of specialist DX, there may be relevant meeting frequencies. Those chasing US counties will want to check into the County Hunters Net on 20m. IOTA enthusiasts will look on 14260 and 21260kHz on SSB and on 14040 and 21040kHz on CW as a starting point. On VHF, an expedition to, say, a rare square, will probably call CQ on the recognised DX calling channel and then move elsewhere in the band as the pile-up starts to build.

So you've done your homework and thought about all the relevant factors necessary to maximise your chances of finding the DX station you are looking for. It's time to turn on your radio and turn the antenna in the right direction (remembering that, in some cases, you will be checking the long-path which is 180 degrees different to the short-path bearing). It's time to start tuning the bands around those frequencies that you have determined are most likely. Careful tuning pays dividends. Make a note of stations you are hearing. Are they in the same part of the world as the one you are looking for? Check the beacons, for example the NCDXF beacon chain [7] on the HF bands or one of the very many beacons available on the VHF/UHF bands (a list of 2m and 70cm beacons can be downloaded from [8]). How loud are they? What does this tell you about actual propagation, as against what was predicted? Incidentally, on CW it is a good idea to get used to tuning with a fairly wide filter setting, or it is easy to tune over a weak signal. Narrow the filters down when you want to home in on a specific station.

Often an immediate pointer to a rare station is the existence of a pile-up. This is bad news in a way, as it means you are going to be in a competitive situation. Better to be the first one to stumble across the DX station, when he calls CQ! There is an alternative which is to call 'CQ DX' yourself, but this tends not be terribly productive, although some DX stations will prefer to call others rather than call CQ themselves, so as to avoid getting into a pile-up situation. You may be able to give yourself a head start. Looking for Tahiti, for example, not only would you want to be aware that French-speaking stations tend to congregate around 14130kHz, but if you choose to call CQ, you will enhance your chances of that FO5 contact enormously if you call in French.

So you have found the DX station. You hear ZK1ZZZ on what appears to be a clear frequency, but apparently working stations, although you can't hear them. What do you do when he ends a contact? The temptation is to fire up on all cylinders and call him, "ZK1ZZZ, this is G3XTT, Golf Three X-ray Tango Tango". Wrong, on several counts! The first thing is to determine what is going on. Spend a minute or two listening. It will pay dividends. The chances are that the reason you can't hear the people he is working is because he is operating split-frequency, in other words listening on a frequency different to the one he is transmitting on. Assuming he is a competent operator, he will announce his listening frequency from time to time or, at the least, indicate whether he is listening 'up' or 'down', ie above or below his transmitting frequency. If he is indeed operating split, then this will dictate how and where you call him (see the section below, on split frequency operation). Whatever, you do, *never ever* ask on his frequency "Where is he listening?", "What's his call?" or "QSL info?" or the like. This simply causes interference for everyone else.

Regardless of whether the DX station is listening split or co-channel, keep any call short. Normally give your callsign just once, phonetically if on SSB. If he is working quickly through a pile-up, don't give his callsign, he knows it already! By giving your callsign just once, you are helping everybody. If you are the first station the DX station hears, he will come back to you immediately and give you a signal report:

The Comoros Islands have hosted many expeditions over the years, including one by the UK Five Star DXers Association, as D68C

Him: "Golf Three X-ray Tango Tango 59".

Me: "QSL 59"

Him: "QSL Zulu Kilo One Zulu Zulu Zulu QRZ"

and away he goes with the next contact. If I had called twice, my second call would just have slowed things down. Or if he had responded to someone's else's first call, I would just have been causing undue QRM. If he had only heard part of my callsign, no problem, I could fill in the gaps on my transmission:

Him: "The Golf Three with Tango, 59"

Me: "QSL, Golf Three X-ray Tango Tango 59"

Him: "Golf Three X-ray Tango Tango, QSL, QRZ"

Bangladesh was very rare for many years but is now activated quite regularly on the HF bands

And so on. Some amateurs advocate calling with only a partial call, eg "Tango Tango". This practice seems to have originated because DX stations often respond with a partial call. That's not actually because they want partial calls, it's simply that that's all they have been able to hear through the pile-up! By coming back with at least a partial call, rather than calling "QRZ?" again, they can press on with the contact rather than wasting time, assuming there was only one station in the pile-up with "Tango Tango" in the call. Assuming, also, that everyone else takes the hint and stands by which, sadly, isn't always the case. But if you send only a partial call rather than your full call, quite apart from the licence issues whereby you are required to identify yourself at least every 15 minutes, you are wasting time. If you only send a partial call and the DX station only hears part of that, he may end up with just a single letter, which is more or less useless. Even if he hears you clearly, it will still require you to give your full callsign on the next transmission. And time really is of the essence. To use our ZK1 example, the opening to Europe may well be no more than an hour or so. If everyone is operating in a slick manner, the DX station can make maybe 150 contacts or more an hour on CW, 200 or more on SSB. That's a contact every 20 seconds or thereabouts. Waste 20 seconds and you have potentially deprived someone else of a contact. If the DX station wants to have a chat, or announce his QSL information, that's his prerogative. But don't slow things down with unnecessary requests or questions, unless things are quiet and he is repeatedly calling CQ with no response. If you need his QSL information, check on the Internet or wait for him to announce it. If you want to know when he will be on another band, wait for him to announce that, leave him on loudspeaker while you do something else in the shack, and wait for him to close on that band and move to another, or go back to your propagation predictions and consider when, if you were in his shoes, you would think about moving to another band.

If you are used to exchanging pleasantries with other amateurs, these brief exchanges with DX stations can seem rather terse and impersonal, but DXing is immensely popular and most DXpeditions want to give as many people as possible the chance for a contact. You can chat with them to your heart's content when they get home to their regular locations. VHF operators in particular get frustrated if a DX station fails to give his QTH locator but VHF openings, for example by Sporadic E on 6m or 2m, can be extremely fleeting and the DX operator will want to get as many callsigns into the log as possible. No doubt he will ensure that his QTH locator is prominently featured on his QSL card.

Perhaps the main piece of advice is always to take your cue from the DX station, even if he appears to be inexperienced and leaves you feeling frustrated. The better DX operators, though, will always give clear indications of what they are doing. For example, if the pile-up gets very large, a DX operator may listen by prefix or by numbers, "Only stations with Number One in the call". If he starts with one and you are a G8, it can be pretty frustrating to sit while he works his way through all the other numbers, but if the callers step out of line all it does is slow things down even more and, in the extreme, the DX operator will throw in the towel and switch off.

This sounds all well and good, but life isn't always so simple. You may have only a modest station, and find that you are getting nowhere in calling the DX, despite doing all the right things. Well, you could try to be first on frequency the following day. If it's a big expedition, there for a week or two, you might just have to wait things out, hoping that, towards the end, the number of callers diminishes and you stand a better chance. But it's always worth hanging in there, as propagation may suddenly change and favour you, or the DX station himself might switch the odds to your favour: "Stand by southern Europe, I'm looking for UK stations for the next five minutes", or whatever.

Some DX stations deliberately try to favour the more attentive callers, for example by suddenly announcing a spot listening frequency elsewhere in the band. If you're on the ball you can move there, call and work him, while the masses are still calling on the original frequency.

While the foregoing is generally applicable, there are plenty of variations which will be learned through regular operation on the bands. There are also some helpful books around, such as that by W9KNI [9] which, while coming mainly from a CW DXers perspective, is absolutely full of useful hints and tips. However, it is worth covering just a few of them here, in no particular order.

Prearranged schedules

TO SOME EXTENT, prearranging scheduled contacts on the HF bands in order to work a DX station tends to be frowned on, although on the higher VHF and microwave bands few DX contacts would take place without prior arrangement, other than when a contest or major band opening is in progress. But there are good arguments for making schedules on the harder bands, for example 160m. Nowadays this is often very simple, using e-mail. For example, let's suppose you are trying to work a South American station who you know to be reasonably active and with a reasonable signal. There may be a good chance that several nights of listening at the time of optimum propagation would result in a contact. But the optimum time is likely to be around 0200/0300 local in the UK, which may not be conducive to domestic bliss if pursued several nights in a row. So it may well be worth contacting the distant station by e-mail and, at the least, checking which nights he is likely to be active, even if not making a schedule for a specific time and frequency.

Related to this is an arrangement made on another band. For example, you may work a DX station on 80m, and mutually agree to move to 160m, either immediately or fairly soon thereafter, on the basis that if signals were good on 80m there is a reasonable probability of the path being open on 160m, albeit with higher absorption. The same may apply at the other end of the spectrum, working a station on 12m, for example, and mutually agreeing to move to 10m to see if the band is open.

Split frequency operation

NOWADAYS, WITH the huge interest in DX chasing, most DXpeditions and many DX operators choose to operate split frequency. This is by no means confined to HF operation, being quite common on 6m. The concept is simple. By transmitting on one frequency and listening on another, callers can hear the DX station clearly, rather than through a mass of other callers, and therefore know when to go ahead with their contact and, more importantly perhaps, when to remain silent while another contact is taking place. And rather than listening on a single frequency, the DXpedition may choose to listen over a range of frequencies, thereby making it easier to pick out callers.

If you hear an expedition making plenty of contacts, but you can't hear the callers, then the chances are that you are listening to a split-frequency operation. Indeed, before calling any DX station on his own frequency, it's always worth waiting a moment to determine whether he is working split. Otherwise, if you call him co-channel, you risk the wrath of others who have been waiting and will almost certainly inform you of the error of your ways!

If a DX station is working split, what do you do? In the past many amateurs may have had a problem in that their transceiver was only capable of transmitting and receiving on the same frequency. In practice most transceivers came equipped with RIT and XIT (Receiver and Transmitter incremental tuning) allowing for a limited degree of split operation (typically up to 10kHz between transmit and receive frequencies). Most modern transceivers go one step further and have two quite separate VFOs, giving total flexibility (though it's worth practising split operation in the peace and quiet of your own shack before you try it on the air and end up pressing the wrong buttons!). Most radios also allow you to check your transmit frequency, which is handy, because as well as listening to the DX station, half the trick can be finding the people he is working, and putting your transmitter onto that frequency. The more expensive radios go one step further still, with a second receiver. With that capability, you can listen to the DX station in one ear of your headphones (I never use a loudspeaker for anything other than casual ragchews, and I suspect most DXers are the same) and the pile-up in the other ear. Then you know exactly what is going on.

Always listen to the DX station carefully. Often he will announce his receive frequency, and may also be giving other instructions (such as "UK stations only") which should always be followed carefully to avoid creating unnecessary interference and slowing things down. If no listening frequency is announced, the general rule is to call about 1-2kHz up on CW, or 5kHz up on SSB. But, again, a few moments' listening should, in any case, quickly allow you to find the callers he is working. Listen for a little longer and you may also determine a pattern. For example, does the DX station always respond to callers on the same frequency or does he, for example, listen a little higher up the band after each contact, finally dropping back down the band and starting the whole process anew. Does he respond to stations only giving part of their callsign or does he, like many DX operators, only respond to callers when he has their full callsign? And so on. Some intelligent listening can pay dividends, compared with simply calling at random. This is how experienced operators running low power can often get through more quickly than less experienced operators running high power (no surprise there, I suppose; experience counts for more than brute force in most competitive sports and activities).

Unless the DX station is specifically taking 'tail enders', ie stations who call as the previous QSO is coming to an end, never call over the top of a contact in progress but wait until the DX station signs and calls "QRZ?" or similar. Otherwise chaos ensues.

There is another form of split frequency operation which needs to be covered. This is split frequency when working less exotic DX, but where band plans and practical consider-

PA3GIO, an inveterate expeditioner, activated rare island and DXCC entity Lord Howe Island in 2001

ations demand it. On 40m SSB for example, although the situation is currently changing, UK stations, along with most of IARU Region 1, have historically been restricted to operation below 7100kHz, whereas US station can only operate on SSB above 7150kHz. The answer is to operate split-frequency. The UK station will listen up in the US part of the band, the US station listening down in the European part of the band. Provided you know how to operate your transceiver in split-frequency mode, there should be no fundamental problem, but some basic considerations need to be taken into account. If you are calling for US stations, you will need to find two clear frequencies, the first for your own CQ call and the second, in the US part of the band, to listen on. This latter can be easier said than done, as most of that part of the band is currently occupied by loud broadcasting stations. When calling CQ, announce your listening frequency clearly, and give potential US callers time to set up their VFOs for split operation and be ready to answer you. While conducting the ensuing QSO, be sure to check your own frequency regularly to ensure that you are not causing interference to other European stations, or being interfered with by them. This is a case where having a transceiver with dual-receiver capability really comes into its own, as you can then monitor both frequencies simultaneously. Similar considerations apply to 80m operation where, although there is an overlap between US and European allocations, the US allocation extends to 4000kHz, so it is often more convenient to operate split. The same is true when working certain other countries outside Region 1 which have allocations extending above 3800kHz. It also used to be common practice to operate split-frequency on 160m when working the US or Japan, in the latter case because Japanese stations had only a narrow allocation centred on 1910kHz. Nowadays most regular activity on 160m is co-channel, but occasionally split-operation may be appropriate for US contacts, given that the US allocation starts at 1800kHz whereas the UK allocation starts at 1810kHz.

Lists and nets

IF YOU SPEND ANY time at all on the HF bands will quickly run across list and net operations. If you want to participate but are not familiar with the conventions relating to them you can end up getting yourself into hot water.

There are a number of regular nets which exist purely for the purpose of rag-chewing and keeping in touch with friends. Many are associated with a particular organisation, the Royal Signals Amateur Radio Society, for example. This section is more concerned with lists and nets specifically run for the purpose of enabling participants to work DX.

It is important to deal with one aspect right at the start. Many DXers consider lists and nets to be a form of cheating, in that you are enlisting the help of a third-party (the Master of Ceremonies, or MC) to run the operation and keep other stations at bay while you make your call to the DX station. Sometimes it gets even worse, when the MC or one of the other participants, perhaps getting restless, 'helps' things along by passing all or parts of callsigns or signal reports. A 'contact' made in this way is surely not a true two-way exchange. But a well-run list or net will avoid these pitfalls; guidelines for list and net operations are shown in the box.

Lists and nets - a Code of Practice

1. The 'master of ceremonies' (MC), when taking the list, should endeavour to ensure a fair and even representation from all those countries calling to participate.

2. It is not desirable to take a list for use at some future date. In the case of poor propagation, however, a running list may be held over and continued when possible.

3. It is desirable to establish with the DX station beforehand how much time he or she has available, or how many stations can be worked in the time available.

4. A valid QSO requires some minimum two-way exchange of information. As stations are usually addressed by callsign this information has already been imparted to the DX station; nevertheless the MC should seek to avoid passing the whole callsign if possible. Convention has established that the exchange need only be a correctly received RS report by both parties. It is therefore the responsibility of the MC at all times to ensure that this is accomplished fairly, accurately and without assistance. While repeats are in order, if necessary, verification of partly received reports is not. Should a relay or a guess be suspected by the MC, the transmitting station should be instructed to make a second attempt with a changed report. The MC should not flinch from giving "negative QSO" when not satisfied with the exchange.

5. It is acceptable practice for the MC to nominate another station to monitor and assist with the procedure in difficult circumstances due to interference or linking for example.

6. If conditions fail the MC should terminate the operation rather than allow a 'free for all' under the guise of the list.

7. It is very important that the MC gives information out at regular intervals, relating to new lists, QSL managers, length of current list etc. This will be of great assistance to waiting stations not on the list, and minimise breaking and interference.

DX Nets meet regularly on (or near - a DX net has no more 'right' to a particular frequency than any other amateur) frequencies that are usually well-publicised and at regular times. 20m is a particular favourite for such nets, as propagation is reasonably consistent, but you will find them on other bands too (AC6V's web site [10] is one source of information on regular net operations). Usually, at the beginning of the net, the MC will ask for 'DX' check-ins, at which point everyone hopes that one or more rare stations will turn up on frequency. Then other check-ins will be called, sometimes by country or some other form of selection if things get hectic. This is your chance to call in, taking care to follow the MC's instructions carefully. The MC will then go round each of the participants in turn, asking them if they wish to call any of the DX stations. When your turn comes, make any calls you require, complete the contacts as quickly and efficiently as possible, and hand back to the MC. You will appreciate from the description that there may well be lots of sitting around awaiting your turn, by which time the DX station you particularly wanted to call may have upped sticks and gone to work or whatever. But when things work well it means you don't have to compete in a howling pack with all those amateurs using linear amplifiers and stacked Yagis, who worked the DX yesterday but want to do so again just for some personal ego trip (yes, such amateurs do exist!).

Lists are similar, but tend to happen spontaneously, often at the request of a DX station. Let's suppose I was operating from North Korea as P5/G3XTT, using just low power and a dipole. The demand for North Korea is such that, when I come on the air, I am swamped by callers. I try the obvious solution and operate split frequency (previous section), but my signal isn't loud enough in Europe to compete with those causing interference on my own frequency and my rate of making contacts falls almost to zero. What I could do (though, personally, I have never resorted to this when operating from a DX location) is to ask one of the louder, better-equipped European stations on frequency to act as MC, or 'take a list'. He will take maybe 20 callers at a time, and then indicate to each of them in turn as to when they should call. This way only one will be calling me at a time, so the frequency should remain clear and both callsigns and signal reports exchanged without problems from the screaming masses. It stands to reason that the MC should not pass complete callsigns to me, or assist the contacts in any way (for example by relaying signal reports) - if I cannot hear the calling station myself or he cannot hear me, then no two-way contact has taken place. Always with nets and lists, follow the instructions of the MC or chaos will result.

Low Power and QRP operating

RELATIVELY FEW amateurs are able to build highly competitive stations, with large Yagis and full legal power. Planning constraints and the proximity of neighbouring properties render this a dream for the majority. But having a modest station should not preclude you from chasing DX. Indeed, QRP DXing (generally, 5W or less) has been very much a growth activity in recent years. There are several reasons. Although organisations like the G-QRP Club [11] have published some excellent designs for home-built QRP transceivers, there have been few commercial designs specifically developed for QRP operation (though most can have their power reduced to QRP levels if required). But, of late, all the major manufacturers have filled this gap and with equipment that is fully featured in every respect other than power output. Most have add-on automatic aerial tuning units available, too, so they will work comfortably into almost any length of wire. The QRP DXer need not necessarily handicap himself further by using a non-optimum antenna, but local circumstances may dictate this. Nevertheless, improvements in QRP transceivers, coupled with many more DX operations equipped to hear and work even the weakest of signals, has meant that QRP DXing can be a very satisfying pursuit. It is certainly harder than DXing with high power, requiring more subtlety and operating skill to make up for the lack of brute force, and therefore is perhaps more suited to experienced DXers who want a new challenge than to the newly-licensed amateur. But, equally, if your licence category restricts you to low power levels, this shouldn't discourage you from chasing DX.

All the advice given up to this point is equally applicable to low power and QRP DXing, but you will usually be waiting in line behind those with higher effective radiated power (ERP). I use the phrase advisedly. It's not transmitter power, as such, that is relevant but the combination of that and antenna gain. So the low power or QRP DXer may need patience. Not for nothing do some amateurs sport T-shirts bearing the saying "Life is too short for QRP"! This said, there is plenty you can do to use your DXing time in the most effective manner. For example, there is a lot to be said for being active in the major DX contests, whether you consider yourself a contester or not. The benefits are twofold. Firstly, the bands will be full of activity, including plenty of DX activity. So the chasers won't all be after just one DX station. They will be scattered throughout the bands, divided between lots of DX stations to chase. So you shouldn't have so much competition, especially if you wait until well into the contest, for example the second day of a 48-hour event. The other significant factor is that many groups go out and set up very big stations for the contest weekends (in fact, lots of these will usually be active up to two or three days ahead of time, while they check everything out; an even better chance to catch them). Places like the Caribbean islands, or islands off the African coast are especially favoured as they are good places to operate from to achieve a high score. But these groups know they will not achieve a high score simply by working the more competitive entrants. They need to make lots of contacts with casual participants, too, which means they need to be able to hear well. Some of the stations are set up on a permanent basis, for example the HC8L/HC8N contest station in the Galapagos Islands, with four 135ft towers, each sporting large monoband Yagis and with a take-off directly over the ocean. Another example is the A61AJ contest station in the UAE, also with multiple towers and huge antennas. When these stations are active in a contest, you will hear them and be able to work them!

The same is true of an increasing number of major DXpeditions, which set out to ensure that they work not only the best-equipped DXers, but those with more modest stations, too. They recognise that many amateurs have restrictions on the sort of stations they can put together, but nevertheless want to participate in the DX game. The UK-led Five Star DXers Association expeditions to D68C (Comoros) and 3B9C (Rodrigues) are good examples. They had round-the-clock operation on all bands, with good monoband antennas, on a waterfront site, and on site long enough to work their way through all the loudest callers and be left with more than enough time to ensure that the weaker stations found their way into the log. At least one UK amateur worked 3B9C using an FT-817 transceiver and Miracle Whip antenna, while out for a walk.

One of the key pieces of advice to give to a QRP operator is to learn to listen. While someone with a huge signal can afford to be lazy and wait for Cluster spots, moving to the

Victor Brand, G3JNB, has worked much DX with this low power station constructed from popular kits

announced frequency and shouting over the top of other callers, the QRP operator doesn't have that luxury. You simply won't be able to compete when the hordes arrive on frequency. So it's a case of spending more time tuning the bands, with the hope of being the first to find a DX station before it is 'spotted' on the Cluster network. The other key piece of advice is to use CW. It is far more effective than SSB in getting through when signals are weak. The only caveat is that some of the new data modes have similar advantages. Some would argue with PSK31, for example, that it can decode signals that cannot even be heard by the human ear because they are masked by band noise. This is probably not strictly true; use a narrow enough filter and you will be aware that a signal is present, but certainly the software is excellent at decoding extremely low signals.

If your interest is in two-way QRP contacts, you will tend to confine much of your operation to the well-known QRP calling frequencies, where other QRP operators tend to congregate. But you cannot assume that DX stations will necessarily happen by these frequencies.

Two final comments. Firstly, it is not considered legitimate to call with high power to attract the attention of the DX station and then to drop to QRP to conduct the exchange of signal reports. Secondly, do not append /QRP to your callsign when calling DX (or anyone else for that matter). Quite apart from the fact that it is, strictly speaking, against your licence conditions, as the only allowable appendages are /P, /M, /MM etc, it is also counter-productive. Your time is better spent giving your callsign. Nothing is more frustrating to a DX station than to hear part of a call and then /QRP. He would rather hear the call repeated twice, which gives him twice the chance of copying it correctly. Very few DX stations will actually stand by specifically for QRP stations for the simple reason that some high power stations will, sadly, abuse this by calling anyway. If you want to chase DX as a QRP enthusiast, then you simply have to be prepared to join in with everyone else and take your chances.

Duplicate QSOs and DXing ethics

ONE OF THE QUESTIONS that comes up with respect to working DX, is the extent to which it is ethical to make duplicate QSOs. In days gone by, this might have been taken as making more than one QSO with a DXpedition or DX station, full stop. Anything more might have been considered bad form, as it potentially deprived another station of a contact. This said, through to about the late-50s and early-60s when modern-style DXpeditioning started to come about, even DX stations expected a QSO to consist of a full exchange of name, QTH, equipment used, the local weather conditions, and so on. This started to change when DXpeditioners such as Danny Weil VP2VD, Gus Browning W4BPD and Don Miller W9WNV began their global DXpeditions. These operators aimed to move on from rare spot to rare spot, staying only a few days in any one location. Therefore they expected a quick-fire exchange of signal reports and nothing more, just as is common nowadays. But what has changed, as described in an earlier paragraph, is that there are now many more DXCC and similar awards, recognising achievement on every band and mode. It is therefore considered fair game to work a DXpedition on every band/mode combination (though

The various US possessions in the Pacific are relatively easy to work from Japan or North America, but are always a nice catch from Europe

you may not wish to do so, or be able to do so). So a duplicate QSO is a second QSO on the same band/mode combination, for example 20m SSB or 30m RTTY. Why would anyone want to do so? The most likely reason is that you were unhappy with your first contact. Perhaps the DX station got your callsign wrong to start with and, although you corrected it, he didn't acknowledge the fact. A duplicate QSO in this situation is fair game, though often it is no longer necessary because many DXpeditions post their logs to the Internet even while the DXpedition is still in progress and you can check to ensure that your QSO is there in their log. If it isn't or your callsign has been copied incorrectly, don't ask the DXpedition operators to change their log. After all, it was your responsibility at the time of the contact to ensure that they had your call correctly. Instead, try to work them again.

Another valid reason for a duplicate QSO might be that you worked the DXpedition on high power, and wish to do so again using QRP. Most DXpeditions will accept this.

A third reason might be that you hear the DXpedition calling CQ repeatedly but with no callers. This is most likely to happen on one of the 'edge' bands, for example 160m or 6m. In this situation, most DXpeditions would welcome your duplicate call, to assure them that they really are being heard and that it is worth continuing.

Duplicate contacts to ask for schedules on other bands, ask for QSL information because you haven't been able to find it elsewhere, to try out another antenna, and so on, are generally frowned upon unless the DXpedition really is running out of stations to work and the DXpedition operator is looking for any contacts to relieve his boredom. This rarely happens. Even those DXpeditions making around 100,000 QSOs or higher find that, even when they are coming to an end, there are still plenty of stations calling for their first QSO on a particular band and mode. The demand nowadays really does seem to be almost never-ending and every unnecessary duplicate QSO you make potentially deprives another station of a QSO he desperately wanted.

This leads on to ethics about working DX more generally. If you already have a particular DX entity worked and confirmed on a specific band/mode combination, should you work the next DXpedition to that location on the same band/mode, or should you refrain to allow more recently-licensed operators to have a contact? There is no easy answer to this. If your particular amateur radio interest is DXing, then you will want to contact every DXpedition that appears on the bands regardless of whether you have the entity in your log already or not. But the next question might then be, if you already have a DX station (maybe a resident in a rare location) in your log, is it legitimate to work him again on the same band/mode each and every year, maybe for an annual table that you participate in, perhaps at your local club. Again, there is no simple answer. Some DX stations actually lay down their own rules, perhaps refusing to acknowledge your call if they already have you in the log from a previous year. If you hear them operating a contest, that's a different matter. They are then fair game, as they will want you in their log for points, regardless of whether you worked them recently outside the contest.

Operating as DX

THERE MAY BE times when you find yourself as the DX station, rather than chasing DX. This can even happen from the UK if, for example, you are operating a sought-after special event station or undertaking an Islands on the Air operation off the British coast.

There is a lot that could be said, so what follow are some brief guidelines. The first point to make is that, when you have a lot of callers because you are the perceived 'rare' station, it is up to you to take control of the situation or it may quickly get out of hand. This can happen all too easily.

There are several methods available to you and most are equally applicable whichever operating mode you are using. The first is to start operating split frequency, as described on earlier in this chapter. This time, though, it is you who stays in one place and ask others to call you away from your transmit frequency. When it becomes clear that you will need to operate in this manner, ask the pile-up to stand by while you look for a suitable frequency to listen on. It should be close by, usually slightly high of the frequency you are operating on (by about 1kHz or so on CW or data modes, 5kHz on SSB). But try to find a clear frequency rather than moving your pile-up onto the top of an existing QSO in progress. Now the callers will, at least, be able to hear you clearly, so that your instructions to the pile-up will (hopefully) be understood and followed.

Once one of the rarest DXCC entities, it is nice to see regular operation again from Libya

G4ODA makes regular trips to northern climes to give out rare squares on the VHF bands

That might be sufficient to bring things under control. What you want to achieve at this point is a clear pattern of operating. Try to pick a complete call out of the pile-up within the first few seconds or, if not a full call, then enough of a callsign that there is no doubt who you are answering. But do ensure you transmit regularly; if you are having trouble copying anything at all then say something like: "the station with Alpha in the call". There probably is one and, more importantly, if you stay silent for long periods the callers will engage in longer and longer calls, just adding to the level of interference.

Whatever system you use to pick out calls, never work someone other than whoever you have tried to answer. For example, if you go back to "Tango Tango", then don't work November Kilo One Golf, however tempting it might be that he is still calling and very loud. Once you are heard to do this, the rest of the callers will take it as the green light for a total free for all. But if you stick to your guns, the message will eventually get through that they are only slowing things down.

If it is still too hectic, you can try to spread the callers over a range of frequencies, though keep it to no more than 2-3kHz on CW or 10kHz on SSB, or you will start to take over the band. Even these sort of splits are really only acceptable if you are on a major expedition to a very rare spot. The other alternative is to make directional calls, for example by taking stations with, progressively, number, 1, 2, 3, etc. in their calls, or perhaps by country (but this is very slow - there are lots of them - and callers will quickly get frustrated and start causing QRM). Never take more than, say, ten calls from one area before moving on, or the frustration factor will quickly increase. More common, and more importantly, it can be helpful to stand by for a particular continent. For example, if you are operating close to Europe, the European stations will be workable for many hours at a time, whereas band openings to North or South America may be fleeting. So make a point of asking European stations to stand by while you check for calls from other continents.

In contests, or with a less rare operation, split-frequency operation is neither desirable nor necessary, but you can still use the other suggestions to thin the pile-up.

In these situations, keep your operating crisp, avoiding unnecessary exchanges of information. Do give your callsign every QSO, or certainly every two or three QSOs, but QSL

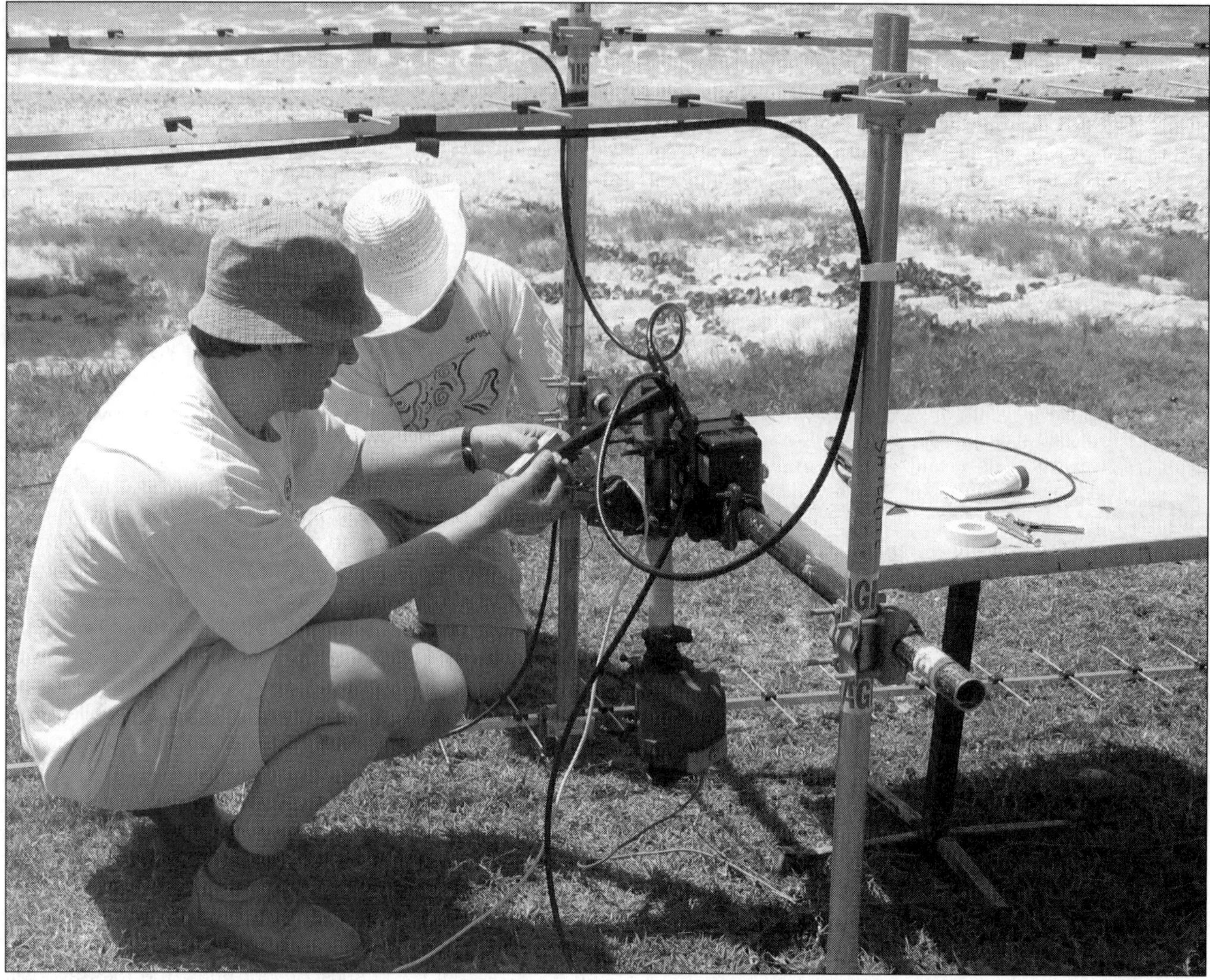

David, G0MRF, and Dave, G4FRE, set up the array of four 70cm Yagis for the first EME and satellite contacts ever made from Rodrigues Island, 3B9C

information can be given less frequently, and there is usually no need to give out lots of information about name, weather, etc. You can indulge in longer chats when you are operating from home, but when you are sought after, then it is courteous to try and accommodate as many of the callers as possible, as presumably you will only be operating that rare station for a limited period of time (or it wouldn't be rare!).

Whatever you do, try to avoid being drawn into list or net operations if at all possible, including taking your own 'lists'. These only increase the overall number of exchanges that need to take place, and hence reduce the total number of contacts that can be made in the time available. One of the few times that it may be necessary is, as has happened with some IOTA operations, when you have limited battery power and therefore want to keep your transmit time to an absolute minimum, when it may be reasonable to ask for someone to maintain a list of callers for you. Ideally, in such an instance, the list taker should be in the same part of the world as you are. It simply doesn't work when, for example, a European station takes a list of other Europeans on behalf of a weak Pacific station. He will hear those other Europeans who are loud with him on short-skip (quite possibly because they have high-angle antennas) but who may have zero chance of working into the Pacific. On the other hand, he may well not hear the well-equipped European station in his dead zone who could easily have made the contact. In any case, when operating as the DX station in a list operation, the guidelines on List and Net operation which have already been mentioned do very much apply.

G3SXW's book [12] is an excellent and entertaining account of what it's like to be at the DX end of the pile-ups.

VHF and UHF DXing

MUCH OF THE foregoing applies to VHF and UHF DXing, except that, in many instances, the so-called DX station is not a DXpedition or rare station, but rather a perfectly ordinary station like yourself who happens to be a long way away (in VHF terms). On HF, propagation is rarely an issue, at least on the main bands, and DX is determined by the rarity of the station worked, but the situation on VHF is different. Other than on 6m which can, at times, exhibit properties similar to any HF band, the issue on the VHF and UHF bands is very much one of distance, pure and simple. For UK stations, for most of the time, the DX they are working will be other European stations, not necessarily in rare locations, but rarely available simply because suitable propagation only occurs occasionally. Or, indeed, the path may only exist because strenuous efforts have been made to achieve it, maybe through setting up your equipment on a mountaintop or, perhaps, building a more effective station (high gain antenna, low loss feeder, mast-head pre-amp, etc).

Let's take, as an example, a tropospheric opening on 2m or 70cm. Propagation may be quite stable for periods of several hours, even days at a time. And you won't necessarily be competing with many others for a particular contact, unless there is an identifiably 'rare' station on the band (perhaps an expedition to an otherwise inactive locator square, for example). So you should be able to call and work stations to your heart's content. However, given that propagation may change quite quickly and that others may be waiting in turn to work the station you are in contact with, it is usual to keep contacts relatively short. An exchange of signal report, QTH locator and, perhaps name. The same is especially true when using those even more ephemeral propagation mechanisms such as Sporadic E and Aurora, which could disappear at a moment's notice. Keep contacts slick and efficient. Unlike on HF, for the reasons outlined above, on VHF each participant in the QSO is likely to be DX. If he is DX to you, then you are probably DX to him, in respect of distance if nothing else.

Finding DX on the VHF bands is rather different to HF. It's not so much a case of researching newsletters or the Internet, but one of keeping a weather eye (quite literally in the case of some types of propagation!) out for band openings. The chapter on propagation deals with how to spot the signs of possible Sporadic E, tropospheric or other VHF band openings. When the band opens, much of what you hear will be, in VHF terms, DX. Take part, make contacts and enjoy. One major difference between HF and VHF is that VHF antennas have much higher gain and narrower lobes than typical HF beams, so more care needs to be taking in changing beam direction a little at a time and tuning carefully for weak signals. To help the process along, there are recognised calling frequencies on most of the VHF bands for DX activity. When the band is dead but an opening is possible, the simple solution is to leave your receiver on the calling frequency and wait for something to happen. The other solution is to monitor the various beacon transmissions. Often you will hear a beacon before other amateur signals start to appear. The Cluster system is extremely effective nowadays in alerting the more casual DXers to VHF band openings, but the more serious DXers will continue to make their own efforts to spot potential DX opportunities, monitoring constantly when enhanced conditions are expected. The other modern tool which helps enormously is the spectrum scope, incorporated into many current transceivers or a software 'scope such as *Spectran* with the receiver on a distant beacon, for example. This enables you to monitor not just one frequency, but a whole range. This can give an instant visual indication when signals start to appear. And as well as in-band signals, serious VHF DX operators are well aware of commercial and other stations operating close to the amateur bands and whose signals can often give an indication of enhanced propagation.

Moving up to the microwave region, DXing takes on rather a different flavour again. Many contacts are prearranged, for example during an 'activity period' or contest, even to the extent of both parties heading out to separate hilltops to achieve a long-distance contact, perhaps to qualify for one of the various distance awards. This said, much of the current microwave DX happens from well equipped home stations - portable operation is no longer 'mandatory' Another popular technique is to set up a contact on one of the lower bands and, often , to maintain a link on that lower band until the higher band contact is completed. To take a simple example, two stations may establish contact on the 70cm band and agree to try a contact on 10GHz. Although they may have a line-of-sight path, their 10GHz antennas, probably dishes, will have very high gain and narrow beamwidth and have to be aligned with great accuracy before a contact becomes possible although with some contacts, especially by forward troposcatter, rain scatter or aircraft scatter, alignment accuracy is less critical. Not only will the alignment of their 70cm antennas give a good starting point for aligning the 10GHz antennas, but the 70cm link can be used for communications until the 10GHz link is working.

Operating during a Sporadic E opening

Sporadic E operations on 50MHz and 70MHz are relatively common each summer and at some other times of the year, and propagation can exist for several hours at a time. Using Sporadic E to make QSOs is therefore no different to how you would conduct a QSO via any other day-to-day mode of communication. However, the probability of Sporadic E propagation declines rapidly with increasing frequency. 144MHz Es openings are infrequent and often very short-lived, so efficient operating is essential and an exchange of report and QTH locator is the most that should be attempted. It is possible for a station to appear, calling CQ, be worked and disappear totally in less than a minute. Avoid using the SSB calling channels - there is no hope of establishing an Es contact and then changing frequency as is normal practice with other propagation. All too often a station fades out during a contact and there is usually nothing to be gained by waiting in the hope it will reappear - it is best to 'cut your losses' and look for someone else. The ionised reflecting layer, which may be relatively small in area, can move very rapidly and also tilt. For example, Maltese stations may be very strong one minute then fade out to be replaced by Sicilians which are in turn replaced by Sardinians - all in the space of a few minutes.

Monk Apollo is the only amateur in Mount Athos, probably the rarest DXCC entity in Europe. He was active on 6m during the 2004 sporadic-E season

CQ calls should be brief, perhaps 10-15 seconds, and used with discretion - if an operator is in an area of high activity, any DX station is likely to have many UK stations calling him and be unlikely to reply to a call. Conversely, if an operator is isolated, he may have an opening all to himself and a pile-up of DX may call him. In this case he will want to work as many as possible, just exchanging reports with each station but giving the locator on every third or fourth contact - the waiting pile-up will have heard it already. However, always remember that Sporadic-E can be very localised and it is possible for a DX station which is S9 to one operator to be inaudible 10km away - and that a CQ call may well pay dividends, especially just as the band is opening.

Auroral operating

The beacon stations closest to the auroral zones are usually the first auroral signals to be heard in the south. The Swedish beacon, SK4MPI (144.412MHz), and the Lerwick beacon, GB3LER (144.445MHz), in Shetland are good auroral indicators as is the Faroes beacon, OY6SMC (50.035MHz).

Auroral events are usually first noticed by amateurs in Norway, Sweden, Finland and northern Russia, who will be on the band making contacts before the auroral reflections extend to the south. Due to their northerly locations, they see far more visual auroras and participate in more radio events than stations in southern England. Amateurs have noticed that the larger the change in geomagnetic activity, the farther south the area of auroral ionisation extends, and stations as far south as Italy make auroral contacts in major events.

If you hear someone calling "CQ aurora" and you have not operated in an auroral opening before, resist the temptation to call indiscriminately, and listen only. There are going to be hundreds of future auroras and this is your chance to learn the entirely new operating techniques required for auroral contacts. First select horizontal polarisation and beam between north and east at 45°. Tune the beacon band between 144.412MHz and 144.445MHz; it will take some time to get used to the rough sounding keying of the beacons which will be slightly off their usual frequencies due to Doppler shift. If you hear GB3LER and SK4MPI, check whether DL0PR on 144.486MHz is readable. If these three beacons are heard the aurora is extending to at least as far as Germany, and is therefore a large-scale event which will probably last for a few hours and may repeat later in the evening.

Turn the beam between north and east on each beacon heard and it will be noticed that different beam headings give peak signals for different countries. Generally the farthest DX is worked with the beam well to the east. Next tune the SSB section between 144.160MHz and 144.400MHz and try listening to an experienced local station who is working auroral DX. Due to the distortion he will be speaking slowly, using correct phonetics and possibly end-of transmission tones. Remember that you will hear the local station direct but the DX stations will be replying via the aurora and will be slightly off his frequency. A typical SSB auroral contact starts like this:

"CQ aurora, CQ Aurora, GM8FFX, Golf Mike Eight Fox Fox X-ray calling CQ aurora . . ." (repeated slowly several times) "and GM8FFX listening." pip (end of transmission tone).

"GM8FFX, GM8FFX, LA2PT calling. Lima Alpha Two Papa Tango, LA2PT calling GM8FFX . . ."

End-of-transmission tones which give a low-frequency pip are very helpful in auroral openings when signals are weak - the tone readily identifies the end of each station's transmissions and could be a 'K' tone or 'pip' tone. Receiver independent tuning (RIT) is a 'must' for auroral reception as the amount of Doppler shift often changes in the middle of a contact. It will soon be seen that SSB contacts are difficult due to the distortion, and contacts tend to be limited to exchanging reports, names, and locators. Many amateurs also exchange and log the beam headings used at both ends of the contact as a study of these figures can reveal the particular area of ionised E layer being used. During weak auroral events SSB operators in England, Northern Ireland, North Wales and Scotland can work each other and operators with better facilities can contact Norway and Sweden. During strong auroral events SSB stations all over the UK and north-west Europe can work each other.

A new operator listening in the CW section between 144.020 and 144.120MHz will hear a great many rough-sounding hissing CW signals during a strong event. Experienced operators are used to the strange sounding notes and contacts are completed quickly and efficiently. The letter 'A' is added when calling CQ and is also added after the readability and signal strength report, in place of the normal tone reports which are not sent during aurora openings as no signal sounds T9. The best auroral DX is always worked on CW, just as on other propagation modes - CW is easier to copy in weak signal conditions and contacts are therefore completed much faster.

Some auroral operators use full break-in technique on CW, allowing them to listen for stations breaking in during the sending of a CQ. During the large-scale aurora on 1 May 1978 GM4COK worked more than 150 stations in 20 countries on 144MHz CW.

Auroral openings can occur in three separate phases in a single 24-hour period. The first phase can start as early as 1300UTC but usually takes place between 1500 and 1900UTC.

An aurora can benefit VHF radio signals well to the south of the spectacular visual display

The second phase can occur between 2100 and 2300 and a third phase can run from after midnight till 0600. Very few auroral contacts take place around 2000 and there is often a fade-out between the evening phase and the after-midnight session. Some auroras have no afternoon phase and start in the evening, often continuing again after midnight. Some auroras have no afternoon or evening phase, only starting after midnight. These are almost always weak events, sometimes heralding a larger occurrence on the next day.

Due to the Doppler shift and distortion on signals, auroral contacts can only be made on CW and SSB. High power is not essential but helps greatly in weak events. During strong events almost anyone can participate - mobile-to-mobile contacts have been made from southern England to Scotland using halo antennas and 10W SSB transceivers. Signals reflected from the auroral curtain on 144MHz do not change polarity, and high-gain horizontal antennas give the best results. Operators who are blocked to the south and south-east enjoy auroral openings as they can work stations, normally unheard due to the obstructions, by beaming well to the north of the direct path.

The amount of Doppler shift is proportional to the frequency band in use. For this reason auroral signals on the 50 and 70MHz bands are easier to read and have less distortion than on the 144MHz band. Inter-UK signals are generally stronger on 50 and 70MHz and the openings start a little earlier and finish a little later than on 144MHz. Auroral contacts have been made on both CW and SSB on the 432MHz band but signals are about 40dB weaker than on 144MHz, and the Doppler shift can be as much as 4kHz. No auroral contacts have yet been made on the 1.3GHz band but as power levels increase and receivers improve this will doubtless occur soon. Professional studies reveal that radar reflections have been received at over 3GHz.

Some useful advice on predicting the occurrence of auroral propagation is given in Chapter 6 (Propagation).

Specialist techniques

Meteor Scatter

Most amateur Meteor Scatter (MS) operation takes place on 144MHz and 50MHz, although 28 and 70MHz are also good bands for this. Operation on 432MHz is also marginally possible, but the path losses approach those experienced in EME operation. Commercial MS links tend to use the low VHF region, as the path availability is greater than at the higher frequencies. The distances which may be covered by typical MS operation are similar to those possible via sporadic-E. Assuming most signals are reflected from a region at an altitude of 110km, the maximum range possible with an antenna exhibiting a main lobe at 0° elevation is about 2300km. Typical amateur antennas have a main lobe at 2-5° and thus the ranges to be expected are somewhat less. Most MS contacts on 2m take place during periods of more-or-less predictable meteor activity - the so-called showers. Rather fewer contacts are made via sporadic meteors during the intervals between, but 6m meteor scatter activity is possible on most days of the year using the specialist *JT6M* software (see below and Chapter 8 on modes).

Table 9.2 lists the major meteor showers, which occur on the same dates each year as the earth passes through those bands of particles on its passage round the Sun. Serious meteor scatter enthusiasts ensure they are ready for these events, with no distractions in their diaries! Nowadays, though, more casual operators may become aware of meteor scatter opportunities as they watch the DX Cluster and see stations exchanging sked information for MS QSOs. This is an example where VHF use of the Cluster system differs from HF use. While on HF it is deemed unsporting to arrange skeds or

Table 9.2: Principal meteor showers

Shower name	Limits	Max	ZHR	N - S	NE - SW	E - W	SE - NW
Quadrantids	1-5 Jan	3-4 Jan	110	02-06 (W) 11-16 (E)	11-17 (SE)	23-03 (S) 15-17 (S)	00-05 (SW)
April Lyrids	19-25 Apr	22 Apr	15-25	22-02 (W) 06-10 (E)	23-03 (NW) 08-11 (SE)	03-06 (N)	22-01 (SW) 05-08 (NE)
Eta Aquarids	1-12 May	3 May	50	03-04 (W) 10-11 (E)	04-09 (NW)	05-11 (N)	08-12 (NE)
Arietids	30 May-18 Jun	7 Jun	60	04-08 (W) 11-15 (E)	05-09 (NW) 14-16 (SE)	08-12 (N)	04-06 (SW) 10-14 (NE)
Zeta Perseids	1-16 Jun	9 Jun	40	05-10 (W) 13-17 (E)	06-11 (NW) 15-17 (SE)	09-14 (N)	07-07 (SW) 11-15 (NE)
Perseids	20 Jul-18 Aug	12 Aug	95	23-04 (W) 09-13 (E)	08-17 (SE)	11-01 (S)	18-04 (SW)
Orionids	16-27 Oct	22 Oct	25	00-03 (W) 07-09 (E)	00-04 (NW)	03-06 (N)	05-08 (NE)
Taurids S	10 Oct-5 Dec	3 Nov	25	02-05 (E) 20-22 (W)	20-01 (NW)	22-03 (N)	00-05 (NE)
Geminids	7-15 Dec	13-14 Dec	110	04-09 (E) 20-01 (W)	22-02 (NW) 05-09 (SE)	01-04 (N) 03-07 (S)	03-07 (NE) 19-23 (SW)
Ursids	17-24 Dec	22 Dec	15	-	07-01 (SE)	00-24 (S)	16-09 (SW)

Operating procedures for meteor scatter QSOs

Note. These procedures were adopted at the IARU Region 1 Conference in Miskolc-Tapolca (1978), later slightly amended at the IARU Region 1 Conference in Noordwijkerhout (1987), Torremolinos (1990), de Haan (1993) and San Marino (2002). The meeting in Vienna 2004 accepted a slightly reworded version.

1. INTRODUCTION

The goal of the procedures described is to enable contacts to be made by meteor scatter (MS) reflection as quickly and easily as possible. Meteor scatter is unlike most other propagation modes, in that neither station can hear the other until an ionised meteor trail exists to scatter or reflect the signals. As the reflections are often of very short duration the normal QSO procedure is not readily applicable and specialised operating techniques must be taken to ensure that a maximum of correct and unmistakable information is received. The two stations have to take turns to transmit and receive information in a defined format, following the procedures as detailed below. Some meteor showers are strong enough to make some of these measures unnecessary but to encourage use of all generally listed showers there is no reason why the suggested procedures should not always be used.

As with operating procedures in general, the virtues of the MS operating procedures are mainly that they are standard and are widely understood throughout IARU Region 1.

2. SCHEDULED and RANDOM CONTACTS

Two types of MS contacts, arranged in different ways, may be distinguished:

(a) A scheduled contact, where two interested stations arrange in advance the frequency, timing and duration of the test, as well as the transmission mode (eg Telegraphy, SSB or FSK441) and call signs to be used. Scheduling may be carried out, for example, by exchange of letters or e-mail, by radio via the European VHF Net on 14.345MHz, by Internet chat-rooms or packet radio.

(b) A non-scheduled contact, where a station calls CQ or responds to a CQ call. Such contacts are often called 'random MS'. Random contacts are far more difficult and because you're starting entirely from scratch, it's particularly important for both stations to follow the standard IARU meteor scatter QSO procedures.

3. TIMING

Accurate timing of transmit and receive periods is important for two reasons: to maximise the chances of hearing the other station, and to avoid interference between local stations. The recommended time period for random contacts is,

(a) Telegraphy - 2.5 minute periods,

(b) SSB - 1 minute periods,

(c) FSK441 - 30 second periods.

This practice gives quite satisfactory results. However growing technical standards make it possible to use much shorter periods and amateurs may wish to arrange 1-minute schedules for telegraphy and shorter periods for SSB especially during major showers. If non-standard time periods are used the first priority is to avoid causing interference to local stations that are using the standard periods.

The recommended standard period for both random and scheduled SSB contacts is 1-minute. However time periods shorter than this are encouraged during major meteor showers. Quick-break procedures within SSB contacts can be very effective. This could involve, for example, taking a break every 15 seconds in case the QSO can be completed within one long burst.

Prior to any MS activity it is absolutely vital that clocks need to be set to better than two seconds of standard time. This can be accomplished, for example, by using TV Teletext, telephone 'speaking clock' or GPS time signals. Any clock inaccuracy will result in wasted time and will cause unnecessary interference to other MS stations.

4. TRANSMIT PERIODS

(a) All MS operators living in the same area should, as far as possible, agree to transmit simultaneously in order to avoid mutual interference.

(b) If possible, northbound and westbound transmissions should be made in periods 1, 3, 5 etc, counting from the full hour. Southbound and eastbound transmissions should be made in periods 2, 4, 6 etc.

5. SCHEDULED DURATION

(a) Every uninterrupted scheduled period must be considered as a separate trial. This means that it is not permissible to break off and then continue the contact at a later time.

(b) Scheduled contacts using telegraphy or SSB are usually arranged for up to 1-hour duration although during shower periods this can be significantly reduced. Operators using the more efficient FSK441 transmission mode often use 30-minutes or less.

6. FREQUENCIES

Scheduled Contacts: These contacts may be arranged on any frequency, taking into consideration the mode and band plan. Scheduled contacts should avoid using known popular frequencies and the random MS frequencies.

Non-Scheduled Contacts: For non-scheduled contacts reference should be made to the relevant IARU Region 1 band plan.

7. QSY FREQUENCIES

To avoid continent-wide interference, which results from a large number of stations attempting to complete contacts on the various MS calling frequencies, a QSY method is recommended. The procedure for moving a beginning QSO off the calling frequency without losing contact is as follows.

(a) Telegraphy: During the CQ the caller indicates on which frequency he/she will listen for a reply and carry out any subsequent QSO. Refer to the relevant band plan for QSY frequencies.

i) Select the frequency to be used for a QSO by checking whether it is clear of traffic and QRM.

ii) In the call, immediately following the letters "CQ", a letter is inserted to indicate the frequency that will be used for reception when the CQ call finishes. This letter indicates the frequency offset from the actual calling frequency used. For instance, CQE would indicate that the operator will listen on the calling frequency plus 5kHz.

A	=	1kHz	(CQA)	N	=	14kHz	(CQN)
B	=	2kHz	(CQB)	O	=	15kHz	(CQO)
C	=	3kHz	(CQC)	P	=	16kHz	(CQP)
D	=	4kHz	(CQD)	Q	=	17kHz	(CQQ)
E	=	5kHz	(CQE)	R	=	18kHz	(CQR)
F	=	6kHz	(CQF)	S	=	19kHz	(CQS)
G	=	7kHz	(CQG)	T	=	20kHz	(CQT)
H	=	8kHz	(CQH)	U	=	21kHz	(CQU)
I	=	9kHz	(CQI)	V	=	22kHz	(CQV)
J	=	10kHz	(CQJ)	W	=	23kHz	(CQW)
K	=	11kHz	(CQK)	X	=	24kHz	(CQX)
L	=	12kHz	(CQL)	Y	=	25kHz	(CQY)
M	=	13kHz	(CQM)	Z	=	26kHz	(CQZ)

In all cases the letter used indicates a frequency higher than the CQ frequency.

iii) At the end of the transmitting period the receiver should be tuned to the frequency indicated by the letter used in the CQ call.

iv) If a signal is heard on this frequency, it may well be a reply from a station who has heard the CQ call and replied on the frequency calculated from the letter used during this call.

v) When the caller receives a signal on the frequency indicated during the call and identifies the reply as an answer on his CQ, the transmitter is moved to the same frequency and the whole QSO procedure takes place there.

(b) FSK441: A similar QSY procedure to that of telegraphy is used by operators using FSK441 transmissions. However instead of using a letter system, operators should use a number system. Users of FSK441 should indicate the frequency they intend to carry out the QSO by adding the three digits of the nominated frequency. For example CQ383 indicates that the station will listen on 144.383MHz for a subsequent contact.

(c) SSB: The letter system should not be used for SSB contacts!

8. QSO PROCEDURE FOR SCHEDULED CONTACTS AND RANDOM OPERATION

(a) Calling:

The contact starts with one station calling the other, eg "G4ASR OH5LK G4ASR . . . .".

(b) Reporting system:

The report consists of two numbers:

First number (burst duration)	Second number (signal strength)
2: up to 5 sec.	6: up to S3
3: 5 - 20 sec.	7: S4 - S5
4: 20 - 120 sec.	8: S6 - S7
5: longer than 120 sec.	9: S8 and stronger

(c) Reporting procedure.

A report is sent when the operator has positive evidence of having received the correspondent's or his own callsign or parts of them.

The report is given as follows:
"G4ASR OH5LK 37 37 G4ASR OH5LK 37 37 ....".

The report should be sent between each set of call signs: three times for telegraphy, twice for SSB and twice for FSK441.

The report must not be changed during a contact even though signal strength or duration might well justify it.

(d) Confirmation procedure

(i) As soon as either operator copies both callsigns and a report he may start sending a confirmation. This means that all letters and figures have been correctly received.

You are allowed to piece the message together from fragments received over a period of bursts and pings, but it's up to the operator to ensure that it's done correctly and unambiguously.

Confirmation is given by inserting an R before the report: "G4ASR OH5LK R37 R37 OH5LK ...".

A station with an R at the end of the call sign could send "SM7FJE G4ASR RR26 RR26 ...".

(ii) When either operator receives a confirmation message, such as "R27", and all required information is complete he must confirm with a string of Rs, inserting his own call sign after each eighth R:

"RRRRRRRR HG5AIR RRRR . . . ."

When the other operator has received Rs the contact is complete and he may respond in the same manner, usually for three periods.

(e) Requirements for a complete QSO

Both operators must have copied both callsigns, the report and a confirmation that the other operator has done the same. This confirmation can either be an "R" preceding the report or a string of "RRRR. . ."'s as explained in paragraph 8.d.ii.

Contacts using SSB are conducted in the same way as telegraphy or FSK441. When attempting random contacts, speak the letters clearly, using phonetics where appropriate. It may not be necessary to use phonetics during a scheduled SSB contact, but still speak clearly.

9. MISSING INFORMATION

If a confirmation report (R**) is received it means that the other operator has copied both call signs and the report, yet you may still need something from that station. At that stage, you can try to ask for the information needed by sending a missing information code string.

The following strings may be utilised by operators using Telegraphy to ask for missing information:

BBB	both callsigns missing
MMM	my callsign missing
YYY	your callsign missing
SSS	duration and signal strength missing
OOO	all information complete
UUU	faulty keying or unreadable

The other operator shall respond by sending only the required information. This approach must be used with great caution to prevent confusion.

self-spot via the Cluster system, on VHF the Cluster becomes a useful tool for setting up contacts on specialist modes. Skeds can also be arranged via the Meteor Scatter reflector on the Internet (*meteor-scatter@mailman.qth.net*).

MS QSO procedure: The intermittent nature of MS propagation means that special operating procedures are necessary. Within IARU Region 1, they are the subject of international agreement (see panel), and should thus be employed. Failure to do so has resulted in not a few lost contacts.

On CW, high speeds are employed. During skeds, speeds from 200 to over 2000LPM (letters per minute) are in use. In random MS work 800LPM is the recommended maximum speed. Most operators nowadays use computer software to deal with these speeds.

Some useful links on software, procedures and an MS Internet reflector for skeds appear on the Meteor Scatter web page [13].

JT6M and FSK441 users should consult the WSJT documentation [14] for the best way to set up their station and conduct MS QSOs.

Equipment: Meteor-scatter contacts are possible with low power, particularly on 50MHz, but on 144MHz higher ERP is necessary for consistent success. 100W RF at the feed point of a 10-14dBd gain antenna should be aimed for. A genuine system noise figure of less than 2.5dB is highly desirable. Many commercial transceivers, especially the earlier models, have inadequate front-end performance but a new generation of DSP transceivers has helped somewhat. Masthead preamplifiers are used by serious operators but care should be taken to avoid too much gain which could degrade the performance of the transceiver.

Frequency setting is of paramount importance. A tolerance of ±500Hz is demanded on CW and 200Hz on SSB. A stability of better than 100Hz/hour is necessary which requires accurate calibration and a stable oscillator. Today, modern transceivers employ much more stringent frequency-derived systems which are very accurate and stable. Stability is perhaps even more important when using software such as WSJT, using DSP techniques to integrate signals received in a very narrow bandwidth.

Most 2m MS signals will be quite weak so the antenna system should be as large as possible within environmental, structural and financial constraints. Long Yagis are popular, particularly the commercial 13- and 17-element models, although smaller antennas are capable of good results. With a high-gain array, such as a box of four 17-element Yagis, received signals will be much stronger than those from a single 9-element antenna. However, many MS operators have found that a too 'sharp' array often misses signals coming into the broader capture angle of a smaller single Yagi.

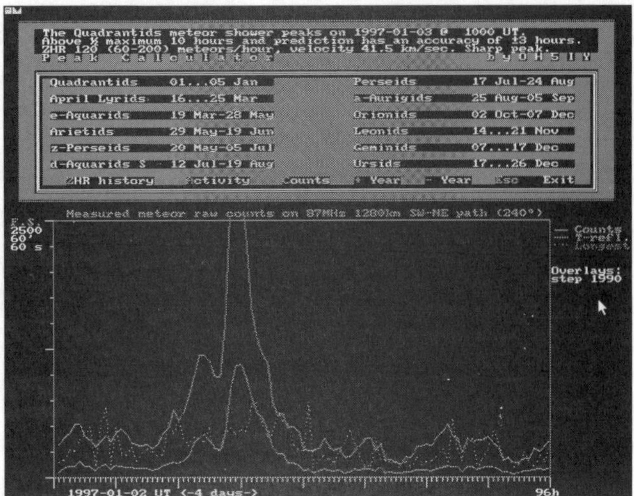

A screen shot from OH5IY's *MS Soft* Meteor Scatter software

Experienced operators tend to favour two or more stacked Yagis since these give extra gain while retaining a broader E-plane lobe.

The timing requirements of MS technique are stringent but not too difficult to meet. A radio-controlled clock or watch is probably the most popular timepiece now found in many shacks. These clocks or watches incorporating radio receivers phase-locked to radio transmitters such as MSF and Droitwich are now priced very reasonably. There are radio receiver boards available for plugging into your PC which will ensure the computer's clock is always spot on, or your PC can easily be locked to one of the standard time sites available via the Internet (Windows XP has an option for locking your PC clock in this way). Mains-driven clocks are to be avoided as they have poor short-term stability.

On CW, two other items of equipment are required; a means of sending repetitive messages at the speeds involved and a means of decoding the received CW. Nowadays this is usually by way of suitable PC software. The PC can generate CW, store incoming CW for replaying at lower speed and, if required, archive whole QSOs as WAV files for future reference. Modern MS operation is a far cry from the early days of multi-speed reel-to-reel tape recorders and endless tape loops for sending!

This said, the majority of operators have now made the logical move to software such as WSJT. After all, if you are already using your PC for CW why not, instead, use a mode which has actually been designed for PC operation rather than one which was designed well over 150 years ago for manual operation? When using the WSJT modes, though, be aware that transmissions can be continuous for many seconds at a time, whereas many transceivers and, especially, amplifiers, are designed for the low duty cycle of CW or SSB, so you may need to reduce your output power accordingly.

Arranging skeds: Once the procedures used for MS have been understood, and the necessary equipment gathered together, the intending MS operator has to find someone to work! There are really two choices: to make a first contact directly on the frequencies set aside for random MS operation or to arrange a sked with an active MS station. Of the two, the latter is the approach most likely to be fruitful. In order to maximise the chance of success, skeds should be arranged at optimum times. The sporadic meteor rate peaks at 0300 local time for north-south contacts and around 0600 local for east-west contacts, but with shower meteors it is possible to be more specific. Knowledge of the propagation mechanism and the astronomical co-ordinates of the individual showers makes its possible to calculate the optimum time for any given path.

When arranging an MS sked, a certain minimum amount of data needs to be exchanged:

(a) The date
(b) Times of start and finish (2h duration is usual)
(c) Length of transmit and receive periods
(d) The frequency
(e) Which station transmits first
(f) CW speed

One of the most useful tools when thinking about skeds or random MS operation is the public-domain software from OH5IY [15]. It features predictions of the peak times of the major and many minor meteor showers, and times when reflections will be optimum for the required path. The program can be used to key the transmitter at speeds of 100-9999LPM, receive and playback the CW if the PC has a sound card and the Windows operating system. It features a comprehensive sked editor, automatic logging and will even wake you up with an alarm call when it is time for a sked in the middle of the night! Within days of a major shower, the observed radio data for it is posted on the Internet.

Moonbounce

Probably the most challenging type of VHF/UHF DX communication is that using the Moon as a passive reflector, popularly known as 'EME' (Earth-Moon-Earth) or 'moonbounce'. The first known use of the Moon as a relay was by the United States Navy which set up a circuit between Washington, DC and Hawaii using 400 megawatts ERP. The first amateur EME contact was on 1296MHz in July 1960 between W6HB and W1BU. The majority of EME work takes place on the 144, 432 and 1296MHz bands although nowadays there is also regular activity on 50MHz, made possible largely as a result of weak-signal software such as WSJT. The microwave bands up to 10GHz are also used for moonbounce as more stations equip themselves with the capability.

The logistics: The mean distance between the Earth and the Moon is 385,000km. The Moon's diameter is 3476km so a little simple trigonometry shows it appears a mere 0.52° wide as viewed from Earth. Bearing in mind the three-dimensional polar diagrams of typical amateur antenna arrays, it is obvious that only a very small amount of ERP will illuminate the disk. Moreover the Moon is a sphere, not a flat mirror, so only radio waves that hit the middle region will be reflected back to Earth. In other words, the path loss is enormous. To put some figures on it, the minimum round-trip path loss at 144MHz is 251.5dB rising to 270.5dB at 1296MHz. Even so, it is possible to work a few of the biggest EME stations on 144MHz using a few hundred watts and a single long Yagi under favourable conditions.

For stations without antenna elevation capability, EME communication is only possible around moonrise and moonset. At such times, depending upon the height of the antenna above ground, advantage can be taken of so-called 'ground gain' whereby the apparent gain of a horizontally polarised antenna can be up to about 5dB more than the free-space figure. This is equivalent to increasing the size of an array from a single Yagi to four - and all for free!

Arranging EME tests: The best time to arrange EME tests is when the Moon is nearest to the Earth, known as 'perigee'. At 'apogee' (furthest from the Earth) there is an extra 2dB path loss to overcome. However, this is not the only consideration since the background sky temperature and/or Sun noise at new Moon periods may mitigate against perigee operation. Unfortunately there can be periods lasting several years when conditions are far from ideal, particularly on 144 and 432MHz.

The 2 Meter EME Net: A good place to get information on the air about EME operation is the 2m EME net which meets every Saturday and Sunday on 14.345MHz at 1600 during summer daylight savings time, and 1700. Schedules and EME operating information are exchanged on this net, not only for 2m but for the other VHF bands too. The W5UN web page [16] is an excellent place to find information on how to get started with EME, with advice on equipment, antennas, operating procedures, etc. G3SEK's web [17] page is also an invaluable resource.

The EME Directory: The *EME Directory* is a database of known 2 meter EME stations which contains detailed information about those stations. This database is managed by WB5LBT, and is available from WB5LBT as well as from several internet on-line sites. Software that will display the EME Directory data includes *PCF* and *SKYMOON*.

Tracking And Operating Aids: There are several computer programs available that will assist in EME. A basic moon tracking program called *MoonBrat* can be downloaded from the W5UN Web site. Advanced and more powerful tracking programs that are available include *Skymoon*, *Nova4*, and *The VK3UN EME Planner*.

EME QSO procedure: There are internationally agreed operating procedures for EME work and, as with MS operation, timing is all-important. On 144MHz 2-minute periods are used and on 432MHz and above, 2.5 minutes. The convention is that the station whose call appears first on a sked list transmits first then in following 'odd' periods. In the absence of a formal list the convention is that the furthest east station transmits first on 144MHz but on 432MHz it is the one furthest west. There is a special TMOR reporting system for EME work.

On 144MHz these letters denote the following:

- T Signals just detectable
- M Portions of calls copied
- O Both calls fully copied
- R Both calls and 'O' report copied.

On 432MHz and above, these reports have slightly different meanings:

- T Parts of calls copyable
- M Both calls fully copied weakly
- O Both calls copied comfortably
- R Both calls and 'M' or 'O' report copied.

In favourable conditions RST reports are exchanged. At the start of a sked both callsigns are sent for the complete period of 2 or 2.5 minutes, depending on the band. Only when both callsigns have been copied completely may you send a report which will be 'O' on 144MHz, and 'M' or 'O' on other bands. At this stage the first 1.5 minutes on 144MHz, or the first 2 minutes of the period on other bands, will be devoted to sending callsigns, and the final 30 seconds the reports. Reports are acknowledged by sending "RO" on 144MHz and "RO" or "RM" on 432MHz and above and when this is received by the other station a series of 'R's is sent. As in MS work, random EME contacts are made especially during contests. If you hear a station calling CQ, reply by sending his and your own calls. If the calling station does not copy your complete call he will reply with "QRZ", "???" or perhaps "YYY", the latter indicating he has not copied your call. In this case, send your call for the whole of the next period until you receive an 'O' or 'M' report. If you receive "GGG" it means the other station needs your grid (Locator), eg IO91, for scoring purposes in a contest.

WSJT: The advent of the WSJT (see Chapter 8) software suite has revolutionised EME operation, just as it has Meteor Scatter. The JT65 mode within WSJT is optimised for EME communications, and can make a contact possible where CW would be inaudible below the noise level. JT65 uses the digital signal processing (DSP) capabilities of the PC to integrate the received signal over time and extract the required data. WSJT also offers a Measure mode for testing Sun noise, etc, and an EME Calculator to help you predict the maximum strength of your own and other stations' echoes from the moon. Full help information is available in a user manual downloadable from the main WSJT site.

This is the 5.4m dish antenna built by Howard Ling, G4CCH, for 23cm EME operation

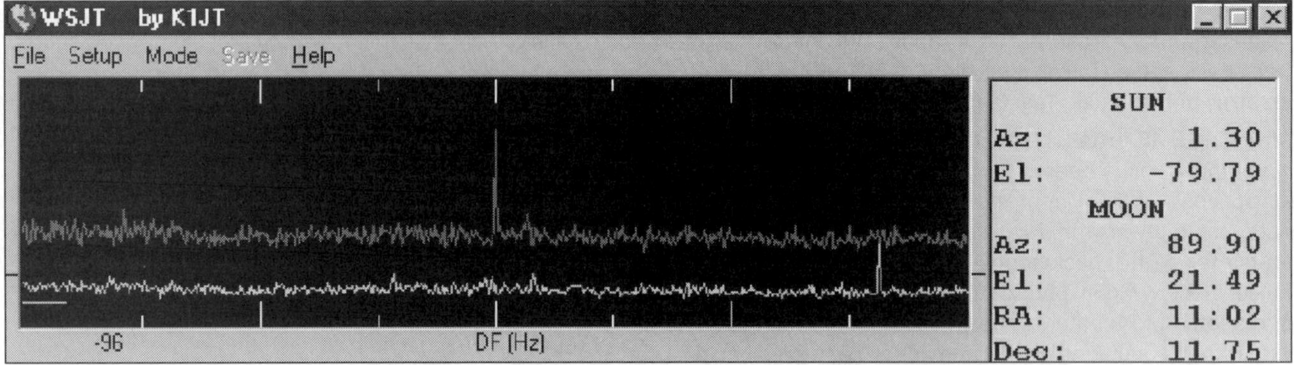

Detail of the EME-Echo screen from the *WSJT* suite of programmes. This gives visual evidence of receiving your own echoes

Equipment: As mentioned earlier, on 144MHz it is possible to work a few of the stations using very large antenna systems with a few hundred watts and a single Yagi. However, if serious EME operation is contemplated you must be prepared to make a considerable investment in time and money. On the receiving side it is essential to achieve the lowest possible system noise figure and this usually means fitting a high performance low-noise preamp at the masthead. To avoid damage to the preamp it is vital to incorporate a properly-designed, fail-safe transmit/receive switching system - this is known as 'sequential switching', so that the transmitter power is removed before going into receive, and vice versa.

The antenna array should have as much gain as possible combined with a clean polar diagram. On 144 and 432MHz, Yagi antennas are the most popular because of their ready availability. Collinear arrays have been used with success by some VHF operators and have the advantage of not being as 'deep' as an equivalent array of long Yagis. On the microwave bands, dishes are favoured and there are plenty of graphs and tables in the handbooks to enable you to design your own. Supporting a large EME antenna array should be regarded as an engineering project, the safety of the complete structure under all weather conditions being of paramount importance. A weak point can be the steering system, commonly referred to as the 'az-el rotator'. Obviously the rotator(s) must be able to deal with the weight and inertia of the load imposed so it is essential to ascertain from the supplier that it/they will cope. The system will have to be carefully calibrated so the array can be aimed accurately at the Moon. Some operators adapt the screwjack systems from satellite TV dishes to elevate their EME antennas. The Japanese are very active with large antenna systems on EME and have developed a mighty elevation chain-driven rotator, but at a price!

On the transmitting side the aim should be to deliver the maximum licensed power to the antenna array, usually the transfer relay at the masthead. The lowest loss feeder that can be afforded, for the power involved, should be used; there is not much point in generating lots of RF at the output of the PA then wasting 25% of it in the feeder! Such feeder and the appropriate connectors are not cheap if purchased new but sometimes surplus lengths become available from commercial sources. Some surprising bargains can also be found at radio rallies by way of hefty relays and connectors. Commercial amplifiers are available capable of delivering many hundreds of watts, but if you have the time, skill and a proper understanding of RF engineering, it is very satisfying to build your own amplifier. Surplus valves are fine as long as they are new - don't go out and buy well used ones and expect them to perform cleanly in your newly designed amplifier. There are many designs on the Internet, including several tried and tested designs by G4ICD and others which include the Russian surplus tubes GS35B (1.5kW at 1GHz), GS31B (1kW at 1GHz). All the latter tubes are triodes and offer simple construction of the power supply and RF circuitry.

Summary: Interest in EME communication is growing steadily, largely thanks to the availability of the WSJT software. Many regular operators are those who have been, and still are, MS enthusiasts. Both modes have similar equipment and operating requirements. However EME operation can be very frustrating. Having arranged a sked with a much-sought-after station, conditions may be ruined by an unpredicted aurora, high winds or static rain. Or you can copy your sked partner perfectly but he hears nothing from you, and vice versa, due to Faraday rotation. Sometimes you hear nothing from your partner then learn later it was because he had a local power failure. But it is these challenges which attract EME enthusiasts, being such a contrast to the wholly-predictable communications that are now possible by other means.

Locator squares

LOCATOR SQUARES are sometimes referred to as Maidenhead squares, having been formulated by Dr John Morris GM4ANB, and tabled at an IARU Region 1 VHF Managers meeting being held in Maidenhead in April 1980. The system formally came into use on 1 January 1985. They are derived by dividing the earth's surface into 324 'fields', each one being 20 degrees (longitude) by 10 degrees (latitude) thus dividing the Earth into an 18 by 18 grid. These fields are given two-letter indices, 'AA' to 'RR', with the first letter specifying the longitude and the second the latitude; the origin being at the South Pole at 180°W. Thus the field AA runs from 180° to 160°W, 90° to 80°S. North of this is AB, east is BA and so on. The field covering most of the UK (50° to 60°N, 20° to 0°W) is then IO. These fields are divided into 100 squares, each 2° wide and 1° high, labelled from '00' in the southwest corner to '99' in the northeast. Each of these Locator Squares can be further divided into 576 Sub-squares, each one being 5' wide by 2.5' high. The subsquares are labelled using two letters, again the first specifying the longitude and the second the latitude, starting

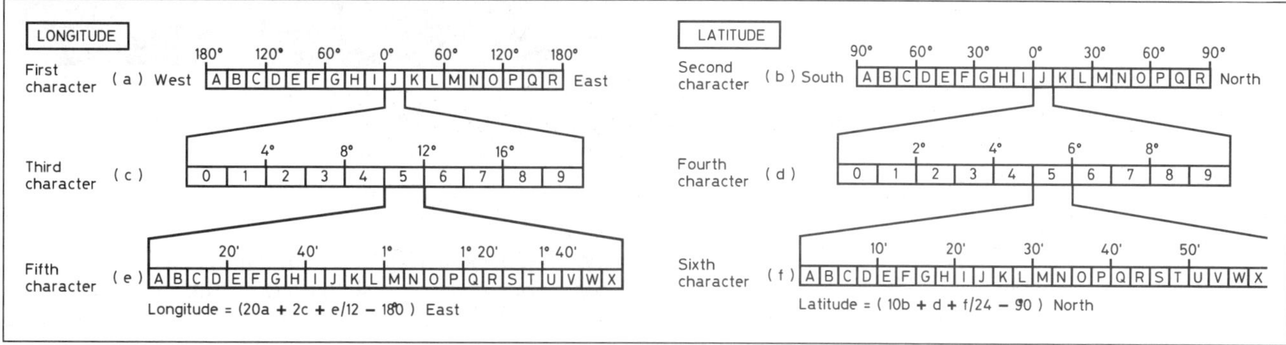

Fig 9.1: How the Locator system is built up into fields, 'squares' and 'sub-squares'

from 'AA' in the southwest corner, and running to 'XX' in the northeast. A full locator thus consists of two letters, two numbers and two letters, with a typical reference being IO91IP.

Fig.9.1 shows how the locator is built up from fields, squares and sub-squares. It may be noted that all of the longitude-defining characters - the first, third and fifth - run from west to east, while the latitude defining characters - the second, fourth and sixth - go from south to north. In addition, at all levels the east-west size, in degrees, is always twice the north-south size. In distance terms, each sub-square is about 4.6km from south to north. The east-west size varies with latitude, but in the middle of Britain (55°N) it is about 5.3km. If you take the accuracy of the system as being the farthest you can get from the middle of a sub-square without actually leaving it, this gives a maximum error of about 3.5km (at 55° latitude), which is quite adequate for most normal operation. It is worth noting, though many operators are unaware of this, that the nearer one gets to the equator, the larger are the squares and, conversely, the closer one is to the poles, the smaller they become.

You can find out your locator by consulting one of the web sites which will calculate your locator from your latitude and longitude [18]. If you don't have Internet access, the following step-by-step procedure can be used to calculate your locator, using nothing more than pencil, paper and a simple calculator.

First of all you must find your latitude and longitude. These can be derived from the popular 1:50,000 series of Ordnance Survey maps but you should note that the blue grid lines do not run exactly north-south and east-west. Along the top and bottom margins of each map the longitude is given and along either edge the latitude, both at 1' intervals. In the main body of the map the corners of 5' by 5' squares are identified by faint blue crosses. By pin-pointing your location within the appropriate square and pencilling in the sides you will be able to determine your latitude and longitude with great accuracy by proportion. The latitude should be round-

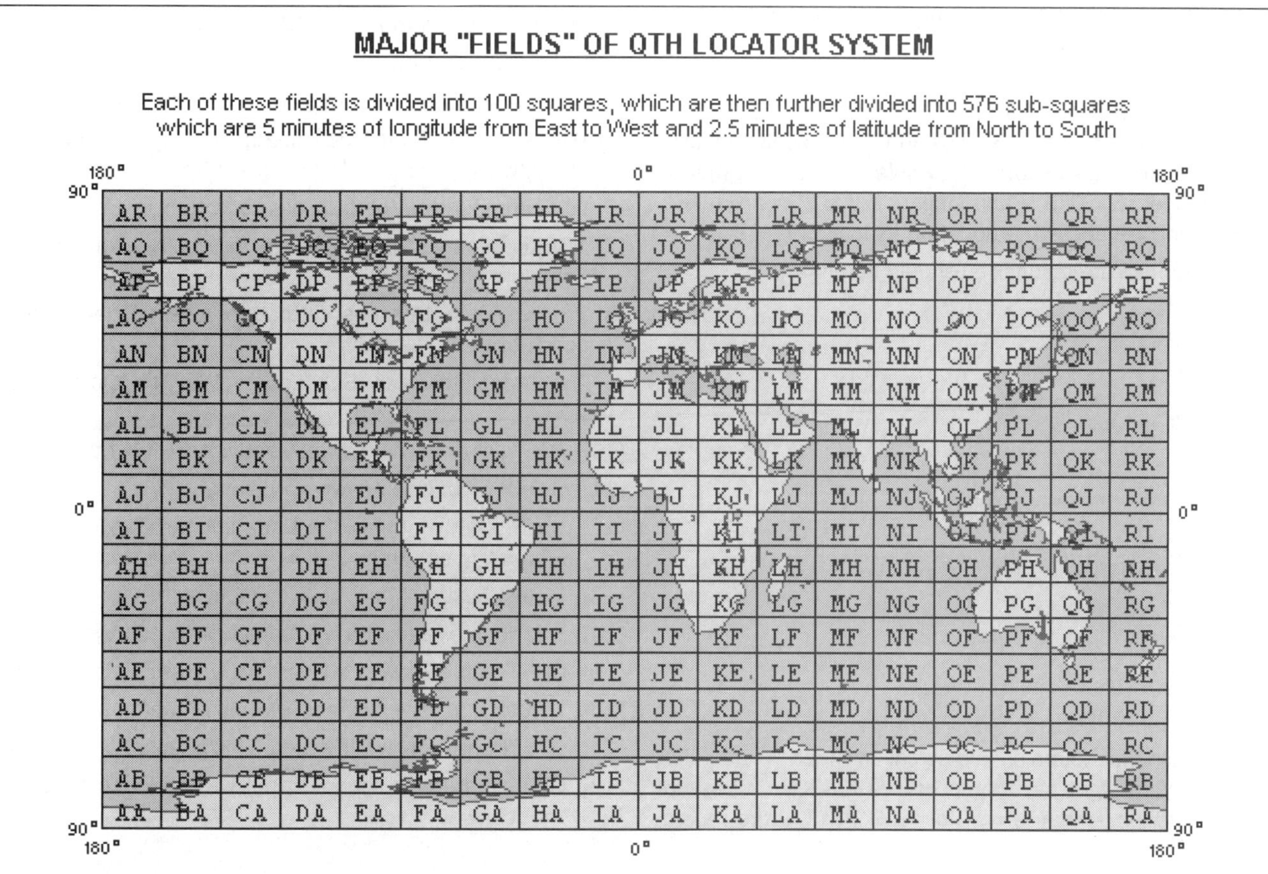

ed down to the next half of a minute south and the longitude to the next whole minute west.

Having established your latitude and longitude the procedure is as follows:

1 First deal with the longitude. Convert the longitude to decimal degrees. This is done by dividing the minutes part by 60 and adding the result to the degrees part.
2 If you are east of Greenwich, add 180.
3 If you are west of Greenwich subtract the value from 180.
4 Divide the result by two.
5 Now divide the value obtained by 10, and note the figures to left of the decimal point. These give the first letter of the locator, on the basis of 0 = A, 1 = B, 2 = C and so on, as shown in **Table 9.3**.
6 Multiply by 10, and note the single digit immediately before the decimal point. This is the third character of the locator.
7 Take just the fractional part of the value (the part to the right of the decimal point), and multiply by 24. The figures to the left of the decimal point give the fifth character of the locator, once again using Table 9.3.
8 Now follow a similar process for latitude. Convert the latitude to decimal degrees.
9. If you are north of the equator, add 90.
10 If you are south of the equator subtract the value from 90.
11 Divide by 10, and take the second letter of the locator from the digits to the left of the decimal point, using Table 9.3.
12 Multiply by 10, and note the digit to the left of the decimal point. This is the fourth character of the locator.
13 Take the fractional part, and multiply by 24. The figures to the left of the decimal point give the last letter of the locator, again using Table 9.3.

As an example, take Edinburgh Castle. From the map, its latitude is somewhere between 55°56.5' N and 55°57' N, and its longitude between 3°l l' W and 3°12' W. Rounding to the next half minute south and whole minute west means that latitude 55°56.5' N and longitude 3°12' W are taken. Verify, using the above method, that its locator is IO85JW.

The intermediate results you should obtain are:

1 3.2
2 No action
3 1768
4 88.4
5 8.84, ie 'I'
6 88.4, ie '8'
7 9.6, ie 'J'
8 55.94166667
9 145.9416667
10 No action
11 14.59416667, ie 'O'
12 145.9416667, ie '5'
13 22.59999984, ie 'W'

On the air, the system should be called simply 'locator'. For example, you might say "My locator is IO83QP", or ask of another station, "What is your locator?". On CW the recommended abbreviation is 'LOC', so that the CW equivalent of "What is your locator?" is simply "LOC?" The various divisions of the locator, fields, squares and subsquares, have just those names. A VHF DX chaser might claim to have worked 300 'squares', or, for the real enthusiast, 20 'fields'.

Table 9.3: Number-to-letter conversion table for hand calculation of a locator

0	A	4	E	8	1	12	M	16	Q	20	U
1	B	5	F	9	J	13	N	17	R	21	V
2	C	6	G	10	K	14	O	18	S	22	W
3	D	7	H	11	L	15	P	19	T	23	X

While the six-character locator system is accurate enough for VHF/UHF use, more accuracy may be necessary for identifying locations and calculating distances and antenna bearings when operating in the microwave bands above 24GHz. At the IARU Region 1 conference in Belgium in September 1993 an RSGB proposal for an extended locator system was approved. The 5' wide by 2.5' high sub-squares are divided into 100 'micro-squares' each 30" wide by 15" high labelled from '00' in the southwest corner to '99' in the northeast. Thus a full micro-locator would be IO91IP37 and at 55°N latitude, the maximum error is reduced 10-fold to about 350m.

It is worth noting that, although developed for VHF use, locator squares are also used nowadays by HF operators, for example as a contest exchange in several specialist HF contests, the scoring system being based on distance worked.

References

[1] QRZ DX & The DX Magazine: http://www.dxpub.com/

[2] 425 DX News: http://www.425dxn.org/

[3] OPDX Bulletin: http://www.papays.com/opdx.html

[4] Weekly DX& Daily DX: http://www.dailydx.com/

[5] WD4NGB DX Telnet download: DX Telnet download: http://www.qsl.net/wd4ngb/telnet.htm

[6] DX Summit: http://oh2aq.kolumbus.com/dxs/

[7] NCDXF Beacons: http://www.ncdxf.org/Beacon/Beacon Schedule.html

[8] 2m & 70cm beacons: http://www.qsl.net/la0by/beacons.htm

[9] The Complete DXer, Bob Locher W9KNI, Idiom Press 2003.

[10] AC6V list of HF nets: http://ac6v.com/nets.htm

[11] G-QRP Club: http://www.gqrp.com/

[12] Up Two - Adventures of a DXpeditioner, Roger Western G3SXW, Idiom Press 2003.

[13] Meteor Scatter: http://www.meteorscatter.net/soft.htm

[14] WSJT Home Page: http://pulsar.princeton.edu/~joe/K1JT/

[15] OH5IY: http://www.kolumbus.fi/oh5iy/mssoft/mssoft.htm

[16] W5UN: http://web.wt.net/~w5un/primer.htm

[17] G3SEK: http://www.ifwtech.co.uk/g3sek/

[18] Grid square calculation: http://www.amsat.org/cgi-bin /gridconv

10 Contest Operating

Like DXing, contest operation appeals to our competitive instincts. Contests are sporting competitions between amateur stations on specific bands and modes according to published rules. In some countries the activity is actually referred to as 'radiosporting', and it enjoys the same sort of recognition as other sports activities. The main difference is that it is generally undertaken from the privacy of our own homes and radio stations. An exception is the World Radio Teamsport Championships, held every four years, which are an attempt to bring the world's top contesters together to compete on the closest possible radio equivalent to a level playing field.

The nice thing about radio contests is that, like marathon races, there will be serious competitors but there is room for everyone, competitor or casual participant, to take part and enjoy the fun. In practice, the casual participants invariably outnumber the serious entrants by a large margin. But there is a lot to be said for building up your contesting skills as the years go by. Serious contesters spend countless hours improving their stations, practising their operating skills and even undertaking physical exercise in order to be able to maintain high levels of concentration for many hours at a time. These efforts spin off into other aspects of the hobby, too. In emergency situations, contesters have on several occasions come to the fore. Their stations are usually able to put out a stronger signal and hear a weaker signal than those of day-to-day ragchewers and DXers. Their operating skills are more honed to short, concise, accurate exchanges of information. And they are physically able to maintain a high level of operating skill over long hours in front of the radio.

The antenna system at G0IVZ, an active HF contester

Benefits of contesting

CONTESTS ATTRACT flack from some sections of the amateur radio population, usually because they have a habit of filling up the bands at weekends, at just the time that many amateurs want to get on the bands and chat with friends. But the very fact that the major contests tend to fill up the bands is evidence that contesting is a very popular activity. The two legs of the CQ World-Wide contest, undoubtedly the biggest contest each year, each attract several thousand entries, and some tens of thousands of different callsigns appear in entrants' logs, indicating that a very large number of amateurs are making contest contacts, if not actually sending in an entry.

There are certainly good arguments for the fact that there may be too many contests on our bands, but the truth is that many are short, geographically-limited events which have little impact on other band activity. And if you do want to avoid contests, the 30, 17 and 12m bands are kept contest free at all times. On the VHF bands, contests are often very welcome, bringing activity to what might otherwise be a dead band.

This is, at the basic level, why contests appeal. They bring about a level of activity which guarantees that there will be stations about for you to work. That may be general activity, or it may be specific to a particular band, mode or country. For example, if you are chasing US states for the Worked All States award, the ARRL International DX Contests are an ideal opportunity. Not only will there be lots of US activity, but US stations include their state as part of the contest exchange, so you know immediately which state you have worked. When the PSK31 mode started to become popular with data modes enthusiasts, activity was low and you could call CQ for hours without finding another station equipped for the mode. So some short contests were introduced, with the result that PSK31 operators could go on the bands, knowing that other like-minded enthusiasts would be on at the same time. This helped to build interest in the mode to the critical level needed to ensure its ongoing success.

So contests help to create activity on the bands, which is great if you are chasing countries, islands, Swiss cantons, or whatever. There will undoubtedly be one or more contests each year which bring on to the bands the very stations you are looking for.

For those of a competitive disposition, contests are obviously a way of enjoying competition in the context of amateur radio. This is no different to most other hobbies. There are angling competitions, competitions for the best researched and presented stamp collection on a specialist theme, photographic competitions; every group of enthusiasts tends to find ways in which individuals can compare themselves with fellow enthusiasts and measure their progress as the years go by. DXing, too, is a competitive activity, but one which is much longer-term. It will take many years to build up a serious squares total on 2m, or achieve DXCC Honor Roll on the HF bands. But a contest is a defined activity, with a clear start and finish time, so that even the busiest people can plan their diaries to be available for the duration.

Surprising as it may seem to anyone who hasn't actually participated, contests are also social occasions. Admittedly, in a major HF contest, where the winners are likely to be averaging 100-200 contacts an hour for the whole of the event, there isn't much time for an exchange of pleasantries, though if you know the amateur who calls you, there is usually time for a quick "Hello Don" or whatever. In the less frenetic events, which includes most VHF contests and quite a few of the HF ones, there is more than enough time to exchange greetings without adversely prejudicing your final score. To this extent, contesting is more sociable than DXing, where everyone sits in the same pile-up calling the DX stations, so the chasers never get to speak to one another. When you contest regularly, you will soon get to know the regular participants, and there is a level of recognition, even if you aren't always aware of their name. There is also the opportunity to be part of a multi-operator team, which involves a great deal of camaraderie, as well as being ideal for picking up operating and technical skills from more experienced contesters.

Contests are also an ideal focus for developing our stations and our operating skills. If a DXpedition is active for a couple of weeks, then provided you follow the sort of advice offered in Chapter 9, and have a half-decent station, you will eventually manage to work them, even if you spend an hour or two in the pile-ups. But a contester doesn't have that sort of time to spare in an event which may be only 12 or 24 hours long in total. He wants to be able to call stations and work them on the first or second call, if at all possible. So he will squeeze every decibel out of his station, focusing on antenna system, feeder cables and everywhere that improvements are possible. On the operating side, while at first sight it may seem that contesters simply sit at the radio saying "5914" or something similar, there's a whole lot more to both the strategy and the tactical side to consider, as well as the actual operating itself, as this chapter will try to show. If ever there was a clear focus to the self-training, which is one of the major justifications for our hobby, then contesting is it.

(l to r) G3SXW, G4PIQ and G4IFB operating XT2DX in the 2001 *CQWW* CW Contest

This chapter also gives a short introduction to Amateur Radio Direction Finding (ARDF) events, a rather different kind of competitive activity, but one which appeals to those who enjoy the outdoors and which, by its very nature, isn't restricted to holders of an amateur licence. Listeners can take part too.

Not covered here, but perhaps of interest, are the High Speed Telegraphy Championships, organised under the auspices of the IARU (see [1], for example). These take place indoors, not over the air waves, so, like ARDF, you don't have to be a licensed amateur to take part. They are very popular in some countries, but never seem to have taken off in the UK. However, there is nothing to stop UK enthusiasts attending and taking part in these events.

The challenge of contesting

LISTENING TO A contest in progress, it is easy to assume that it is simply a matter of calling CQ and exchanging reports, or tuning the bands and calling stations to do the same. But like most competitive activities in life, there is much more to it than this. Every contest has a unique set of rules, and radio propagation is a constantly changing phenomenon, affected by the sunspot cycle, time of day, solar disturbances, etc. So every contest requires a particular strategy, determined by its scoring and multiplier structure, but entrants also need to be flexible, ready to respond to band conditions and activity on the day. This is what makes contests fun; the mix of skill and chance.

For example, in RSGB HF Field Day, 10m and 160m contacts count double points, so savvy entrants will be sure to check these bands at every opportunity, because even a handful of extra contacts on them could make a big difference to the final placing. Missing a short Sporadic E opening on 10m could cost your group several places in the final listing. So before the contest you will have made sure you have a radio and antenna system which can change bands very quickly to check and, if necessary start to operate, on 10m. When the contest is in progress you will translate that into practice, remembering to check 10m even when you appear to have a reasonable QSO rate on, say, 15m. Similarly, preparing for a summer 6m contest, you will be hoping for some Sporadic E openings but preparing for the eventuality that you have to make every contact the hard way. It is this mixture of skill and chance which makes contesting so enjoyable. Who knows, the day may come when propagation favours your particular location, your equipment performs faultlessly for once, and everything falls into place for a great contest score that brings a certificate or plaque for the shack wall.

How to take part

CONTESTS ARE organised by clubs, magazines, even individuals. Some are designed to appeal on a local level, and perhaps aimed at beginners as a way of improving operating skills. Others are truly global in scope, running for up to 48 hours, demanding the most of both station and operator. So the first question you need to ask yourself is what sort of event appeals? Many amateurs have their first experience of contesting during a Field Day event. In the UK there are HF Field Days, both CW and SSB, and the annual VHF Field Day. All are geared round the idea of being able to set up and operate in emergency conditions, so you are only allowed to move onto the site 24 hours or less before the contest, and may not use mains power. Some clubs take Field Days very seriously indeed. Others use them as a social event, an occasion for club members and friends to get together for a barbecue and some operating. For your first Field Day, you may be asked just to help with the logging, and do some of the heavy lifting involved in setting up the station and antennas. Or you may get to do some operating. But whatever your level of participation, you will undoubtedly find it a valuable learning experience.

Alternatively, you may be pressed into, for example, taking part in one of the RSGB Club Championship events, short (90 minute) single-band contests where even the most modest score contributes to your local club's total in the final listings. Most countries have similar events. Hopefully, one of the other club members will walk you through what is required, and probably one of the committee members will be designated to collect and submit the logs.

It is important to note that you don't have to pre-register in any way to take part in a contest. This is perhaps one of the commonest misconceptions. If you tune around the bands and hear a contest in progress, then by all means start to make a few contacts. It's a great way of getting your feet wet. Call one of the participants who doesn't appear to be too busy at the time. When he answers you, with a contest report and exchange, be prepared to ask him what he needs from you in return by way of a contest report. Once you have an idea of what's going on, make some more contacts. You don't need to worry about how to send in an entry at this stage, just log the contacts in the way you would any other day-to-day contact.

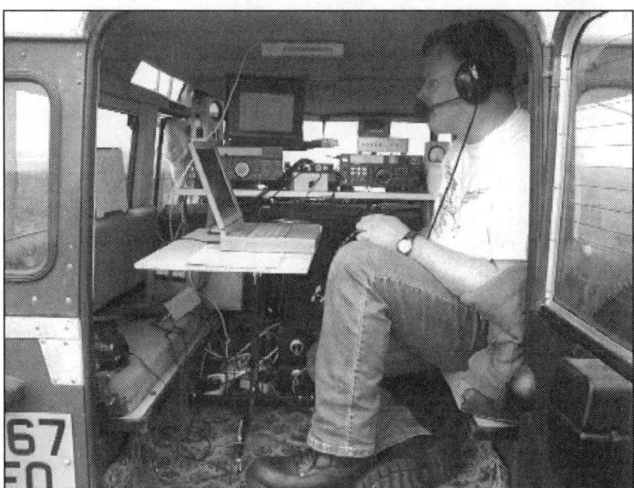

A compact portable contest station

Club contesting can involve more skills than simply operating

Incidentally, one of the joys of contest operating for some amateurs is that, because they are for short periods only, it is sometimes possible to put up temporary antennas that far exceed anything you could leave up on a permanent basis. I well remember a US amateur living in the UK some years ago, who was in a rented house on a housing estate where no external antennas were permitted. But on contest weekends he put up 30ft of mast, topped by an HF tribander, and enjoyed great success. There were no planning issues as this was a (very) temporary installation, just like putting up a marquee for the weekend, or similar.

Types of contest

ONCE YOU ARE READY to think about participating a little more seriously, you will want to prepare yourself before the event. Every contest is different, quite deliberately so, to make for interest and variety. They differ in who can contact whom, they differ in the scoring system, they differ in length, in the modes and power levels, even antennas, you can employ, and they are at different times of the year which makes for a variety of different propagation experiences. Most are at weekends, obviously to avoid clashes with work and other commitments, but some short events take place on weekday evenings to encourage band activity. Some are specifically aimed at, for example, portable operation (Field Days are one example, but the popular Backpackers events are another).

Contests also range from domestic events, where you will mainly be working other stations in your own country, to fully-fledged international events. The former are usually organised by national radio societies or by other local and national clubs and bodies. The major international contests have a much higher profile, though again are organised by national societies or, in some cases, by magazines (the *CQ* contests being the best-known example). The smaller domestic events are usually the best place to cut your teeth, as they are less intimidating than the big international events. Neophyte contesters sometimes complain, for example, at the CW speeds being used by most contesters in the *CQ*WW CW Contest. But several of the RSGB-sponsored domestic CW contests specifically have a 'QRS Corral' where participants are encouraged to slow their speed and look for contacts with less experienced operators. If you were interested in motor racing you wouldn't expect to start at the Formula 1 level, and it's a little bit the same.

Whatever your particular interest, by band, mode, etc, and whatever your level of proficiency, there will almost certainly be contests suited to you. So do take the plunge.

Where to start?

THE FIRST STEP IS to locate the contest rules. Many will appear in national society magazines, but nowadays they will almost certainly appear on the Internet and this should be your first port of call. A number of specialist sites list all contests, with links to the relevant rules and results pages. Once you have the rules, you can start planning your strategy for the contest. If you can't track down the rules, or come across a contest already in full flow on the bands, you may well be able to determine at least the basics (for example, the contest exchange) just by listening to a few QSOs being made.

Some contests are limited in their participation, perhaps to a certain country or club. The RSGB's Commonwealth Contest is a good example. Only amateurs in Commonwealth countries can be worked for points. But by far the majority of contests allow all comers. The serious participants will welcome the points they make from contacting you. Other participants will simply enjoy the activity, to which you and they are contributing.

Equally, just because you take part in a contest, there is no obligation to send in a log. However, most contest organisers welcome every log received, if only because it enables them to be more thorough in checking the logs of the leading participants (where life can get very competitive, with small margins between the leading players). Some organisers will offer incentives to get your log, for example a certificate for everyone making more than a certain number of contacts. In any case, there are usually many separate sections in which you can compete, so although you may not be competitive at the highest levels, you may be able to enter a section alongside entrants similar to yourself (Low Power or QRP for example) and even win a trophy of some sort.

Rules for RSGB Contests appear in the *RSGB Yearbook*, and also on the RSGB HF Contests Committee [2] and VHF Contests Committee [3] web pages. In any case, always check the web sites as any late changes to the rules will be found there. Several web sites provide links for other contests around the world, the SM3CER [4] and WA7BNM [5] sites being good starting places. The ARRL site [6] covers not only ARRL events, but the popular IARU contest too. And rules for the *CQ Magazine* contests appear on the magazine's web site [7]. If you don't have access to the Internet, you can usually get hold of the rules by sending a request to the contest organisers, though you may well have to ask someone with web access to get hold of the relevant address for you. The rules for most major contests stay the same, apart from minor changes, over long periods, partly because it is hard to ensure that rule changes are propagated to all possible participants (the Internet has made this easier) and partly because it allows scores to be compared year on year. And most major contests have dates which are entirely predictable year on year, too. **Table 10.1** shows the weekends on which a number of major HF contests take place.

Table 10.1: HF Contest Calendar

This calendar shows a number of the RSGB and International Contests which have dates that are predictable year on year. To find the dates of other events, check the appropriate websites.

January	
First full weekend (but never 1 January)	ARRL RTTY Round-up
Second Sunday	RSGB AFS CW
Saturday following AFS CW	RSGB AFS SSB
Last full weekend	*CQ* WW 160 CW
February	
Second full weekend	RSGB 1st 1.8MHz
Third full weekend	ARRL International DX CW
Last full weekend	*CQ* WW 160 SSB
March	
First full weekend	ARRL International DX Phone
Second full weekend	RSGB Commonwealth
Last full weekend	*CQ* WPX SSB
April	
First Sunday	RSGB ROPOCO
Second Saturday	EU Sprint Phone
Third Saturday	EU Sprint CW
May	
Last full weekend	CW WPX CW
June	
First full weekend	RSGB National Field Day
Third full weekend	All Asia DX CW
July	
Second full weekend	IARU HF World Championship
Sunday of third weekend	RSGB Low Power
Last full weekend	RSGB IOTA
August	
First Sunday	RSGB ROPOCO
Second full weekend	Worked All Europe CW
September	
First full weekend	All Asia DX Phone
First full weekend	RSGB SSB Field Day
Second full weekend	Worked All Europe SSB
Last full weekend	*CQ* WW RTTY
October	
First Saturday	EU Sprint Phone
First Sunday	RSGB 21/28MHz Phone
Second Saturday	EU Sprint CW
Third Sunday	RSGB 21/28MHz CW
Last full weekend	*CQ* WW Phone
November	
Second Saturday	RSGB Club Calls
Third full weekend	RSGB 2nd 1.8MHz
Last full weekend	*CQ* WW CW
December	
Second full weekend	ARRL 10m Contest

RSGB Online | VHFCC | IOTA | UK Contest Reflector

Radio Society of Great Britain Contest Committee

RSGB HFCC

www.rsgbhfcc.org

Radio Society of Great Britain. HF Contests Committee.

The web sites of the RSGB HF and VHF Contest Committees are a good place to start (see References)

Planning for a contest

MOST SERIOUS contesters plan their contest calendar several months in advance, blocking out the key dates and warning friends and family of their unavailability. You can participate in a contest on a casual basis, with relatively little planning, just taking part for a portion of the time, and enjoying the fun of making a few contacts. However, whatever your level of participation, there are things you can do beforehand to enhance the experience.

Once you have the rules to hand, you need to determine a number of key things. What is the contest exchange? Typically, it will be RS(T) plus maybe a serial number plus, in many cases, one other item of information such as your QTH locator or Club name. You may be able to deduce this by listening to other participants, but it isn't always possible. For example, you might hear an entrant send 59927. Is the 27 a serial number, the ITU zone, or maybe the number of years he has been licensed? Then there is the major question of what the scoring system is. This is less important if you are intending to operate casually. You can score your log afterwards and nowadays you often don't even need to do that. Even if you intend sending in an entry, the adjudicators normally rescore every log from scratch. But if you are proposing a serious entry, it is essential to know the scoring system beforehand to determine your plan of attack. More about this in a moment.

What else do you need to know? Obviously the start and finish times are vital, translated into local time (most rules specify contest times in UTC). Perhaps also operating times; some contests, for example, allow single-operators to take time out for resting, eating or whatever. You will need to understand what the rules are regarding these 'time outs', and plan to use them in the most effective way so as to have least impact on your final score.

The RSGB IOTA Contest brings lots of island stations and expeditions onto the bands during the last full weekend of July each year

It is also very important to know who you can work in a contest. Some contests are of the 'everyone works everyone' variety. Others are along the lines of 'everyone works Francophone stations - France and its overseas territories' or something similar. Such contests can be excellent opportunities to collect counters towards specific awards (in the example given, maybe French départements). Beware that some contests are closed to all except those in a particular category, eg Russians, so your participation may not be welcomed.

The rules will also tell you about the contest categories in terms of power, bands, etc. A look at previous years' results may suggest that you have a better chance of winning one particular category rather than others, maybe because you have a more effective antenna on one particular band, for example. You may also be swayed by the trophies and certificates on offer, which may encourage you to enter a particular category.

Your contest callsign

IN RECENT YEARS, special short calls have been available for use by UK clubs in certain RSGB and international contests. These callsigns have just a single-letter suffix, the idea being that they save time in a contest, when you may have to send your call several thousand times. A number of other countries have adopted a similar system, too. If your club has requested one of these callsigns, you may decide to use it instead of your regular callsign. The rules for requesting and using these special callsigns, including a list of contests in which they may be used, appear in the *RSGB Yearbook*. In practice, some amateurs take great pride in using their own callsign regularly in contests, to the point where it becomes well known on the air. Others value special callsigns, especially if the callsign concerned has an unusual prefix, as this may attract additional callers who you might not otherwise work. It is very much a matter of personal preference.

Contest scoring

WHATEVER THE SPORT, the way you approach it from a competitive point of view will depend on the rules and, especially, the system of determining the final result. In the case of amateur radio contesting, although each event has its own distinct flavour, the basic system is that every qualifying contact will generate points while, in many cases, there is scope for increasing the score through bonuses or multipliers.

To take QSO points first. In the popular *CQ* Worldwide contests, contacts with your own country count zero points, with other countries in your continent one point and contacts with other continents three points (there is one exception to this, but it is not necessary for the present discussion). Clearly there is an advantage in trying to make contacts outside your continent, which is very much the thrust of the event which is billed as a 'DX' contest. So if, as a UK station, you can be making 25 QSOs an hour on 15m, most of which are with the USA, that is better than, for example, staying on 40m to work European stations at 60 an hour (75 points an hour, to 60). In many VHF contests the scoring system is based on distance, computed from the QTH Locator of the station worked (fortunately, modern computer logging software makes this computation trivial). Again, depending upon band conditions, there may be a strategic decision to take as to whether to beam to a nearby population centre and make lots of low-scoring QSOs, or whether to try and seek out those higher scoring distant contacts, even if they are few and far between.

Bonuses and multipliers

A bonus is an additional score added each time a specific goal is reached. It might be a new county, country or zone, or even based on working a specific station on additional bands. A multiplier is similar except that, instead of being added to the QSO points, it is used to multiply them. It may well be based on the same goals - counties, countries, zones, etc. So the final score could be made up of:

QSO points + bonuses, or

QSO points x multipliers.

Again, the scoring system will help to determine your strategy. If a QSO is worth three points and a new country adds a bonus of 15 points, then it's worth missing five other QSOs while chasing that new country. But if the new country is a multiplier, it could be worth very much more than five QSOs, and it may well be worth making a much greater effort to put it in the log.

Some examples

All in all, a close study of the rules is well worthwhile. A couple of examples may help to put flesh on the foregoing discussion.

CQ WPX Contest: Each year there are three events, SSB, CW and RTTY. which are popular events in the calendar. Let's consider the *CQ* WPX CW Contest, held annually on the last full weekend of May. The contest exchange is RST plus serial number. Scoring is based on points per QSO, multiplied by the total number of prefixes worked, regardless of band. QSO points are one for contacts with your own continent and three for contacts with other continents. However, these point scores double on the low bands (40, 80 and 160). So, for example, working US stations at a rate of 40 an hour on 20m (generating 120 points an hour) is equivalent to working European stations at 60 an hour on 40m. But in May, in the northern hemisphere, the nights are quite short. What's more, single operators are only allowed to operate 36 out of the 48 hours of the contest (which starts at midnight UTC, or 0100 local in the UK). Where are the QSO points going to come from? Mainly, perhaps, assuming you are operating from the UK (depending on where we are in the 11-year sunspot cycle), from working Europeans at two points each on LF, and North Americans at three points each on HF. This tends to suggest operating throughout the hours of darkness on LF, and during the afternoon and early evening on the HF bands (when they are most likely to be open to North America). It means that sleeping and eating should probably be done during the mornings. A similar thought process should be followed wherever in the world you are, though the conclusions may be different. As for multipliers, there are so many prefixes around and you only need to work each one once, that it probably isn't worth spending a lot of time searching for new ones. If you have a good enough signal, call CQ and they will come to you. To that extent, *CQ* WPX is what is generally considered to be a 'rate' contest, where the aim is to get as many contacts into the log as possible and the multipliers will largely take care of themselves.

6m Contest: Let's take a completely different example. Suppose you intend to operate a 6m contest in June (many are scheduled for this time of the year, as there is a high likelihood of Sporadic E propagation). The rules may require you to exchange RS(T) and QTH Locator, with the score based on the distance for each QSO. Let's also suppose this is a mixed-mode contest, but you are only allowed to work each station once, regardless of mode. And the contest is for 24 hours.

How to maximise your score? Clearly it isn't simply a matter of getting lots of contacts in the log. A large number of local contacts won't score anywhere near as highly as a handful of distant contacts. So you need to focus on making those long-distance contacts. Some will come, hopefully, from Sporadic E openings. When Sporadic E comes along, you should be able to make contacts with even a modest station, but it is essential that you are alert to the band opening up. Don't stray from the radio just because the band has been quiet for a while. A Sporadic E opening may be short, and it can happen at any time during quite a wide time window. For example, from the UK in June, it is not uncommon to have multi-hop Sporadic E to North America around 0100 to 0200 local time. For the times when the band isn't wide open, though, you will want to maximise your score by working the best distances you can during flat conditions. If you live on a hilltop you may be well-placed to do so. Otherwise, you may consider operating the contest from a portable site, selecting the site with consideration to where the main populations of activity are likely to be (major cities, for example). The nature of VHF propagation and antennas also means that you can easily miss stations who are at the limit of propagation. A QSO may only be marginally possible when you are beaming directly at the distant station and he at you. With high-gain antennas with narrow beamwidth, the probability of this can be quite small, but you need to maximise it. There are several things you can do, for example by ensuring that

Not only a rare country (Guinea) but quite an unusual prefix. This operation was by regular DXpeditioner Baldur, DJ6SI

Code of Practice for VHF/UHF/SHF Contests

1. Obtain permission from the landowner or agent before using the site and check that this permission includes right of access. Portable stations should observe the Country Code.

2. Take all possible steps to ensure that the site is not going to be used by some other group or club. Check with the club and last year's results table to see if any group used the site last year. If it is going to be used by another group, come to an amicable agreement before the event. Groups are advised to select possible alternative sites.

3. All transmitters generate unwanted signals; it is the level of these signals that matters. In operation from a good site, levels of spurious radiation which may be acceptable from a home station may well be found to be excessive to nearby stations (25 miles away or more).

4. Similarly, all receivers are prone to have spurious responses or to generate spurious signals in the presence of one or more strong signals, even if the incoming signals are of good quality. Such spurious responses may mislead an operator into believing that the incoming signal is at fault, when in fact the fault lies in the receiver.

5. If at all possible, critically test both receiver and transmitter for these undesirable characteristics, preferably by air test with a near neighbour before the contest. In the case of transmitters, aim to keep all in-amateur band spurious radiation, including noise modulation, to a level of -100dB relative to the wanted signal. Similarly, every effort should be made to ensure that the receiver has adequate dynamic range.

6. Remember that contesters cannot claim exclusive use of any part of any band. Please respect other operators at all times by avoiding using, or causing interference to, frequencies set aside for other legitimate users. This applies whether the other use is prescribed by an official bandplan (e.g. the 144.300MHz SSB calling frequency on 2m), by recognised code of practice (e.g. the 50.100-50.130MHz DX window on 6m), or by common convention (e.g. the GB2RS news broadcasts on 144.250MHz). If asked to QSY because of interference to any such use, please do so quickly and courteously.

7. Above all, be friendly and polite at all times. Be helpful and inform stations apparently radiating unwanted signals at troublesome levels, having first checked your own receiver. Try the effect of turning the antenna or inserting attenuators in the feedline; if the level of spurious signal changes relative to the wanted signal, then non-linear effects are occurring in the receiver. Some synthesised equipment has excessive local oscillator phase-noise, which will manifest itself as an apparent splatter on strong signals, even if there is no overloading of the receiver front-end. Preamplifiers should always be switched out to avoid overload problems when checking transmissions.

If you receive a complaint, perform tests to check for receiver overload and try reducing drive levels and switching out linear amplifiers to determine a cure. Monitor your own signal off-air if possible. Remember that many linear amplifiers may not be linear at high power levels under field conditions with poorly regulated power supplies. The effects of over-driving will be more severe if speech processing is used, so pay particular attention to drive level adjustment. If asked to close down by a Government Official or the site owner, do so at once and without objectionable behaviour.

you keep moving your own beam heading and calling CQ regularly to all parts of the compass (a voice keyer may be a good idea for this!). You should also spend time tuning the band each time you change beam heading, to catch stations you haven't already worked - there may not be another opportunity. And you probably need to be comfortable with CW operating, for those contacts where conditions are marginal and CW may be the only way of completing.

These two examples show why it is important to think ahead. Once you have decided what category to enter, and what sort of strategy will be required to be effective, then you can start planning in earnest. What antenna system will you need? Does this require changes to what you already have, perhaps by supplementing it with some additional hardware for the contest weekend? If you plan to go out portable, then you need to locate and arrange a site, maybe organise a generator and camping equipment, and so on.

And then there's your station itself. It may be fine for day to day ragchewing or DXing, but will it be suitable for the contest. There are several aspects. Is the equipment itself optimised for the contest or maybe you need to add more filters or borrow a second receiver for finding multipliers. Is your PC fully integrated for logging (and Cluster access if you intend to enter an 'Assisted' category)? The more automated your station, the better. Whilst you may be happy to change bands manually on the PC for day to day logging, for example, 40 hours into a 48 hour contest and you may be too tired to remember to do so. Station ergonomics are important, too. Your operating chair, the position of the tuning dial and the keyboard. Again, what works fine for casual operating may lead to backache over an extended period of contest operation. And what about arrangements for eating and other requirements during the contest? Really serious contesters arrange to have food prepared beforehand or have someone to bring it during the contest, so that they don't have to leave the operating chair. Some even go to the extent of having an empty container in the shack to avoid breaking off the pile-ups to go to the bathroom! Do you have logging software that is tailored for the particular contest, so that you can track your progress as you go along? This makes a big difference. But take time to be familiar with the software before the contest; there will be too much happening during the event itself to be in a learning situation.

Obviously there is plenty of other pre-contest preparation you could be doing: station maintenance; analysing logs from previous years; running propagation predictions in order to have some idea of which bands to be on at any given time, and which directions you should be targeting as the contest progresses; maybe taking part in some smaller contests in order to improve your operating skills, or using one of the various contest simulators for the same purpose; checking the Internet and other sources to see what expeditions may be active during the contest, or try to identify where your major competition is likely to be coming from; planning your sleep patterns before the contest, so that you start the event alert and ready to be awake for long periods, and so on. For many contesters, this period of preparation and anticipation is at least as rewarding as the contest itself. This is especially true when planning a multi-operator event, maybe a Field Day entry with a local club. Planning such an activity can be a great social experience, bringing club members closer together.

Finally, do read the 'Introduction to VHF Contests' and 'Introduction to HF Contests' sections which appear in the *RSGB Yearbook*, and mesh nicely with what you will find in this chapter.

Your contest station

THE PREVIOUS SECTION made some references to the particular requirements of a contest station. Most of the things you can do to improve a contest station, such as thinking about equipment positions on the operating table, or improving your antennas, will help your day-to-day operating as well. However, any limitations in your station are much more likely to become a real nuisance in the hothouse atmosphere of a contest. Some have described DXing as a form of much extended contest. For example, if a rare station appears on the band and it takes you a couple of hours to make a contact, this is all part of the fun (unless the family are waiting for you to join them for dinner!). But in a contest, if a new multiplier appears, it may only be worth, say, five ordinary QSOs, so if you don't manage to work that multiplier in the space of a few calls you are wasting time. This is why contesters are the ones who seem to build the biggest and best stations. But this doesn't mean that you need to have something which emulates Voice of America or the BBC to be a successful contester. You might, for example, focus on a particular band, and set up highly-effective antennas for that one band. And if you are plagued by EMC problems, you could set your sights on entering the Low Power or QRP categories which most contests have nowadays. But there is no excuse for settling for second best. Just because you focus on QRP, for example, doesn't mean you have to use an elderly direct-conversion transceiver and a compromise wire antenna. Aim to do the best you can within the rules. Stick within the limits for transmit power, but ensure you have an excellent receiver, and the best antenna you can put up at your location. Install low-loss co-axial cable. Automate your station to a high degree so that during the contest you can focus your energies on the actual operating. In other words, set your sights high, and try to improve with every contest you enter.

Most of the relevant equipment considerations have already been dealt with in Chapter 3 (Setting Up your Station). The major additional concern for contest operations is perhaps being able to listen on one band (for multipliers, for example) while transmitting on another (sending an automated CQ call from a voice or CW keyer). On the HF bands you may well find that you start to suffer breakthrough between bands. There are several solutions in terms of bandpass filters and tuned coaxial stubs, and a number of suitable commercial products are available if you don't feel able to build something yourself. The problem is multiplied many times in a multi-operator multi-band contest station, and great care needs to be taken not only with filtering but with the orientation of antennas and feeder cables, earthing, and so on. Usually these multi-operator stations will have one or two team members who are well versed in tackling such problems.

On the VHF bands, it is not unusual to hear very wide signals during contests. This may be because the other station is over-driving his amplifier or it may be because your own receiver really isn't up to handling the very strong signals often encountered in the contest environment. Many of the earlier VHF-only transceivers were designed for casual day-to-day operating, and struggle in contest situations. One solution is to use a modern HF transceiver with transverter for the VHF bands. And to pull out those very weak signals, you may well need to think in terms of a masthead preamplifier. Of course, you may also take the opportunity, especially if you go out portable, to put up a bigger antenna system than your usual one, perhaps a stacked array of some sort.

Because contests are repetitive in the sense of needing to make repeated CQ calls, and of sending certain parts of the contest exchange during every QSO, voice and CW keyers are absolutely invaluable in taking some of the load off the operator. Modern logging software is designed to integrate closely with these. It saves your voice (or keying hand) and also frees you to be doing other tasks, such as tuning another band or checking propagation predictions with a view to changing antenna direction, for example. There is also a strong case for recording contests, something which has always been possible with tape recorders but which is now so much easier using the sound card and hard disc of your PC. You then have a permanent record if there are later queries, or for analysis when preparing for the next contest.

Operating the contest

THE JOY OF operating an amateur radio contest is that you never know exactly what to expect. Radio propagation, like the weather, doesn't lend itself to accurate predictions, and there will always be surprises. A successful contester learns how to play these to his advantage, rather than being thrown by, say, a solar storm or an unexpected band opening.

The trick is to be continually aware of what is happening in the contest environment. If you are entering a multi-band contest, you will need to be forever evaluating whether you are on the right band. Is there likely to be an opening on another band that you need to take advantage of? Propagation predictions, tables of sunset and sunrise times and previous years' logs can help here. So can having a second receiver, so that you can check the other bands at regu-

GU0SUP operating in an RTTY contest from Guernsey

lar intervals. Those modern transceivers with spectrum displays can be invaluable too; when a band opens the spectrum display will suddenly start showing lots of signals.

One of the key tactical decisions in any contest is when to call CQ and when to tune the bands ("search and pounce"). There is no simple answer to this. It depends on the contest rules, for example. If there is a finite number of multipliers, it may be worth spending substantial amounts of time tuning the bands to find new ones. It will also depend on how loud you are. Weaker stations will almost certainly spend more time tuning and calling, because their CQ calls are less likely to be heard. Louder stations will almost certainly spend more time calling CQ. But there is no hard and fast rule. Even a QRP station can sometimes call CQ successfully, when a band is wide open to a major area of population. It depends on the contest, too. In the biggest international contests (CQWW, for example) the number of participants runs to many thousands, and the HF bands, especially the narrow ones such as 40m, simply cannot accommodate everyone calling CQ at once, and it can be hard if not impossible to find a clear frequency on which to call CQ. In contrast, on the VHF bands there is usually plenty of room for everyone to call CQ, should they wish to do so.

The actual operating is very much the same as during day to day ragchewing and DXing, except that it needs to be very tight, with no wasted words or transmissions. Serious contesters don't indulge in pleasantries, and have recognised that in a contest where, say, they might make 4,000 QSOs (an average of 43 seconds a contact over a 48-hour contest), a second saved on every contact is 4,000 seconds saved, or time for an additional 93 contacts over the course of the contest, which might be all the difference between a first and second place. Of course, this is less of an issue in, say, a VHF contest, where time is unlikely to be a crucial gating factor. There are many ways to save time in a contest. The most obvious is to keep the transmission to only the essential data:

"*CQ CONTEST FROM MIKE ZERO CHARLIE*"

"GOLF THREE X-RAY TANGO TANGO" - no need to give his call, he knows it already.

"*GOLF THREE X-RAY TANGO TANGO 5991013*" - he gives my report just once. If I miss it, I can always ask for a repeat.

"QSL 599784" - All he needs now is his report from me.

"*THANK YOU, MIKE ZERO CHARLIE, CONTEST*" - And away he goes, looking for the next contact.

The same principles apply on other modes. Some RTTY contesters are notorious for including unnecessary information in their transmissions, presumably because it is easy to program other data into the buffers, but it wastes time. It's no different to runners in a race. They might be the best of friends, but during the race they don't chat with each other, they are focused on being first at the winning post. There is no group of amateurs more animated than contesters when they get together at social events. They are always anxious to swap contesting stories and share hints and tips. But during the contest itself they are totally focused on maximising their scores.

When calling CQ, keep your calls relatively short, but remember that stations tuning the bands will not only hear you, but need time to check whether they have already worked you. So allow a moment or two after your CQ call for them to respond. On VHF, longer calls are generally more appropriate, as distant stations may need to adjust their beam heading to maximise their reception of you.

The author, G3XTT, at the HC8N contest station (Galapagos) for the 2002 *CQ*WW CW Contest

When everything is going well, there may be times when you have two or three stations calling you at once. The trick, which comes with experience, is not to get flustered but to try and keep up a steady rhythm, going back to one station at a time. If you didn't get his full call, then make it clear, and acknowledge later in the QSO that you have it correct:

"CQ CONTEST, CQ CONTEST, GOLF THREE X-RAY TANGO TANGO"

"MIKE ZERO ALPHA INDIA MIKE"

"MIKE ZERO ALPHA STATION, 59123"

"MIKE ZERO ALPHA INDIA MIKE 59005"

"MIKE ZERO ALPHA INDIA MIKE, THANK YOU, GOLF THREE X-RAY TANGO TANGO CONTEST"

Many contest programs take care of this automatically, when you are using them to key your transceiver in a CW or RTTY contest. In other words, if you amend the callsign on the screen during the course of the contact, they will send the corrected call with the final exchange, so that the other station knows you have his callsign correct in your log.

By the way, before calling CQ in a contest, as at any other time, always check that the frequency isn't already in use. It isn't always obvious.

When you are in 'search and pounce' mode, tuning the band, you need to be alert to every station you hear. Some contesters have a routine, for example always tuning from the bottom end of the band upwards. If you hear a station you haven't worked, assess whether you should call immediately. Is he loud and unoccupied? Is he a multiplier, or a high scoring contact? If he is busy, you may decide to put the frequency into one of the memories on your transceiver, to come back later. If you are paper logging, you will need to have kept dupe sheets, to be able to see whether you have worked the station before. These are paper check sheets, usually ordered by first letter of suffix, but different people use different systems. One of the joys of computerised contest logging programs is that they take care of all this and you can put in any part of a callsign, and it will immediately show you which stations you have already worked with that particular combination of letters in the call. On the HF bands in a major contest, a good search and pounce operator using computer logging should be able to maintain QSO rates of 60 an hour or better. This may be slower than you could achieve by calling CQ but if, by tuning the band, you are also collecting multipliers, then your score may be going up faster than if you stayed in one place letting others call you.

There are plenty of other tricks for maximising your contest score. Depending on the scoring system, it may be worth moving callers from one band to another, for additional points, for example. With modern transceivers this is quite feasible. You can move bands, work the station concerned, and be back on your original frequency before anyone realises you had gone. In the days of valve transceivers, requiring elaborate tuning-up every time you moved frequency, this would have been quite impossible! Many VHF contesters will also recall the days when many stations were limited to a few crystal-controlled frequencies and it was a case of calling CQ and then tuning the band for replies. Thankfully, those days are long gone!

Contesting with Cluster assistance is a rather different matter again. Every time a 'spot' appears for a station you haven't worked, especially if it is a multiplier, you have to make a conscious decision whether to move from what you are doing to chase that spotted station (knowing that many others are probably about to do the same). Not for nothing is the Single-Operator Assisted category sometimes referred to as "Single-Operator Distracted!" To use the Cluster to advantage is an art that can only be developed over time.

After the contest

THE SERIOUS CONTESTER finds plenty to do after the contest. Fortunately, in these days of PCs, the actual log submission has got immeasurably easier than it used to be. In the past it was common to have to rewrite the log, using a huge paper check-sheet to root out any duplicate contacts, and then it would be necessary manually to score the whole thing. Once all the paperwork was ready, you would have to take it along to the Post Office and perhaps pay a substantial amount for overseas mailing. Nowadays, most contest logging programs generate the required log (usually in the widely-accepted Cabrillo format, where both log and summary data are in one electronic file - see the sidebar), which can then be e-mailed instantaneously to the organisers. In theory, it should be possible to submit your log within minutes of the contest ending. In practice, it is rarely a good idea to do this. There are mixed opinions about the extent to which it is legitimate to edit a log after the contest has finished. For example, you logged G3XTT but, after the contest, you read that I had actually been operating from Wales as GW3XTT. Should you change your log? The answer is "no", in that you clearly made an operating error, and once the contest is finished the log is effectively closed. But suppose you logged E15DI, knowing perfectly well that this was EI5DI but simply hitting the wrong key on your PC. Most contesters would accept that it is legitimate to correct this before sending in your log (especially if you made a note at the time to go back and fix it). Most importantly, though, check the Summary information in the log. Are all the details (Name, Address, e-mail address, category entered, etc) correct? If you belong to a club and need your score to count towards the club score, are the details in there?

Members of the Flight Refuelling ARS put together their monster 6m and 4m antennas for the 2002 VHF National Field Day

The trend towards electronic submission of logs is well advanced and very much to be encouraged. It helps both you and the adjudicators. It helps you because you don't have to do all that manual work any more, especially if you were using a computer to log during the contest itself. All you need to do is enter the relevant details (name, address, section entered, etc) into the header of the log and e-mail it to the published address. With Cabrillo submissions, there is no need to identify duplicate QSOs, or even to score the logs, as all this will be done anyway during the adjudication process.

For the organisers, the advent of electronic log submission removes the days of wading through heaps of paper logs, often in undecipherable handwriting, and it allows computers to do what they do best and human beings do badly, which is to plough through perhaps millions of QSO records, identifying those which tie up, and those where there are errors (for example, a miscopied callsign). Once this checking is complete, the computer can calculate the final scores. This helps to speed up the whole process of adjudication and, to help matters along even more, results are usually posted on the web, saving the inevitable delays in publishing in some sort of paper medium (magazine, results booklet, etc).

Incidentally, the adjudicators are the unsung heroes of contesting. Despite the impact of computers, there is still a huge amount of work to be done in adjudicating a major contest, right through from ensuring the rules are published correctly, to checking the logs and tabulating the results, maybe writing some sort of commentary to go with the results, organising the distribution of trophies and certificates, and reviewing the rules in readiness for the following year. Given this level of effort, adjudicators tend not to take kindly to those who have made the minimum of effort in sending in their entry - most adjudicators can tell tales of logs without key information such as section entered, logs in formats which bear no relation to that detailed in the rules, even logs for a different contest entirely! Most adjudicators are unpaid volunteers, who like to contest themselves when time allows!

For RSGB VHF contests, you can submit your log files either in Cabrillo format (which is not yet supported by many

A Cabrillo Primer

The RSGB HF Contests Committee has recently moved to adopt the Cabrillo format for RSGB contest entries. This is not to say that other formats won't be accepted, at least for the time being, but Cabrillo will be preferred, and the hope is that an increasing proportion of logs will follow the format as time goes by.

Why Cabrillo?

The first thing to say is that it makes the Adjudicators job a lot easier if logs are in a common format. Many proprietary contest logging programs generated unique log formats, which often could not be read by contest adjudicators or, even if they could, were time-consuming to convert. The RSGB HFCC has, in the past, made some attempt to adopt a standard, both by way of a straightforward text format, and also by recommending the use of ADIF (Amateur Data Interchange Format, used not only for contest logs, but for a wide variety of station log conversion purposes). Neither of these has really taken off, for a variety of reasons. Partly because they may not be supported by the major software authors, and partly because ADIF never really seems to have made a major impact as a data interchange standard.

The good news is that a standard does exist, which is already well supported and gaining ground all the time. That standard is Cabrillo. ARRL faced exactly the same issues as RSGB in dealing with many log formats, and asked Trey N5KO to work on a standard which would meet their requirements for something which was simple to implement, but would give them what they wanted. The thinking behind Cabrillo is essentially:

1. Text based, no html or other tags, both for simplicity of implementation and with the added benefit that a log can easily be eyeballed to determine whether it contains the required information.

2. All information in a single flat file, rather than having separate log and summary files, which would need to be sent as attachments. As a result, the log can usually be sent within the body of an e-mail (Attachments are treated in a variety of ways by different mailing programs and different ISPs, which can lead to problems. Note though that some contest sponsors require the Cabrillo file to be sent as an attachment but, please, always as the .log file, never as a .zip file or other form of encoding).

3. Header information (name, mode, power, etc.) is, as far as possible, generic, rather than contest-specific. This simplifies the job of the software authors, but when correctly implemented the contest sponsors should easily be able to determine which category has been entered.

4. Each QSO record contains all data relevant to that QSO (callsign of both stations, band, mode, etc.), allowing the log to be sorted in various ways for checking, but easily recreated as required.

5. The data format, while specifying desired character position and format for each item of QSO data (time, call, band, sent and received exchanges, etc.) is actually very undemanding. Essentially, provided there is white space (tab or space is fine, no slashes, commas or full stops please!) between each element, the adjudicator should be able to make sense of the log.

Cabrillo deliberately doesn't ask for data which can perfectly well be determined by the Adjudicator. So, for example, it doesn't ask you to indicate multipliers, QSO points, duplicate contacts, off periods, etc. Too many entrants mess these things up, or handle them in disparate ways. All can be figured out as and when required by the checking software.

What does a log consist of?

Let's have a look at a typical Cabrillo log:

START-OF-LOG: 2.0

CONTEST: CQ-WW-RTTY

CALLSIGN: G3XTT

CATEGORY: SINGLE-OP ALL-BAND HIGH-POWER

CLAIMED-SCORE: 484750

OPERATORS: G3XTT

CLUB: Chiltern DX Club

NAME: Don Field

ADDRESS: 105 Shiplake Bottom, Peppard Common,

ADDRESS: Henley-on-Thames, RG9 5HJ

ADDRESS: England

QSO: 21000 RY 2002-09-28 1146 G3XTT 599 14 DX RV3WU 599 16 DX

QSO: 21000 RY 2002-09-28 1146 G3XTT 599 14 DX SP9LJD 599 15 DX

END-OF-LOG:

Much of this will be common to all contests, but obviously the actual QSO data varies (typically the contest exchange). So the early part of the QSO line will remain the same (Band, Mode, Date, Time, MyCall) while the rest will vary by contest. To deal with this, preferred formats are specified on N5KOs Web page, and for RSGB contests there will also be links from the HFCC Web page. Software authors will be encouraged to support the preferred format for the various RSGB events (In the IOTA contest, by far the majority of logs are generated from just a handful of popular contest logging programs CT, SD, NA, Writelog, N1MM, LuxLog being the favoured ones). But the good news, as you may have figured by now, is that you can produce a Cabrillo log in any text editor or Word processor with the greatest of ease. Also, many station logging programs such as Turbolog allow you to output log data as ASCII text in whatever order you specify, so it is easy to set up what you require. Equally, you could keep your log in a spreadsheet, sort the columns into the required order and save as a text file. If you need to manipulate the Cabrillo file once you have generated it, then life may be a little easier if you get hold of one of the many text editors that will allow you to edit columns as well as lines (several of these exist, including both shareware and freeware programs downloadable from the Web)

Note that the minimum the organisers want is the log file. If you get a tracking number, then that's fine. The robot is happy with your entry. If you forgot some additional information (Club name, for example), or spot some error with your log, don't panic. Just resend the log. Providing it arrives before adjudication has started, it will overwrite the original log on the server, and you'll be fine.

That's it!

And that's about all you need to know. For many contests which have already adopted Cabrillo, the server runs a little routine to check for key fields in the log, and will generate an error message back to the sender if data is missing or suspect (for example if the dates and times don't correspond to the contest which is being entered). Entrants are then able to resubmit their log, when the problem has been fixed. This saves the adjudicators a lot of time which might otherwise have been spent in correspondence.

of the common logging packages) or in the standard log file format of any of the common logging packages in use. If your logging program doesn't include all necessary information such as name, address, section entered etc in the log file, you need to submit a separate cover sheet file with this information. Again full details on how to do this are on the VHF Contests Committee web page. If you don't have access to a computer to submit your log, you can obtain sample paper log sheets and summary sheets from a VHF Contest Committee member, or someone can download them for you from the web site.

Incidentally, even if you do enter casually, most contest organisers are keen to have your log as it helps them to check the logs of the serious entrants, so do take a few moments to submit it after the event.

But even when you have sent off the log, there is plenty you could be doing. The main thing is to make notes of anything you need to be aware of. Problems with your station that need to be addressed. Unexpected band openings that you need to plan for in advance of next year's contest. Strategic and tactical errors which you need to be aware of when planning for the next one. This is the time to capture all this data, while it is still fresh in your mind. It is this sort of attention to detail which separates the good contesters from the great contesters, just as in any other competitive area of life.

Contest adjudication

IT'S WORTH SPENDING a little time describing contest adjudication. It's the part that you, the entrant, don't see, but it helps to understand something of what goes on behind the scenes.

Contest adjudication is not there to penalise you (unless there are very good reasons to do so!), but to ensure that the final scores accurately reflect the relative standings of all the entrants. For example, it isn't uncommon for some entrants to use the wrong scoring system, so their claimed score is in error. Even if you think your log is scored correctly, the adjudicators may have additional information. A good example would be the Shetland Islands in the *CQWW* contests, where they count as a separate multiplier to the rest of Scotland. Many participants who work Shetland may not even realise they have done so, but the adjudicators will have a database of who is where, and will rescore those logs accordingly.

While it is possible for an experienced log checker to cast his eye down a paper log and see any obvious incorrectly-copied callsigns, there is a limit to the amount of cross-checking that can be done. To take the IOTA contest as an example, the received logs account for a total of, typically, about 400,000 contacts. Some of these cannot be cross-checked, as the station worked has not sent in a log. But a high proportion of them can be. With the best will in the world, cross-checking, say, 200,000 contacts for callsign, band, mode, report, serial number and IOTA reference is going to take an awful lot of time. But by ensuring that all logs are in a single database (paper logs have to be retyped to achieve this), the cross-checking can be done in a matter of hours with a suitable computer program.

The key thing that you, the entrant, need to know is what happens when there is an error in your log. Perhaps you have miscopied a callsign or a serial number, or mislogged the band. In the case of most RSGB contests you will probably lose all points for the contact and, if it is a multiplier, you will lose that as well (but you may, of course, have worked another station which would also count for that multiplier). Some contest organisers apply additional penalties, to encourage participants to ensure logging accuracy. In the case of the *CQ WW* contests, the penalty is three times the value of the QSO, so if it's a one point QSO, you lose three points, and if it's a three point QSO you lose nine points. Knowing this helps you to decide what to do if, at the time of the contact, you are unhappy about whether you have logged it correctly.

The adjudication of a contest, therefore, takes on several distinct stages. The first is to record all incoming logs and ensure they are assigned to the right category (high power / low power, single- / multi-band, CW / SSB / Mixed mode or whatever is applicable). If the entrant hasn't included this information in his log, the adjudicator will either try to contact the entrant and find out (this is where it helps if you have provided an e-mail address) or simply default the entrant to the lowest common denominator (so a Low Power entrant who has failed to mention this might end up consigned to the High Power category).

The next step is to get all the logs into a single database. This is where it is much easier if entrants use the recommended log format. The RSGB contest committees try to be flexible, but some logs are extremely difficult to convert if they are in an odd format and some paper logs can be pretty much unreadable!

Once the database is complete, the cross-checking can take place. Comprehensive cross-checking relies on a good proportion of the participants (or the more active participants, at least) sending in their logs, either as an entry or as a checklog (where it will be used in adjudication but not list-

A telescopic mast on a trailer provides an easy way to erect a contest antenna

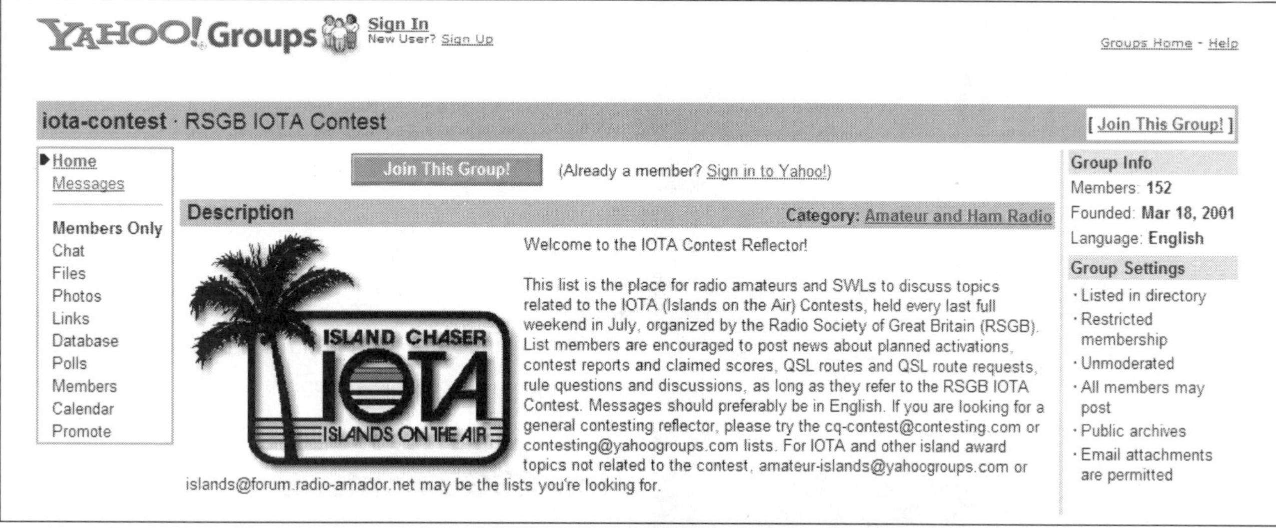

There are several places on the Internet for contesters to exchange news and information

ed in the final results). The computer software will then identify errors. At this point it may rescore the logs immediately or, in most cases, require human intervention to decide what penalties, if any, should be applied. The final scores are then drawn up.

It then remains to publish the scores and a write-up of the event. Nowadays, many contest results are published on the Internet. While, at the time of writing, the RSGB still carries scores and placings in *RadCom*, results are also available on the Internet, usually in advance of publication on paper. The ARRL has adopted a system for its contests whereby extended write-ups are available on the Members' web pages, which is a real boon for contest aficionados.

One of the great benefits of computerised log checking is that many contest organisers now offer feedback on your log. The best known are the UBN (UBN standing for Unique, Broken and Not in Log) reports which are available after *CQ* WW log checking. The title makes it clear that the feedback is essentially on how well you copied the other station's callsign. Unique calls are ones which do not appear in anyone else's log. Normally they are not penalised.

You may really have worked someone who came on and made just one contact, though it is also possible that you miscopied his callsign. Broken calls are those where the other party to the contact has sent in a log and it is clear who you actually worked. Not in Log is where you think you worked someone, but he hasn't logged you. For contests other than *CQ* WW the type of feedback varies. For the IOTA contest, which I adjudicate, I am happy to provide a copy of the submitted log, annotated where contacts have been nulled, with an explanation (wrong band logged, serial number copied incorrectly, or whatever).

Of course, the adjudicators will have other work to do, dealing with correspondence and queries from entrants, organising certificates and trophies for the winners, and reviewing the rules for the next year's event. When you need to contact them, do remember that, for most contests (and all RSGB contests) these are unpaid volunteers, with jobs and families and who like to get on the air occasionally and take part in contests themselves!

Contesting and the Internet

BECAUSE THE PROCESS described above inevitably takes many weeks, or months for a major contest, several informal means have evolved for contesters to compare notes and claimed scores shortly after a contest has taken place. The so-called '3830 Reflector' (so named because it replaces a net which used to meet on 3830kHz in the USA after major contests) has become a focal point for posting claimed scores for many of the more popular international contests.

There are also several contest 'reflectors' on the Internet specifically set up for contesters to share news and views. The US-based CQ-Contest reflector is the best known and, in the UK, the UK-contesting reflector. There is also one for the IOTA contest. To subscribe to these send blank e-mails as follows:

- To post a score to the 3830 Reflector, go to http://www.hornucopia.com/3830score/ To subscribe, simply send a message to 3830-request@contesting.com. In the body of the message type 'subscribe' only. No subject is necessary. You should receive a confirmation message back within a few minutes.
- To subscribe to the CQ-contest Internet Reflector, send a message with the single word subscribe in the subject line to: cq-contest-request@contesting.com. Within a few minutes you will receive an email giving full details of the contest discussion group. Full details may also be found on the web page www.contesting.com.
- To subscribe to the UK-contest Reflector, send a message with the single word subscribe in the subject line to: uk-contest-request@contesting.com. Within a few minutes you will receive an email giving full details of the contest discussion group. Full details may also be found on the web page www.contesting.com.
- To subscribe to the IOTA Contests Reflector (iota-contest@yahoogroups.com) send a blank message to iota-contest-subscribe@yahoogroups.com

If it seems that contesting is heavily software and Internet-based, that is no surprise. Contesters are, by their very nature, a competitive sub-group within our hobby, and use

The American *CQ Magazine* runs several of the largest amateur radio contests

every new development that comes along if it helps them achieve higher scores, reduces their overall workload, or generally improves their lot (like getting contest results out quicker). The PacketCluster system was introduced in the first instance by one of the US east coast contest groups, to enable their members to exchange data about contest multipliers. Only later did it come into use as a tool for the wider DXing community. Nowadays there are those who argue that the Cluster system should be turned off during major contests, perhaps unaware of the network's genesis!

Which takes us nicely to the use of the Cluster system in contests. The use of 'spotting' during contests goes back to when multi-operator contest categories were first introduced. Major contest clubs would have several operators at the contest site, but would encourage other club members to tune the bands and pass information about contest multipliers to the main station, usually over a 2m FM link. The advent of packet radio allowed the development of software (PacketCluster by AK1A), to make the process easier. Once PacketCluster nodes had grown up around the world and been linked (see Chapter 9 for more on the Cluster network and its use), single-operator contesters saw its potential for helping them to achieve higher scores. But clearly that would put contesters without the facility at a disadvantage. Contest organisers respond in various ways. The most common is that entrants are welcome to use Cluster to aid their contest efforts, but are put into a separate 'Assisted' category where they compete with others who have done the same, or are classified along with multi-operator entrants (the latter is the case with most RSGB contests).

Having said all this, there is a widespread view that the use of Cluster in contests has now become counter-productive. A Cluster spot often leads to huge pile-ups, inundating the potential multiplier. Those who dislike Cluster consider that it de-skills contesting, presenting new multipliers like 'fish in a barrel'. Even those who support it are sometimes heard to refer to Single-Operator Assisted as "Single-Operator Distracted", as it can be a real time-waster chasing a Cluster spot, only to find that everyone else is, too.

Nevertheless, for better or worse, the Internet is here to stay and undoubtedly will have much more impact on contesting in years to come. Already, so-called Internet Sprint contests are organised in the USA, whereby entrants are expected to submit their log by Internet within 24 hours of the contest ending, in return for which the adjudicators commit to publishing the final results on the Internet within a week. This is a huge improvement on the turn-around times of most contests, and is only possible by insisting on the use of standard log formats and Internet submission. The RSGB has now taken a similar approach with the 80m Club Championship events, and it has been well received, as participants and clubs get early feedback on how their scores are accumulating compared with other clubs.

You will find more on this topic in Chapter 4 (Computers in Your Shack).

Non-RSGB contests

THIS SECTION GIVES a summary of the rules of the non-RSGB contests most popular with UK amateurs.

CQ *World-wide (CQWW) & Worked Prefix (WPX) Contests*

CQ Magazine runs these major events annually on CW, SSB and RTTY. Each is a full weekend (48 hours) long on each mode and literally thousands of amateurs enter. *CQ*WW usually provides great opportunities to work rare countries, often activated by 'DXpeditions' who go there specifically to operate in the contests. In *CQ*WW the contest exchange is signal report and 'CQ Zone', which for the UK is '14'. DXCC Countries and *CQ* Zones worked on each band (160 - 10m) count as multipliers. In the WPX contests, scoring is by multipliers for each prefix, rather than country. This contest is unusual in that multipliers may be counted only once, regardless of band. The full rules are published in *CQ* Magazine, and on their web site.

ARRL DX contests

The American Radio Relay League (ARRL) organises major International DX contests on SSB and CW. These events, where the rest of the world works the 48 mainland US states plus Canadian provinces on all six bands 160 to 10m, are as popular as *CQ*WW. US/VE stations send report and state/province while all other stations send report and power output. The multiplier is the number of states/provinces contacted on all bands. ARRL also run single-band contests on 160m and 10m.

IARU HF Championship

The International Amateur Radio Union runs this major multimode (SSB and CW) event on all the HF bands in mid July. The RSGB Headquarters station, GB5HQ, is one of several around the world representing a country's national society. All such stations count as additional multipliers.

WAE DX Contests

Europe works the rest of the world. In this contest extra points can be earned by DX stations sending back to European stations details of their previous QSOs (called QTCs). The rules are quite complex and anyone intending to enter should obtain a copy from the German national society (DARC) who organise the events.

Portable and guest contesting

EVERYTHING THAT HAS been said so far applies as much to VHF contests as to HF contests. Perhaps the major difference with VHF contests is that, for many entrants, it makes sense to operate away from home if you want to achieve a good score. Long-distance VHF propagation is much more reliant on a high or at least a clear take-off, which isn't possible from many suburban locations. Rather than deal with portable operating here, it is covered in Chapter 11 as it is also applicable to special event and DXpedition operations. Of course, some HF contests will require portable operation, especially the Field Day events.

Another way to achieve a higher score in a contest than you might from home is to become a 'guest operator' at another amateur's station. This can be an informal arrangement, but some amateurs offer their stations for rental for the major contests, especially if those stations are on exotic islands and ready-equipped with antennas, transceiver and amplifier. The DX Holiday Web site [8] is a good starting point, and the US National Contest Journal (NCJ) [9] also maintains a list of amateurs willing to lend out their contest station to guest operators.

Amateur Radio Direction Finding

AMATEUR RADIO Direction Finding (ARDF) is a competitive activity, but rather different to the sort of contesting described so far in this chapter. ARDF (sometimes known as Amateur Radio Foxhunting) involves competitors being asked to locate one or more hidden transmitters (the Fox). It should immediately be apparent that the competitors themselves are not involved in transmitting so anyone, whether licensed amateur or not, can take part. The hidden transmitter, of course, has to operated by a licensed amateur.

ARDF events take many forms. Many radio clubs organise ARDF events, when a club member is elected to be the Fox. Other members are given some idea of the general area

A topband direction finding contest gets under way

VHF 'foxhunting'

where he is located, and then have to find the transmitter. To do so, they will usually use specially built or modified receivers, with directional antennas. By taking a series of bearings from several locations, they try to triangulate (ie locate where the bearings cross), and progressively home in the Fox. Typically, these local events will take place on the 2m or 160m bands.

For more serious enthusiasts both national and international events take place. The main UK events are organised by the RSGB ARDF Committee [10], with events run in accordance with the IARU rules. These events are run mainly on 2m, but with some on the 80m band, and at locations around the UK. The IARU rules make provision for up to six hidden transmitters (usually five in practice), located within a clearly defined area, and the event runs for a defined time period, usually 90 minutes or two hours. There are several entrant categories, by sex and age. The more serious UK enthusiasts frequently travel to other parts of Europe and farther afield to take part in IARU-organised events.

As well as VHF DF events, the UK has a long history of DF events run on the 160m band (dating back to the 1920s), and these continue under the auspices of the British Top-Band DF Association [11]. A number of events are held each year at various locations around the country, culminating in a National Final. The winner of the final receives the highly-coveted RSGB trophy which dates from 1951. There may be anything from one to four hidden transmitters to be found at any particular event. These events usually require competitors to have access to transport, though it will be necessary to revert to foot when getting close to the Fox.

Equipment

A typical club event, as described earlier, may consist of the Fox hiding in a local wood, possibly locating himself some distance from the actual transmitter to avoid giving its location away. Members set out in their cars, stopping from time to time to take bearings, until they have a rough idea of the Fox's location. They will probably use a typical commercial handheld transceiver with a small Yagi antenna, and try to find the direction of maximum signal. As they get closer to the Fox, they will almost certainly have to abandon their vehicles and head off on foot, so it is important that they are properly attired. Obviously it is also vital to have a suitable Ordnance Survey map of the area, and a compass. As they get close to the Fox, it is helpful to have an attenuator in the antenna lead, to avoid overloading of the receiver, which can give false indications.

Those taking part in the national and international events follow a similar procedure, but the IARU events take place entirely on foot, and most competitors will use equipment that has been specially designed or adapted for the purpose. Sources of both designs and kits are detailed on the RSGB ARDF web page. The various hidden transmitters will have an orienteering marker and the terrain may be quite demanding. The event has a strong element of orienteering in addition to the radio aspects.

In the case of 160m DF events, suitable equipment designs are available on the British Top-Band DF Association web page. As in the IARU events, the terrain can be demanding and rugged construction is a good idea.

Getting started

If you are interested in becoming involved in ARDF activities, you may find that your local radio club organises casual ARDF events, and you can team up with one of the more experienced members and start to learn the necessary skills. To get involved in the more demanding series of events at national level, start by reading up the relevant Web page(s), perhaps find an event that is taking place close to where you live, and go along to see what happens. Talk with the competitors (but not during the event itself!) to learn more about the type of equipment they use and recommend, and about the best way of acquiring the necessary skills. The great thing about ARDF is that it is very much a social event, unlike most amateur radio contesting where you are closeted in your own station and only meet other competitors over the airwaves. It's also a great way of getting out and about and keeping fit, though it's certainly not restricted to the younger generation.

References

[1] High Speed telegraphy: http://www.morsecode.dutch.nl/hst.html

[2] RSGB HFCC: www.rsgbhfcc.org

[3] RSGB VHF Contests: www.blacksheep.org/vhfcc/index.html

[4] SM3CER contest pages: http://www.sk3bg.se/contest/

[5] WA7BNM contest pages: http://www.hornucopia.com/contestcal/

[6] ARRL Contest Page: http://www.arrl.org/contests/

[7] CQ Contests: http://www.cq-amateur-radio.com/awards.html

[8] DX Holiday: http://www.dxholiday.com/

[9] NCJ: http://www.ncjweb.com/

[10] RSGB ARDF Committee: http://www.ardf.btinternet.co.uk/index.html

[11] British Top-Band DF Association: http://www.topbanddf.org.uk/

11 Mobile and Portable Operating, Special Event Stations

WHILE THERE IS a huge amount of fun to be gained from operating our home stations, one of the joys of the hobby is that, because we are not constrained to wires, we can conduct our operations from almost anywhere. This includes mobile and portable operation, special event stations set up at local and national events and venues, and DXpedition operating in every sense, from activating a hilltop for the Summits on the Air programme [1,2] to participating in a major DXpedition to a remote Antarctic island. And with the advent of cheap air fares, ever more compact transceivers, and international licensing agreements, especially through the CEPT Common Licence (see Chapter 2), there are few barriers to taking your hobby with you around the world. This chapter addresses these matters, giving some pointers for successful operations away from home.

Mobile operating

MOBILE OPERATING has been popular since cars first started to be generally available, probably around the 1950s, but is so much more accessible nowadays with compact, yet highly-featured transceivers, and a huge network of repeaters developed primarily to enable mobile operators to extend their range. In some countries the regulations also allow these repeaters to be interconnected with the telephone network. The advent of Internet linking has extended the scope even further.

Although the approach in this book has been to try and minimise the historical distinction between HF and VHF operation, it remains quite relevant to mobile operation. Mobile operators fall very much into two categories. Firstly, there are those who enjoy the ability to chat with other local amateurs, perhaps during the commute to the office, using one of the VHF/UHF bands, usually through a repeater which will be located on a convenient hilltop. This allows reliable communication over a relatively wide area, provided that the mobile station is effectively line-of-sight to the repeater. In some parts of the world, where repeaters can be set up high on mountains, mobile to mobile range can extend to well over 100 miles. The use of channelised operation and repeaters with a wide coverage area allows the mobile operator to communicate safely, as there is little or no necessity to adjust the transceiver once a QSO has been established. But with Internet linking (see Chapter 12), even VHF operators can enjoy worldwide contacts from their mobile stations.

G0OII who, in 2004, used his mobile station to call for help when he came upon a motorcycle accident

The other category of mobile operators is those who operate the HF bands. Often this is done as an alternative to struggling from an unsuitable home location. Although a mobile operator is constrained by way of antennas (even on 10m, a full-size quarter wave vertical is about 8ft long), there are compensations. The mobile operator can find an unrestricted hilltop or seaside location, taking advantage of the propagation benefits of such sites, and perhaps avoiding EMC problems that might occur from home. In many cases, the actual operation will take place while the car is stationary, to allow attention to be focused on tuning the transceiver, perhaps setting up for split-frequency operation, making adjustments for QRM and changing signal strengths, and all the other aspects which are part and parcel of HF operating. The more successful HF mobile operators have country totals which would be the envy of many fixed-station operators, and there are some fascinating success stories even on the LF bands, for example New Zealand to Europe on 80m, with the mobile station at the New Zealand end located right on the coast for best signal take-off.

Equipment and antennas

Mobile transceivers have to contend with relatively inefficient antennas, high electrical noise levels and rapidly fluctuating signals. A high-sensitivity receiver is required, with efficient AGC and a noise blanker (SSB) or with excellent limiting characteristics and a correctly adjusted squelch (FM). The acoustic noise level will be high and a reasonable audio output of at least about 2W will be found necessary. The good news is that there is a wide range of transceivers, both for HF and VHF (many combining both) which have been designed specifically with mobile operation in mind.

Adequate protection of the RF power amplifier against high VSWR is essential. Many mobile antennas exhibit high VSWR when wet, and if a loaded whip is used this may well have a narrow bandwidth, giving a high VSWR when out-of-tune. Many modern HF and VHF/UHF transceivers feature automatic ATUs which can be very useful in allowing the matching of a mobile whip which is slightly off-resonance. However, such radios are larger than those without ATUs and space considerations may necessitate the use of one of the separate remote-controlled ATUs which can be mounted elsewhere in the vehicle.

Mobile safety is paramount, and this demands a minimum of controls, easy-to-operate, with clear and unambiguous dials and meters, preferably illuminated at night.

The 12V power requirements should not exceed the spare capacity of the vehicle generation system. In practice this may, for example, confine the use of a 100W HF transceiver to daylight hours when the vehicle lights are not required. The average vehicle voltages fluctuate considerably and are 'spiky'; therefore internal transceiver voltage regulation and over voltage protection are very desirable. Vehicle interference may be a problem and require suppression.

A mobile transceiver should be small enough to fit in or under the dashboard - such transceivers are available in HF as well as VHF/UHF models from all the major manufacturers Some transceivers are available with a remote head for the dashboard, allowing the rest of the rig to be tucked away out of sight. Security is increasingly a problem for equipment mounted in vehicles and such head units can be easily stowed in a glove box or even taken away from the vehicle. No matter what the attractions of larger equipments are, they will demand special mountings which will spoil the car interior and may lack operating convenience.

Rugged mechanical construction is essential, because a great deal of vibration will be encountered. Note that extremes of temperature and humidity are common in vehicles.

When planning a mobile installation, consideration should be given to the possibility of using the transceiver in other modes of operation, particularly as a portable station, where the requirements are in many ways similar. For example, if a hand-portable SSB or FM transceiver is available, all that needs to be done is to obtain an add-on RF amplifier and antenna, and leave these permanently in the vehicle.

Recent editions of the UK *Highway Code* [3] have warned against the dangers of operating equipment while mobile. The present edition states (rule 127) "You MUST exercise proper control of your vehicle at all times. You MUST NOT use a hand-held mobile phone, or similar device, when driving or when supervising a learner driver, except to call 999 or 112 in a genuine emergency when it is unsafe or impractical to stop. Never use a hand-held microphone when driving."

Despite the recent changes in the law which prevent the use of a handheld mobile phone when driving, there are currently no restrictions applicable to amateur radio operation, other than the guidelines mentioned above.

The Department of Transport, in a letter to the RSGB, adds: "The *Highway Code* is an advisory code of practice in that a failure to observe any of its provisions is not in itself an offence. Such failure, however, may be used in any court proceedings which may arise. Current legislation already places the responsibility on drivers to have proper control of their vehicles at all times. A motorist who fails to do so as a result of distraction or lack of concentration is liable to prosecution". It follows that radio amateurs who operate mobile stations while actually driving should take great care not to be distracted by the radio. The basic necessity is to leave both hands free for driving and to allow the driver's head unrestricted movement, while keeping the mouth-microphone distance roughly constant. A boom microphone with headset has two disadvantages - it is conspicuous and the ear muffs will seriously impair the driver's hearing. A lightweight microphone similar to those used for hands-free mobile telephony is more appropriate.

Whichever alternative is chosen, operators should bear in mind the recommendations of the *Highway Code* and the need to maintain good audio quality. This can only be achieved by making sure that the microphone is reasonably close to the operator's mouth and that the audio gain is not excessive. It may be that if the vehicle is excessively noisy the audio gain must be kept low and the operator must speak more loudly to compensate. It must be borne in mind when making adjustments in the relative quietness of a stationary vehicle that we all tend to speak more loudly when the vehicle is moving. There is a need to ask for reports over the air and to take action to improve the quality if unfavourable ones are received. It may not be possible to operate in a noisy car or lorry travelling at 70MPH with all the windows wide open as the readability of the signal can become R3!

The rear bumper is a good site for an HF mobile antenna

The best positions for HF mobile whip antennas are the rear wings or the rear bumper bar. Commercially made bumper mounts are available and can considerably lessen the risk of unsatisfactory mounting. Many modern vehicles have plastic bumpers and care therefore needs to be taken to ensure that an effective earth connection to the bodywork of the car can be obtained so that the performance is not compromised. If the car is fitted with a towing hitch this can also serve as a very effective mounting point for a HF antenna. The ideal position for VHF or UHF mobile antennas is the centre of the roof, but this is not always possible or desirable for other reasons. Various types of mounting are available for those who do not wish to drill the car metalwork. These include gutter mounts, window-clip mounts, magnetic mounts and boot-lip mounts. An alternative method of mounting HF antennas is the triple magnetic mount which is quite an effective way of mounting a whip, although difficulties may be experienced when travelling at high speed, especially if there are gusty cross winds.

Whatever antenna is chosen, the fixing must be mechanically strong enough not to be damaged when the vehicle is travelling at high speed, or succumb to a blow caused by a low-hanging branch or other obstruction. Care should also be taken that the antenna does not project horizontally from the vehicle, even at speed, in such a way that it becomes a danger to other vehicles or pedestrians.

On the HF bands, the antenna system is the most critical component in any mobile installation, even more so than with fixed stations. The whip antenna with loading coil normally used has a low feedpoint impedance and a narrow bandwidth, and this involves careful tuning and matching for optimum results [4].

Most VHF FM operators use a 5/8-wave or 7/8-wave whip mounted on the rear wings, although in some cases this may have only marginal advantages over a /4-wave whip mounted on the roof. The most popular UHF antenna is the collinear, usually roof mounted. However, dual or even triple-band antennas are growing in popularity as they can cover several bands with only one mounting. All popular VHF and UHF mobile antennas are a good match to 50 ohm coaxial cable, and no special matching circuit is necessary.

Expensive radio equipment left permanently attached to the vehicle should always be insured against theft, and the driver's ordinary insurance may not cover this eventuality. A burglar alarm should always be fitted and, if possible, the transceiver disguised or removed completely when not in use. Information on insuring equipment can be obtained from specialist insurers.

Last but not least, it is important to ensure that the radio equipment will not affect the vehicle's electronics. This is increasingly an issue with the complex electronic engine management systems in many cars, and some models have proven to be particularly susceptible to RF, especially at the power levels typically used on the HF bands.

Operation

Mobile operation on the HF bands (and in the DX portion of the VHF and UHF bands) is little different to normal SSB fixed station operation in that there are no specific mobile calling frequencies or sub-bands allocated. The HF SSB mobile operator is usually more interested in working DX stations in fixed locations rather than other mobile stations, and mobile-mobile contacts are fairly rare, except perhaps on 1.8MHz SSB and 29MHz FM.

As the frequency is raised, the effects of the terrain through which the vehicle is passing become more pronounced. On the HF bands this is usually confined to a relatively slow variation in signal strength but on VHF, and especially UHF, individual buildings and trees will markedly affect the radio path, giving rise to a rapid and characteristic signal 'flutter' when the vehicle is on the move. Sometimes a poor VHF signal may be obtained when the car is parked in an apparently good position on the side of a hill. This may be caused by the vehicle being in a 'null', and the solution may be to move the car forward a few metres and try again. A number of HF DXers confine their operations to when the car is stationary, but enjoy excellent results through careful choice of operating site, for example a hilltop or a location close to saltwater. For those with limited antenna facilities at their homes, this sort of operation can be especially pleasurable.

Mobile operation includes "inland waterways"

RSGB mobile safety recommendations

1. All equipment should be so constructed and installed that in the event of accident or sudden braking it cannot injure the occupants of the car.
2. Mobile antennas should be soundly constructed, taking into account flexing at speed and possible danger to other vehicles or pedestrians. The maximum height must not exceed 14ft (4.3m) above ground.
3. Wiring should not constitute a hazard, either electrical or mechanical, to driver or passengers.
4. All equipment should be adequately fused and a battery isolation switch is desirable.
5. The transmit/receive switch should be within easy access of the operator and one changeover switch should perform all functions.
6. The microphone must not impair the vision or movement of the driver.
7. A driver/operator should not use a hand microphone or double headphone.
8. All major adjustments, eg band change by a driver/operator, should be carried out whilst the vehicle is stationary.
9. Essential equipment controls should be adequately illuminated during the hours of darkness.
10. Logging must not be attempted by the driver whilst the vehicle is in motion.
11. All equipment must be switched off when (i) fuelling, (ii) in close proximity to petrol tanks and (iii) near quarries where charges are detonated electrically.
12. A suitable fire extinguisher should be carried and be readily accessible.

Most mobile-mobile working takes place on the FM sections of the 144 and 432MHz bands. 50 and 70MHz are also popular, especially as there are several 50MHz repeaters and it is also possible to work into the Continent during the sporadic E season on the DX portion of the band. There is one UK 10m FM repeater licensed, and others around Europe, and this band offers the possibility of working DX relatively easily during the appropriate parts of the sunspot cycle and sporadic E season. Operating in these FM sections is channelised, which is a considerable safety and convenience advantage for the mobile operator. Instead of fine tuning a VFO dial, the operator can click a rotary switch round to change frequency and, with practice, this can be done without taking the eyes off the road. Many HF and VHF/UHF transceivers feature memories and these are extremely useful for mobile operators in that they allow fast, accurate frequency changes while on the move.

If you want to know more about mobile amateur radio, this is the book to get

The use of FM is convenient in this case because one of its characteristics is that strong signals will completely obliterate weak ones in the receiver (the 'capture effect'). Therefore operation on the same channel ('co-channel working') is often possible with two pairs of stations only 20km apart, without the annoying heterodynes typical of AM operation. The channels are spaced 12.5kHz apart in IARU Region 1, and to avoid the necessity of giving long strings of digits when specifying frequencies on the air, they have been given identification codes. This supersedes the earlier S20, RO, SU20, RUO system. Under the current system the coding starts at 145.000MHz which becomes RV48 (formerly RO), 145.500MHz becomes V40 (formerly S20), 433.000MHz becomes RU240 (formerly RUO) and 433.500MHz becomes V280 (formerly SU20).

The channel numbers are prefixed with 'V' for VHF (145MHz) or 'U' for UHF (433MHz). In addition 'R' is also used to denote a repeater channel. Lists of repeater channels are given in the *RSGB Yearbook*.

The normal way to set up a simplex contact while operating VHF/UHF mobile is to make (or answer) a CQ call on the mobile calling channel and to change frequency as soon as contact is made to one of the 'working' channels. For example, the mobile calling channel on the 144MHz band is V40 (145.500MHz) and the working channels are V16 (145.200MHz) to V46 (145.575MHz) although some of these channels are designated for particular priority uses such as emergency communication and RTTY. As mentioned elsewhere in this book, it is important to be aware of the bandplans at all times. This procedure does have its difficulties: one or more of the working channels may be occupied, but sometimes this is not apparent to both stations.

Using the standard 10-50W transceiver and a 5/8-wave whip it will usually be found that the range for mobile-mobile simplex work is very unpredictable in low-lying urban areas, and that mobile 'flutter' is a problem, particularly when both stations are on the move. One solution is to fit an add-on RF amplifier to boost the transmitter power, and perhaps also a preamplifier to improve the receiver sensitivity. Although these measures can give a useful increase in range, the extra expense, spectrum pollution and power consumption involved have led to a different and much more sophisticated technique being preferred - the use of repeaters. Repeater operation, along with Internet-linking, is covered in detail in Chapter 12.

Finally, if you decide that mobile operation is for you, the RSGB's Mobile Handbook is a useful resource [5].

Maritime Mobile operation

MARITIME MOBILE operation is an excellent way of combining an interest in the sea with one in amateur radio. The two go well together, amateur radio acting as a way of keeping in touch with friends and, if the worst should happen, a means for securing assistance. VHF operators will also welcome the activation of 'wet' squares, those Locator squares which consist purely of sea.

Chapter 2 dealt with the licensing issues related to using your UK licence from a seagoing vessel. However, if you operate from a vessel of foreign registry, as well as obtaining permission from the ship's Master, you must obtain a reciprocal operating authorisation from the country of registry. This may be relevant if, for example, you wish to operate from a cruise ship. This is analogous to obtaining licensing authority from the country concerned, and discussions elsewhere in this book regarding CEPT licensing, reciprocal licensing, etc are equally valid.

Complications can arise when you leave International waters and enter the territorial waters of another country, and the licensing situation can vary according to any bilateral, multilateral or other operating agreements in place with the country concerned. You are advised to check carefully if you anticipate wanting to operate maritime mobile under these circumstances. You should also be aware of which ITU Region of the World you are in, as amateur radio frequency allocations vary between regions.

Equipment

Favoured equipment, both by yachtsmen and ships' radio officers, is the smaller portable transceiver which will operate on 12V DC. While not a problem in a large ship's wireless room, the climatic conditions encountered on board a small yacht, especially in the tropics, were certainly not envisaged by the manufacturers of the rig, who thought their equipment was destined to be tucked, warm and dry, beneath the dashboard of a car. Initially many yachtsmen make the mistake of locating the rig among their other radio gear around the chart table. Such a position is almost inevitably going to expose the equipment to a splash of sea water sooner or later. Better to put it inside a locker next to the chart table, and run a multi-way cable to a remote alternative operating position in the cockpit.

Spares

If a yachtsman is going to set off across the Atlantic working regular skeds with friends back home it is irresponsible to do so without both spares and some knowledge of the potential weaknesses of the particular 'black box' that will be aboard. While retailers and manufacturers will normally maintain that the gear they are selling just never goes wrong, they will usually become a lot more helpful if approached with a full explanation of just why the enquiry is being made! If a /MM station goes suddenly off the air with equipment failure in mid-ocean, great concern is likely to be caused to friends who have been keeping skeds. Certainly, they know that the most likely cause is radio equipment failure, but when it actually happens they can hardly be blamed for fearing worse.

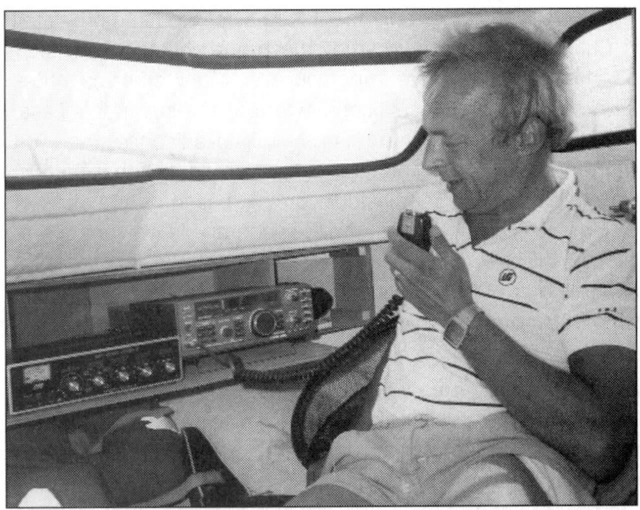

Roger Wheeler, G3MGW, operating on his boat

Power supplies

Even a modern 150W PEP transceiver will represent quite a considerable drain on a yacht's batteries and at sea it is easy to become involved in quite long operating periods without thinking. Ideally a separate battery should be carried specifically for the rig, with suitable means to isolate it from the ship's main batteries. Here again, not a 'big ship' problem for in that case the ship's AC supply will be available.

Antennas and earths

Due to its ability to operate with a near-perfect earth system a radio on a boat will put out a remarkably good signal with quite modest power. For instance, when working the UK from the West Indies, a yacht running 150W to a vertical dipole may well be given the same report as a shore station on an adjacent island which is running 500W to a two-element cubical quad! The problem is more that of the antenna being non-directional, and with the pile-up of callers who may be anxious for a contact there is no way to notch out any of the interference. In these circumstances the infallible solution is to plead a sudden navigational problem and switch off!

Shipboard antennas are normally vertically polarised and radiate an excellent low-angle signal. The favourite seagoing antenna is normally a vertical $\lambda/2$-wave dipole, although if the boat is of steel construction then a $\lambda/4$-wave ground plane driven against the ship's hull may be better.

Seagoing RF

On a merchant ship the antenna is usually well elevated and the operating position is adequately screened, but on a yacht the reverse is true and everything can easily become live with RF. The stray resonant circuits provided by the stays, rigging and wiring on a yacht can be positively dangerous when excited by a strong RF field. It is therefore far better to keep the power level down and make a really serious effort to get maximum radiation and minimum reflected power. If part of a boat's rigging is used as a radiator, remember that rigging usually comes in symmetrical pairs. For example, if one of the mast stays is a convenient 15m long, its opposite number must be detuned the favourite technique is to bridge across about 500mm with 1.2mm (18SWG) copper wire with a 500pF mica capacitor in the middle.

Even with low power, other electronic equipment on board may seriously misbehave when subjected to RF fields - remember, the makers of equipment used in small yachts never had it in mind that their gear would have to tolerate a 14MHz SSB signal in close proximity. Electronic speed/distance logs and quartz crystal clocks should be carefully checked out for RF tolerance before setting out on any major voyage.

Operating frequencies

Throughout the world, most /MM operation is carried out on the 14MHz band, irrespective of the stage in the sunspot cycle. Each region has its own net frequencies and sked times. Several web pages carry details of Maritime Mobile nets around the world [6], and it is worth carrying an up-to-date list for the areas in which you will be travelling. If you are neither /MM nor keeping regular skeds with a /MM station, a wanted contact and subsequent card will be more readily forthcoming if it is borne in mind that the net operations should be allowed to proceed without interruption to their natural conclusion before an attempt to contact is made. Most /MM operators are always delighted to chat and reciprocate a card provided they not interrupted when talking to their friends in the Mediterranean - after all, exchange of information about harbours, fishing and RF in the rigging is to the /MM operator what life is all about!

Portable and expedition operating

PORTABLE OPERATING can cover a multitude of situations. The best-known is the typical Field Day situation, mainly because this has been a feature of amateur radio operating for decades. Field Day events have been encouraged as a form of emergency preparedness, encouraging self-training in setting up and operating an amateur radio station under some sort of pseudo-emergency conditions. For example, some Field Day contest rules restrict access to site until 24 hours before the contest, and most insist on battery or generator powered operation. In the days of high-voltage valve transceivers, setting up and operating a Field Day station over a weekend could be quite a challenge. Nowadays many Field Day stations are highly sophisticated, with motor caravans ready-equipped with operating positions and even pneumatic masts, so that the whole station can be driven onto site and set up in a matter of minutes, and operations can take place in relative comfort.

As transceivers have become smaller and more power-efficient, other forms of portable operation have evolved, particularly what might be described as backpacker-style operations. In the UK the Summits on the Air awards programme is growing rapidly in popularity, especially among the younger generation of amateurs, combining as it does the joys of hill walking with the specific goal of making contacts from the summit. Often, these operations will take place with a handheld transceiver, but it is quite possible to carry enough materials in a backpack for a more ambitious operation. For example, a lightweight fishing pole can make an extremely effective antenna support for a wire dipole on HF, or can even support a lightweight VHF beam of some sort.

For all types of portable operation, one issue to consider is access and permits. It is essential to have the landowner's permission to operate if the hobby is to avoid getting a bad

Field day events are team efforts and can be great fun

name. Many Field Day groups have long and fruitful relationships with landowners and return to the same site year after year. This is unlikely to happen if there are problems, for example by leaving litter behind after the operation or leaving guy pegs in the ground which may harm animals. Common sense obviously applies here.

The term DXpedition suggests something more than a portable or Field Day type of operation. It is more likely to be from some sort of fixed location where mains power is available (though obviously not in the case of DXpeditions to uninhabited islands). There may be facilities for reasonably ambitious antennas. There are even holiday homes available to rent in several exotic locations which come ready equipped with antennas and/or equipment. All you have to do is turn up and operate.

Let's assume, though, that you are planning an expedition where you need to take everything with you. Whether a small, holiday expedition or a major multi-person effort, the same approach applies which is to plan every aspect before you go. The tick list is essentially the same, though the actual inventory will be much greater for the bigger expedition. The main headings will be licence, accommodation, equipment and antennas (including transportation) and participants. If the expedition is to a remote location, it may also be necessary to consider power and living essentials (shelter, food, drink, sanitation). And in all instances there is the matter of safety.

Licensing

In the UK, licensing is not a problem, and straightforward portable operation requires only that you sign /P (and change your prefix as appropriate, eg GW3XTT/P if I were operating portable from Wales). Nowadays licensing in many other countries is extremely straightforward, too. The European Common Licence arrangements, which also cover many countries outside Europe, enable licence holders from any of the qualifying countries to operate from any of the other applicable countries without any prior authorisation. All that is required is to prefix your home callsign with the relevant prefix of the country visited, for example LX/G3XTT if I were operating from Luxembourg.

The CEPT licensing arrangements are discussed in more detail in Chapter 2; you should study these and check for any later developments before starting your trip. Many other countries have so-called reciprocal licensing arrangements. In this case, it is necessary formally to request a visitor's licence when you want to operate from the country concerned, but that permission will usually be readily forthcoming, based on the class of your home licence. Incidentally, the general rule with any sort of overseas licensing is that you are allowed the lowest common denominator of the two licences, though this is no longer universally true. You should always check if you are unsure.

Where no reciprocal licensing arrangements exist, the situation can vary enormously from country to country. Most countries are happy to issue licences to visitors, but many will want you to apply in person at the local licensing office when you arrive in country. In some of the emerging nations the process can take several days, requiring repeat visits to the licensing authority. A search of the web will often turn up the information you require to obtain a visitor's licence, and OH2MCN maintains a web site [7] with detailed information. Alternatively, track down someone else who has operated from the same location in the past, and they will almost certainly be willing to help.

It is important to point out that licensing alone is not enough in some locations. For example, although the European Common Licence covers the French overseas territories, operation from several of the Indian Ocean islands requires additional permits from the local administration dealing with those islands. Without this additional authority, any operation is likely to be closed down by the authorities and, in any case, will not be accepted by any of the major Awards issuers (eg ARRL's DXCC or the RSGB's IOTA programme).

Sites and accommodation

Finding somewhere to operate from away from home can be difficult. Unlike most tourists, radio amateurs have very specific requirements. Even to do some casual holiday operating, you will need to be able to erect an antenna of some sort. And it doesn't make sense to try and sneak an antenna out of your hotel room without first discussing this with the hotel management, as there may well be difficulties if the management later discover what you are doing.

G4ODA and G1GSN operated on the 6m and 2m bands, just 2.5km south of the Arctic Circle in Iceland.

The antennas at XT2DX, Voodoo Contest Group operation from Hotel Splendide, Ouagadougou, Burkina Faso

Usually, by far the best way is to contact your hotel beforehand, explaining your specific requirements, and seeking their help. For a modest operation, you may simply be asking for something like a top floor room, with access to the roof to be able to string a wire dipole or erect a vertical. Surprising as it may seem, given that most hotels in Europe or North America would probably look askance at such a request, in many parts of the world it will be readily accommodated. Often one of the hotel employees will be made available to help with your project, climbing palm trees, running cables, or whatever is required. All that is asked in return is a very modest tip.

For more ambitious operations, other options need to be considered. You may want to seek out a location with specific attributes, such as space for several antennas or a seafront location, to take advantage of the enhanced propagation which is characteristic of a take-off over saltwater. Renting a villa or caravan may be preferable to hotel accommodation. Given that more and more radio amateurs are undertaking 'DX vacations' it isn't surprising that there is a web site called 'DX Holiday' [8], where you can find suitable venues to rent. Many are owned by radio amateurs, and can often be rented to include antennas and/or equipment. The only limitation is that most will be booked for major contest weekends well in advance. In the case of expeditions to uninhabited islands, for example for IOTA purposes, different considerations will apply, and it may be necessary to take tents, along with a generator for power, and the necessary prerequisites for cooking and general outdoor living.

On HF, the best sites for expedition or Field Day operations are usually somewhere wet, ideally close to the sea but otherwise with a high water table. However, it is worth bearing in mind that additional antenna gain can also be achieved from a high site where the ground slopes towards the direction(s) of most interest. At VHF there is something of a myth that height above sea level is everything, but this is far from being the complete story. What is more important than plain elevation is whether the site has a clear unobstructed take-off in the important directions. This can mean that even a small rise of a few tens of metres can be a very good location if the surrounding land for a good number of miles is essentially flat. If you happen to live near to the coast, a site on or very close to the water can be excellent, particularly on 70cm and higher, since you will be able to take advantage of the fragile marine ducts which sometimes form over water and break up very quickly when they hit land. This said, nothing is ever hard and fast, and these sorts of conditions are not present for so very much of the time, so under normal circumstances you could well be better off on a site which is further inland but higher. If, like many people, you are planning to use a site which is some way inland, then height certainly seems to become more important and ideally you want to be a good few hundred feet above the surrounding terrain. However, even away from the coastal plains of the country there are many flattish parts of the country where sitting on top of a relatively small 'dimple' will pay big dividends. The alternative view, propounded for example by W6JKV, with numerous successful 6m DXpeditions to his credit, is that a low takeoff angle and maximum signal are best achieved from a seafront location, benefiting from 'ground enhancement' and low signal absorption over saltwater. The final decision depends on what sort of operation you envisage, and the various constraints you may be facing.

Suppose, for example, you were looking for a site for a VHF contest. Since there is no 5000ft mountain in the UK which has a clear shot for 360°, and which is only 10km from the coast in all directions - and even if there were it would already be well and truly booked by a major contest group - it is very important to try and decide what directions are important to you, and these may vary from contest to contest. For a major Europe wide contest, the bulk of activity is likely to be in Central and Southern England and in the rest of Europe - for this sort of event you will want to pick a site with a good take-off in those directions. However, a UK-only contest with postcode multipliers will lead you to wanting a different site,

A vertical antenna mounted close to the sea can be surprisingly effective

This simple VHF/UHF portable station has the mast supported by the car and a ground spike

with a good take-off to most of the UK, and you may be prepared to sacrifice some performance into Europe. If you are planning to travel any distance, you will probably make your initial choice of site from looking at the Ordnance Survey maps; however, you cannot rely on this alone - you really need to go and take a look at your proposed site before the contest to check out how to get access etc. At this point a good hint is to take a small station with you - perhaps even just a mobile - and make sure that the beacons or even repeaters at your proposed site are as loud as or louder than in the rest of the surrounding area. If you do not have any amateur station with you, you can get a fair idea from just using ordinary broadcast VHF stations on the car radio.

As a quite different scenario, you may be planning an HF expedition to a Pacific island, with the hope of making plenty of European contacts. It probably won't be feasible to make a reconnaissance trip, but you may be able to contact others who have operated from there and ask their advice on locations. Perhaps a particular hotel is well sited or has been especially helpful to DXpeditioners in the past. But you will also want to check out the topography of the island to ensure that, for example, there isn't a mountain between you and the path to Europe. Even when you locate a suitable hotel, there may be a need to negotiate for a particular room, for example one that is away from other parts of the hotel and with access to land on which you can site your antennas, or perhaps roof access for the same reason. Some DXpeditioners, when undertaking such operations, actually leave the final decision on location until they arrive, building a day or two into their itinerary to seek out the most suitable location.

Whatever your portable site, whether a field for a 24-hour contest or a hotel location for a three-week DXpedition it is usually a bad idea simply to turn up on the day and hope for the best. Good Field Day sites are usually already known to and used by active contest groups. DXpedition rental locations also tend to be booked for major HF contests. So, unless you choose the approach described at the end of the previous paragraph, do make contact with the owners well in advance, discuss your requirements and, if possible, make a site visit or, at the very least, try to find another amateur or group of amateurs who have operated from that location, and seek their advice. It is especially useful to make contact with local amateurs if they exist. If you do so, then you stand a good chance of building up a relationship which could prove extremely valuable. If you fail to do so, you risk alienating them, with the complaint that you are somehow invading their 'turf'. This is true also of local radio clubs.

When setting up temporary antennas and station, whether in a field or in hotel grounds, both in the UK and overseas, do be sensible - don't obstruct gateways and paths, don't damage any of the surroundings, don't leave litter (many of the items we use such as tape and cable can be harmful to animals) - basically, observe the Country Code.

Equipment and antennas

The choice of equipment and antennas for expedition operations will be determined largely by the goals of the operation. For Field Day and other UK-based contest and temporary operations, there may be little to limit you. Some groups have been known to tow several trailer-mounted towers to a site and set up multiple antennas, along with quite sophisticated stations, perhaps in a caravan or other similar vehicle. One very successful German group even managed to transport a station of this magnitude overland (and by ferry) to Morocco, to set multi-operator records in the CQWW Contests which will probably stand for many years. If you are planning, say, a Restricted entry in Field Day, the rules will limit what you can use, but it does make sense to take back-up equipment, as Murphy invariably joins the team on such occasions too!

For many overseas contest and expedition operations, there may well be limitations imposed by airline or other baggage restrictions. Airline baggage restrictions vary according to ticket type, by airline and by geography. A limit of 20kg for hold luggage plus 5kg for hand luggage is not untypical. Given that a portable transceiver probably weighs around 7kg, a suitable switched-mode power supply a further 2kg, and a laptop maybe 5kg, the allowance will usually preclude heavy antennas or a linear amplifier, especially if you need to take along some clothes and other essentials, too! If there are several people in the group, then it may be possible to take advantage of part of their baggage allowance in addition to your own. If weight restrictions are critical, the easiest antenna to pack is a pre-cut piece of wire, with lightweight co-axial feeder, which can then be suspended from a suitable support on site. For example, a sloping dipole can be tied to a hotel room balcony at the high end, and to a suitable tree at the lower end. If you need to take your own support, a 10m fibreglass mast, suitable for both verticals and light-

A big expedition will involve transporting a lot of equipment, and sorting it all out on arrival!

weight dipoles or loops, will weigh only about 2kg. You can always pay for an additional baggage allowance, if you so wish, but be aware that most airlines charge on the basis of 1% of the First Class fare per kg of baggage above the agreed limit. An alternative is to ship some of your equipment ahead through one of the many freight companies such as UPS or FedEx, but beware that it may well sit in customs at the far end until you arrive, along with local licence and the necessary duty, to arrange for its release.

Depending on your destination, it is always advisable to take along a basic toolkit for sorting out the kind of problems which inevitably arise. A screwdriver, wire cutters and insulating tape are probably the bare minimum, but a small multimeter, soldering iron and solder and perhaps an antenna analyser may also prove invaluable. In many countries you will be able to buy basic tools at a local hardware store if necessary. Equally, if you are heading for a remote island, it will be necessary to prepare for a wide range of eventualities and to anticipate what tools and spares might be needed. Don't try to ship lead-acid batteries. This is dangerous and they are, in any case, heavy. It is usually possible to rent such batteries and/or a generator at your destination. After all, every car uses one.

In this day and age, it is particularly necessary to be aware of restrictions placed by airlines on the sort of items which can be carried. For the most part, amateur radio equipment is best sent as hold baggage, as many of the items we use are nowadays prohibited from carriage in your hand luggage. However, this then runs the risk of your baggage being delayed or misrouted. Unfortunately, these are inevitable consequences of the world in which we live.

Nowadays, there should be few problems with customs when shipping a modest amount of amateur radio equipment, though it is always sensible to carry photocopies of the original receipt, to show that it was bought, duty-paid in your home country. For large amounts of equipment, it is more sensible to do the job properly and use the internationally-accepted *carnet* procedure, which involves itemising every piece of equipment that will be shipped in and out of the destination country. Be aware that the charges for processing such a *carnet* are quite high.

Much more could be said about planning for, and successfully undertaking portable and expedition operations. Check the references at the end of this chapter for suitable further reading.

Special Event Stations

SETTING UP A SPECIAL event station, perhaps as part of a local show or celebration, is physically much the same as setting up a portable Field Day style station. What is different about a special event station is that there will be members of the public around the station. Indeed, its very purpose is to showpiece our hobby to the public at large. This has a number of implications for those organising the station. Firstly, safety aspects must be paramount. See the section on safety later in this chapter. It applies to all portable and expedition operations, but is particularly important when members of the public are in the vicinity, as they will not be familiar with the hazards of antenna systems (guy wires, trailing cables, winches, etc) and equipment (high voltages, interference if they accidentally touch a key or microphone, etc). Secondly, attention must be given to ensuring that members of the public understand what the amateur radio station is about, or the effort will be wasted. Thirdly, there may be issues of interaction with other activities at the event (radio control aircraft, PA systems, etc). Let's consider these in turn.

There is nothing worse as a member of the public than arriving at an amateur radio demonstration, only to see the backs of the operators, perhaps busy on CW, with no information about what is going on. Unfortunately, this scenario is all too common. It's not easy to ensure that a nice 59 phone contact is in progress at all times, for visitors to listen in to. Most will not be able to read CW and many will have trouble with the sound of SSB. Even when signals are crystal clear, if the operators are using amateur radio jargon, the conversation may well be impenetrable.

The GB50 special event station at Windsor Castle, celebrating the Queen's Golden Jubilee, was an excellent example of how a special event station should be put together. Visitors were met in a 'meet and greet' area where they could be given a quick overview of what was happening and were able to see some exhibits of radio equipment, new and old, as well as a display of posters explaining something of the hobby. They were then taken into the operating room, where they were able to watch and hear contacts being made, with their host there to explain what was going on. The operators themselves wore headphones so as not to be disturbed by this noise in the background, but their contacts were audible on loudspeakers. A world map was kept up to date with pins

A few friendly faces, some posters and a couple of radios being operated in full view of passers-by was the welcoming scene at GB2STF

showing contacts being made. There was also an APRS (see Chapter 12) demonstration, with a map display showing the location of mobile stations in the vicinity. The station log was being echoed in the public area on a large LCD display, with statistics such as countries worked, number of contacts made, etc. Visitors were able to take away a leaflet about the hobby and a sample QSL card, along with details of clubs in their home area and a contact number for one of the organisers, should they wish to learn more.

Putting on such a massive effort is beyond the means of most clubs (GB50 was a joint effort of two active radio clubs and the RSGB itself), but there are many aspects which even the most modest clubs could copy with sufficient forward planning.

As far as possible EMC issues with other aspects of the event is concerned, this again requires proper pre-planning and tests. At a local show, for example, it is important to check before the show opens to the public that there is no interaction with the PA system or other key installations. Be ready with clip-on ferrite rings and other anti-breakthrough measures.

Publicity and public relations

This is not the place to go into a great deal of detail about these topics, which are covered elsewhere ([9] for example). However, suffice to say that at the planning stage of any expedition, contest operation or special event it is worth thinking about what sort of publicity is required and how best to achieve it. Many operations will benefit from some sort of pre-announcement in the various amateur radio bulletins and magazines, though this is less appropriate for contest operations unless they are from somewhere rare and exotic. Special event operations, to be successful, also need wider publicity, perhaps in the local press. Have material ready, and be prepared to ghost-write any articles, to avoid a reporter who knows little or nothing about the hobby putting the wrong slant on what you are trying to do. The RSGB, either directly from headquarters or via its various regional representatives, can usually help with background material, but you will also want to put together a story that links this to the particular event that you are attending. When the operation is underway, take plenty of photographs and perhaps video, for later use. Nowadays, the Internet is also a great way to promote what you are doing. Most DXpeditions, many contest operations, and quite a few special event operations have excellent web sites, which help to generate interest throughout the amateur radio community and beyond. Some examples are included at the end of this chapter [10, 11, 12], to show you what is possible.

Sponsorship

A word, too, about sponsorship, as this often comes up in the context of DXpeditions and special event operations. It is rather less appropriate to contesting, which amateurs do very much for their own gratification, so that it is unreasonable to expect others to cover the costs (though it can be argued that this happens in many sports!). Sponsorship can range from having a local company help with the production of QSL cards, in return for some publicity, to the loan of the latest transceivers and antennas. When seeking sponsorship, always put the case not only for why you believe it is appropriate (for example, by explaining the nature of the special event and its significance to radio amateurs and/or the public), but also what the sponsor can expect to gain from it. Sadly, many radio amateurs, having successfully obtained sponsorship for an event or expedition, rapidly forget about their sponsors after the event, neither mentioning them in articles or talks, or even extending the courtesy of a thank-you letter with some words about how well the event went. Sponsors remember this next time!

A special event station can be a good way to introduce amateur radio to youngsters

GB50, from Windsor Castle, was one of the highest profile special event operations to have taken place in the UK. One of the visitors was RSGB Patron HRH the Duke of Edinburgh

Safety

SAFETY COVERS MANY aspects, and every portable, DXpedition and special event operation will be different. This section can do more than give guidelines, starting with antenna erection, which is potentially one of the more dangerous activities you will be involved in.

Antenna erection

Portable operating generally means that antennas should be erected as high as practicable, usually supported by means of a tubular mast. Carefully select the antenna you intend to use - small tri-band beams can give quite good performance but for superior gain the quad is hard to beat. However, being three-dimensional, it can be tricky to get in the air. Best of all, use monoband yagis, which are lighter and have less wind resistance than trapped antennas.

Now for the mast itself, the erection of which may well be the most dangerous activity contemplated in setting up for the contest, special event or expedition - so do have sufficient help and carefully plan exactly what you are going to do. Make sure that everyone helping understands what is expected of him. If you have not erected a mast before or have a limited amount of help, do not be too ambitious. Choose thick-wall scaffolding poles, not the thin-wall TV antenna masts which tend to buckle very easily. The tubular section should be joined with external sleeve clamps, *not* the

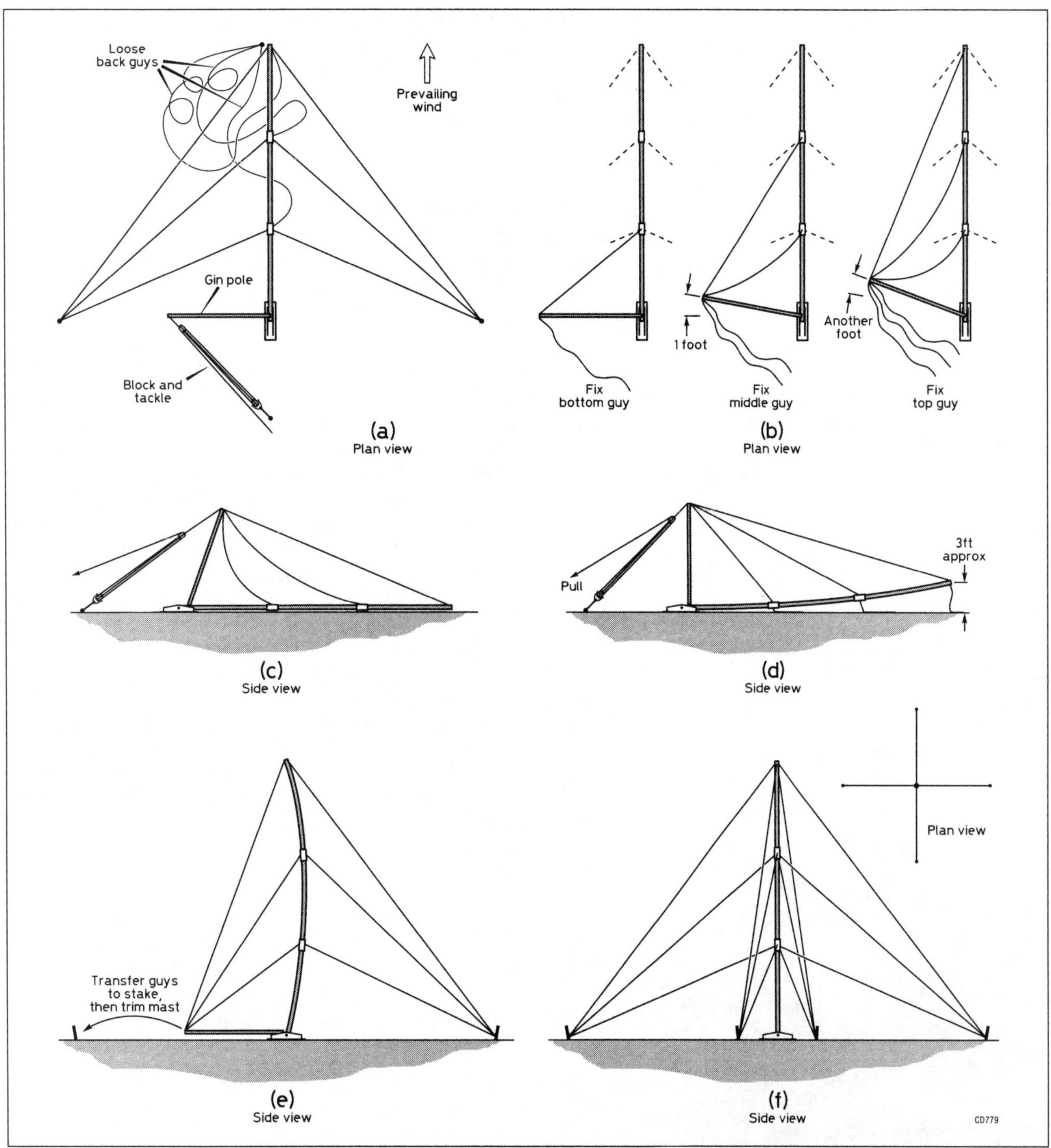

Fig 11.1: Erecting a mast using the gin-pole method. The mast typically consists of three scaffold poles giving 60ft, with another pole for the gin-pole. Guys are 8mm polypropylene. (a) Overhead view showing the mast and gin-pole laid out on the ground prior to erection. (b) Setting the pre-bend; the amount varies the top load. (c) Side view showing the gin-pole being raised using the block and tackle. (d) As the guys take the strain, the mast should be slightly bent as shown. The antenna can now be fitted to the top of the mast. (e) With the mast in position, the gin-pole guys are transferred to stakes and adjusted to remove the bend (the other two sets of guys are not shown for clarity). (f) The mast in final position. Note the procedure should be reversed to lower the mast, ideally lowering away from the wind

interior expanding type of connector. When using a sleeve with a bolted flange arrange the flanges to oppose the bending during lifting, or better still weld two more ribs at 90° to the bolt flange to provide additional rigidity. The person in charge of the group erecting the antennas should check personally that all of the bolts have been tightened. It is worthwhile using shake proof washers. A gin-pole is practically essential, and if properly constructed will simultaneously ease erection of the mast and increase the overall safety of the operation (**Fig 11.1**).

As a rule of thumb, the gin-pole should be a third of the length of the mast. If a base plate is being used it should be securely fixed to prevent slipping when lifting the mast. There should be a ring of four guys for each section of the mast. Calculate the length of guys beforehand and have them already prepared and clearly marked - allow a reasonable amount of spare for handling and tying off. The guy stakes should be placed on a circle with a radius not less half than the height of the mast. Use substantial lengths of angle iron driven into the ground at an angle away from the mast. The depth required will depend on the soil composition but usually if they are driven in about 60/90cm they should be adequate for most installations. Strips of reflective material to mark the low end of guys and stakes may prevent one of the helpers driving or walking into them in the dark. Be especially careful in placing guys and stakes if you are on public property and near to public footpaths.

If there is a wind blowing, always raise and lower the antenna into the wind. The force that can be applied to a beam at 15m by a strong breeze may take the guys right out of everyone's hands. Be prepared to accept reduced height rather than risk the loss of the entire installation to a powerful gust of wind.

Use gloves to handle rope, and everyone working close to the mast should wear some form of protective head gear. As shown in the plan view in Fig.1 the side guys should be securely tied to the stakes though they will probably need adjustment once the mast is up. The back guys should be tied to the back stakes rather than risk the mast going 'over the top'. The gin pole must *always* have side guys and these should be tied to the side guy stakes. It is best to allow some slack when side-guying the gin pole.

If the mast does get out of control and starts to fall, call to everyone on site to stand clear and if possible, let it fall gradually. Heroics could mean a trip to the hospital - antennas are easier to mend than bones!

Portable operation doesn't have to involve a lot of equipment. The author is operating 'backpacker-style' on Blencathra (LD-008 in the Summits on the Air program)

Generally, with a knowledgeable and experienced team, it is realistic to think in terms of heights of up to 60ft for a gin-pole erected mast which will support only wire antennas, and up to 40ft for a mast supporting some sort of HF Yagi or VHF array. A useful, and safer alternative to the gin-pole arrangement is a push up (or pump-up) mast, which is often available on the surplus market.

Other aspects of safety

Electrical safety is also very important when using mains-powered equipment literally 'in the field'. Check the continuity of all earth leads on distribution boards and cables that are likely to be used. Do not rely on the generator frame sitting on the wet grass as the safety earth return - use a proper earth spike and bond it to the generator - this can also reduce interference. All gear should be fully enclosed against misplaced fingers.

Never erect masts near overhead power lines. Finally, remember that weather can play strange tricks on high exposed locations. Go prepared with plenty of warm clothing as well as some in reserve, sleeping bags and the means of obtaining some hot food under extreme conditions.

There are many other aspects of safety which you should think about before undertaking any sort of operation away from home. In the UK, from a site not too far from a major town, it may be sufficient to have a First Aid kit and mobile phone available on site, preferably with at least one member of the team knowledgeable in First Aid. At a more remote location, you might need to let others know where you will be and when you are expected back. Expeditions to remote overseas location may be faced with a wide range of other hazards. The UK-based Five Star DXers Association, for example, in planning its recent DXpeditions to Indian Ocean islands, has had to plan for the dangers of malaria, tropical cyclones, and the need for medical evacuation off the island for anyone likely to need a blood transfusion or anything more than basic medical treatment. The group has also tried to ensure that at least one team member is a qualified doctor. In addition, one section of the *DXpedition Manual*, which all participants are expected to be familiar with, deals specifically with health and safety matters. DXpeditions to the more remote Antarctic islands often have to go to the extreme of having a ship with helicopter standing off, in case a rapid evacuation is required.

It is also worthwhile, if you are going to be in a remote location, to be aware of any medical concerns relating to team members. For example, there may be a diabetic on the team who needs to ensure that he has sufficient supplies of insulin, and the team doctor or first aider needs to be aware of where these are kept.

Whatever safety considerations are appropriate for the type and location of operation you are undertaking, do ensure that all team members are aware of them and know what to do in the event of an emergency.

Has all this sounded rather negative? It is difficult to treat a subject such as safety in anything but a serious manner. Above all safety on site is the application of common sense. Being aware of the potential dangers and doing something about them can help to ensure an enjoyable and successful operation.

Generators

FINDING A SOURCE of power at any portable site is a major consideration for many operations. If you are just running a few tens of watts you may well be able to get away with battery power (many Islands on the Air and Summits on the Air operations do, for example), but more substantial stations require an inordinate amount of effort to ensure a ready supply of battery power - particularly if you are at the top of a mountain! The obvious alternative is a generator, and these can be extremely reliable and behave just as you expect. However, equally, they can be an immense source of frustration and the cause of hours of lost operating. The basic choice is between diesel and petrol (although gas power is also feasible) but nevertheless all the options are expensive to buy or hire! Most sets produce 220VAC or 240VAC, although battery charging 12VDC or 24VDC sets produces an attractive alternative solution for modest power stations. Petrol or gas engines can both stop in driving rain, and have been known to lose regulation upwards, which is potentially dangerous. Putting a box in line between the generator and equipment which will cut the load if voltage outside the limits 200-270V is detected is an excellent insurance policy. Some groups opt to use a UPS (uninterruptible power supply) between generator and station. This has several benefits, ensuring constant voltage and an uninterrupted supply should the generator fail or need to be stopped for refuelling.

You should bring the generator up to its governed speed before connecting the load, and also isolate the load before stopping the generator. Sometimes it is necessary to have a steady load such as an electric fire constantly connected to ensure steady operation of the generator, as the requirements of an SSB or CW station are very variable and can be more than the generators governor can cater for.

Both petrol and gas engines use spark-ignition which can cause potential EMC problems, and the storage and transport of upwards of 20 gallons of petrol needs to be considered. 'Hot' filling of petrol generators can be very hazardous, especially in windy weather.

Diesel generators run on very cheap fuel but can be difficult to start

Nowadays, some portable operators use alternative sources of energy

Diesel sets can be difficult or impossible to start after long periods of storage unless they are 100% healthy, and summer grade fuel can freeze in March. Diesel is very prone to develop bacteriological contamination during storage, particularly in the summer, and especially when stored in clear or white vessels/pipework. Diesel sets are bigger and heavier than similarly-rated petrol sets, but are far more economical and, as an extra bonus, fuel can be tax-exempt 'red' diesel, available from boatyards etc. Anything bigger than 5kVA is best trailer mounted in order to reduce the manhandling hazards in rain or snow.

Generators of all types need to be sited away from the main antenna lobe, downwind, and where cables do not cross footpaths. One big issue is how big a generator do you need? In general, a much bigger one than you might at first expect! This because most transmitters have capacitor-input power supplies which draw current only on waveform peaks, causing high copper losses in the alternator. As a 'sizing' guide, aim for a generator with a VA rating fourfold greater than the required transmitter output PEP. Even with a generator significantly bigger than this, with most valve amplifiers you should not expect to see the same power output on the generator as you do at home, mainly because the HT will be down. As an example, on a 240V mains supply a typical amplifier using a pair of 4CX250s has the EHT supply sitting at 2.6kV off load, and the amplifier will deliver about 600W - on a 9kVA 230V generator it is down to 2.3kV, and will only deliver 450W, and on a 2.5kVA petrol generator you are down to 300W RF output! The only real solution to this problem is either to have much bigger amplifiers than you need, or to use those with choke-input supplies which take current over the whole mains cycle. Some forms of switched-mode supplies can also be a good option.

Cable size may be less significant than expected, because of the high source impedance of the generator as compared with domestic mains. Ex-building-site alternators are often 220VAC brushless types and produce a square-wave EMF. Better types with proper sine wave output exist, but these have brushes, and may therefore be less reliable and present possible EMC problems. Beware of heavy oil consumption - smoky generators could run out of oil and seize if run continuously for 24 hours. Also beware of vibration - avoid the temptation to get 240VAC out of a 220VAC mechanically governed set by raising the governed speed by 10%. The engine mountings etc may have a high Q and be ineffective (or worse) at anything other than the intended mechanical frequency.

Many alternators have the neutral connected to the frame, but others have the L-N output fully insulated. Chalk hilltops in summer present earth conductivity problems, even assuming it is possible to drive in an earth stake, and in all cases it is necessary to think carefully about safety in terms of fusing and RCCB/ELCB performance, especially if using multiple generators as part of a single installation (see previous section). If you don't fully understand this side of the system, get good advice from someone who really does!

One final point is that of physical safety - when using a crank handle, fingers and thumb must go on the same side to avoid risk of injury in event of kickback, and all belts, chains and shafts must have guards.

References

[1] SOTA: Summits on the Air, RadCom, July 2004, page 47

[2] SOTA: http://www.sota.org.uk/

[3] *Highway Code*: http://www.highwaycode.gov.uk/

[4] *Radio Communication Handbook*, 7th edn, ed Dick Biddulph, M0CGN, RSGB, 1999.

[5] *Amateur Radio Mobile Handbook*, RSGB

[6] Maritime nets: http://www.cruiser.co.za/radionet.asp

[7] Overseas licensing: www.qsl.net/oh2mcn/license.htm

[8] DX Holiday: www.dxholiday.com

[9] *DXpeditioning, Behind the Scenes*, Neville Cheadle G3NUG & Steve Telenius-Lowe G4JVG, RadioActive Publications, 2000.

[10] GB50 (Special Event Station): www.gb50.com

[11] 3B9C (DXpedition): www.fsdxa.com/3b9c

[12] K2KW (Contest operations): http://www.k2kw.com/tv.html

12 Repeaters, Packet Radio, APRS and Internet Linking

MUCH OF THIS book relates to real-time, point-to-point communications, where you are in direct contact with another amateur station, either line-of-sight, or taking advantage of various propagation modes to send your signals beyond the horizon. This form of communication has its limitations. The station you are in communication with must be on the air at the same time as you are, and propagation must be such as to make the contact possible.

Not surprisingly, amateurs have sought means to overcome both these limitations; time and distance. The chapter discusses those means, and how to take advantage of them.

The first mechanism we will discuss is the use of voice repeaters. These have now been in use in amateur radio for thirty years or so and exist in order to permit communications over distances well beyond the horizon, even when band conditions are 'flat', in other words when signals really are limited to line-of-sight. As such, they operate mainly on the VHF and UHF bands, though there are also some repeaters on 10m. The solution, quite obviously, is to site repeater stations at a high point such as a hilltop or on top of a very high mast, so that it can receive signals from a wide area and retransmit them over a similar area. **Fig.12.1** illustrates this diagrammatically. Depending on the location of the repeater station, contacts can be made reliably over quite large distances. I recall operating from a car in California and talking on the 2m band with other amateurs some 200 miles or so away. This was possible because the repeater I was using was on a mountaintop.

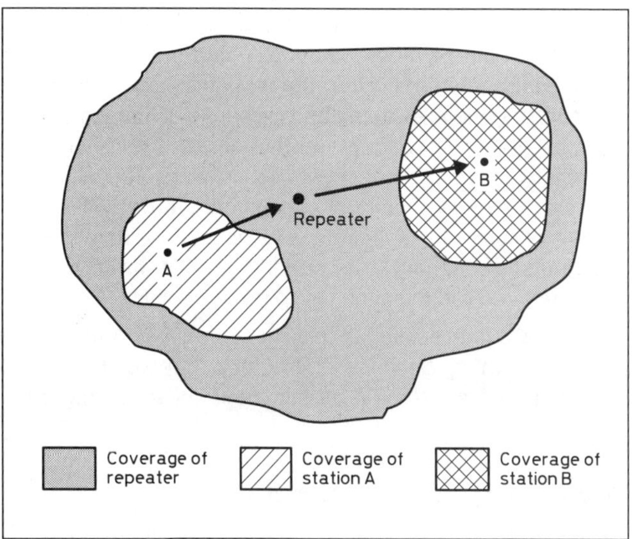

Fig 12.1: The improved range of communication available between mobile stations using a repeater. The simplex coverage areas of stations A and B shown are constantly changing shape as the two vehicles pass through different terrain, and thus the two stations would have to be quite close before reliable simplex communication was possible

The licensing of repeaters requires that they can be remotely switched off if necessary, as they are normally unmanned and often in quite remote locations. They may also share a commercial mast with other users, so it is essential they are built and maintained to professional standards so that they don't cause interference to other services. Satellites are, of course, simply a repeater on a *very* high 'mountain'! However, given the specialised nature of operating through satellites, they are given a separate chapter in this book.

With the advent of data communications, especially Packet Radio, the way was opened up for dealing not only with distance but time. The Packet Radio network which evolved in the 1980s allowed global distances to be covered, by passing data from node to node, using an addressing and routing system which ensured that the messages got to the correct place. But it also removed the need for both parties to be in their radio shacks at the same time, as messages could be left at mailboxes, from which they could be collected later.

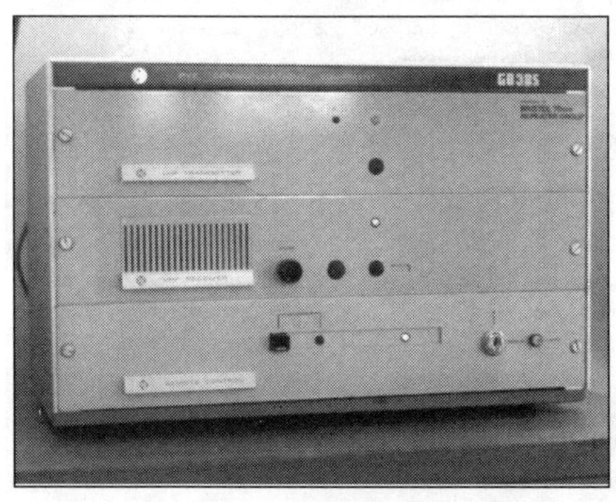

Ex-commercial equipment is often used to form the heart of a repeater [Photograph: GB3BS 70cm Bristol]

More recent developments, mainly as a result of the Internet, take both voice and data networks a step further. The linking of voice repeaters and other nodes to the Internet, which required special licensing arrangements, has removed any distance restrictions so that it is now possible to use a handheld VHF radio to talk to someone on the other side of the world, very much as you might do with a mobile phone. In a sense, this is nothing new. Many voice repeaters in the US have been linked to the telephone system for 20 years or more, but there is a substantial cost associated with long-distance telephone calls and, in any case, many countries (including the UK) did not allow such linking. The Internet, not so much because of its technology but because of the commercial structure under which it operates, is essentially distance-independent, so that there is no more cost or difficulty in linking voice repeaters in Australia and the UK than there would be in linking similar repeaters in London and Birmingham. And unlike the telephone system which is based on point-to-point communications, the Internet allows anyone to connect from anywhere, so that many parties can participate simultaneously in such communications. At the same time, the Internet has become the backbone for linking national Packet Radio networks, so that it is no longer necessary to use limited HF or amateur satellite facilities to carry packet traffic around the world. The Automatic Positioning Reporting System (APRS) described later in this chapter takes full advantage of Internet linking, although it can certainly be used independently of the Internet for specific applications.

It is not unreasonable to expect the convergence of amateur radio and the Internet to move on further as the years go by. Cheap storage means that voice and image, as well as data, could be stored within the repeater network, allowing the sort of voice messaging and exchange of images that we take for granted nowadays in other areas of our lives. Your handheld or mobile transceiver (quite possibly including a camera, as many mobile phones already have) will be the means of communicating with voice, image and data to other amateurs throughout the world, marrying fixed network (Internet) and radio technology for total flexibility.

There is a final section in this chapter on ATV (Amateur TV) repeaters which, because of the much greater bandwidth required for fast-scan TV, remain independent of the other systems discussed here.

Voice repeater operation

VOICE REPEATERS were introduced initially to facilitate mobile operation. As you travel round in your car, perhaps talking to another mobile operator, the distance between the two of you can change rapidly, and you may lose communications. Repeaters were installed to help avoid that. However, they also facilitate operation with small handheld transceivers. There is nothing to stop them being used by fixed stations either, though the normal code of conduct is that mobile and portable stations take priority. Having said this, some clubs set up repeaters with the specific aim that they allow members, whether from home or car, to communicate with one another around the club's catchment area. The repeaters on the 10m HF band allow extended range operation at times when the MUF is low (ie times of sunspot minimum), allowing the band to be useful for more than just ground-wave communications when ionospheric propagation is impossible.

A repeater is a device which will receive a signal on one frequency and simultaneously transmit it on another frequency. Thus a low-power transmitter, for example in a vehicle, can transmit on the repeater's 'input channel' and the signal will be faithfully reproduced on the repeater's 'output channel'. Careful design has meant that repeaters can receive and transmit in the same band. This means that one antenna can be used for both reception and transmission.

In effect the receiving and transmitting coverage of a mobile station becomes that of the repeater and, since the latter is favourably sited on top of a hill or high mast, the range is usually greatly improved over that of unassisted or 'simplex' operation. Typically the effective range is increased from the order of 10-25km from the mobile station to something like 50km in any direction from the repeater, depending upon terrain and band used. Another advantage is that contact with other stations becomes more predictable. The coverage of stations A and B in Fig 1 continually changes shape as the two stations pass through different terrain. Thus it is never easy for the mobile operator to estimate his simplex range. In contrast, the repeater service area is a known and much less variable factor. One further advantage is that mobile 'flutter' is usually diminished due to the superior antenna location at the repeater site.

How a repeater works

A repeater is an unmanned relay station and therefore requires an automatic system to control its operation. This logic system must ensure as far as possible that the repeater only relays signals intended for that repeater, and that those signals it does relay come up to an acceptable standard in respect of frequency, strength and deviation. For example, there is little point in the repeater relaying a signal which is so weak that it is unintelligible.

It would be very wasteful of power to have an FM repeater transmitter left on continuously if there were no signals being relayed and so it is arranged (with the exception of 23cm repeaters) that it is only switched on when a signal for relaying is present on the input channel. To ensure that signals which are not intended for relaying cannot accidentally switch on the repeater transmitter, UK repeaters on 2m and 70cm conform to IARU Region 1 specifications which, traditionally, has required a short audio tone (toneburst) to be sent by a user at the start of a transmission (tone access). This tells the repeater to switch on its transmitter. Once this has been done other stations may carrier re-access the repeater indefinitely until it is no longer required. It will then automatically switch its transmitter off and another toneburst will be required if further use is to be made of it. It should be noted that the use of

Code of Practice for voice repeater operation

1 Avoid using a repeater from your base station; it is really for the benefit of the local mobiles. If you really must use it, use the lowest possible power and a directional antenna to avoid interfering with other repeaters on the same channel which you may not be able to hear. To be sure, use a CTCSS tone to access only the repeater you want.

2 Listen to the repeater before you transmit to make sure it is not in use. If you hear a local station you wish to call, listen on the input frequency to check whether the station is within simplex range before calling.

3 Unless you are specifically calling another station, simply announce that you are "listening through", e.g. "G1XYZ listening through GB3ZZ". One announcement is sufficient. If you are calling another station, give its callsign followed by your own callsign, e.g. "G2XYZ from G1XYZ".

4 Once contact is established:

(a) at the beginning and end of each over you need give only your own callsign, e.g. "From G1XYZ";

(b) change frequency to a simplex channel at the first opportunity (especially if you are operating a fixed station);

(c) keep your overs short and to the point or they may time-out, and do not forget to wait for the 'K' or 'T' (if used);

(d) do not monopolise the repeater as others may be waiting to use it;

(e) if your signal is very noisy into the repeater, or if you are only opening the repeater squelch intermittently, finish the contact and try later when you are putting a better signal into the repeater.

5 If the repeater is busy, emergency calls may be made by tail-ending before the 'K', and announcing (a) that you have emergency traffic, and (b) which facilities you wish a station to provide. This will normally in most 'risk-to-life' situations be a telephone so that the other station can alert the emergency services. Do not reply to an emergency call if you cannot provide the services requested.

Table 12.1: UK repeaters, CTCSS tones

Tone A = 67.0Hz	Tone B = 71.9Hz	Tone C = 77.0Hz
Tone D = 82.5Hz	Tone E = 88.5Hz	Tone F = 94.8Hz
Tone G = 103.5Hz	Tone H = 110.9Hz	Tone J = 118.8Hz

the 1750Hz access tone is gradually being replaced by CTCSS (Continuous Tone Controlled Squelch System) access and CTCSS is now mandatory for all new UK repeaters. 1750Hz tone burst access, to the current standard, will continue to be permitted in addition to CTCSS. CTCSS consists of a sub audible tone in the range of 67 to 254Hz which is continuously transmitted in addition to the actual voice signal. In the UK, each repeater will have a designated CTCSS access tone, determined by its geographical location (see the Repeater Management Committee web site [1]), and will only respond when the correct tone is used. The use of sub-audible tones was first introduced for 29MHz and 50MHz repeaters (for which it is the sole means of access) to avoid the problems of co-channel interference during periods of enhanced conditions with Continental repeaters which share the same frequency. The system has been successful, hence the extension of its use to repeaters in the higher VHF and UHF bands. There are nine tones in use in the UK, each designated by a letter of the alphabet (**Table 12.1**). Repeaters with the CTCSS facility available transmit the appropriate letter in Morse code after the callsign so that users can know what tone is required.

In order to make the best use of a repeater it is desirable to have knowledge of how the repeater control logic works in outline, and a typical sequence of events during a transmitting over is as follows. The repeater receiver is switched on continually and monitors the input channel, using a squelch system.

When a signal appears on the input the control system determines if:

- the signal has tripped the squelch (ie it is of adequate strength);
- there was an audio tone (toneburst) or CTCSS tone of correct frequency and duration present; and
- the received signal is correctly deviated.

If these initial conditions are satisfied (known as a 'valid access') the control system will switch the repeater transmitter on and allow the receiver audio output to modulate it. During the transmission, the control logic continuously monitors the incoming signal level and, if it falls at any time below the standard required for valid access, may switch off the transmitter or disconnect the receiver audio from the modulator. When the transmission is finished and the incoming signal disappears from the input channel, the repeater squelch will close and indicate to the control logic that it must ready itself for the next over. After a short delay the repeater will signal it is ready by transmitting either a 'K' or 'T' in Morse code.

The short delay between the end of an over and the 'K' (or 'T') is quite important. During this interval the repeater will still relay any new signals on the input channel. Consequently this interval may be used by a third station quickly to announce its presence by giving its callsign. The use of 'Break' is unnecessary as the repeater users will already be listening for such a call. This practice is termed tail-ending and is a good way of inserting urgent or emergency messages between overs. If the repeater has relayed a signal for more than a certain period of time (typically two minutes on 144MHz and five minutes on 432MHz) the control system may go into a 'time-out' mode, close the talk-gate, and possibly transmit some form of 'busy' signal until the incoming signal disappears off the input channel. This is done primarily to prevent overs from being too long, but is also a useful anti-jamming measure. It should be noted that some repeaters do not incorporate time-out devices, but it is good operating practice to keep repeater overs to less than a minute whether or not time-out is fitted.

Equipment considerations

Modern VHF transceivers incorporate CTCSS as a standard feature, so that the use of voice repeaters presents no problems. If you are using a modified PMR or a homebrew transmitter, do ensure that the transmitter, receiver and toneburst or CTCSS are operating correctly before you try using a repeater - *do not align equipment through a repeater.*

UK 144MHz repeaters have their inputs 600kHz lower than the outputs according to IARU Region 1 recommendations, while the 432MHz repeaters have their inputs 1.6MHz higher than the outputs. Most commercial transceivers have the useful ability of being able to reverse this frequency shift at the touch of a button. For example, assuming the transceiver was set to channel RV62 (145.175MHz transmit, 145.775MHz receive) the frequencies would be reversed as soon as the REVERSE-REPEATER switch was depressed, becoming 145.175MHz receive, 145.775MHz transmit. It thus allows the operator to listen on the repeater input channel (the ability to listen on any frequency in use for transmission at the station is required by UK licence regulations).

50MHz repeaters use a 500kHz shift system with the transmit frequency below the receive frequency. 1.3GHz repeaters use a 6MHz shift with outputs from 1297 to 1297.375MHz and inputs from 1291 to 1291.375MHz. There is just one 29MHz UK repeater licensed at present and this uses the standard worldwide system of output channels above 29.600MHz with 100kHz downshift.

Repeater antennas may be mounted on a high building. [Photograph: GB3BS Bristol 70cm repeater]

Table 12.2 gives a list of voice repeater frequencies in use in the UK, along with their designations. The RMC web page and the *RSGB Yearbook* include a full list of all repeaters, including frequencies and required CTCSS access tone.

Using a repeater

The proper use of a repeater requires a high standard of operating ability and courtesy. Knowledge of the way in which repeaters work and confidence that one's own equipment is 'spot-on' does help, but also required is an ability to express yourself concisely; this being especially important on a repeater with a high level of activity. It must also be remembered that the purpose of repeaters is to facilitate mobile communication, and therefore mobile stations should be given priority at all times. If it is required to test access into a repeater, the callsign and purpose of the transmission should be stated, eg "G3XTT testing access to GB3ZZ". The repeater will respond with a 'K' or 'T' if access has been made. CQ calls are not normally made through repeaters; instead stations usually announce they are "listening through" the repeater, eg"G3XTT listening through GB3ZZ". One such announcement is sufficient.

If it is apparent after setting up a contact that the stations are likely to be within simplex range of each other, the input channel should be checked. If signals are reasonable, the repeater should be vacated and the contact completed on one of the simplex channels. This is especially important if both stations are fixed.

Sometimes stations outside the repeater's service area will access the repeater successfully, but their signals will be very noisy and they may only open the repeater squelch intermittently. If this is the case, the contact should be terminated and another attempt made when a better signal into the repeater can be obtained. Repeaters are not intended for DXing. If there is a lift in propagation, this is the opportunity to make long-distance simplex contacts, not to try and access distant repeaters.

If you wish to join an existing contact on the repeater, you should transmit your callsign in the gap immediately after one of the participating stations drops carrier but before the 'K' or 'T'. Don't worry if you are a little slow in doing this as the repeater will inhibit the 'K' or 'T' as soon as it senses another transmission is taking place. The use of "Break" on its own is unnecessary and illegal as an amateur should always identify his/her transmission using a callsign. To insert emergency or urgent messages, use the time before the 'K' or 'T' to announce your callsign and the problem, eg "M0CDX/M emergency, road traffic accident A46/A606 junction".

Because many UK repeaters will time-out after a few minutes, lengthy repetition of callsigns wastes the time available for each transmission. For example, "From G3XTT" is quite sufficient at the beginning and end of each over. A spell of listening will soon show that two common operating errors are timing-out and forgetting to wait for the 'K'. As a result, the repeater may eventually interrupt communication and the user, quite unaware of this, may spend up to a minute or so blocking the repeater to no avail. A simple time-out warning device may therefore prove useful.

There are two selfish attitudes that should be discouraged. The first is the practice of "taking another 'K'". This defeats the idea of sharing out the available air time to all users, ie it defeats the time-out of the repeater. The second bad practice is to use the gap before the 'K' to make a comment about the previous over. A good operator waits for his/her over before commenting because they realise that otherwise they are preventing the proper use of the gap to allow others to join in by inserting their callsign.

Certain repeaters, especially those outside the UK, may have different requirements, but if the rule 'listen before transmitting' is followed this should present no particular problem.

Repeater groups usually have available literature with full details of their repeater and its facilities, which is well worth studying. Contact the keeper (see *RSGB Yearbook*). Several UK repeaters can link to one another and this is usually achieved by sending an appropriate DTMF tone to the repeater which activates the link. Further information on this is available from the RMC web site.

The UK repeater network

UK FM repeaters are operational in the 29, 50, 144, 432MHz and 1.3GHz bands, giving coverage of most of the country. All repeater callsigns are in the series GB3-plus-two-letters, and callsign identification is regularly given in Morse code at 12WPM.

All UK repeaters are designed, built and maintained by groups of enthusiasts under the overall management of the RSGB Repeater Management Committee which has full responsibility to the licensing authority for all aspects of repeater operation, including technical standards and frequency allocation etc. There are no 'closed' or private

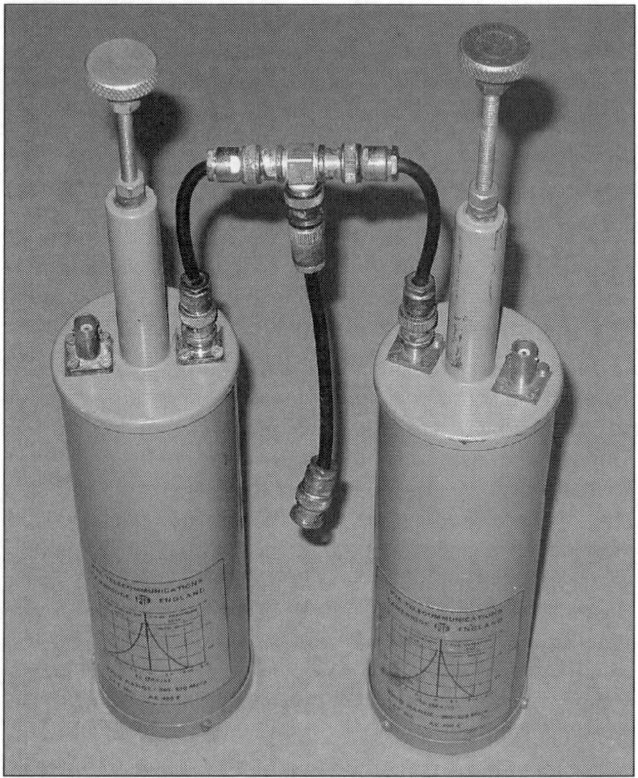

Repeaters use cavity filters to ensure that the receiver is not blocked by the transmitter. [Photograph: GB3BS Bristol 70cm repeater]

Table 12.2: Voice repeater frequencies in use in the UK

HF

10m

INPUT FREQ	OUTPUT FREQ
29.540MHz	29.640MHz

VHF/UHF

6m

CHAN	INPUT FREQ	OUTPUT FREQ
R50-0	51.210MHz	50.710MHz
R50-1	51.220MHz	50.720MHz
R50-2	51.230MHz	50.730MHz
R50-3	51.240MHz	50.740MHz
R50-4	51.250MHz	50.750MHz
R50-5	51.260MHz	50.760MHz
R50-6	51.270MHz	50.770MHz
R50-7	51.280MHz	50.780MHz
R50-8	51.290MHz	50.790MHz
R50-9	51.300MHz	50.800MHz
R50-10	51.310MHz	50.810MHz
R50-11	51.320MHz	50.820MHz
R50-12	51.330MHz	50.830MHz
R50-13	51.340MHz	50.840MHz
R50-14	51.350MHz	50.850MHz
R50-15	51.360MHz	50.860MHz
R50-16	51.370MHz	50.870MHz
R50-17	51.380MHz	50.880MHz
R50-18	51.390MHz	50.890MHz

2m

CHAN	INPUT FREQ	OUTPUT FREQ
RV48	145.0000MHz	145.6000MHz
RV49	145.0125 MHz	145.6125MHz
RV50	145.0250MHz	145.6250MHz
RV51	145.0375MHz	145.6375MHz
RV52	145.0500MHz	145.6500MHz
RV53	145.0625MHz	145.6625MHz
RV54	145.0750MHz	145.6750MHz
RV55	145.0875MHz	145.6875MHz
RV56	145.1000MHz	145.7000MHz
RV57	145.1125MHz	145.7125MHz
RV58	145.1250MHz	145.7250MHz
RV59	145.1375MHz	145.7375MHz
RV60	145.1500MHz	145.7500MHz
RV61	145.1625MHz	145.7625MHz
RV62	145.1750MHz	145.7750MHz
RV63	145.1875MHz	145.7875MHz

70cm

CHAN	INPUT FREQ	OUTPUT FREQ
RB0	434.600MHz	433.000MHz
RB1	434.625MHz	433.025MHz
RB2	434.650MHz	433.050MHz
RB3	434.675MHz	433.075MHz
RB4	434.700MHz	433.100MHz
RB5	434.725MHz	433.125MHz
RB6	434.750MHz	433.150MHz
RB7	434.775MHz	433.175MHz
RB8	434.800MHz	433.200MHz
RB9	434.825MHz	433.225MHz
RB10	434.850MHz	433.250MHz
RB11	434.875MHz	433.275MHz
RB12	434.900MHz	433.300MHz
RB13	434.925MHz	433.325MHz
RB14	434.950MHz	433.350MHz
RB15	434.975MHz	433.375MHz

70 cm (wide)

CHAN	INPUT FREQ	OUTPUT FREQ
RU66	438.425MHz	430.825MHz
RU68	438.450MHz	430.850MHz
RU70	438.475MHz	430.875MHz
RU72	438.500MHz	430.900MHz
RU74	438.525MHz	430.925MHz
RU76	438.550MHz	430.950MHz
RU78	438.575MHz	430.975MHz

23cm

CHAN	INPUT FREQ	OUTPUT FREQ
RM0	1291.000MHz	1297.000MHz
RM2	1291.050MHz	1297.050MHz
RM3	1291.075MHz	1297.075MHz
RM5	1291.125MHz	1297.125MHz
RM6	1291.150MHz	1297.150MHz
RM8	1291.200MHz	1297.200MHz
RM9	1291.225MHz	1297.225MHz
RM13	1291.325MHz	1297.325MHz
RM14	1291.350MHz	1297.350MHz
RM15	1291.375MHz	1297.375MHz

repeaters in the UK - all are available for general use. The annual cost of running a repeater is around £500 (licence, electricity, etc) and every regular user of a repeater should join the repeater group to support it and contribute to its funds.

Over ninety 144MHz FM repeaters are licensed, using IARU Region 1 repeater channels RV48-RV63. The network was originally planned on a basis of non-overlapping service areas, but additional repeaters have been brought into service to cope with the increasing popularity of FM mobile operation, especially in the major cities where the amateur 'population density' is high.

432MHz repeaters far outnumber those on 144MHz in the UK. The IARU Region 1 frequencies are used, but the input and output channels have been transposed to avoid placing the output adjacent to the amateur fast-scan TV band. The channel number prefix 'RB' is used instead of 'RU' to denote the UK system. UK 432MHz repeaters were originally planned on a grid basis, each one nominally serving a 33km square. Consequently each has more of a local and community character than the VHF repeaters.

About a dozen 1.3GHz repeaters are currently licensed. These use channels RM0 (input 1291.00MHz, output 1297.00MHz) to RM15 (input 1291.375MHz, output 1297.375MHz), ie 25kHz spacing and 6MHz shift. Unlike repeaters on the lower bands, these repeaters mostly use horizontal polarisation and radiate a continuous carrier (to act as beacons) when not being used for talkthrough.

The *RSGB Yearbook* includes a full list of UK repeaters, including some useful coverage maps. You can also find a full list on the RMC web Site.

Problems with repeaters

From time to time in urban areas there is abuse or jamming (mostly on 144MHz band repeaters). The best advice is:

" Do not respond in anyway at all on the air to unlicensed transmissions or abusers.

" Do not approach suspected offenders as this can encourage further abuse and may prejudice investigations already underway.

" Help to gather as much information about the problem as possible.

For example, write down dates, times, and frequencies when the interference took place. Note any pattern of operation, suspected location of offenders, details of any bearings obtained with DF equipment etc. Tape recordings of the interference can be useful. Also details of other callsigns, names and addresses of those who have heard the interference as well. A copy of this information should be sent to the repeater keeper (see the *RSGB Yearbook*). If problems per-

Guidelines for the Use of the Packet Radio network

The packet radio network in the UK and throughout the world is an immensely useful tool for the dissemination of information, the seeking of help and advice and the publication of amateur radio related news. It is not uncommon to find messages giving information on AMSAT, RAYNET or other similar AMATEUR RADIO related activities.

The *GB2RS* news is also available on the network, as is local club news in the area of a particular mailbox. This use of the network is what was in many operators' minds when they spent large amounts of time and money in developing it. With the advent of high speed modems and use of dedicated links, some in the microwave bands, the Packet Radio Network is developing and hopefully will continue to do so for many years to come.

The RSGB Data Communications Committee, in consultation with the Radiocommunications Agency, has devised the following guidelines with which all operators are urged to comply. These guidelines have been split into five sections in order to reflect:

1) The need for messages to be within the terms of the licence conditions and the implications if they are not.

2) Messages which could result in legal action being taken by other amateurs or outside bodies.

3) Actions to be taken when amateurs identify cases of abuse.

4) Unattended Operation.

5) General Advice.

SECTION 1: Types of Message

a) All messages should reflect the purposes of the amateur licence, in particular "self training in the use of communications by wireless telegraphy".

b) Any messages which clearly infringe licence conditions could result in prosecution, or revocation, or variation of a licence. The Secretary of State has the power to vary or revoke licences if an amateur's actions call into question whether he is a fit and proper person to hold an amateur licence.

c) The Radiocommunications Agency has advised that the Amateur Radio Licence prohibits any form of advertising, whether money is involved or not.

d) Messages broadcast to ALL are considered acceptable but should only be used when of real value to other radio amateurs, in order to avoid overloading the network.

e) Do not send anything which could be interpreted as being for the purpose of business or propaganda. This includes messages of, or on behalf of, any social, political, religious or commercial organisation. However, our licence specifically allows news of activities of non profit making organisations formed for the furtherance of amateur radio.

f) Do not send messages that are deliberately designed to provoke an adverse response. Debate is healthy but can sometimes lead to personal attacks and animosity which have no place on the Packet Network.

g) Unfortunately the very success of the network has resulted in messages appearing which are of doubtful legality under the terms of the UK Licence. The use of 7+ and other like programs to pass text and binary based material in compressed form via the Network has become common practice.

Users must always be aware of the licence conditions in BR68 (also copyright, and illegal use of software, or software which when decoded and used may contravene the License) when entering such messages into the Network via their local BBS. If in doubt consult your local Sysop or your local RSGB Data Comms Committee representative.

SECTION 2: Legal Consequences

a) Do not send any message which is libellous, defamatory, racist or abusive.

b) Do not infringe any copyright or contravene the Data Protection Act.

c) Do not publish any information which infringes personal or corporate privacy e.g. ex-directory telephone numbers or addresses withheld from the Yearbook.

SECTION 3: Action in Cases of Abuse

a) Any cases of abuse noted should be referred in the first instance to the DCC Chairman care of RSGB HQ.

b) It is worth noting that any transmissions which are considered grossly offensive, indecent or obscene, or contain threatening language, may contravene the Wireless Telegraphy (Content of Transmission) Regulations 1988 and should be dealt with by the police. This action should also be co-ordinated through the RSGB DCC initially.

c) Mailbox Sysops have been reminded by the Radiocommunications Agency that they should review messages, and that they should not hesitate to delete those that they believe to contravene the terms of the licence or these guidelines. It is worth remembering that their licence is also at risk as well as your own.

SECTION 4: Unattended Operation

a) As of July 1994 unattended operation of Digital Communications cannot be carried out without giving 7 days notice in writing of operation to the Manager of the Local Radio Investigation Service (RIS). (BR68 Para 2(5)) The manager may, before the commencement of operation, prohibit the Unattended Operation or allow the operation on compliance with the conditions which he may specify.

The RSGB Data Communications Committee recommends supplying the following information when applying to your local RIS office for permission to operate unattended digital operations.

1) An external close down switch or other means of closing down the station, which is separate from the rest of the premises.

2) A list of 4 persons including telephone numbers who can close down the Station. (Not all need to be amateurs)

3) Travelling times and availability times (I.E.: 24hrs) of close down operators of the Station.

4) Frequencies of operation (within BR68 clause 2 4(c)) antennas and powers used.

5) Use of Station for Digital Operation. (I.E. PMS, NODE etc)

6) Only the licensee can reactivate the Station after permission from the RIS.

SECTION 5: General Advice

a) With the advance in software writing it is now possible for packet users to set up intelligent software nodes (G8BPQ and similar applications) via a PC and radio. The RSGB DCC strongly recommends that users contact their local packet group and local BBS Sysop before starting operation of such nodes.

Appearance of such nodes without co-ordination causes problems within the local and inter-BBS/DXCluster/TC/PIP Network routing tables.

Network Sysops work closely with each other to determine route qualities and node tables, to aid the fast movement of traffic via the National Trunk System.

The appearance of uncoordinated ("rogue") nodes causes in some cases severe problems in traffic routing.

Packet users can experiment with software nodes without affecting the node tables of local network nodes, by setting the software parameters of the node to stop propagation of the node into the Network. Advice can be sought on the setting of software parameters from local node Sysops or BBS Sysops.

b) Do not send "Open Bulletins" to individuals.

c) Do not write in the heat of the moment. Word process your bulletin first, then reread it. You may feel differently after a few minutes.

d) Stop to think before sending GIF images and the like which sometimes are in large multi-part files, do you really need to send them, are they amateur radio related, would they be better sent on disc in the post ?

e) Please try to show some consideration for your local Sysop. Remember that you are using, in most cases his own equipment, which is in his home. Try to comply with any requests he makes of you.

f) When accessing your local Mailbox at busy time and are having problems holding the link, try not to turn your power up just to maintain the link, try later when it is not as busy.

g) Obey the Golden Rule -If you would not say it on voice do not send it on packet.

sist, copies of all correspondence and information should be sent to the Repeater Management Committee Chairman c/o RSGB HQ. Further information on procedures to be followed can be obtained by contacting the Zonal Repeater Manager or the AROS Co-ordinator c/o RSGB.

The packet radio network and packet mailboxes

MOST VHF/UHF data communications are carried out these days using packet radio. There are two protocols in use, AX.25 (which is an amateur radio derivative of X.25, a packet protocol used in professional communications) and TCP/IP, the very same Internet protocol used for routing data over the Internet. Without going into detail, each packet of data contains routing information (based on your amateur callsign) and data. The data can be text, a program, an image, or indeed pretty much any information at all. Messages, like the e-mail seen on the Internet, can be posted to or taken from a local packet bulletin board (BBS). The network of stations currently in use also provides other facilities such as conference (even worldwide) and DX information nets. In cases where the distance between stations is too high for normal point-to-point working, a network of stations, called 'nodes', exists for the purposes of relaying these messages to their destination. In this respect, they are akin to the voice repeaters discussed in the previous section. One of the benefits of packet radio is that, because it uses a protocol which can handle 'collisions' between packets (where two stations transmit at once), several stations can share a common frequency. So a number of users can be accessing a mailbox or DX Cluster node at the same time, without necessarily being aware of each other (data throughput starts to slow down when the channel becomes congested).

The typical station

A typical installation for operating VHF/UHF packet radio comprises a number of parts:

1. A VHF/UHF FM radio.

2. A terminal node controller (TNC) which converts the computer data into a suitable form for transmission (or a computer add-on which makes it appear as TNC signals), along with its power unit. However, it is worth noting that nowadays it is possible to install software in conjunction with the soundcard on your PC which then emulates a TNC.

3. A personal computer with suitable software.

Packet radio needs a dedicated Terminal Node Controller (TNC), or some computer software to emulate it

The radio

The choice of radio may require a little thought. Several makers of amateur equipment now incorporate a connector for data communications at 1200 baud and 9600 baud. Furthermore, various suppliers are able to supply ready-made cables for many of the amateur radios on the market. But unlike the other data modes discussed in chapter 8, your packet station may remain connected for long periods at a time. Use of your favourite radio can tie up what amounts to a considerable investment. Many operators, therefore, have purchased surplus (ex-PMR) equipment. These radios can represent a sound investment.

One thing is important: deviation. Most amateur FM radios are set to too wide a deviation. Many nodes and BBSs are run with ex-PMR equipment which often features narrow filters for the commercial standard 12.5kHz channel separation, and 5kHz and more deviation is simply too much. Reliable communication, particularly at 1200 baud, is satisfactory with a lower deviation than one might use on voice. So, when you set up the radio, set the packet deviation to about 3kHz on the high tone and no more.

It is not usually necessary to have a couple of hundred watts into a large Yagi antenna - useful though that is in some cases. This is because there are many stations out there and a lot of nodes which will act as a means of relaying your signals onwards to the final destination. These days, even satellites can be accessed on the power of a hand-held radio and a very modest antenna.

Getting started

It is worth spending some time configuring your TNC, transceiver and software to ensure that everything is working in the optimum way. Read the manuals carefully, as there are many parameters that can be adjusted. That said, however, most packet radio software nowadays comes with suitable set-up files for the majority of TNCs, so that much of the process is automatic and relatively painless.

Real-time contacts

You can, of course, establish real-time contacts over great distances using packet radio, by networking through other nodes along the way. How successful this is depends upon the quality of the backbone network. In a sense, the development of packet radio has been disappointing. When first developed in the mid-80s, packet radio was quite revolutionary, and the work which amateurs did quickly found its way into commercial use, for sending data to and from vehicles on the move. Amateurs typically used 1200 baud packet on 2 and 4m, but soon moved to 9600 baud on the higher bands, with a number of backbone (node to node) links being established on 23cm. The expectation was that higher speeds would gradually be introduced, perhaps with very high speed backbone links on, say, 3cm. This really hasn't happened, despite efforts by a number of experimenters. But over the same period, Internet access speeds have increased out of all recognition, with many users now satisfied with nothing less than a good broadband connection. As a consequence, packet radio seems slow for real-time communications, though it still has a place for specific applications such as messaging via the BBS network and for local access into PacketCluster (see Chapter 9).

The personal mailbox system (PMS)

Several types of TNC are fitted with a system which makes it is possible to leave a message for the recipient in the manner of using a full-sized BBS. It's rather like an automatic telephone answering machine but looks a bit like a bulletin board. Users of these handy gadgets leave them on for long periods, thus ensuring that they can get any messages from, or even sending to, the local BBS.

Bulletin boards

Your local bulletin board system (BBS) or packet mailbox is operated by a sysop (system operator). It usually comprises a computer and a number of TNCs and radios which enable a station to access on a number of frequencies. Typically these are 144.650 and 432.650MHz, although there are some in the 4m, 6m and 23cm bands. Most BBSs operate on 1200 baud, but many forward mail to other BBSs on special RF links running at 9600 baud.

Messages from one person to another in a more distant location are generally passed via a series of BBSs, which behave to the packet operator in the same way as those on the telephone system. Messages can be sent to individuals, to groups of stations or to all users, just as you might when using Internet-based e-mail. Ask your local sysop for details on how to use the BBS, as various versions of BBS software are in use, or you can usually download a help file.

Addressing

In the same way you address an ordinary letter properly, with the postcode and so on, packet messages should be similarly addressed correctly. This is particularly true of mail to foreign parts. This is a typical UK address:

G8UYZ@GB7IPT.#28.GBR.EU

This shows that G8UYZ has GB7IPT as his normal home BBS but the rest is a bit trickier. Reading from the back, the address is broken into parts. 'EU' is the particular part of the world. For example, America is broken into two: 'NOAM' and 'SOAM', while Australia is in OC (Oceania). Countries also have a code: 'GBR' is obviously Great Britain, whilst France is 'F'. Countries are broken down in turn to smaller areas, usually indicated by a '#' symbol. '#28' shows that the station is located in region this and county that.

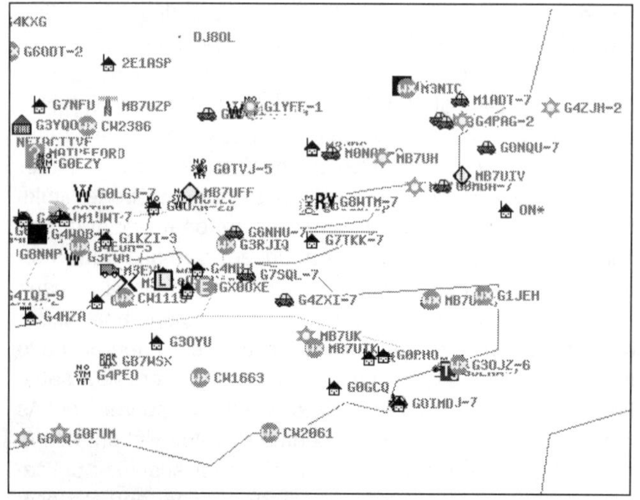

Fig 2: APRS screen shot

File transfer

Given a good path, text and text files are not the only thing that can be sent between stations using packet. It is possible to send binary files from one to another, given that the computer software and the TNC wiring are appropriate. As the packet network is an essentially text-based message system, anything other than text distributed on the network needs to be converted into a form which can be sent as if it is text. Such utilities are called 'ASCII code converters' and examples are 7-PLUS and UUCODE.

You are reminded not to send commercial software or material unrelated to amateur radio.

A full list of current packet network nodes is available on the RSGB Datacomms Committee web site [2].

Automatic Positioning Reporting System (APRS)

APRS DIDN'T get a mention in the last edition of this book, but has established itself rapidly in recent years, mainly due to the links which have developed between it and the Internet (APRS-IS, the APRS Internet System). Many amateurs who are familiar with the system regard it as existing for tracking vehicles on the move using packet radio and, indeed, this is probably the best known application. Amateurs operating mobile are able to use the packet radio network, along with a GPS (Global Positioning System) set in their car, to transmit their location on a continual basis to other connected stations. Nowadays those other stations can, thanks to the Internet, be anywhere in the world. Indeed, anyone, not just licensed amateurs, can access APRS data on the Internet. The map (**Fig.2**) is a view of south-east England, showing the position, in real-time, of amateur stations connected to the network and transmitting APRS data. With an APRS terminal in your car, your family can connect to the Internet and watch your progress as you drive around the country or farther afield.

But this is getting ahead of the story. APRS started life back in 1992 as a real-time digital communications protocol for exchanging information between a large number of stations connected simultaneously to a single network. In this respect it differs significantly from conventional packet radio, which relies on point-to-point connections between specific stations. APRS is well-suited to real-time applications involving multiple parties, for example emergency and other public service communications. When information is sent, it can immediately be seen by all parties connected to the network. This capability is enhanced by the integration of maps and other data displays to organise and display data. This can be useful for the tracking of key assets. Where is the Event Leader? Where are the emergency vehicles? What's the weather at various points in the locality?

It is not the purpose of this section to go into a detailed technical explanation of how APRS works. Suffice to say it is based on traditional packet radio technology, but builds on the capability of packet radio to send 'beacon' messages without being connected to a specific station. The content of those beacon packets is enhanced in APRS to contain data such as location and type of station (home, mobile, digipeater, weather station, etc), which can then be used by the network or the receiving station to generate maps, reports and other summary data as required. Position information can be fed into the system from a GPS unit, but also manually. For example, a weather station could feed in data about the location of a severe weather event, and this could then be tracked over time. This is probably more useful in the Caribbean or southern United States than in the UK but, with global warming, who knows!

It is probably obvious at this stage that APRS isn't relevant purely to amateur radio, although it was developed by radio amateurs, principally by Bob Bruninga, WB4APR. Of course, having at least some stations on a network connected by radio means that they can be mobile or portable, but that link could just as well be via CB, PMR or mobile phone.

Getting started with APRS is relatively simple, especially if you already have packet radio capability by way of a PC, TNC and a VHF transceiver. All you will need to do is download suitable APRS software (there are programs available for all the usual operating systems, including those for Personal Digital Assistants (PDAs)). Any TNC-2 compatible TNC will be suitable. If you want to add real-time positioning data, then you will need a GPS which you can connect to your PC or, with some late-model TNCs, directly to the TNC. Just to simplify matters even more, some recent VHF transceivers come APRS-capable, with internal TNC and APRS software. Add a GPS and you are ready to go.

As far as software is concerned, the most popular Windows-based package appears to be UI-View by Roger Barker, G4IDE. It can be sourced from the UI-View Web site [3].

APRS and satellites

Many amateur satellites (see Chapter 13) have supported data communications. With the increase in popularity of APRS, several recent satellites have incorporated a facility specifically to support APRS. This is known as ASTARS (APRS Satellite Tracking and Reporting System) and is simply a general term for any satellite that allows end-user-to-end user real-time digital data exchange, typically between mobiles and handhelds. The PCSat download page on the Internet [4] is a good place to get an idea of what is available. It shows, both on a map and in a table, the callsigns and positions of last 50 amateur stations copied by PCSat, as well as the positions of several other ASTARS-equipped satellites. The intention is that the system can be used by ground stations using something as simple as the Kenwood THD-7E handheld transceiver, which comes with APRS capability.

Further information about APRS can be found in references [5,6,7].

Voice over IP (VoIP)

VoIP IS A NATURAL evolution of voice repeaters, linking through the Internet to provide global networking. It brings together the best of amateur radio and the Internet to provide a whole new means of communication. Like APRS, its development is very recent, benefiting from the huge increases in Internet speed and the availability of broadband connections at affordable rates. Internet gateways operate on VHF and UHF simplex channels and repeaters using FM. The quality of the audio is generally excellent. To some amateurs this convergence signals the end of amateur radio as we know it, as it is no longer necessary to struggle with the vagaries of HF propagation to achieve worldwide communication. Instead anyone with a VHF transceiver who is within reach of a VoIP node can chat around the world in exactly the same way that millions already do from their homes using their home PC as a VoIP terminal. For others, though, it represents not the death of amateur radio through the Internet, but the use of the Internet to complement amateur radio, opening up new opportunities, for example for those who spend a lot of time on the road but wish to enjoy long-distance conversations. Or for an amateur who has perhaps had to relocate to a home where he is only able to put up limited antennas or none at all, he can use the Internet to remain part of the amateur radio community, continuing to keep in touch with amateur friends around the world. Or imagine travelling to the USA on holiday, but continuing to check into your local club's 2m net by using your handheld to connect to a VoIP gateway in the USA.

Computer card for an IRLP node

VoIP, like APRS, was born and nourished in the USA, partly because both systems lend themselves well to emergency communications, which is a much greater aspect of amateur radio in the US than it is in the UK (think hurricanes in Florida, taking out traditional landline telephone systems, for example). There is also a history in North America of being able to connect voice repeaters to the telephone network, something which was never allowed in the UK. Having said this, several UK amateurs played an important part in the development of early Internet-linking protocols. K1RFD [8], for example, mentions Graeme Barnes M0CSH and his development of iLINK and Paul Davies M0ZPD, developer of eQSO [9].

In the UK, the licensing of Internet gateways to amateur radio was authorised by the Radiocommunications Agency (now Ofcom) in 2000. Worldwide, there are now over 4,000 amateur radio Internet gateways, many available 24 hours a day. Several different systems have been developed to make these gateways possible, given that there needs to be some way of identifying yourself to the gateway and routing your call to a particular distant gateway, controlling the QSO while it takes place, and then logging off when you are finished. Some have dropped by the wayside and there are now three main gateway systems in use, namely Echolink [10], eQSO and IRLP [11, 12] With Echolink and IRLP it is possible using a hand held radio with DTMF or a DTMF microphone on a base station individually to call a station via the gateway. So for example on IRLP if you wanted to call an amateur in Sydney, Australia using your handheld you would press the PTT and press the DTMF key numbers 6 0 0 0 then release and listen. You would hear a voice announcement telling you that the link was connected. You would then talk and carry on a QSO normally as you would if you were working a local station. When you have finished you press the PTT and then press DTMF 7 and then 3 which closes the link. You will hear another voice announcement informing you the link has been closed. You should always listen first on a gateway frequency to see if it is in use. You can also send a '0' to see if it is connected to anywhere.

Echolink and eQSO can also be used from a PC, providing the computer has a soundcard with microphone and speakers attached. IRLP can only be used with a transceiver. This ability to connect to a VoIP network directly from the Internet raises some security issues, as the system can only be used by radio amateurs. After all, even if the connection at your end is via your PC, at some point on the network your voice will be carried over an amateur radio frequency. The different systems handle this in different ways, but all require that you provide some sort of proof of identity (a copy of your licence) and then issue you with a username and password or security key to enable you to access the network.

Obviously, non-licensed people can listen in and monitor what is happening via the Internet, just as they can listen over the airwaves. Also, if you have an Internet connection, you can see the live status pages showing which nodes are connected on all three systems. You can get a full list of nodes including their addresses, which you will need if you want to use the network.

If you want to set-up your own RF gateway you need an NoV from Ofcom. You must hold an Intermediate or Full licence to do this.

ATV repeaters

AMATEUR TELEVISION (ATV) operation is covered in Chapter 7. ATV repeaters differ in their purpose from voice repeaters. While voice repeaters are essentially designed to extend operating range for mobile and portable operators, ATV repeaters are designed for use by fixed stations. ATV repeaters are needed because path losses at 23cms and above, along with the very high signal strengths needed for good reception of high bandwidth signals, mean that direct contacts are much more difficult to achieve than on CW or SSB. ATV users are not usually chasing DX, but wanting to exchange good quality pictures, and the repeaters facilitate this. ATV users can leave their antenna pointing towards the repeater and their station monitoring the repeater output, and see immediately if any other ATV-equipped station is active. The *RSGB Yearbook* shows the callsigns, locations, coverage area and operating channels of operational ATV repeaters in the UK, as well as those still in the licensing process. The BATC [13] and RMC web sites also carry this information, regularly updated, as well as links to repeater group websites and a full repeater list in the form of an *Excel* file which can be downloaded. The file includes a handy macro to calculate the distances from your own location, based on your QTH locator. It will be seen that ATV repeaters now cover most of the major areas of the country. All use FM with horizontal polarisation. All currently operate on 23cm, 13cm or 3cm, or some combination thereof (some are cross-band, with input on 13cm and output on 23cm, for example). As with voice repeaters, Morse code ID is given at regular intervals on the audio channel. **Table 12.3** shows the various frequency pairs used by ATV repeaters.

There are four very important differences between voice and ATV repeaters, from a user standpoint:

1. To access an ATV repeater, all you need is a fast-scan FM TV signal with the video conforming to the CCIR specifications for 625-line television (ie exactly what you get from your camera, camcorder, VCR etc);
2. ATV repeaters do not require a toneburst or CTSS for access, but switch out of beacon mode to repeat mode whenever they receive a valid ATV signal on their input;
3. Most ATV repeaters have no timeout; and
4. Perhaps most importantly for the constructor, when a repeater is not repeating a received picture it broadcasts its own pictures, from test cards, colour test screens, textual information screens, outside mast-head cameras shots, etc all scrolling round in an endless loop. When in repeat mode many ATV repeaters have large selections of options available, from relaying weather pictures to giving signal and picture reports, to

Table 12.3: Amateur TV Repeater frequencies

Band	INPUT FREQ	OUTPUT FREQ
23cm		
	1246MHz	1310MHz
	1248MHz	1310MHz
	1249MHz	1310MHz
	1280MHz	1310MHz
	1280 / 2388MHz	1310MHz
	1248MHz	1308MHz
	1249MHz	1311.5MHz
	1249MHz	1312MHz
	2390MHz	1312MHz
	1249MHz	1316MHz
	1255MHz	1316MHz
	1280 / 2388MHz	1316MHz
	1249MHz	1318.5MHz
13cm	INPUT FREQ	OUTPUT FREQ
	2330.0MHz	2435.0MHz
	2335.0MHz	2435.0MHz
	2340.0MHz	2440.0MHz
	2328 / 2388MHz	2440.0MHz
	2388.0MHz	2440.0MHz
	2388 / 10315MHz	2440.0MHz
10GHz	INPUT FREQ	OUTPUT FREQ
	10.315GHz	10.065GHz
	10.425GHz	10.065GHz
	10.425GHz	10.240 GHz

being able to select which of several antennas you are being received on.

In other words, ATV repeaters are operational 24 hours a day, either radiating on-board generated pictures or repeating incoming received pictures.

With an ATV repeater, as with a voice repeater, there is no reason why multi-way contacts cannot occur, each station taking it in turns to transmit video. As with any other form of operation, you will need to identify at least every 15 minutes, in this case both in vision and sound.

References

[1] RSGB Repeater Management Committee: http://www.coldal.org.uk/rmc.htm

[2] RSGB Datacomms Committee (list of Packet nodes, Internet gateways, etc): www.dcc.rsgb.org

[3] *UI-View*: http://www.ui-view.com/

[4] PCSat download page: http://www.findu.com/cgi-bin/pcsat.cgi

[5] *APRS, Moving Hams on Radio and the Internet*, Stan Horpzepa WA1LOU, ARRL, 2004.

[6] 'APRS - an Introduction', Ciemon Dunville G0TRT, *RadCom* December 2000.

[7] APRS: www.aprs.org

[8] *VoIP, Internet Linking for Radio Amateurs*, Jonathan Taylor K1RFD, ARRL, 2004.

[9] *eQSO*: http://www.eqso.net

[10] *Echolink*: http://www.echolink.org

[11] *IRLP*: http://www.irlp.net

[12] *UK IRLP*: http://www.ukirlp.co.uk

[13] British Amateur Television Club: http://www.batc.org.uk/

13 Satellites and Space Communications

THE OSCAR (Orbiting Satellite Carrying Amateur Radio) programme started back in the sixties (the first was launched in 1961), with some very simple satellites riding piggyback on commercial spaceflights. It's not surprising that amateurs were keen to take advantage of satellites. They are, after all, simply flying relay stations, not unlike ground-based repeaters (see previous chapter), but at a very great altitude. This gives them excellent coverage, allowing intercontinental contacts to take place on the VHF and UHF bands. But there are some specific issues associated with satellites, which mean that operating through them isn't quite as straightforward as operating through a terrestrial relay station. This chapter gives an introduction to those issues and how to get started with satellite operation.

Satellites differ from ground-based repeater stations in several ways. Perhaps the most important to be aware of is that they have a limited power budget, as they are dependent on batteries which are recharged from solar panels. It is important not to overload them with your transmitted signal and in some cases you will also need enough gain on your receiving system to be able to copy their weak signals. As you will read in this chapter, though, amateur satellites vary enormously. Some require sophisticated equipment and antennas on the ground while some of the more recent amateur satellites are themselves more sophisticated and powerful, allowing them to be used by more modestly equipped ground stations. Most cater for SSB, CW and packet rather than continuous modes like FM, to keep the duty cycle (and hence power consumption) to a minimum. Another factor to bear in mind is that whereas a terrestrial repeater station is fairly limited in its coverage, a satellite can be "seen" by amateurs across a very wide area, with the result that many users may be trying to access it at once. While satellites generally relay a band of frequencies, rather than just one channel (as with terrestrial repeaters), it is important to keep contacts short and allow others to take advantage of the facility. Yet another aspect is that satellites track across the sky, which means that your antenna system needs to be able to follow them. Amateurs have yet to launch geostationary satellites, for reasons which are explained later. As a consequence of their movement across the sky, the signals will be subject to Doppler shift, meaning that the receive frequency will keep changing as the relative velocity of the satellite changes with respect to your location on the earth. Finally, for technical reasons, it is normal for satellites to retransmit on a different band to the one on which they receive signals (unlike terrestrial repeaters, which normally retransmit within the same band). None of these issues are insurmountable and, nowadays, there is plenty of help around, for example computer programs for tracking of satellite orbits and multiband transceivers designed very much with satellite operation in mind.

Astronaut Mike Foale, KB5UAC, on board the International Space Station

Fig 13.1: Footprint of the International Space station at a specific moment in time, produced using the Nova program (available from AMSAT-NA)

Another popular aspect of space communications is communicating with astronauts in orbit. Many of the shuttle missions have carried out amateur radio operations, as did many of the astronauts on the MIR space station. And nowadays, the majority of the astronauts in the International Space Station (ISS) hold an amateur radio licence and try to make some contacts. NASA, in particular, appears to be very keen on this, as it helps to make the space program more accessible to the public at large and contacts are often set up specifically to allow schoolchildren, with the help of an accommodating amateur on earth, to talk to the astronauts and ask questions.

A concept to grasp early on with satellite communications is that of its footprint. This is the area of the earth which has a line of sight path to the satellite at any given time. **Fig 13.1**, for example, shows the footprint of the International Space

Station at a specific moment in time. A satellite orbiting higher the space station will have a larger footprint. The footprint is different to overall coverage because, as the satellite tracks across the sky, its footprint will move. Of course, the size of the satellite's footprint is dependent on the height of the satellite above the earth and, in any case, can never be more than half the earth's surface. Think of how the sun, even at 93,000,000 miles from earth, can only illuminate half the earth at any given time, but the sun's footprint (daylight!) moves across the earth as the earth rotates. But because the satellite is tracking across the sky, many countries will be accessible during its pass from the moment it first appears over your horizon until it finally disappears again over the opposite horizon.

Another key concept is that of a transponder. A transponder is the device which takes your signal and retransmits it. It may be like a terrestrial repeater, receiving just one channel and retransmitting it. Or it may take a band of frequencies and retransmit them. A satellite may carry one or several transponders, each operating in a different mode (see later in this chapter for an explanation of modes in this context).

Amateur satellites have come a long way since the relatively primitive devices launched in the 'sixties, and those currently in orbit include sophisticated communication and research satellites which would have cost millions of dollars if constructed on a commercial basis. One of the main organisations involved with the launch of amateur satellites is the Radio Amateur Satellite Corporation (AMSAT-NA) [1] with its headquarters in the USA. There are affiliated groups across the globe, including AMSAT-UK [2]. Many of these AMSAT groups have been actively engaged in the design, building and launch operations.

Russia (and the former USSR) has also launched several amateur satellites, co-ordinated by the Radio Sport Federation (RSF) in that country. These are designated RS (Radio Sputnik), followed by a number.

The satellites constructed by AMSAT Groups in the USA, UK, Germany, Mexico, Israel, South Africa, and Japan, loosely known as AMSAT-International, are generically known as OSCARs (Orbital Satellites Carrying Amateur Radio). These OSCARs will have their own name in their own countries and organisations, but in general all amateur satellites now have an OSCAR numbering, e.g. The Japanese satellite OSCAR 29 is also known as FUJI OSCAR 29, OSCAR 50 is Saudisat OSCAR 50 and the Amsat ECHO satellite launched in June 2004 is known as Amsat OSCAR 51. An indication of just how many amateur satellites have been launched over the years.

The various amateur satellites have been classified into five phases:

- Phase 1 - experimental (Oscar 1-5), long since dormant or decayed.
- Phase 2 - long-life, medium-orbit, satellites with transponders (linear or inverting) allowing two-way communication (Oscars 16, 18, 19, 20, 22, 23 etc)
- Phase 3 - high-altitude elliptical orbit satellites with sophisticated control systems (Oscars 10, 13 and 40, for example).
- Phase 4 - Geostationary
- Phase 5 - Non earth orbiting. For example, P5A, a Mars orbiter, is currently being designed in Germany.

Not all amateur satellites carry transponder capabilities. Some simply operate beacons in the amateur bands, allowing ground-based research and experimentation to take place. Most which do carry transponders allow all modes to be received and retransmitted, so SSB, CW and FM operation are possible. Other satellites carry packet radio mailboxes, so that messages can be left in the satellite mailbox, and accessed later in its orbit by a station on the other side of the globe.

Design criteria

TO A LARGE EXTENT, amateur satellite design is determined by launch opportunities and complexity (which affects overall cost). Amateur satellites are launched by sharing space on rockets carrying commercial payloads. The type of orbit is therefore determined by the company which is paying for the 'primary payload'.

There are two common types of commercial launch:

- LEO (low earth Orbit) for ground observation satellites. LEOs are frequently launched into a "Sun synchronous orbit" This is where the satellite appears at a similar time every day. e.g. 1100 and 2300.
- GTO (Geostationary transfer orbit). GTO is used for satellites which will eventually be stationed in the 'Clark belt' of geostationary satellites. The GTO is used because it's not possible to launch a satellite directly into a geostationary orbit. Instead the launch initially places the satellite into a highly elliptical orbit (as used by Phase 3 amateur satellites). From there the satellite's own propulsion system is used to move it into the correct orbit. A typical GTO is highly elliptical. The highest point (apogee) is typically 30,000 to 40,000km but the lowest altitude (perigee) can be as low as 250km. This orbit cannot be maintained for a long period as the satellite is dangerously close to the atmosphere. The satellites must include a rocket motor to raise the perigee to a safe level.

Amateur Phase 3 satellites are launched into a GTO around the equator with the commercial satellites then are moved into an orbit with a higher and safer perigee and usually with a higher inclination. This means they orbit more

AMSAT-UK member Malcolm, G7NFO, provided this image of his shack with the Yaesu FT847 and satellite tracking display

'pole to pole' and not around the equator. An orbit with a zero degree inclination would orbit around the equator. An orbit with a 90 degree inclination would orbit from pole to pole. Oscar 40 and other Phase 3 satellites have planned inclinations of around 60 degrees.

Complexity is determined by several factors. The number of transponders and types of antennas, of course. The power system, with its solar panels and batteries. And radiation protection. LEO satellites generally do not suffer from high levels of radiation. HEO satellites, however, pass through the Van Allen radiation belts twice each orbit and use specialist radiation hardened components. Computer firmware can generally be loaded from the ground command stations and onboard memory is configured so that any individual locations that have been damaged by radiation can be bypassed when the firmware is loaded.

LEO satellites

LEO (Low Earth Orbit) satellites are perhaps the easiest to get started with. Because they are not very high, signals are strong and you can access them with a simple station. They orbit the earth at heights of somewhere between 400 and 1,000km, meaning they will be accessible for anything up to about 20 minutes on a given orbit. Usually they operate in the 2m and 70cm bands, and it is possible to work through some of them with a dual-band handheld transceiver and suitable dual-band antenna, perhaps a handheld Yagi. There is even tracking software available for use on PDAs (personal organisers), so your whole satellite station is something you can carry round with you.

In practice, a more typical ground station would consist of a crossed- or circularly-polarised Yagi or helical antenna, with control of both elevation and azimuth, run directly from a suitable program on your PC, a full-duplex multiband transceiver with computer-controlled tuning, TNC and soundcard for data modes, and a masthead preamp to improve reception

HEO satellites

AO-40 (AMSAT Oscar 40) is typical of an HEO (High Earth Orbit) satellite. Its orbit is actually elliptical, so that it comes close to the earth for part of its orbit, but then swings way out into space, 35,000km or so, while over the northern hemisphere. The intention is that the satellite spends most of its orbital period above the more heavily populated parts of the earth (in amateur radio terms), allowing more time for contacts to take place. Pass time can range from 12 to 18 hours, simplifying the tracking and allowing more time for contacts to take place. Unfortunately a problem with AO-40's power system means that, at the time of writing, it is unavailable for amateur use, although the ground stations are still in touch with it and hope to bring it back into service at some time in the future.

Geostationary satellites

Geostationary satellites are worth mentioning here, as it may not be immediately apparent why they are not used by amateurs. After all, they are very popular for professional communications and broadcasting. Firstly, a geostationary satellite can cover a large but limited area of the earth's surface and, by definition, because it has an orbital period of 24 hours it appears to remain stationary above the earth's surface, so its footprint is constant. To give global coverage two or three satellites would be needed and signals would need to be passed between satellites. In contrast, a single Phase 3 satellite can give coverage to 90% of the world, albeit with limits on the time it can provide communications between any two locations. Secondly, geostationary satellites need some form of propulsion to maintain their position in space. This limits their useful life. Finally, the area of space used for geostationary satellites is heavily congested with commercial spacecraft. This may seem surprising, but to remain in a constant position above the earth a satellite must be located at a height such that its orbital period is exactly 24 hours, and it must sit above the equator. Thus all geostationary satellites are competing for the same band above the earth.

Table 13.1: Early satellite operating modes

Mode	Uplink	Downlink
Mode A:	2m uplink	10m downlink
Mode B:	70cm uplink	2m downlink
Mode J:	2m uplink	70cm downlink
Mode K:	15m uplink	10m downlink
Mode L:	23cm uplink	70cm downlink
Mode S:	70cm uplink	12cm downlink
Mode T:	15m uplink	2m downlink

Operating modes

WHEN YOU READ about satellite operating, you will see reference to various operating modes. Don't confuse these with modes as in SSB, RTTY, etc. Rather, they refer to the bands on which the satellite receives and retransmits signals. The best-known are shown in **Table 13.1**,

More recently, a new type of designation has come into use, whereby two or more letters are used for each mode, the first to designate uplink and the second the downlink eg Mode-B would be called Mode UV; uplinks on both 435 MHz and 1.2 GHz linking to 145 MHz and 10 GHz downlinks would be called Mode ULVX. The letter assignments are consistent with the usual microwave band designations, where "K" for example means 18-26.5 GHz. The reason for changing the system was that, with the launch of the P3D (AO-40) satellite, there were so many possible combinations, that the previous system simply couldn't cope. The full list is shown in **Table 13.2**.

Table 13.2: New satellite mode identifier

Letter	Frequency	Remarks
A	29MHz	
T	28 MHz	Uplink only
H	21 MHz	Uplink only
V	145 MHz	Uplink and Downlink
U	435 MHz	Uplink and Downlink
L	1.2 GHz	Two Uplinks only, L1 and L2
S	2.4 GHz	2 Uplinks, 2 Downlinks, S1 and S2
C	5.6 GHz	Uplink only
X	10 GHz	Downlink only
K	24 GHz	Downlink only
Q	47GHz	

AMSAT-NA President Robin Haighton, VE3FRH, with OSCAR-51 just before the launch

Current satellites

PERHAPS THE LEAST useful thing to do in an introductory chapter of this sort is to list the various satellites, because it really is a moving feast. New ones are in the pipeline to be launched, existing ones will eventually fail or be put on a reduced duty cycle. But it's nevertheless useful to know of some of those which could be available to first-time satellite operators.

Oscar 7

Launched back in 1974, this satellite suffered battery failure in 1981 but, in 2002, spontaneously came back into service working directly off its solar cells. This means, of course, that it is only operational when in sunlight. It has transponders for both Modes A and B, SSB and CW. The mode B transponder inverts, so that LSB signals transmitted at the low end of the uplink band will return as USB signals at the high end of the downlink band.

Fuji-OSCAR 29 (JAS-2)

Built by Japanese amateurs and launched in 1996 into a polar orbit, FO-29 operates a Mode JA inverting transponder, i.e. an uplink of 145.9 to 146MHz LSB/CW, with downlink of 435.8-435.9MHz USB/CW.

AMRAD Oscar 27

Launched in 1993, this satellite has a single-channel FM transponder with uplink on 145.85MHz and downlink on 436.795MHz. Like many of the satellites, it suffers power problems and its use is limited to 6 minutes on each south to north pass over the northern hemisphere and it is turned off midsummer and midwinter.

AMSAT Echo (AO-51)

Launched in June 2004, AMSAT Echo has several facilities. Firstly, an FM voice repeater with uplink on 145.92MHz (requiring a PL-67 tone to activate) and downlink on 435.225MHz. There is a 9600bps AX.25 packet mailbox, with uplink on 145.86MHz and downlink on 435.15MHz. And there is a linear (SSB/CW) transponder with uplinks on various bands, downlink on 13cm.

Packet satellites

There are several packet satellites, some for APRS (see Chapter 12) and some with packet bulletin board facilities. The former include PacSAT (AO-16), Sapphire (NO-45) and the ISS (Zarya) on the International Space Station. The latter include UOSat-5 (UO-22), Sapphire (NO-45), ISS (Zarya), GerwinSat (GO-32), TuingSat (MO-46) and Echo (AO-51)

Cubesats

There are many picosats (very small satellites) currently in orbit, all based on a standardized 10cm cube design [3]. The intention is that the cubesat approach can be used to launch a wide variety of payloads into space at relatively low cost. Applications include everything from simple telemetry to PSK31 repeaters. Software is available for decoding the CW beacons, Hamscope being popular, and Cute-1, for example, has downloadable analysis software to convert the decoded CW into spacecraft data. Cubesat XI-IV, from the Intelligent Space Systems Laboratory as the University of Tokyo, callsign JQ1YCW, carries telemetry on FSK and AX25 (1200bps) on a frequency of 437.490MHz. Transmitter power is 800mW to a half-wave dipole. The signals have been well received in the UK.

Future satellites

AT THE TIME OF writing, scheduled launches include:

- VUSat (by AMSAT India), a LEO satellite with SSB/CW transponder (scheduled launch September 2004)
- BLUEsat (by University of New South Wales), carrying a packet mailbox (scheduled launch 2005)
- PCSat-2 (US Naval Academy) to put an APRS digipeater on the ISS, but only when the Shuttle is back in operation.
- P3E "Express" (by AMSAT DL, Germany), an HEO satellite with multimode linear transponder (scheduled launch 2006)
- Eagle (AMSAT-NA), an HEO satellite with multimode linear transponder (scheduled launch 2006/07)
- SSETI Express. (European Space Agency) Launch date May 2005. 80kg 680km LEO. FM voice U/S repeater. 437 to 2401MHz. Data Downlink on U band at 9600Baud and S band at 38k4 from onboard camera and other experiments. S band transmitter by AMSAT-UK.

It is important to note that all of the recently launched LEOs running FM have CTCSS access (used for many years with terrestrial repeaters). So far SO-50 (Saudi Oscar 50) and

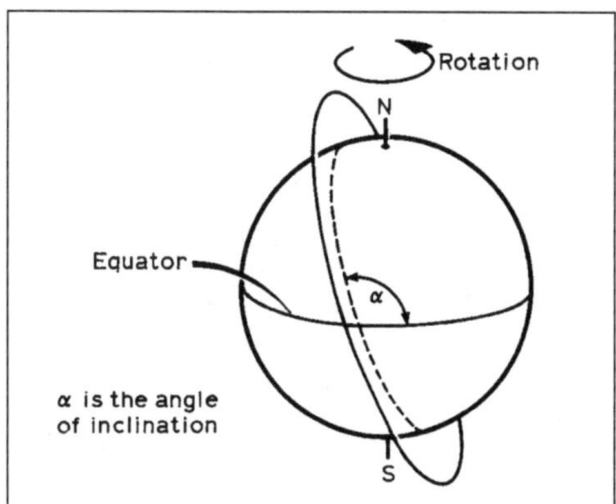

Fig 13.2: Phase 2 satellite orbit viewed from space

AO-51 (Echo) have used 67Hz. This will also be implemented on the SSETI Express satellite. Once the CTCSS signal is lost the transmitter remains active for between 5 and 10 seconds and is then cut. This allows amateurs using split frequency operation to confirm that they have been received by the satellite. The 5-10 second delay also prevents losing the signal for short periods of time as the satellite spins (known as spin fading). The overall idea of the CTCSS is power saving, by ensuring that only legitimate amateur signals are passed by the satellite (in some areas of the world that satellites pass over, it has been found that unlicensed transmissions can inadvertently activate some amateur satellites).

Tracking satellites

SINCE RADIO communication via an amateur satellite is essentially line-of-sight, it follows that it can only take place when the satellite is above the user's horizon, and it is therefore necessary to determine the periods when this occurs. In addition, if beam antennas are in use it will be necessary to ascertain the beam headings of the satellites during these periods. Furthermore, many satellite stations use antennas adjustable in elevation as well as azimuth rotation (az-el antennas), and in this case it is also desirable to know the approximate elevation of the satellite above the horizon at any time. All this information can be derived quite simply from orbital data or Keplerian elements which can be obtained from a number of sources. It helps to have a basic understanding of the terms involved. Some of these will be clarified by the following description - much more complete orbital information concerning amateur satellites is given in references [4] and [5].

Orbital data

The simplest way to understand satellite orbits is to imagine one is out in space observing the Earth rotating on its axis from west to east with the north pole at the top (**Fig.13.2**). If an object as small as a satellite could be detected it would be seen coming from behind the Earth over the Antarctic region, proceeding northwards across the equator, then disappearing over the north polar region. This part of the orbit is known as the ascending node. The remaining half of the orbit, when the satellite travels from north to south is called the descending node.

It will be noticed that the orbit is tilted anti-clockwise from the north-south line, or is retrograde in space terminology. The satellite never goes right over the poles. The time which a satellite takes to complete one orbit is known as the period, during which the Earth will have rotated eastwards. The satellite will therefore cross the equator at a different longitude, the difference being the longitude increment.

An orbit is said to commence when a satellite crosses the equator travelling north. All orbit predictions consist of this time, given in Co-ordinated Universal Time (UTC) and degrees west of the Greenwich meridian where the crossing occurs. This method of stating longitude often confuses the uninitiated who are more used to degrees east and west of Greenwich. It is really quite simple; up to 180°W there is no problem, after that 170°E is equivalent to 190°W, 160°E equates with 200°W, and so on round to the Greenwich meridian again; hence 5°E is given as 355°W. The first orbit each day is called the reference orbit; these orbits are usually out of range of the UK. Future orbits can, however, be calculated with fair accuracy, given any reference orbit information. In the past, you might have gone to an organisation such as AMSAT-UK for an orbital calendar, but nowadays it is usually a case of do-it-yourself. The tracking of satellites has got very much easier with the introduction of suitable PC software. Popular programs for the PC include Nova, SatPC32, SCRAP, Satscape and Orbitron. There are also suitable programs available for Macintosh and PDAs.

Polarisation

Imagine a satellite in orbit without a sophisticated stabilisation system. That satellite is likely to roll and tumble according to external influences of solar and terrestrial origin, and so the orientation of the satellite's antennas, as seen from the ground, can (and does) change in direction. The polarisation to cater for all orientations and combat fading (except when the antenna is end-on to the observer) is circular. Satisfactory results can be obtained with horizontal or vertical polarisation alone for most of the time but fading will occasionally be troublesome; better results can be obtained by having both polarisations available and switching between them to select the strongest signal.

Some satellites' antenna systems are themselves circularly polarised (on VHF and upwards) and some advantage can be gained by ground stations using the same sense of circular polarisation, but only when the satellite antenna system is pointing towards the observer. At other times selected lin-

An array of antennas especially for satellite working being set up by G0AKI on the roof of the RSGB's demonstration vehicle GB4FUN

ear polarisation will be better. The best all-round results will be achieved by the station which can switch between horizontal, slant, vertical, left-hand circular and right-hand circular polarisations. However, this is by no means essential, and very few stations go to this extreme.

Doppler shift

The impact of Doppler shift has already been mentioned. This is a frequency- and velocity-related effect all too obvious in amateur satellite operation (typical speed of a satellite is about 17,000MPH). It appears, as the satellite approaches, that its frequency starts high and is drifting lower. To use RS15 mode A as an example: Doppler shift on the 145MHz uplink added, via the linear transponder, to that on the 29MHz downlink will give a cumulative 'drift' of up to 5 or 6kHz per pass. The degree of Doppler shift will depend on the frequency and the velocity of the satellite relative to the observer. So, for a given velocity the Doppler shift at 1GHz will be 10 times the Doppler shift at 100MHz. Remember that the shift of both links has to be taken into account and, in the case of Mode A, the 4 or 5kHz of 145MHz added to the 1kHz of 29MHz to give the total amount. Designers of transponders can, however, go some way to mitigating the effects of Doppler shift by using inverting transponders. In an inverting transponder frequencies at the top of the uplink band come out at the bottom of the downlink band and vice versa. The mixing scheme which is used to achieve this plays off the Doppler shifts of the uplink and downlink to reduce the overall amount of frequency shift to the difference between the two. This is why many of the satellites, especially those which use the higher bands, employ inverting transponders.

Getting started on satellites

NOW THAT YOU HAVE read through the basics, perhaps you are fired up to try satellite operating. It is well worth looking at the various Web sites listed at the end of this chapter for the latest information on each of the satellites and plenty of additional advice on getting started. The AMSAT-UK frequency list [6] is also a useful source, and is regularly updated. On the AMSAT-NA Web site there is a link called START which takes you to an excellent beginners guide by Emily Clarke W0EEC which you can download as a PDF file.

FO-29 analogue satellite

Inverting transponder frequencies at zero doppler

CW Beacon	435.795	145.945	435.855
		145.950	435.850
TX LSB	RX USB	145.955	435.845
145.900	435.900	145.960	435.840
145.905	435.895	145.965	435.835
145.910	435.890	145.970	435.830
145.915	435.885	145.975	435.825
145.920	435.880	145.980	435.820
145.925	435.875	145.985	435.815
145.930	435.870	145.990	435.810
145.935	435.865	145.995	435.805
145.940	435.860	146.000	435.800

A handy quick-reference table. The frequency translation equation for FO-29 is: Downlink (MHz) = 581.800 - uplink (MHz) +/- Doppler

You will also want to download one of the tracking programs, so that you can know when each satellite will be "visible" at your location.

UK Foundation Class licensees should be aware that they are not permitted to operate through amateur satellites. This also applies to contacts through the ISS when it is unmanned, at which time it is treated as though it were another satellite.

Before thinking about transmitting through a satellite, select one for which you have a suitable receiver and start to listen to its beacon transmissions and to amateur signals. This will allow you to get used to tuning into satellites and tracking them across the sky. If you are using an omni directional antenna (which may be sufficient to hear some of the LEO satellites) you won't even have to worry about tracking your antenna and even if you use a Yagi, most of the LEO satellites are low enough in the sky that an antenna fixed at an elevation of around 30 degrees will be sufficient, avoiding the need for elevation adjustment.

Once you are confident that you can predict a satellite's appearance and receive signals at reasonable strength, then you can think about making your first transmission. You will need to work out the correspondence between up and down frequencies which can be a little confusing, especially with inverting transponders where an increase in transmit frequency results in a decrease in receive frequency. Transmit through the satellite and find your signal on the downlink. You must then learn to adjust the transmit frequency so that the downlink frequency remains constant in the face of the Doppler shift.

If you plan to operate SSB, the accepted practice is that the downlink should be USB. This means that if you are working through an inverting transponder you must transmit LSB to the satellite.

Now you should be ready to answer someone's CQ call, or call CQ yourself, and start to enjoy making satellite QSOs.

The way you actually conduct a QSO through a satellite is fundamentally no different to making any other sort of amateur radio contact. You can call CQ or answer someone else's call, and exchange signals reports, location, etc. Of course, at the same time you will be keeping an eye on tracking the satellite and compensating for Doppler shift, so you may be a little distracted! A degree of courtesy is appropriate, especially when the satellite is busy. It is sensible to listen for one of the satellite beacon signals or for other users before transmitting yourself, so that you know you are able to hear the satellite (meaning that your antenna is correctly pointed, etc.). Unlike most terrestrial operations, you should always aim to work duplex so that you can hear your own transmitted signal at all times, as it comes back through the satellite. Headphones are recommended as working duplex with an open speaker and microphone has the potential to create a spectacular feedback loop. Use as little power as possible, to avoid overloading and desensing the satellite (this is especially important with AO-7, as it operates purely on solar power). And when the satellite is busy you should obviously keep contacts short, exchanging the minimum of information (typically callsigns, signal reports, QTH locator and perhaps name).

Code of Practice for satellite operation

Naturally the same ethics of amateur conduct and behaviour apply as they do to normal terrestrial communication on both the HF and VHF bands but, because each satellite is a DX 'band' with limited and power-sharing openings, certain additional points should be observed.

DO NOT turn on your carrier, whistle, send CW or otherwise until you can hear the satellite beacon. If you have a poor downlink receiver and a good uplink, as most European users seem to have, the chances are that someone else's DX contact will be ruined by your signal.

DO NOT run more than the recommended EIRP at any time (if you don't know what 'EIRP' and other buzz words mean why not try and find out?), or you will ruin contacts for those who are 'playing the game', and give them grounds for the same irresponsible behaviour. Calculate your EIRP, don't guess it.

DO NOT call stations in your own area when the satellite is near the horizon - they have but a few seconds a day to work DX stations but most of any orbit to work you.

DO NOT call Satgate incessantly. The old-time operators' 3 times 3 de K is really the way to call CQ these days as well on a satellite. Short bursts are enough, then listen, otherwise you are just depressing the satellite's AGC and using its battery power unnecessarily. Many of the rarer stations are crystal controlled so it is necessary to listen for them.

DO pay maximum attention to your receiving system - when it is good enough you will hear returns from even 100mW uplink power, and hence work much more DX for less power. Attention to higher gain, lower angle and less noise on your downlink reception is cheaper and far more productive than anything else you can do.

DO use the outer limits of the passband, thus avoiding the over-crowded centre, and encouraging others to spread out and avoid mutual interference.

DO visit the AMSAT Web site and subscribe to the AMSAT-NA Bulletin Board (these effectively replace the AMSAT Nets).

DO try to have proper amateur contacts via amateur satellites, rather than merely exchanging a few numbers contest- style. Try spreading the word about new stations, schedules or other satellite-interest information.

DO pay attention to special service channels and avoid transmitting on these. They may be required at that time to control the spacecraft for your better enjoyment.

DO NOT work stations obviously using more power than required for a reasonable signal. These stations are stopping the enjoyment of all other users of the satellite and they degrade the transponder efficiency. If they are louder in your receiver than the beacon (telemetry) they are in excess of design parameters for the transponder. This is a fact, not a myth, and can be easily proven by you the listener.

Do persuade all stations to reduce power to the minimum for a satisfactory QSO.

As far as data modes are concerned, you should find out what speeds, protocols and applications are applicable to the satellite you wish to use. The PACSATs, for example, deal with the potentially large number of stations wanting to upload and download data by ordering them into queues, and handling each request in turn. The data is effectively "broadcast", so that all users can see all the data being sent. There is special software available to handle this, PB/PG DOS, for example, and WiSP is for Windows. Both are available from the AMSAT download page.

For some amateurs, working through any sort of repeater, whether ground-based or on a satellite, isn't "true" amateur radio, in the sense that it doesn't rely on the vagaries of propagation. If the satellite is there and operational you will be able to work through it. But, in another sense, it is exactly what amateur radio is about, because there are real technical challenges to be overcome in working through the various satellites, which is yet another aspect of what "self-training" is all about.

Awards

A NUMBER OF awards are available for operating through amateur satellites, ranging from the Satellite Communicators' Club award for making your very first satellite contact to awards for working 100 countries or 1,000 two-way satellite contacts (endorsable for each additional 1,000 contacts). At the time of writing, some 18 amateurs had gained the 5,000 QSO level of the Robert W. Barbee Jr., W4AMI Satellite Operator Achievement Award, which demonstrates the high level of activity which exists on amateur satellites to make this achievement possible. Many other awards are available or can be endorsed for satellite operation. For example, the ARRL's popular DXCC program (Chapter 14) includes an award for contacts made via satellites, while the IARU Worked All Continents Award (available through the RSGB) can be endorsed for satellite contacts. Visit the Amsat NA web site for a list of awards.

International Space Station

ARISS (AMATEUR RADIO on the International Space Station) [7] is a volunteer body which supports amateur radio from the International Space Station. It is entrusted by the major space agencies with co-ordinating contacts with the space station. Normally these would be scheduled contacts with schools, limited to the ten minutes that the space station is in range of a single location on earth as it passes overhead. Other amateurs are, of course, more than welcome to listen in to these communications, but are asked not to transmit on the ARISS frequencies and cause interference.

The frequencies concerned are:

Worldwide packet uplink:	145.990 MHz FM
Region 1 voice uplink:	145.200 MHz FM
Region 2/3 voice uplink:	144.490 MHz FM
Worldwide downlink:	145.800 MHz FM
USA Callsign:	NA1SS
Russian callsigns:	RSOISS and RZ3DZR
Mailbox callsign:	RSOISS-11
Digipeater alias:	ARISS

The ARISS station consists of several units, permanently installed into the ISS, including a VHF FM transceiver and a separate, multimode transceiver. A voice repeater was activated in late summer 2004, with uplink on 437.800MHz and downlink on 145.800MHz. No toneburst or CTCSS is required. Given that the Space Station is in a relatively low orbit, this voice repeater should be workable with a low power and an omni-directional antenna. When the repeater is in use, it is likely that the audio will be streamed through the AMSAT conference server on Echolink, so that anyone can listen in via the Internet. There is talk of mounting a camera on the outside of the Space Station, which will send back pictures of the earth. This is likely to be of great interest schools, who can use it to enhance their geography, science and communications studies. This project may also include an ATV repeater, with input on 1.2GHz FM ATV and output on 2.4GHz digital TV. Further details are available from the ARISS Web site and the ARISS News page on the AMSAT Web site.

To determine where the Space Station is, in real-time, check [8]. For predictions up to three days in advance, you can use the pcsat decoder program [9].

References

[1] AMSAT-NA: www.amsat.org

[2] AMSAT-UK: www.uk.amsat.org

[3] Cubesat chart: http://home.earthlink.net/~maenpaa.cubesat_table.pdf

[4] *The Guide to Oscar Operating*, Richard Limebear - G3RWL, AMSAT UK.

[5] *Orbital Mechanics and Satellite Technology*, Bob Phillips, G4IQQ

[6] Laminated Satellite Frequency List, AMSAT UK

[7] ARISS Europe: http://www.ariss-eu.org/

[8] ISS location: http://science.nasa.gov/temp/StationLoc.html

[9] pcsat decoder download: http://www.ui-view.com/uiview32/pcdec242.msi

14 Operating Awards and QSLing

WHILE IT'S GREAT fun to get on the bands and make some interesting contacts, there has always been additional pleasure for many amateurs in sending and receiving QSL cards. This goes back to the very earliest days of the hobby and the concept is still very much as it was, though improved printing techniques mean that many modern QSL cards tend to be quite elaborate.

A QSL card is simply a written or printed confirmation of a two-way contact (or of a heard station in the case of listeners). It serves as a reminder of the contact and most amateurs take pleasure in displaying their cards on the shack wall, collating them into albums or, when the collection gets too large, into filing cabinets or perhaps shoe boxes. Because QSL cards are a confirmation of a contact, they are also the common currency for claiming amateur radio awards and certificates (though some awards require only a certified extract from your logbook or, increasingly nowadays, some sort of electronic verification).

This chapter looks at QSLing in some depth, and then takes a quick canter through some of the major awards programmes. It is not appropriate to try and mention all awards in these pages. Not only are there far too many of them and application details change as voluntary awards managers come and go, but awards themselves also come and go, often focused around a specific event. For example, as I prepare this chapter in mid-2004, we have seen several awards available for working stations related to the expansion of the EU, some awards built around the Euro 2004 soccer competition, and several awards focused on the 2004 Athens Olympics. What I can do is point you to useful sources of information about awards and give you some hints and tips on how to gain awards.

What is a QSL card?

A QSL IS A confirmation that a contact has taken place. The name obviously derives from the more formal Q code, QSL "I am acknowledging receipt". For awards purposes or, indeed, for your own records, it can take several forms. It could be a handwritten letter from the station you contacted, a Telex or FAX (though generally none of these would be acceptable for claiming awards), or maybe just a rubber stamp and signed confirmation returning a QSL card that you have sent to him. In practice, most amateurs use postcard-size cards printed for the specific purpose of confirming their contacts.

The major requirements are pretty obvious. Firstly, it must show the callsign used, plus the name of the DXCC country somewhere on the card (perhaps as part of the address). Then there should be somewhere for the details of the contact being confirmed - callsign of the station worked, date, time, band, mode, signal report. So far so good. If you're going to enter dates in the European format, it's worth the heading reading something like DATE (D-M-Y) or American recipients might misinterpret and be unable to cross check the contact in their log (most people now realise that 9/11 means something very different in the USA to what it would have done in the UK, for example). Time should always be in UTC, but make this clear in the heading - TIME (UTC). Again, make the units clear for the band description, whether metres or MHz. Otherwise the entry "10" could mean 10 metres (28MHz) or 10MHz (30m). Mode should somewhere indicate two-way, perhaps by using the heading MODE (2x). This is primarily because when the CW DXCC came in, people were having mixed-mode contacts where a non-CW operator might listen for some random dots and dashes from the other station, give a 599 report on SSB, and it was declared a QSO for the new award. The ARRL soon got wise to this, and look for a clear indication that CW contacts in particular were genuinely both-way on that mode.

What else goes on our card? The full address is useful, and if this differs from the station location, then make that clear. Chasers of counties, for example, will get confused if your postal address is, say, Essex, whereas your physical location was, perhaps, in Suffolk. An e-mail address is always useful these days, though many of us change our e-mail addresses more often than we reprint QSL cards. WAB square, IOTA ref-

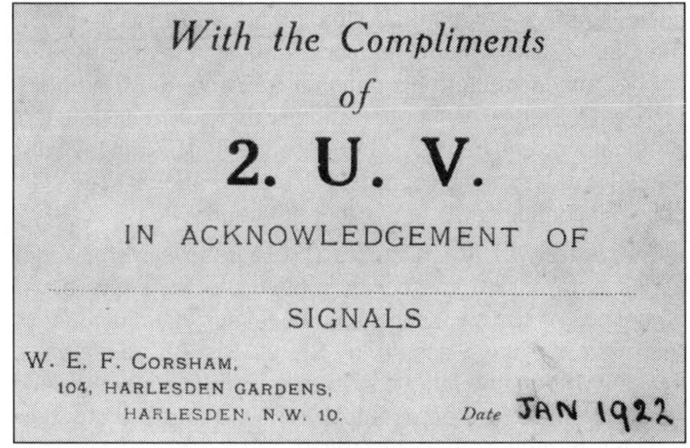

This very early card was much smaller than today's postcard-sized QSLs and is printed in black on coloured card

Modern QSL cards can be quite elaborate. This one from the 2004 3B9C DXpedition is a fold-out card in full colour

erence where applicable (mainland UK is EU-005), CQ Zone, QTH Locator, etc are all helpful to at least some of the people who will receive your card. In fact, the IOTA Awards programme will only accept cards where the actual island name is printed on the card. And, of course, any interesting additional material you choose to include about yourself, your station, your club memberships, your town, or whatever. And a PSE/TNX QSL tick box, or similar, to indicate to the recipient whether you are looking for his card in return, or that you have already received it (many contest stations these days send out QSL cards automatically, but specifically say they do not want your card in return).

Many amateurs like to write out their cards and to sign them as well, to personalise them a little, but nowadays it is common to print the QSO data on to labels, and simply allow space on the card to affix the label. Many QSL managers who use this method use a rubber stamp to overprint the label, to confirm authenticity, though this is not an award requirement. Many logging programs offer sophisticated QSL management facilities, including printing of labels, ready sorted for the QSL bureau.

QSL cards have definitely become more elaborate over the years as printing techniques have improved, bringing quality colour printing into the sort of price bracket many of us can afford. A decent photograph or some interesting graphics is always nice. Make sure, though, that the recipient's callsign can be read clearly by the sorters at the QSL bureau, and also have space to show, even more clearly, if the card is to be routed via a QSL manager in another country, as otherwise your card may end up at the wrong distant bureau entirely. The size of QSL cards has become fairly standardised over the years, averaging around 90mm by 140mm, ie postcard size and able to fit into a C6 envelope or similar. Some amateurs, special event stations and DXpeditions are occasionally tempted to produce outsize cards which may look nice on the shack wall, but will almost certainly have to be folded for mailing in most return envelopes, and when sent by the bureau system really do cause problems. So please stick to standard sizes.

Cards being sorted at the RSGB QSL Bureau

Table 14.1: Countries with no national QSL bureau

3B	Mauritius	KH8	American Samoa
3C	Equatorial Guinea	KH9	Wake Island
3C0	Pagalu Island	KP1	Navassa Island
3W, XV	Vietnam	KP5	Desecheo Island
3X	Guinea	P2	Papua New Guinea
5A	Libya	P5	North Korea
5R	Madagascar	PZ	Suriname
5T	Mauritania	S0	Western Sahara
5U	Niger	S7	Seychelles
5V	Togo	S9	Sao Tome & Principe
7O, 4W	Yemen	SU	Egypt
7P	Lesotho	T2	Tuvalu
7Q	Malawi	T3	Kiribati
8Q	Maldives	T5	Somalia
9N	Nepal	T8	Palau
9U	Burundi	TJ	Cameroon
9X	Rwanda	TL	Central African Rep
9Y	Trinidad & Tobago	TN	Congo
A3	Tonga	TT	Chad
A5	Bhutan	TY	Benin
A6	United Arab Emirates	UK	Uzbekistan
CN	Morocco	V3	Belize
D2	Angola	V6	Micronesia
E3	Eritrea	VP2E	Anguilla
J5	Guinea-Bissau	VP2M	Montserrat
J8	St. Vincent	XU	Kampuchea
KH0	Mariana Is.	XW	Laos
KH1	Baker & Howland Is.	XZ	Myanmar (Burma)
KH4	Midway Island	YA, T6	Afghanistan
KH5	Palmyra & Jarvis Is.	ZD9	Tristan da Cunha
KH7K	Kure Island	ZK1	North & South Cook I

Finally, always ensure any QSLs you have printed also allow you to select 'SWL Report' instead of 'QSO' to be able properly to acknowledge any listener reports that come along, though these are certainly fewer than in days gone by.

How do I go about sending and receiving QSL cards?

WHEN THE CONCEPT of QSLing first emerged in amateur radio, the usual practice was to mail the card to the station concerned. Undoubtedly this was why early QSL cards adopted the postcard format, as the mailing address could be written on the blank side and the card could be mailed for minimum postal rates. However, as the level of activity started to increase and more cards were being exchanged, national societies started setting up clearing houses for QSL cards: the QSL bureau system. The concept is simple enough. The sender sends cards to his national QSL bureau, where they are then sorted by destination country and bulk mailed to the national society in the country concerned. Similarly, the sender can lodge envelopes with his own national society to collect incoming cards from other amateurs.

The exact way in which the QSL bureau system works varies from society to society, though the IARU lays down guidelines as to how it expects national societies to conduct their part of the process. In the UK, at least at the time this is being written, though the system is currently under review, RSGB members are automatically entitled to use the outgoing QSL bureau as part of their RSGB membership. Cards can be sent in bulk to RSGB HQ, but should be pre-sorted by country prefix to simplify the job of the volunteer sorters at

Table 14.2: Countries with restricted QSLing

Countries that currently restrict the forwarding of QSL cards to anyone other than members of that country's national radio society include:

Denmark	Monaco
France	Norway
Germany	Poland
Greece	Portugal
Hungary	South Africa
Italy	Zambia
Japan	

the QSL bureau. Incoming cards are sent to volunteer sub-managers, each of whom handles incoming cards for specific blocks of UK callsigns. Any UK amateur, not only RSGB members, is entitled to lodge pre-paid envelopes with the appropriate sub-manager, in order to receive incoming cards. Normally these envelopes will be mailed when they contain enough cards to use up the postage on the envelope. Alternatively, the recipient can make specific requests, such as mailing an envelope when it contains ten incoming cards, for example.

The international QSL bureau system effectively handles many millions of cards each year, saving individual amateurs a fortune in postal costs. There are limitations, of course, and users need to be aware of these. First and foremost, from sending a card to receiving one in return can take many months, even years. Let's suppose, for example, that you work a station in Brazil and mail your card to the RSGB bureau the following day (in practice you are likely to wait until you have enough cards to fill an envelope). It may be a matter of weeks before the RSGB has enough cards destined for Brazil to justify sending a package to the Brazilian society. That package will probably be mailed surface (it would be hard to justify the additional cost of airmail to save a few days, when the whole process includes so many inherent delays anyway), and arrive in Brazil a few weeks later. But the Brazilian amateur himself may not receive it until several weeks after that, when enough incoming cards have arrived for him from around the world. Of course, you may have short-circuited the system by agreeing at the time of the QSO to send each other QSL cards. But, if not, when he receives your card he may write a reply card immediately, but probably won't mail it until he has enough outgoing cards to justify mailing a package. Then, of course, the whole process starts all over again, but in the reverse direction.

The other major limitation of the QSL bureau system is that many smaller national societies are unable to justify the cost or effort of running a QSL bureau. **Table 14.1** lists those countries believed at the time of writing not have national QSL bureaus (the list is taken from the ARRL web site). For amateurs in those countries, the only recourse is to mail direct to them or via their QSL manager, if they have one. Where a station has a QSL manager in a country that has a QSL bureau, there may not be a problem. Simply make the QSL manager's callsign prominent on the QSL card, indicating that the card should be routed to the QSL manager rather than to the station worked. However, some countries do not allow this without the DX station also being a member of the manager's national society. Even if a country is not on the list, it isn't always safe to assume that the bureau system will work effectively. The author has personal experience of visiting the Ghanaian Amateur Radio Society (GARS) headquarters in Accra and finding unopened bundles of QSL cards received from bureaus in the USA, UK and elsewhere. GARS has neither the funds nor the volunteers to deal with these cards and, in any case, many of the operations were by visitors to the country who had since left, often without a forwarding address and almost always without leaving any funds to cover postage. Most of the cards will eventually be consigned to the circular filing cabinet though on that occasion G4BWP and I did make an effort to track down the holders of some of the callsigns concerned, and pass on the incoming cards on our return to the UK. Generally, other than for the major nations, it is safest to find a direct address or QSL manager if you want to be reasonably certain of getting a return card. Some countries' QSL bureaus restrict incoming cards to those amateurs who are members of the national society (though this goes against IARU guidelines). The countries concerned are listed in **Table 14.2**.

For those cards going to countries where the system works effectively, the question is, how do you go about using the QSL bureau? In the UK, RSGB members can bundle up their outgoing cards (sorted by prefix, please) and mail them to PO Box 1773, Potters Bar, Herts EN6 3EP. There are also deposit boxes for QSL cards on the RSGB stand at many of the major rallies and conventions. You are encouraged to write the destination callsign on both sides of the card, to reduce handling times. For incoming cards, identify your incoming QSL sub-manager (up-to-date lists appear in the *RSGB Yearbook*) and lodge self-addressed envelopes with sufficient postage, depending on how many incoming cards you are likely to expect. You can mark the envelopes with comments such as "mail after 10 cards" or, otherwise, the sub-manager will mail them when they have reached the weight limit for the postage on the envelope. Don't forget to send extra stamps when postal rates increase. And ensure that the envelopes you leave are large enough and strong enough to cope with the weight and bulk of cards that you are expecting each to carry. This advice may seem obvious, but it is surprising how many amateurs send flimsy or tiny envelopes, or forget, for example, that a postal rate increase has just been announced.

Nowadays many DXpeditions offer the option of requesting QSLs via e-mail or a web-based form. Your QSL cards will come back via the bureau, but you have avoided the delay of sending an outgoing card through the bureau system, and very few DXpeditions are interested in collecting your QSL card. It would probably only be consigned to the wastepaper basket once it had been dealt with.

Direct QSLing and QSL managers

IF YOU ARE ANXIOUS to receive a QSL card for a particular contact or DXpedition, you will probably want to QSL direct. This may mean directly to the station concerned or, more likely to a QSL manager, in other words someone who handles the QSLing job for the DX station concerned. In the case of a DXpedition, the need for a QSL manager is obvious, as the DXpedition is a temporary operation from a remote location, but the QSL manager will be someone who is going to be available over a period of time to deal with QSL requests. Other DX stations quite often have QSL managers too. There are several reasons. The DX station concerned may be keen to spend as much time on the air as possible, and therefore want to pass the QSLing role to someone with more time available. Many out of the way countries also have problems with mail going astray, especially when it becomes known that mail to the person concerned quite often contains International Reply Coupons or dollar bills. So a QSL manager will be appointed in a country where this problem is less likely to arise. In some cases, the DX station may feel that he simply cannot afford to print and mail QSL cards, and perhaps a well-disposed amateur in the US or Europe will volunteer to take on the responsibility.

For you as a DXer, the approach to QSLing direct or via a manager is very much the same in every case. Obviously the first task is to determine the QSL manager, where appropriate, and his address. Often the DX station will announce this information at the time of the contact. If not, there are many sources on the Internet, as well as amateur radio newsletter and magazines (the 'HF' column in *RadCom* carries such information, though a monthly column will never have space for every possible QSL manager). The source you use may include the actual address or you may need to find that elsewhere. There are several online callbooks nowadays, and the online FCC database with the addresses of US amateurs is updated daily [1]. The qrz.com web site [2] is widely used, with many DX stations posting their direct address or QSL manager details. Most DXpeditions have web pages where you can find QSL information as well as all kinds of other interesting information. If all else fails, go to one of the popular Internet search engines such as *Google* and simply enter the callsign you are interested in. Almost certainly, if that station has been at all active, you will get several useful hits.

When you send a QSL card direct or to a QSL manager, there are several considerations to bear in mind. Firstly, ensure that your QSL card is correctly filled out. Don't omit the time, or enter it as local time rather than UTC. Ensure that everything can easily be read. Send it off along with a C6 size self-addressed envelope (SAE) and return postage. There is endless debate about how to send return postage. One solution is to send your SAE with local stamps for the country you are mailing to. This can work well, but there is a risk that they may be about to change their postal rates (there is a useful source of international postal rates at [3]) or the QSL manager may actually be intending to mail your card from a different country. If in doubt, enclose the stamps with the envelope, but don't stick them on. And do remember that it is of little use sending UK stamps to be used for return postage from other parts of the world! International Reply Coupons (IRCs) are sold at Post Offices specifically for the purpose of covering return airmail postage from anywhere in the world. However, that will only be for the basic weight band. For example, from the UK an IRC would cover European mail up to 20gm, but outside Europe only up to 10gm. 10gm is sufficient for one heavy QSL card or maybe two lightweight ones. So think about how many QSOs you are asking to be confirmed. You may have printed, say, four QSOs on a label, but the DX station may be using separate cards for each QSO. So err on the generous side. Even if one IRC does cover the necessary weight, it won't leave the QSL manager or DX station anything to cover the cost of printing the actual QSL cards or any other administrative costs. So it is usual to include at least two IRCs. The alternative is to include the ubiquitous 'green stamp', ie dollar bill. These are almost universally accepted nowadays, though some countries are very strict about currency of any sort being sent through their mail system, and some are even more sensitive if that currency is American. Of course, throughout Western Europe and North America, you can expect 'green stamps' to be welcomed with open arms, especially as they are reusable in a way which IRCs aren't (though there is a thriving trade in 'used' IRCs in the amateur radio world).

Amateurs make many mistakes when sending direct QSL cards, making the QSL manager's job more difficult. Odd-shaped and sized envelopes, QSL cards not completed with the correct details, address labels but no return envelope, putting the return envelope with the fold upwards, so that it gets sliced in half when the outward envelope is opened, asking for confirmations for large numbers of QSOs and enclosing just one IRC for return postage, and so on. Always try to put yourself in the position of the QSL manager, and think about how you can make his task as easy as possible.

The other side of the coin is that many amateurs do the job very efficiently and also make a point of including an additional donation, knowing that the cost of mounting a DXpedition is always beyond any monies that will be received but that any donation, however modest, will go some way to offsetting those costs and be by way of a "thank you".

Beware when sending direct QSL cards to countries where the postal system may be suspect (some South American and African countries are particular problems in this regard).

Code of Practice for QSL management

1. Any DX station appointing a QSL Manager must ensure that satisfactory arrangements are in place for receiving and responding to incoming bureau as well as direct cards. Adequate publicity must be given to such arrangements.

2. QSL Managers must respond to incoming SWL cards.

3. Any DX station appointing a QSL Manager must accept responsibility for that Manager's performance.

4. QSL Managers must respond "direct" and within a reasonable period of time if sufficient funds/IRCs/stamps to cover the exact cost of return postage and a return envelope are enclosed with the request. Airmail must be used if sufficient funds/IRCs/stamps are enclosed.

5. QSL Managers must not insist on separate envelopes/applications for different QSOs or different stations. They must establish internal procedures to handle such multiple requests.

6. Recognising that mistakes of time and/or date are frequently made, QSL Managers must make a reasonably diligent search for QSOs that cannot immediately be found in the log.

7. In particular: It is unacceptable to demand a specific number of IRCs or "green stamps" (US$ bills) if a smaller number would cover the costs mentioned in Point 4. It is unacceptable to return cards via the bureau if they were received direct with sufficient funds/IRCs/stamps as defined in Point 4.

8. There should be no time limit for applying for QSL cards. Old logbooks should be passed to responsible DX clubs when the manager no longer wishes to retain them.

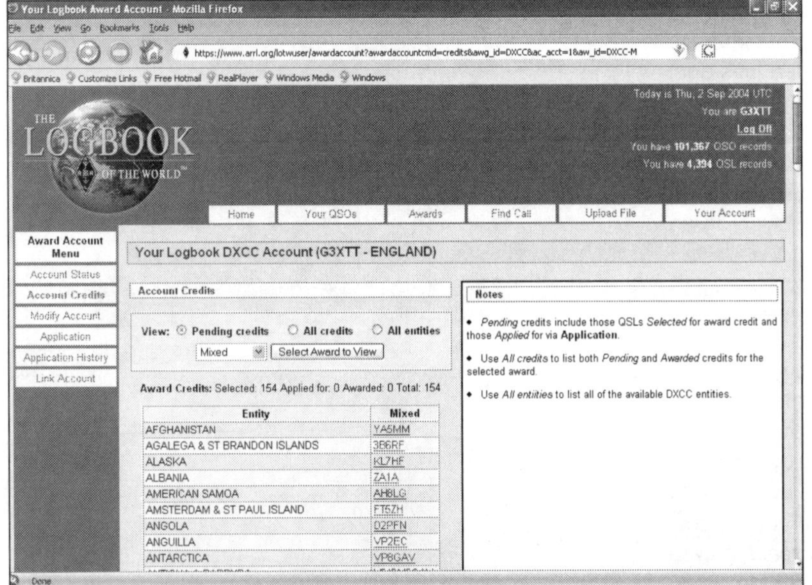

One of the screens available in the ARRL's *Logbook of the World*, showing electronic confirmations, by DXCC entity

If there is any suggestion that the envelope may contain something of value, then there is a good chance that it will be opened and any currency or IRCs removed, after which the envelope will probably be dumped. A callsign on the envelope is often the clue that a dishonest postal worker is looking for. You may decide to send your card registered delivery to be on the safe side, but this can be even more of an invitation to open it up. Amateurs in these countries are usually well aware of any problems, and usually appoint a QSL manager in North America, Europe, Japan, etc.

The IARU Code of Practice for QSL Management appears in the **sidebar**. Hopefully all QSL managers and others who handle direct cards will follow this and, if you find yourself as a QSL manager yourself, these are the guidelines should you aim to adhere to.

Logbook of the World

LOGBOOK OF THE WORLD (LoTW) [4,5,6], introduced in 2004 by the ARRL to support its DXCC Awards Program, addresses the sort of security issues described in the following section on 'eQSL'. It does not, however, purport to be a replacement for QSL cards, as it incorporates no mechanism for generating printed cards. Such a mechanism would have the same limitations described in that section; any printed card could just as easily have been printed from some other graphics program. Therefore LoTW limits its scope to providing QSO matching between electronic logs, for the purposes of applying for DXCC awards. As such, it complements rather than replacing paper QSLs. Many users may still wish to have traditional QSL cards from DX stations, as a memento of their contact, but may not wish to trust these valued cards to the postal service in order to apply for DXCC awards. Instead, the awards chaser can upload his log to LoTW, where any QSOs which match with others on their system, such as the logbook of a major expedition which may have been uploaded, will be available to be used in any DXCC submission. The security comes from the way in which the logs are uploaded. Users must first provide proof of their licence. US amateurs can do so via the FCC database, but amateurs elsewhere need to provide a copy of their licence and some sort of identity document showing name and address, such as a copy of their passport or drivers licence. Once this proof has been presented to ARRL, the user will be sent a digital certificate, which can then be used to sign electronically all QSOs before they are uploaded to LoTW. This electronic signature, based on public key encryption techniques widely used in commerce, prevents the QSO records being tampered with and is the ongoing guarantee of authenticity.

To upload logs, you will need your log to be in Cabrillo or ADIF format (most logging programs support export to these formats nowadays). It is then electronically encrypted, with each QSO record individually signed, as mentioned above, and then either e-mailed to ARRL or uploaded directly via the LoTW Web portal. You will get an acknowledgement e-mail, confirming that all is in order.

When you apply for additional credits for your DXCC awards, you can mix and match traditional paper QSL cards and matching records on LoTW. Charges apply to both, but the charge for dealing with LoTW conformations is lower than for paper QSLs, as less work is required by ARRL staff.

A useful feature of LoTW is that, once you are signed up and have your user ID and password, you will be able to see not only what matches you have through LoTW, but all your DXCC credits. This means that no longer do you have to ask for a printout each year in order to be able to keep track of which new credits you should be applying for.

If the idea of LoTW is anathema to you, fear not. The ARRL has confirmed that it will continue to accept traditional QSLs towards DXCC for the indefinite future.

Electronic QSLing

UNSURPRISINGLY, SINCE many activities are delegated to computers nowadays, there has been a growing interest in electronic QSLing. Rather than wait months or years for a card to be returned via the QSL bureau, why not send one electronically and, therefore, instantly?

The main argument against electronic QSLing is security. I can send another amateur an electronic QSL card, by way of a confirmatory e-mail or, more likely, an image representing the more conventional types of printed card. But, equally, the recipient could use one of the popular painting or image manipulation programs to generate something himself. There is no way of determining which is the 'genuine' card. Therefore the exchange of such electronic QSLs, whilst of some interest, is of limited applicability. The eQSL web site [7] sets out to overcome these objections to an extent, by requiring users to provide proof of their licence before uploading logs, although non-verified logs can also be loaded onto the system. The eQSL system sponsors several awards for contacts confirmed within the system but it has to be understood that the awards are based on matching QSOs within the database, not through the paper QSL cards which the system allows users to print. These cards do not indicate whether they originated from verified or unverified logs and, in any case, there is nothing to distinguish them from any card that an amateur may design and print from his own PC. Of course, the user himself will know which are which, and may therefore be happy to add them to his QSL collection, but they will carry no weight with a third party, such as an external award issuer.

Amateur radio awards

ONE OF THE MAJOR reasons for collecting QSL cards is to be able to use them for gaining a range of operating awards (though not all awards require QSL cards, some simply require an extract from your log, usually certified by two other amateurs or perhaps club officials). This is not the place to try and list all the operating awards which exist. They are covered in other publications, by K1BV on his excellent web pages [8] (you will need to subscribe), and on a wide range of other Internet sites.

It is, though, worth mentioning the principal RSGB and international awards, as they are often the motivation for becoming serious about HF, VHF or microwave bands operation, and may become the goal around which you design your station and focus your operating.

Types of awards

Awards fall into several categories. The following paragraphs discuss some of the major international awards programmes that are well established and keenly fought after. The annual DXCC listing, for example, includes several thousand callsigns. The IOTA Annual Listings have now grown to over 1500 callsigns. To reach the pinnacle of these award programmes takes several sunspot cycles, though the entry levels are set such that even a beginner should be able to gain a certificate within one DXing season (effectively a year). The joy is that, having reached that entry level, you can continue to climb the ladder, and gain recognition as your score improves, with something to keep you going for much of your amateur radio lifetime.

The Islands on the Air (IOTA) award scheme is one of the most popular worldwide

Other awards tend to be more specific, geared to a particular event, to a club or to specialism. Some have a specific time window during which contacts must be made, and then a deadline for applications to be submitted. The Athens 2004 Olympic Awards were typical, requiring amateurs to work Greek stations in the run-up to and during the Olympic Games. To make life even more interesting, a number of special event stations were run from various parts of Greece during that period, using unusual prefixes and counting for additional points towards the various levels of the Award. The Awards were sponsored by the Radio Amateur Association of Greece, and therefore there would be no problem in getting your application processed and receiving the certificate. Whilst awards such as DXCC are well understood by amateurs, explaining them to non-amateurs can sometimes be tricky, especially when our definition of a DXCC entity is often rather different to what a member of the public would consider as a country. But mount an Athens 2004 certificate on your shack wall, and non-amateur friends and family will immediately understand what it is all about!

The RSGB issues awards for excellence on the Microwave and . . .

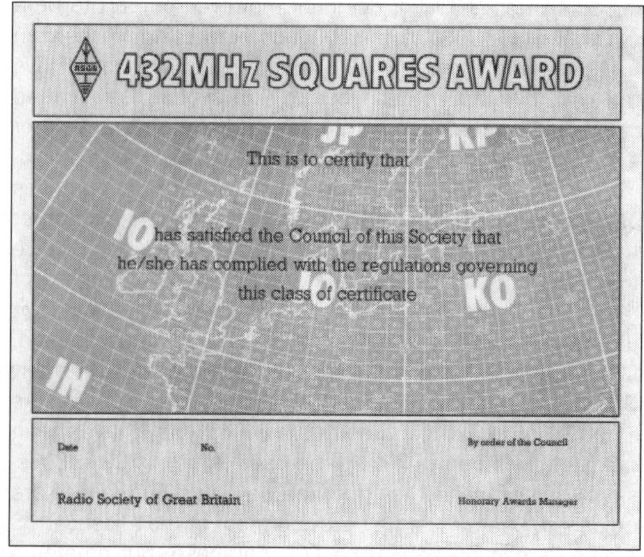

. . . the VHF/UHF bands

Where we move into something of a grey area are those Awards sponsored by local radio clubs. Often they are introduced with the best intentions, but then the originator moves on and a committee member is left to deal with the awards who knows little or nothing about them, or does not have the time to process them. In some cases the Award requirements are trivial and the charge is quite high and it is apparent that they have been introduced purely as a cynical effort to boost club funds. Fortunately these are in the minority, and many amateurs take great pleasure in collecting awards and displaying them proudly on the shack wall.

Chasing awards

Obviously how you go about chasing an award will depend on what it is. The main DXCC awards are effectively what Chapter 9 (DX operating) is all about. Of course, you may chase DX without applying for DXCC, but your DX contacts will certainly amass you the band and mode counters that you will need for DXCC. For more specialist awards, though, different considerations apply. Whilst Cluster has made life much easier than before where it comes to finding specific stations or types of station on the bands, many awards spawn meeting frequencies or regular nets for chasers. A good example is the US Counties awards programme, very popular in North America but also chased by a number of European amateurs. With 3077 counties in the USA, many of them with few or no resident amateurs, working the lot is a huge undertaking (there are, it should be emphasised, lower awards for working 500 counties, upwards). If you participate in US contests (for example the ARRL International DX Contests) and QSL the stations you work, you may well have a few hundred counties confirmed. But the trick to building your score is to join in on the County Hunter nets that take place on 20m. County activators head off in their cars, check into these nets, and may operate from several 'rare' counties in one operating session. If you are checked into the net, you will get a chance to work them all. But otherwise you may never catch these counties in casual day-to-day operation on the bands. Special arrangements are also in place for collecting confirmations for counties, as it would be a huge undertaking to send and receive over 3,000 QSL cards just for one award. Similarly, there are well-known gathering places on the bands for other popular awards programmes such as Islands on the Air (IOTA) and Worked All Britain (WAB)[9].

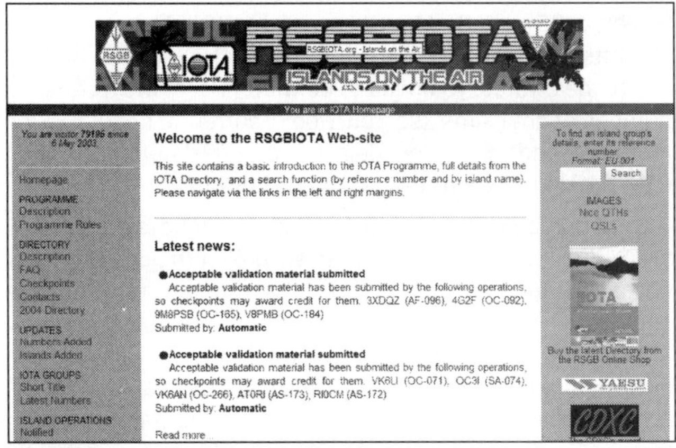

Part of the opening page of the IOTA web site

Sometimes an award is for working just one station which may sound odd, but there can be a challenge in doing so, in that wherever that station is located you will probably have good propagation on some of the bands but will find the chase much harder on other bands. A good example of this type of award is the one that was issued in conjunction with the GB50 operation from Windsor Castle on the occasion of the Queen's Golden Jubilee where points could be accumulated by working the station on different bands and modes, with contacts over the Jubilee Weekend itself counting double points. There was huge interest in this award from around the world, and it would certainly be a talking point when displayed prominently on the shack wall.

Awards chasing can actually be quite educational, as you start to learn about Swiss cantons or Japanese prefectures. Sometimes it can be the motivation you need to start holding QSOs in another language. Or an award may be just the incentive you need to try out a new band or mode. The 136kHz award described later in this section may not in itself be the motivation to become active on that band, but achieving it will be an indication that you have made substantial progress on what is a challenging band.

Finding out about awards

How do you find out about the multitude of short- and long-term awards available? The RSGB awards are all described in the *RSGB Yearbook*. No longer, though, are printed awards handbooks produced as was once the case, because this is a moving feast, catered for much better by the Internet. There are several awards pages, such as that by AC6V [10], which point you to awards from around the world. K1BV, who used to produce a loose-leaf awards handbook with regular updates, now does the same via his awards page, for which there is an annual subscription. However, details of many of the short-term awards are available on his page to all comers.

National magazines such as the RSGB's *RadCom* carry details of new awards from time to time and obviously those clubs who sponsor particular awards will make efforts to publicise them through the various online bulletins and elsewhere (*425 DX News*, *QRZ DX*, the *Daily DX* and the *OPDX Bulletins*, mentioned in Chapter 9 are examples of publications which will carry awards information).

In addition to the foregoing, ON4CAS now operates an Awards Reflector on the Internet, as a forum for awards chasers to exchange views, gather news and generally share with like-minded enthusiasts. To subscribe, send a blank e-mail to: HAM_awards-subscribe@yahoogroups.com.

The main thing to ensure, before you start the time-consuming (and costly, if you need to collect QSL cards) task of chasing credits for an award, is that you have an up-to-date set of rules. There are tales of people spending long periods chasing an award, only to find that it is has been discontinued or that the requirements have changed. Often the rules can be downloaded off a website, or you can send an SAE to the sponsoring organisation (send a reasonably sized envelope, and enough IRCs or other funds to cover return postage).

Fig 14.1: Suggested layout for awards applications

```
John Smith, G9ZZZ
4 High Street
Notown
Blankshire
England
                                  Application for the ZZZ award class 1

Endorsed all 14MHz, all 2X ssb

Date          GMT    Station     His signals    My signals    Band    Mode
13 August 99  1234   G7AS        59             59            14      2X ssb
15 August 99  0750   G7CX        55             46            14      2X ssb
   .           .       .          .              .             .        .
   .           .       .          .              .             .        .
23 August 99  1453   G7NN        59             56            14      2X ssb

Certified that I have complied with my licence regulations

3 September 99                                         John Smith, G9ZZZ
                                                       John Smith
```

Applying for awards

You will have rules, as you will have ensured that you got hold of these when you first started chasing the award in question. So you may well have an official application form, if there is one. Certainly, for the major awards like DXCC, there is a standard form available. Not surprisingly, as well as being able to request it by mail, you can also download it from the ARRL web page. Many other awards simply ask for a 'log extract'. Your application should be legible, and contain the information appropriate to the award in question, usually date, time, callsign of station worked, band, mode, reports exchanged and the relevant award-specific data (county, region, club affiliation, or whatever). If you are applying for a specific class of award, or requiring it to be endorsed ("all CW" or "all 80m" for example), then make this clear in your application.

Quite often the rules will ask for your application to be countersigned by one, or even two, independent persons. Sometimes these can be any other amateurs, sometimes the rules ask for a Club official to do so, sometimes it must the Awards Manager of your national society (in the UK this is John Dunnington, G3LZQ, his address for award applications differs from the callbook address and is given in the *RSGB Yearbook* awards section). What they are certifying is that they have checked your application against your log or, if the rules require it, that they have seen the QSL cards relevant to the application. There are some awards which require you to send the QSLs cards to the issuing body, but very few do, as most amateurs are reluctant to send their QSL cards abroad, in case they are mislaid or damaged.

A typical home-made application is shown in **Fig.14.1**. Always remember to show your own name, callsign and return address. Also an e-mail address if available, so that the awards manager can contact you if anything in your application is unclear.

There is a charge for most awards, usually quite modest and intended primarily to cover printing and mailing costs. Note how this should be paid. Usually there are several options, nowadays most likely to include IRCs, dollars and Euros. Take care if sending cash through the mail. Electronic means of funds transfer such as *PayPal* are likely to become more commonplace in the next few years.

Now your application is ready to mail. Again, check that the mailing address hasn't changed. Most awards managers are volunteers and the position is likely to change hands from time to time. Ideally, send an e-mail prior to mailing your application, to do a final check. When all is well, put your application in the mail and wait for that nice certificate to arrive.

DXCC awards program

The DXCC (DX Century Club) Awards Programme is one of the oldest and most respected awards programmes in the world [11]. It was first proposed in 1935, when Clinton B Desoto, W1CBD, set down the principles for an award based on working countries. Since then the programme has grown from a single award to a whole family of awards, by mode and band. All start at the 100 country level (hence the Century Club name), but all are endorsable for higher levels as you add more countries to your score. The 5-Band DXCC Awards is for achieving 100 countries on each of the five main HF bands (80, 40, 20, 15, 10) and can be subsequently endorsed for 100 countries each on 160, 30, 17, 12 and 6 metres.

Perhaps the most controversial aspect of the DXCC programme has been the definition of what constitutes a 'country' or, nowadays, more accurately a 'DXCC entity' because some of the qualifying entities would not be recognised as independent countries. They count for DXCC for other reasons, such as their geographic separation from the rest of the country concerned. The definition has changed over time, and many countries/entities have come and gone. For example, the former East Germany ceased to be a separate entity on reunification, whereas what was Yugoslavia now consists of the DXCC entities of Croatia (9A), Macedonia (Z3), Slovenia (S5) and Serbia & Montenegro (YU). The current list consists of 335 entities in all. To reach DXCC Honor Roll for any of the awards, you need to be within ten of the maximum number at that time (so you would currently need 326 or more credited). So-called 'deleted countries' appear on your total but do not count toward Honor Roll status.

Even in recent years, it was considered impossible to work all DXCC entities, simply because several of the countries did not allow amateur radio operations under any circumstances. This has gradually changed as countries such as Albania and China have reintroduced amateur radio, and the final domino to fall was North Korea, with a handful of acceptable operations in the last few years, particularly by P5/4L4FN. The result is that many amateurs now have all current DXCC entities worked and confirmed but, of course, they can continue the chase by repeating the process on other bands and modes. The 2m DXCC must be the toughest of them all, only possible if you exploit every available mode including moonbounce.

Full details of the DXCC Awards programme is available from the ARRL, and there are several QSL checkpoints in the UK so that you may not need to send your cards to the USA (nowadays, of course, you may be able to gain some credits for matches via *Logbook of the World*, the *LoTW* web pages explain the process of combining in one application both paper QSL cards and *LoTW* credits).

The UK checkpoints are, at the time of writing:

Fred Handscombe, G4BWP *(who deals with information requests and enquiries)*
Sandholm, Bridge End Road
Red Lodge
Bury St Edmunds
Suffolk, IP28 8LQ
ENGLAND
fredch@homeshack.freeserve.co.uk

Ian Capon, G0KRL *(who deals with postal applications from England)*
Windon, The Green
Beyton
Bury St Edmunds
Suffolk IP30 9AJ
ENGLAND
g0krl@arrl.net

Robert Ferguson, GM3YTS *(who deals with postal applications from the rest of the United Kingdom)*
19 Leighton Ave
Dunblane
FK15 0EB
SCOTLAND
gm3yts@btinternet.com

Jim Kellaway, G3RTE
55 Ladbrooke Drive
Potters Bar
EN6 1QW
ENGLAND
g3rte@tiscali.co.uk

Often, one or more of these volunteers may be available at major conventions and rallies, so that you can have your cards checked on the spot. Alternatively these checkers may accept 'in person' applications at their home address but this *MUST* be by prior arrangement. If you wish to send your cards by post to a UK checker please first contact G4BWP for the required procedure

Islands on the Air

Most popular of the RSGB awards is the Islands on the Air (IOTA) programme [12, 13]. This series of awards celebrated its 40th birthday in 2004, and continues to go from strength to strength, with awards for working island groups worldwide and on a continent by continent basis. There is

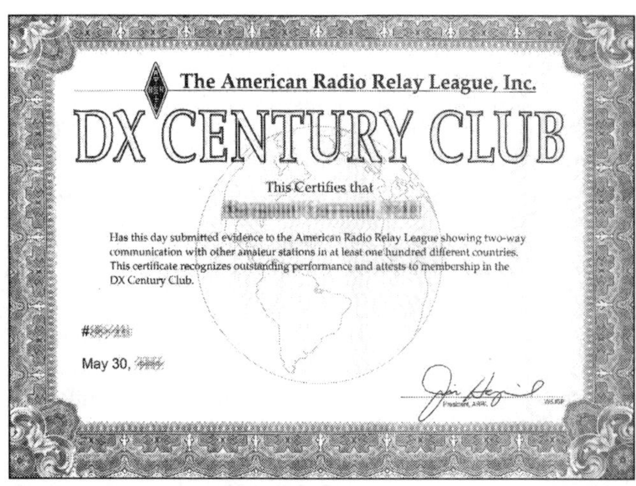

The must-have award for HF DXers

an annual listing of scores, including an Honour Roll of the highest-placed island chasers, which is published in a number of places including the RSGB's *RadCom* and the excellent *IOTA Directories* which also contain the full rules, island lists, and expedition stories. Many IOTA expeditions take place each year, and the annual IOTA Contest (on the last full weekend of July) is a great opportunity to add to your island score. As well as in the *IOTA Directory*, full details of the IOTA awards programme appear in the *RSGB Yearbook* and on the RSGB IOTA web pages [14].

Worked All Zones

The Worked all Zones Award, and 5-band Worked All Zones, are run by the US magazine *CQ* [15]. Like DXCC, the initial idea dates from quite early in the history of our hobby. For purposes of the award, the world was divided into 40 zones (not to be confused with the ITU zones, of which there are 90 in all). The zones are, roughly, of similar size and the idea was that, in days when not every country permitted amateur radio, you might at least be able to work each zone, because there were several countries in most zones, so some at least would probably be active on the bands.

A rule of thumb is that working all 40 zones is of a similar degree of difficulty to working 200 countries, and it is not unknown for contest stations to work all zones in a weekend, even on a single band (20, 15 or 10m). But the award remains a worthwhile challenge and the 5-Band WAZ award is a very tough one indeed. Managing contacts with all 40 zones on 80m is a major exercise, and a huge achievement when completed. Rules are available from *CQ* Magazine or from their web site.

Worked All States

Another popular ARRL awards programme is Worked All States. The name is self-explanatory. There are nine distinct awards in the programme, covering the various VHF bands, 160m, SSTV, RTTY, digital modes and satellite as well as a 5-band award. For UK amateurs, the toughest aspect is often finding those elusive contacts with Alaska (KL7) and Hawaii (KH6) especially, say, on 160m, but some of the mid-Western states can be tough, too, with relatively little amateur radio activity compared with, say, the states of the eastern seaboard.

VUCC

The ARRL's VUCC awards are available to amateurs worldwide, for working grid squares on the VHF, UHF and microwave bands. On 50MHz, 144MHz, and satellite the minimum requirements is 100 squares, but the requirement reduces on the higher bands. As with DXCC and WAS, full rules are available from the ARRL.

Other RSGB awards

The RSGB issues a range of operating awards for HF, VHF and Microwave operation. The HF awards are focused mainly on ITU zones, Commonwealth Call Areas, and Region One countries, as well as administering the Worked All Continents (WAC) award on behalf of IARU HQ. The VHF awards focus on countries, QTH Locator squares and Postal Districts. The Microwave awards are based on Locator Squares and on Distance. There is also a VHF award aimed specifically at Foundation Class licence holders. Again, full rules appear in the *RSGB Yearbook*.

VHF awards

It is worth mentioning, before closing this chapter, that most awards and certificates for HF operating can also be gained for work on the higher frequencies, though this is usually much more difficult. For example, a Worked All Continents award is easy for the average 14 or 21MHz operator to acquire, but a 432MHz WAC is another thing altogether, implying the use of moonbounce techniques, and possibly years of technical refinement. 6m is a different matter and, at least at times of peak solar activity, it is realistic for an active operator to be able to achieve the 6m DXCC award, or to collect enough islands to qualify for one of the IOTA awards. In addition to the RSGB awards mentioned in the previous paragraph, many other organisations issue awards aimed at VHF/UHF and Microwave operators, and many of these will be achievable by UK-based amateurs.

RSGB 136kHz Award

The RSGB's 136kHz award is available in three categories, with endorsements for additional countries heard/worked. The basic award is for confirmed two-way QSOs on 136kHz with five countries from the ARRL DXCC/WAE country list. The SWL Award is for confirmation of SWL reports from five countries. The SWL award may also be claimed by amateurs working cross band to stations transmitting in the 136kHz band. The third category is for cross band contacts, where the station claiming the award has worked five countries by transmitting on the 136kHz band and receiving stations on other amateur bands. Cross mode contacts will be allowed for this award. The categories of this award may not be mixed, but awards from some or all of the categories may be claimed and endorsed concurrently. Once the basic award has been claimed, it may be endorsed in steps of each additional five countries worked or heard.

References

[1] FCC database: http://www.wm7d.net/fcc_uls/

[2] QRZ.com: www.qrz.com

[3] International postal rates: http://www.k4hb.com/postage.html

[4] 'Introducing...Logbook of the World', *QST*, October 2003

[5] 'Logbook of the World', *RadCom*, April 2004, p.48

[6] LoTW Web Page: www.arrl.org/lotw

[7] eQSL: http://www.eqsl.cc/qslcard/Index.cfm

[8] K1BV online Awards directory: http://www.dxawards.com/

[9] Worked All Britain Awards: http://www.users.zetnet.co.uk/g1ntw/wab.htm

[10] AC6V Awards links: http://www.ac6v.com/hamawards.htm

[11] 'From Whence came WAS, WAC and DXCC?', *QST*, April 2004

[12] 'IOTA - A Beginner's Guide', *RadCom*, October 2003

[13] *IOTA Directory*, RSGB, updated annually

[14] IOTA: www.rsgbiota.org

[15] *CQ* Magazine Awards: http://www.cq-amateur-radio.com/awards.html

Appendix A — Glossary of Specialist Terms and Abbreviations

The following list is intended as a reference for those terms and abbreviations appearing in this Manual.

ADIF	Amateur Data Interchange Format, for exchanging data between logging programs
AFC	Automatic Frequency Control
AGC	Automatic Gain Control
AM	Amplitude Modulation
APRS	Automatic Position Reporting System
ARDF	Amateur Radio Direction Finding
AROS	Amateur Radio Observation Service
ARQ	Automatic Repeat Request (used in data communications)
ARRL	American Radio Relay League (the national body representing amateur radio in the USA)
ASTARS	APRS Satellite Tracking & Reporting System
ATU	Antenna Tuning Unit
ATV	Amateur Television
BBS	Bulletin Board System
BPL	Broadband Networking via Power Lines
break-in	Used in CW (Morse) operation, whereby the transceiver reverts to receive between characters
Cabrillo	Series of recommendations for contest logging formats.
CEPT	The European Conference of Post and Telecommunications Administrations
CITEL	Inter-American Telecommunication Commission
CQ	General Call, looking for replies ("Seek You")
CTCSS	Continuous Tone Controlled Squelch System
CVBS	Composite Video and Blanking Signal
CW	Continuous Wave (refers to Morse transmissions)
D-ATV	Digital Amateur Television
DFCW	Dual-Frequency CW
DSP	Digital Signal Processing
DTMF	Dual-Tone Multi-Frequency (refers to the way in which keys are recognised on a touch-tone telephone or microphone keypad)
DX	Long-distance (or rare) in the context of stations contacted
DXCC	DX Century Club (major international awards programme)
DXing	Chasing contacts with rare or distant stations (see DX)
DXpedition	An expedition specifically to activate a DX location
Echolink	System for connecting amateur radio to the Internet
EHT	Extra High Tension (very high voltage!)
EIRP	Effective Isotropic radiated Power (measures the effectiveness of an antenna relative to a point (isotropic) source)
EMC	Electromagnetic Compatibility
EME	Earth-Moon-Earth, using the moon as a passive reflector to make long-distance contacts.
ERO	European Radiocommunications Office
ERP	Effective Radiated Power
FCC	Federal Communications Commission (US licensing body)
FEC	Forward Error Correction
FM	Frequency Modulation
FSK	Frequency Shift Keying
GTO	Geostationary Transfer Orbit
HAREC	Harmonised Amateur Radio Examination Certificate
HEO	High Earth Orbit (satellites)
HF	High Frequency (officially 3-30MHz, but used by amateurs to refer to the bands 30 through 10 metres)
HT	Handie Talkie (handheld transceiver)
IARU	International Amateur Radio Union
IARUMS	IARU Monitoring System
IOTA	Islands on the Air (major RSGB Awards Programme)
IP	Internet Protocol
IRC	International Reply Coupon
IRS	Information Receiving Station
IRT	Same as RIT
ISS	Information Sending Station or International Space Station (used for both)
ITU	International Telecommunications Union
LAN	Local Area Network
LEO	Low Earth Orbit (satellites)
LF	Low Frequency (officially 300kHz-3MHz, but used by amateurs to refer to the 160, 80 and 40 metre bands)
LoTW	Logbook of The World
LSB	Lower Sideband
LUF	Lowest Usable Frequency
MC	Master of Ceremonies (used in net operations)
MCW	Modulated Continuous Wave
MOD	Ministry of Defence (UK)
MOX	Manually operated transmit

MS	Meteor Scatter
MSF	UK based standard frequency and time transmission (similar to US-based WWV)
MUF	Maximum Usable Frequency
NBFM	Narrow-Band FM
NCDXF	Northern California DX Foundation.
NOAA	National Oceanographic and Atmospheric Association (USA)
NoV	Notice of Variation (to UK amateur licence)
NVIS	Near Vertical Incidence Skywave
OFCOM	Office of Communications
OFDM	Orthogonal Frequency Division Multiplexing
OSCAR	Orbiting Satellite Carrying Amateur Radio
Over	A period of transmission
PA	Power Amplifier
PC	Personal Computer
PME	Protective Multiple Earthing
PMR	Personal Mobile Radio
PMS	Personal Mailbox System
PSK	Phase Shift Keying
PSU	Power Supply Unit
PTT	Push-to Talk
QPSK	Quadrature Phase Shift Keying
QRP	Very Low Power (definitions vary, usually 5 watts output or 10 watts input)
QSL Card	Card exchanged by radio amateurs to confirm a successful two-way contact
QSO	Used to refer to a contact between radio amateurs
Ragchewing	An extended contact, where the two parties do more than exchange basic information
RAYNET	Radio Amateurs Emergency Network
RIT	Receiver Incremental Tuning
RMC	Repeater Management Committee (of RSGB)
RSGB	Radio Society of Great Britain
RTTY	Radio Teletype
SCP	Super Check Partial
SID	Sudden ionospheric disturbance
sked	Pre-arranged schedule
SO2R	Single-operator two-radio (as in certain contests)
SOTA	Summits on the Air (Awards Programme)
SSB	Single Sideband
SSTV	Slow Scan Television
STB	Set Top Box
SWL	Short Wave Listener
SWR	Standing Wave Ratio
sysop	System Operator (who looks after a Bulletin Board, Cluster node, etc.)
TEP	Trans-Equatorial Propagation
TNC	Terminal Node Controller
Topband	160m band (1810 to 2000kHz in the UK)
TOR	Teleprinter Over Radio
UBN	Unique, Broken, Not in Log (a form of post-contest accuracy report)
UHF	Ultra High Frequency (officially 300MHz-3GHz, used by amateurs to refer primarily to the 70cm band)
UPS	Uninterruptable Power Supply
USB	Upper Sideband
UTC	Universal Coordinated Time (effectively the same as Greenwich Mean Time)
UTP	Unscreened Twisted Pair (network wiring)
VFO	Variable Frequency Oscillator
VHF	Very High Frequency (officially 30-300MHz, used by amateurs to refer to the 50, 70, 144 and, in N.America, 220MHz bands)
VLF	Very Low Frequency (officially 30-300kHz, but used by amateurs to refer to the 73kHz and 136kHz allocations)
VoIP	Voice over Internet
VOX	Voice operated transmit
VSWR	Voltage Standing Wave Ratio
WAB	Worked All Britain (Awards programme)
WAC	Worked All Continents (an Awards programme)
WARC	World Administrative Radio Conference
WAS	Worked All Zones (an Awards programme)
WAZ	Worked All States (an Awards programme)
WBFM	Wide-Band FM
work	In amateur radio terminology, to work someone is to have a two-way contact with them)
WRC	World Radio Conference (replaces previous WARCs)
WSJT	Weak Signal by K1JT (a suite of programs developed for weak signal working)
WWV	US service providing standard time, propagation and other data.
XIT	Transmitter Independent Tuning
Yagi	The most popular type of directional antenna (named after one of its Japanese inventors)

Appendix B Sources of Information

This Appendix lists a wide range of sources, including those referenced elsewhere in this Manual, where you can find information, software to download, and much else that is relevant to the subject matter of this book. Inevitably, the longest list is of Web sites, as these offer the most up-to-date sources and are easily accessible (and free!). However, it must be remembered that Web sites come and go, and their addresses change, but the list is believed to be accurate at press time. A set of links, including those in this Appendix, will also be maintained via the author's Web site (www.g3xtt.com, and follow Operating Manual and Links). Readers are welcome to send in their own suggestions (to don@g3xtt.com) for inclusion on that site and for possible inclusion in the next edition of this manual.

General/Clubs/Official Bodies

Addresses

International Amateur Radio Union
Box 310 905, Newington, Connecticut 06131 0905, USA.

International Telecommunication Union
Place des Nations, CH 1211 Geneva 20, Switzerland.

Web sites

ARRL
http://www.arrl.org

BARTG (data modes)
http://www.bartg.demon.co.uk

BYLARA (British YL Amateur Radio Association)
http://users.zetnet.co.uk/clivan/bylara.html

Chiltern DX Club
http://www.cdxc.org.uk

eHam (general info.)
http://www.eham.net

European Radiocommunications Office:
http://ww.ero.dk

G-QRP Club
http://www.gqrp.com/

Ham Universe (general info.)
http://www.hamuniverse.com

IARU region 1
http://www.iaru-r1.org

IARU
http://www.iaru.org

ITU
http://www.itu.int/home/

OFCOM
http://www.ofcom.org.uk/licensing_numbering/radiocomms/am_radio/

RAYNET
http://www.raynet-uk.net/

RSGB Spectrum Forum:
http://www.rsgb-spectrumforum.org.uk/

RSGB:
http://ww.rsgb.org.uk

UK Six Metre Group
http://www.uksmg.org/

Licensing

Web sites

Latest T/R 61-01 countries summary table
http://www.ero.dk/documentation/docs/implement.asp?docid=1802

OH2MCN licensing info
http://www.qsl.net/oh2mcn/license.htm

Operating (General)

Articles

'Computer networking and amateur radio'
RadCom, April 2004, p.45

'Morse Code - the Little-Known Facts'
RadCom, November 2001, p.34 and December 2001, p.34.

'The "Fivemegs Experiment"'
RadCom, September 2002, p.44

Books

LF Today **(136kHz)**
Mike Dennison, G3XDV, RSGB

Ham Radio for Dummies
Ward Silver N0AX, Wiley Publishing Inc

Radio Communication Handbook
RSGB

RSGB Prefix Guide
Fred Handscombe, G4BWP, RSGB.

RSGB Yearbook
ed. Steve White, G3ZVW, RSGB (published annually).

The ARRL Operating Manual
ARRL

The Rig Guide
Steve White G3ZVW, RSGB

Web sites

5MHz Experiment
http://www.rsgb-spectrumforum.org.uk/5MHz.htm

Q Signals
http://www.wemsi.org/qsigs.html

The World of LF (G3YXM)
http://www.wireless.org.uk/index.htm

Topband Frequency Allocations (K0CKD)
http://www.machlink.com/~k0ckdennis/topbandfrequencyallocations.txt

Winkey
http://www.k1el.com

DXing and DXpeditions, Special Event Stations

Articles

'One-Man DXpeditioning'
RadCom, August 2001, p.34

'SOTA: Summits on the Air'
RadCom, July 2004, p.47

Books

DXing on the Edge* - *The Thrill of 160 Meters
Jeff Briggs, K1ZM, ARRL

DXpeditioning, Behind the Scenes
Neville Cheadle, G3NUG & Steve Telenius-Lowe G4JVG

Low Power Communication* - *the Art and Science of QRP
Richard Arland, K7SZ, ARRL

Low-Band DXing
John Devoldere, ON4UN, ARRL

The Complete DXer
Bob Locher, W9KNI, Idiom Press 2003.

Up Two* - *Adventures of a DXpeditioner
Roger Western, G3SXW, Idiom Press

YASME* - *The Danny Weil and Colvin Radio Expeditions
James D Cain, K1TN, ARRL

Web sites

3B9C (DXpedition)
http://www.fsdxa.com/3b9c

425 DX News
http://www.425dxn.org/

AC6V list of HF nets
http://ac6v.com/nets.htm

DX Holiday
http://www.dxholiday.com

DX Summit
http://oh2aq.kolumbus.com/dxs/

DX Telnet
http://golist.net/dxt.htm and other sites.

GB50 (Special Event Station)
http://www.gb50.com

OPDX Bulletin
http://www.papays.com/opdx.html

Overseas licensing
http://www.qsl.net/oh2mcn/license.htm

QRZ DX & The DX Magazine
http://www.dxpub.com/

SOTA
http://www.sota.org.uk/

WD4NGB DX Telnet download
http://www.qsl.net/wd4ngb/telnet.htm

Weekly DX & Daily DX
http://www.dailydx.com/

Awards & QSLing

Articles

'Applying for the ARRL DXCC Award'
RadCom, April 2002, p.34

'From Whence came WAS, WAC and DXCC?'
QST, April 2004, p.48

'Introducing...Logbook of the World'
QST, October 2003 (pp.46, 47)

'IOTA - A Beginner's Guide'
RadCom, October 2003, p.56

'Logbook of the World'
RadCom, April 2004, p.48

'RSGB VHF, UHF and Microwave Awards'
RadCom, May 2002, p.36.

'The QSL Bureau Sub-Manager's Tale'
Graham Ridgeway, M5AAV, *RadCom* Sept.2003, p.58

Books

IOTA Directory
RSGB, updated annually

Web sites

AC6V Awards links
http://www.ac6v.com/hamawards.htm

Calculator for locators
http://www.qsl.net/dl3bak/qrb/en/frame.htm

CQ Magazine Awards
http://www.cq-amateur-radio.com/awards.html

eQSL
http://www.eqsl.cc/qslcard/Index.cfm

FCC database
http://www.wm7d.net/fcc_uls/

GO LIST
http://www.golist.net/

IK3QAR QSL Information
http://www.ik3qar.it/

International postal rates
http://www.k4hb.com/postage.html

IOTA
http://www.rsgbiota.org

K1BV online Awards directory
http://www.dxawards.com/

LoTW Web Page
http://www.arrl.org/lotw

Qrz.com
http://www.qrz.com

Worked All Britain Awards
http://www.users.zetnet.co.uk/g1ntw/wab.htm

Mobile/Maritime Mobile

Books

Amateur Radio Mobile Handbook
RSGB

Highway Code
http://www.highwaycode.gov.uk/

Maritime nets
http://www.cruiser.co.za/radionet.asp

Contests

Articles

'A beginner's Guide to RTTY Contests'
John Barber, GW4SKA & Phil Cooper, GU0SUP, *RadCom* Aug 2003, p.54.

Web sites

ARRL Contest Page
http://www.arrl.org/contests/

British Top-Band DF Association
http://www.topbanddf.org.uk/

CQ Contests
http://www.cq-amateur-radio.com/awards.html

CQ WW Contests
http://www.cqww.com/

Data Modes Contesting
http://www.rttycontesting.com

High Speed telegraphy
http://www.morsecode.dutch.nl/hst.html

K2KW (Contest operations)
http://www.k2kw.com/tv.html

Microwave Contest info
http://www.g3pho.free-online.co.uk/microwaves

NCJ
http://www.ncjweb.com/

NG3K Contest Pages
http://www.cpcug.org/user/wfeidt/Contest/index.html

RSGB ARDF Committee
http://www.ardf.btinternet.co.uk/index.html

RSGB HF Contest Committee
http://www.rsgbhfcc.org

RSGB VHF Contest Committee
http://www.blacksheep.org/vhfcc/index.html

SM3CER contest pages
http://www.sk3bg.se/contest/

Various contest resources at contesting.com
http://lists.contesting.com/mailman/listinfo

VHF Contest Mapping software
http://gw3atz.users.btopenworld.com/page5.html

WA7BNM contest pages
http://www.hornucopia.com/contestcal/

World Contest Station Database
http://www.pvrc.org/wcsd/wcsdsearch.htm

Antennas & Planning Matters

Articles

'Aerial Hassles & Planning Permission'
Ian Barraclough, G7DWY, *RadCom* June 2003, p.18.

Books

ARRL Antenna Book
ARRL (available from RSGB)

EMC

Articles

'Living with your Neighbours'
RadCom, September 2001, p.44

Web sites

RSGB EMC Committee
http://www.qsl.net/rsgb_emc/

Propagation/Solar Data

Articles

'Making the Most of Sporadic E at VHF'
RadCom, January 2002, p.34

'Propagation Prediction Software'
RadCom, June 2000, p.24

'The Twighlight Zone: just what is "grey-line" propagation?'
RadCom, July 2002, p.34

'Using DSP Software for VHF Beacon Monitoring'
RadCom, June 2001, p.28

'*WinCap Wizard 3*, Propagation Prediction Software', *RadCom*, December 2002, p.44

Books

Radio Propagation - Principles & Practice
Ian Poole, G3YWX, RSGB

The Shortwave Propagation Handbook
George Jacob, W3ASK, and Theodore J Cohen, N4XX, CQ Magazine

Web sites

2m & 70cm beacons
http://www.qsl.net/la0by/beacons.htm

Build a magnetometer
http://www.payton.cps.k12.il.us/magnet/magnet_welcome.htm

DXLab
http://www.qsl.net/dxlab/

HFRadio.org
http://prop.hfradio.org

IARU/NCDXF Beacons
http://www.ncdxf.org/beacons.html

N6RT propagation data
http://dx.qsl.net/propagation/

NOAA Solar Data
http://www.noaa.gov/solar.html

Real-time Greyline
http://www.worldtime.com/cgi-bin/wt.cgi

RSGB Propagation Studies Committee
http://www.keele.ac.uk/depts/por/psc.htm

Solar weather
http://www.sec.noaa.gov/today.html

Spaceweather
http://spaceweather.com

Sunclock
http://www.mapmaker.com/shadowfacts/index.htm

Sunspot cycle
http://www.sunspotcycle.com/

VHF propagation primer
http://www.anarc.org/wtfda/propagation.htm

W1AW Propagation Bulletin
http://www.arrl.org/w1aw/prop

W6EL propagation software
http://www.qsl.net/w6elprop/

Data Communications

Articles

'An SSTV "how-to"'
RadCom, May 2004, p.24

'Digital Voice Transmission: the AOR ARD9800 Fast Data Modem'
RadCom, July 2004, p.18

'MixW'
QST, August 2003, p.58

'PSK31 - Has RTTY's Replacement Arrived?'
QST, May 1999, p.41

'PSK31: New radioteletype mode with a traditional philosophy'
RadCom, December 1998 and January 1999.

'Simple sound-card-to-radio interface circuits'
RadCom April 2004, p.38

'The Ins and Outs of a Sound Card'
QST, October 2003, p.33

Web sites

AA5AU RTTY Pages
http://www.aa5au.com/rtty/

PSK31 Links
http://members.fortunecity.com/xe1bef/psk31.htm

RSGB Datacomms Committee (list of Packet nodes, Internet gateways, etc)
http://www.dcc.rsgb.org

APRS

Articles

'APRS - an Introduction'
Ciemon Dunville, G0TRT, *RadCom* December 2000.

Books

APRS, Moving Hams on Radio and the Internet'
Stan Horpzepa, WA1LOU, ARRL

Web sites

APRS
http://www.aprs.org

UI-View
http://www.ui-view.com/

Repeaters

Web sites

RSGB Repeater Management Committee
http://www.coldal.org.uk/rmc.htm

VoIP

Articles

'Internet Linking through the IRLP System'
RadCom February 2002

'VoIP and Amateur Radio'
Steve Ford, WB8IMY, *QST* February 2003

Books

VoIP, Internet Linking for Radio Amateurs
Jonathan Taylor, K1RFD, ARRL, 2004.

Web sites

Echolink
http://www.echolink.org

eQSO
http://www.eqso.net

IRLP
http://www.irlp.net

UK Internet Radio Linking project
http://www.ukirlp.co.uk

UK IRLP
http://www.ukirlp.co.uk

Amateur TV

Articles

'A Modular 24cm ATV transceiver'
Simon Lewis, GM4PLM, *RadCom*, May 2003, p.26

Books

Image Communications Handbook
Dr Ralph E. Taggart, WB8DQT, ARRL

Web sites

British Amateur Television Club
http://www.batc.org.uk/

Digital Amateur TV (PE1JOK)
http://www.xs4all.nl/~pe1jok/dvbsvsdatv.html

Satellites/Space

Articles

'A Practical Approach to Operating AO-40'
RadCom, November 2001, p.22 and December 2001, p.29.

'AO-40 for Us Appliance Operators'
QST, November 2003, p.48

'Using Simple Antennas for ISS Contacts'
Keith Zimmerman K5WX, *QST* September 2004, p.34.

Books

Laminated Satellite Frequency List
AMSAT UK

Orbital Mechanics and Satellite Technology
Bob Phillips G4IQQ, AMSAT-UK

The Guide to Oscar Operating
Richard Limebear - G3RWL, AMSAT UK.

Web sites

AMSAT software download
http://www.amsat.org/amsat/ftpsoft.html#pc

AMSAT-NA
http://www.amsat.org

AMSAT-UK
http://www.uk.amsat.org

AO-27
http://www.ao27.org

ARISS Europe
http://www.ariss-eu.org/

Cubesat chart
http://home.earthlink.net/~maenpaa.cubesat_table.pdf

Cubesat XI-IV
http://www.space.t.u-tokyo.ac.jp/index.html

Cute-1
http://lss.mess.titech.ac.jp/ssp/cubesat

Keplerian Elements
http://www.celestrak.com

PCSat download page
http://www.findu.com/cgi-bin/pcsat.cgi

Satellite visibility and tracking
http://heavens-above.com

EME/Meteor Scatter

Web sites

432 and above EME News
http://www.nitehawk.com/rasmit/em70cm.html

EME Directory
http://www.dl4eby.de/

G3SEK
http://www.ifwtech.co.uk/g3sek/

GM4JJJ (MoonSked s/w)
http://www.gm4jjj.co.uk/MoonSked/moonsked.htm

Grid square calculation
http://www.amsat.org/cgi-bin/gridconv

Meteor Scatter
http://www.meteorscatter.net/soft.htm

OH5IY
http://www.kolumbus.fi/oh5iy/mssoft/mssoft.htm

W5UN
http://web.wt.net/~w5un/primer.htm

Software

Articles

'Contest Logging Software Reviewed'
RadCom, November 1999, p.14

Data Modes

Web sites

G3PPT (Hellschreiber)
http://www.lsear.freeserve.co.uk/

G3YXM on Jason
http://www.wireless.org.uk/jason.htm

Hell
http://www.qsl.net/zl1bpu/FUZZY/software.html

Jason software download
http://www.qsl.net/padan/jason/

K6SIX WSJT site
http://personalpages.mcttelecom.com/~b_mobile/6Mweak.htm

MMSSTV download
http://mmhamsoft.ham-radio.ch/#MMSSTV

MMTTY Download
http://mmhamsoft.ham-radio.ch/mmtty/index.html

NB6Z Hellschreiber page
http://home.teleport.com/~nb6z/hell.htm

ON7YD on QRSS
http://www.qsl.net/on7yd/136narro.htm

PSK31 Homepage
http://bipt106.bi.ehu.es/psk31.html

PSK31 links
http://www.psk31.org

PSK63
http://www.qsl.net/kh6ty/psk63/

WA5UFH WSJT site
http://www.qsl.net/wa5ufh/

WOLF for beginners
http://www.computerpro.com/~lyle/wolf/wolf4beginners.htm

WOLF software
http://www.scgroup.com/ham/wolf.html

WSJT
http://pulsar.princeton.edu/~joe/K1JT

Logging Software

Web sites

CT (contest logging)
http://www.k1ea.com/

DX4WIN station logging
http://www.dx4win.com/

LOG-EQF
http://www.eqf-software.com/

N1MM
http://www.n1mm.com

N3FJP
http://www.n3fjp.com

NA Contest Logging Software
http://www.datomonline.com

SD (contest logging)
http://www.ei5di.com

Shacklog
http://www.shacklog.co.uk/shacklog_main.htm

TR Log
http://www.trlog.com/

TurboLog
http://www.turbolog.de/

VHFCONT
http://www.qsl.net/kc6teu

VHFLOG32
http://www.qsl.net/w3km

Writelog
http://www.writelog.com/

Training and Contest Simulation Software

Web sites

G4FON Koch Morse trainer
http://www.qsl.net/g4fon/CW%20Trainer.htm

G4ZFE pile-up trainer
http://www.g4zfe.com/pileup95.html

HSTT
http://je1cka.jzap.com/contest

PED
http://je1cka.jzap.com/ped

Pilemania (JA1DYB)
http://www.jg1vgx.net/etc/pilemania0.09.zip

RUFZ
http://www.darc.de/referate/dx/xedtrsd.htm

VPED
http://je1cka.jzap.com/contest

Mapping/Greyline software

Web sites

DX Atlas
http://www.dxatlas.com/

EI8IC (Maps)
http://www.qsl.net/ei8ic

Geoclock
http://home.att.net/~geoclock/

QSL Management

Web sites

DF3CB (QSL Software)
http://www.df3cb.com/

VHF/UHF/Microwaves

Web sites

4m band:
http://www.70mhz.org/theband.htm

***DUBUS* Magazine**
http://www.marsport.demon.co.uk/dubus.htm

RSGB Microwave Committee Components Service
http://www.g3wdg.free-online.co.uk/

UK Microwave Group
http://www.microwavers.org

Appendix C

Callsign Prefixes and Great Circle Map

Callsigns for the world's nations are determined by the International Telecommunications Union (ITU). This is the United Nations agency that co-ordinates radio activity for all spectrum users. The prefixes used by a country for both commercial and amateur radio purposes are determined from one or more ITU allocation blocks issued to that country. The amateur radio callsigns in use for a particular country might use one or a number of combinations derived from the authorised ITU allocation(s) for that country. The following list shows callsign prefixes currently in use. Most are derived from the callsign blocks allocated to administrations by the ITU for use within the countries, territories and dependencies for which a country is responsible. Also shown are some unauthorised prefixes which may be heard and which may or may not be recognised as a DXCC entity, eg 1S (Spratly Archipelago) and 1A0 (SMOM). Both of these are DXCC countries although the prefixes used are unofficial. 1B (the Turkish area of North Cyprus) and 1Z (Karen State - Myanmar) are unofficial and are not recognised for DXCC purposes. Full information on prefixes is contained in the RSGB Prefix Guide.

Prefix	Entity	Cont	ITU	CQ
1A0	Sov. Mil. Order of Malta	EU	28	15
3A	Monaco	EU	27	14
3B6, 7	Agalega & St. Brandon	AF	53	39
3B8	Mauritius	AF	53	39
3B9	Rodrigues I.	AF	53	39
3C	Equatorial Guinea	AF	47	36
3C0	Annobon I.	AF	52	36
3D2	Fiji	OC	56	32
3D2	Conway Reef	OC	56	32
3D2	Rotuma I.	OC	56	32
3DA	Swaziland	AF	57	38
3V	Tunisia	AF	37	33
3W, XV	Vietnam	AS	49	26
3X	Guinea	AF	46	35
3Y	Bouvet	AF	67	38
3Y	Peter I I.	AN	72	12
4J, 4K	Azerbaijan	AS	29	21
4L	Georgia	AS	29	21
4P-4S	Sri Lanka	AS	41	22
4U_ITU	ITU HQ	EU	28	14
4U_UN	United Nations Headquarters	NA	08	05
4W	Timor - Leste	OC	54	28
4X, 4Z	Israel	AS	39	20
5A	Libya	AF	38	34
5B	Cyprus	AS	39	20
5H-5I	Tanzania	AF	53	37
5N-5O	Nigeria	AF	46	35
5R-5S	Madagascar	AF	53	39
5T	Mauritania	AF	46	35
5U	Niger	AF	46	35
5V	Togo	AF	46	35
5W	Samoa	OC	62	32
5X	Uganda	AF	48	37
5Y-5Z	Kenya	AF	48	37
6V-6W	Senegal	AF	46	35
6Y	Jamaica	NA	11	08
7O	Yemen	AS	39	21
7P	Lesotho	AF	57	38
7Q	Malawi	AF	53	37
7T-7Y	Algeria	AF	37	33
8P	Barbados	NA	11	08
8Q	Maldives	AS/AF	41	22
8R	Guyana	SA	12	09
9A	Croatia	EU	28	15
9G	Ghana	AF	46	35
9H	Malta	EU	28	15
9I-9J	Zambia	AF	53	36
9K	Kuwait	AS	39	21
9L	Sierra Leone	AF	46	35
9M2, 4	West Malaysia	AS	54	28
9M6, 8	East Malaysia	OC	54	28
9N	Nepal	AS	42	22
9Q-9T	Dem. Rep. of Congo	AF	52	36
9U	Burundi	AF	52	36
9V	Singapore	AS	54	28
9X	Rwanda	AF	52	36
9Y-9Z	Trinidad & Tobago	SA	11	09
A2	Botswana	AF	57	38
A3	Tonga	OC	62	32
A4	Oman	AS	39	21
A5	Bhutan	AS	41	22
A6	United Arab Emirates	AS	39	21
A7	Qatar	AS	39	21
A9	Bahrain	AS	39	21
AP-AS	Pakistan	AS	41	21
BS7	Scarborough Reef	AS	50	27
BV	Taiwan	AS	44	24
BV9P	Pratas I.	AS	44	24
BY, BT	China	AS	S	23,24
C2	Nauru	OC	65	31
C3	Andorra	EU	27	14
C5	The Gambia	AF	46	35
C6	Bahamas	NA	11	08
C8-9	Mozambique	AF	53	37
CA-CE	Chile	SA	14,16	12
CE	Easter I.	SA	63	12
CE0	Juan Fernandez Is.	SA	14	12
CE0	San Felix & San Ambrosio	SA	14	12
CE9/KC4	Antarctica	AN	S	S
CM, CO	Cuba	NA	11	08
CN	Morocco	AF	37	33
CP	Bolivia	SA	12,14	10
CT	Portugal	EU	37	14
CT3	Madeira Is.	AF	36	33
CU	Azores	EU	36	14

Prefix	Entity	Cont	ITU	CQ
CV-CX	Uruguay	SA	14	13
CY0	Sable I.	NA	09	05
CY9	St. Paul I.	NA	09	05
D2-3	Angola	AF	52	36
D4	Cape Verde	AF	46	35
D6	Comoros	AF	53	39
DA-DR	Fed. Rep. of Germany	EU	28	14
DU-DZ	Philippines	OC	50	27
E3	Eritrea	AF	48	37
E4	Palestine	AS	39	20
EA-EH	Spain	EU	37	14
EA6-EH6	Balearic Is.	EU	37	14
EA8-EH8	Canary Is.	AF	36	33
EA9-EH9	Ceuta & Melilla	AF	37	33
EI-EJ	Ireland	EU	27	14
EK	Armenia	AS	29	21
EL	Liberia	AF	46	35
EP-EQ	Iran	AS	40	21
ER	Moldovia	EU	29	16
ES	Estonia	EU	29	15
ET	Ethiopia	AF	48	37
EU, EV, EW	Belarus	EU	29	16
EX	Kyrgyzstan	AS	30,31	17
EY	Tajikistan	AS	30	17
EZ	Turkmenistan	AS	30	17
F	France	EU	27	14
FG	Guadeloupe	NA	11	08
FJ, FS	Saint Martin	NA	11	08
FH	Mayotte	AF	53	39
FK	New Caledonia	OC	56	32
FK/C	Chesterfield Is.	OC	56	30
FM	Martinique	NA	11	08
FO	Austral I.	OC	63	32
FO	Clipperton I.	NA	10	07
FO	French Polynesia	OC	63	32
FO	Marquesas Is.	OC	63	31
FP	St. Pierre & Miquelon	NA	09	05
FR/G	Glorioso Is.	AF	53	39
FR/J, E	Juan de Nova, Europa	AF	53	39
FR	Reunion I.	AF	53	39
FR/T	Tromelin I.	AF	53	39
FT5W	Crozet I.	AF	68	39
FT5X	Kerguelen Is.	AF	68	39
FT5Z	Amsterdam and St. Paul Is.	AF	68	39
FW	Wallis & Futuna Is.	OC	62	32
FY	French Guiana	SA	12	09
G, GX, M, MX, 2E	England	EU	27	14
GD, GT, MD, MT, 2D	Isle of Man	EU	27	14
GI, GN, MI, MN, 2I	Northern Ireland	EU	27	14
GJ, GH, MJ, MH, 2J	Jersey	EU	27	14
GM, GS, MM, MS, 2M	Scotland	EU	27	14
GU, GP, MU, MP, 2U	Guernsey	EU	27	14

Prefix	Entity	Cont	ITU	CQ
GW, GC, MW, MC, 2W	Wales	EU	27	14
H4	Solomon Is.	OC	51	28
H40	Temotu Province	OC	51	32
HA, HG	Hungary	EU	28	15
HB	Switzerland	EU	28	14
HB0	Liechtenstein	EU	28	14
HC-HD	Ecuador	SA	12	10
HC8-HD8	Galapagos Is.	SA	12	10
HH	Haiti	NA	11	08
HI	Dominican Republic	NA	11	08
HJ-HK	Colombia	SA	12	09
HK0	Malpelo I.	SA	12	09
HK0	San Andres & Providencia	NA	11	07
HL	Republic of Korea	AS	44	25
HO-HP	Panama	NA	11	07
HQ-HR	Honduras	NA	11	07
HS, E2	Thailand	AS	49	26
HV	Vatican	EU	28	15
HZ	Saudi Arabia	AS	39	21
I	Italy	EU	28	15,33
IS0, IM0	Sardinia	EU	28	15
J2	Djibouti	AF	48	37
J3	Grenada	NA	11	08
J5	Guinea-Bissau	AF	46	35
J6	St. Lucia	NA	11	08
J7	Dominica	NA	11	08
J8	St. Vincent	NA	11	08
JA-JS	Japan	AS	45	25
JD1	Minami Torishima	OC	90	27
JD1	Ogasawara	AS	45	27
JT-JV	Mongolia	AS	32,33	23
JW	Svalbard	EU	18	40
JX	Jan Mayen	EU	18	40
JY	Jordan	AS	39	20
K, W, N, AA-AK	United States of America	NA	6,7,8	3,4,5
KG4	Guantanamo Bay	NA	11	08
KH0	Mariana Is.	OC	64	27
KH1	Baker & Howland Is.	OC	61	31
KH2	Guam	OC	64	27
KH3	Johnston I.	OC	61	31
KH4	Midway I.	OC	61	31
KH5	Palmyra & Jarvis Is.	OC	61,62	31
KH5K	Kingman Reef	OC	61	31
KH6, 7	Hawaii	OC	61	31
KH7K	Kure I.	OC	61	31
KH8	American Samoa	OC	62	32
KH9	Wake I.	OC	65	31
KL7	Alaska	NA	1,2	1
KP1	Navassa I.	NA	11	08
KP2	Virgin Is.	NA	11	08
KP3,4	Puerto Rico	NA	11	08
KP5	Desecheo I.	NA	11	08
LA-LN	Norway	EU	18	14
LO-LW	Argentina	SA	14,16	13
LX	Luxembourg	EU	27	14
LY	Lithuania	EU	29	15
LZ	Bulgaria	EU	28	20
OA-OC	Peru	SA	12	10

Prefix	Entity	Cont	ITU	CQ
OD	Lebanon	AS	39	20
OE	Austria	EU	28	15
OF-OI	Finland	EU	18	15
OH0	Aland Is.	EU	18	15
OJ0	Market Reef	EU	18	15
OK-OL	Czech Republic	EU	28	15
OM	Slovak Republic	EU	28	15
ON-OT	Belgium	EU	27	14
OX	Greenland	NA	5,75	40
OY	Faroe Is.	EU	18	14
OZ	Denmark	EU	18	14
P2	Papua New Guinea	OC	51	28
P4	Aruba	SA	11	09
P5	DPR of Korea	AS	44	25
PA-PI	Netherlands	EU	27	14
PJ2, 4, 9	Bonaire, Curacao (Neth. Antilles)	SA	11	09
PJ5-8	St. Maarten, Saba, St. Eustatius	NA	11	08
PP-PY	Brazil	SA	12, 13,15	11
PP0-PY0F	Fernando de Noronha	SA	13	11
PP0-PY0S	St. Peter & St. Paul Rocks	SA	13	11
PP0-PY0T	Trindade & Martim Vaz Is.	SA	15	11
PZ	Suriname	SA	12	09
R1FJ	Franz Josef Land	EU	75	40
R1MV	Malyj Vysotskij I.	EU	29	16
S0	Western Sahara	AF	46	33
S2	Bangladesh	AS	41	22
S5	Slovenia	EU	28	15
S7	Seychelles	AF	53	39
S9	Sao Tome & Principe	AF	47	36
SA-SM	Sweden	EU	18	14
SN-SR	Poland	EU	28	15
ST	Sudan	AF	48	34
SU	Egypt	AF	38	34
SV-SZ	Greece	EU	28	20
SV/A	Mount Athos	EU	28	20
SV5	Dodecanese	EU	28	20
SV9	Crete	EU	28	20
T2	Tuvalu	OC	65	31
T30	W. Kiribati (Gilbert Is.)	OC	65	31
T31	C. Kiribati (British Phoenix Is.)	OC	62	31
T32	E. Kiribati (Line Is.)	OC	61,63	31
T33	Banaba I. (Ocean I.)	OC	65	31
T5	Somalia	AF	48	37
T7	San Marino	EU	28	15
T8, KC6	Palau	OC	64	27
T9	Bosnia-Herzegovina	EU	28	15
TA-TC	Turkey	EU/AS	39	20
TF	Iceland	EU	17	40
TG, TD	Guatemala	NA	11	07
TI, TE	Costa Rica	NA	11	07
TI9	Cocos I.	NA	11	07
TJ	Cameroon	AF	47	36
TK	Corsica	EU	28	15
TL	Central Africa	AF	47	36
TN	Congo (Republic of the)	AF	52	36
TR	Gabon	AF	52	36
TT	Chad	AF	47	36
TU	Cote d'Ivoire	AF	46	35
TY	Benin	AF	46	35
TZ	Mali	AF	46	35
UA-UI1,3, 4,6, RA-RZ	European Russia	EU	S	16
UA2	Kaliningrad	EU	29	15
UA-UI8,9,0, RA-RZ	Asiatic Russia	AS	S	S
UJ-UM	Uzbekistan	AS	30	17
UN-UQ	Kazakhstan	AS	29- 31	17
UR-UZ, EM-EO	Ukraine	EU	29	16
V2	Antigua & Barbuda	NA	11	08
V3	Belize	NA	11	07
V4	St. Kitts & Nevis	NA	11	08
V5	Namibia	AF	57	38
V6	Micronesia	OC	65	27
V7	Marshall Is.	OC	65	31
V8	Brunei Darussalam	OC	54	28
VE, VO, VY	Canada	NA	S	1-5
VK	Australia	OC	S	29,30
VK0	Heard I.	AF	68	39
VK0	Macquarie I.	OC	60	30
VK9C	Cocos-Keeling Is.	OC	54	29
VK9L	Lord Howe I.	OC	60	30
VK9M	Mellish Reef	OC	56	30
VK9N	Norfolk I.	OC	60	32
VK9W	Willis I.	OC	55	30
VK9X	Christmas I.	OC	54	29
VP2E	Anguilla	NA	11	08
VP2M	Montserrat	NA	11	08
VP2V	British Virgin Is.	NA	11	08
VP5	Turks & Caicos Is.	NA	11	08
VP6	Pitcairn I.	OC	63	32
VP6	Ducie I.	OC	63	32
VP8	Falkland Is.	SA	16	13
VP8, LU	South Georgia I.	SA	73	13
VP8, LU	South Orkney Is.	SA	73	13
VP8, LU	South Sandwich Is.	SA	73	13
VP8, LU, CE9, HF0, 4K1	South Shetland Is.	SA	73	13
VP9	Bermuda	NA	11	05
VQ9	Chagos Is.	AF	41	39
VR	Hong Kong	AS	44	24
VU	India	AS	41	22
VU	Andaman & Nicobar Is.	AS	49	26
VU	Lakshadweep Is.	AS	41	22
XA-XI	Mexico	NA	10	06
XA4-XI4	Revillagigedo	NA	10	06
XT	Burkina Faso	AF	46	35
XU	Cambodia	AS	49	26
XW	Laos	AS	49	26
XX9	Macao	AS	44	24
XY-XZ	Myanmar	AS	49	26
YA	Afghanistan	AS	40	21
YB-YH	Indonesia	OC	51,54	28
YI	Iraq	AS	39	21
YJ	Vanuatu	OC	56	32
YK	Syria	AS	39	20
YL	Latvia	EU	29	15
YN	Nicaragua	NA	11	07

Prefix	Entity	Cont	ITU	CQ
YO-YR	Romania	EU	28	20
YS	El Salvador	NA	11	07
YT-YU, YZ	Serbia and Montenegro	EU	28	15
YV-YY	Venezuela	SA	12	09
YV0	Aves I.	NA	11	08
Z2	Zimbabwe	AF	53	38
Z3	Macedonia	EU	28	15
ZA	Albania	EU	28	15
ZB2	Gibraltar	EU	37	14
ZC4	UK Sov. Bases on Cyprus	AS	39	20
ZD7	St. Helena	AF	66	36
ZD8	Ascension I.	AF	66	36
ZD9	Tristan da Cunha & Gough I	AF	66	38
ZF	Cayman Is.	NA	11	08
ZK1	N. Cook Is.	OC	62	32
ZK1	S. Cook Is.	OC	62	32
ZK2	Niue	OC	62	32
ZK3	Tokelau Is.	OC	62	31
ZL-ZM	New Zealand	OC	60	32
ZL7	Chatham Is.	OC	60	32
ZL8	Kermadec Is.	OC	60	32
ZL9	Auckland & Campbell Is.	OC	60	32
ZP	Paraguay	SA	14	11
ZR-ZU	South Africa	AF	57	38
ZS8	Prince Edward and Marion Is.	AF	57	38

Great circle map centred on London

This map shows the true distance and bearing from London of any place in the world (for magnetic bearings, add 6 degrees to the true bearing).

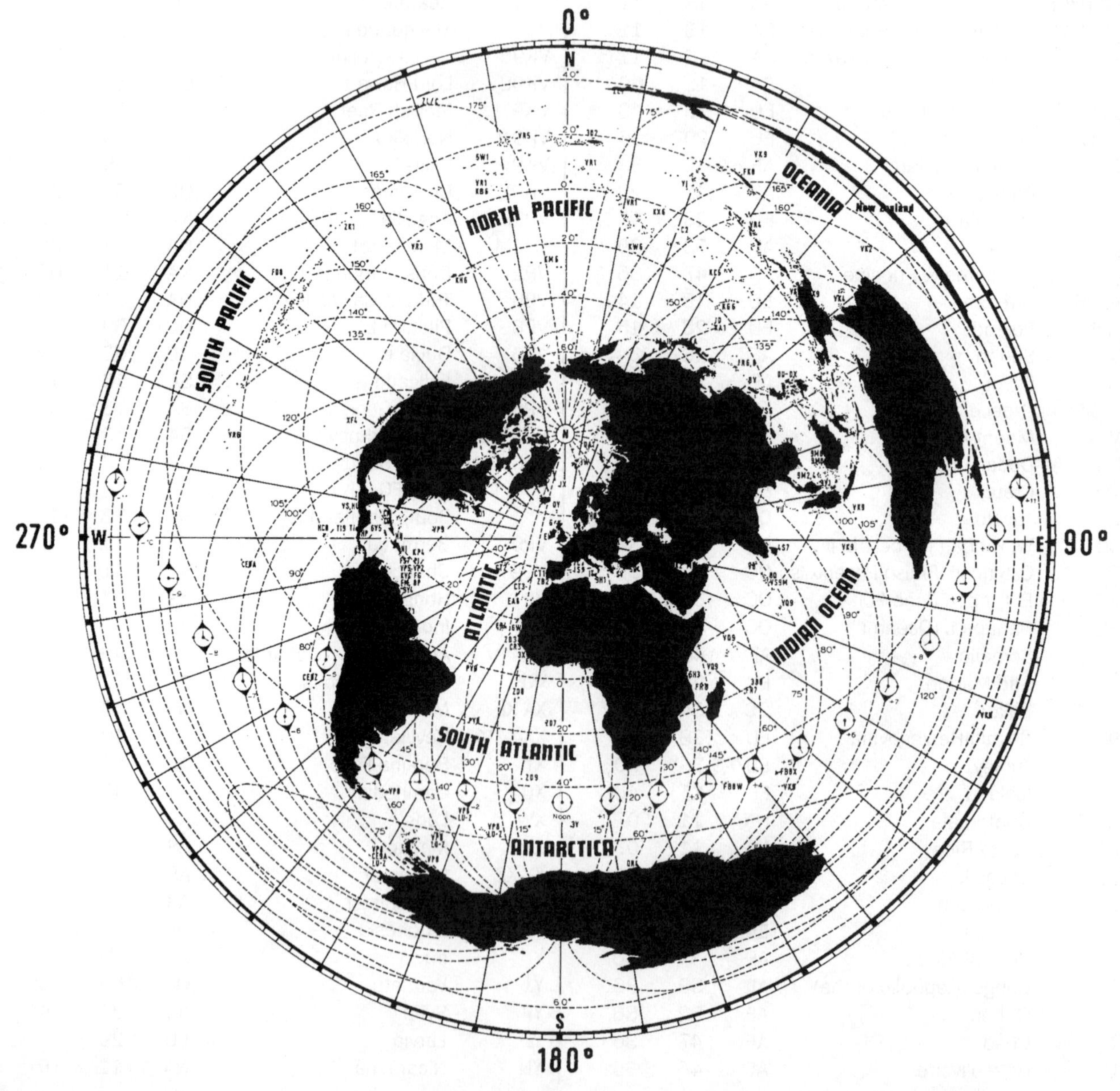

Appendix D

Foreign Language Phone Contacts

Thousands of operators across the world have contacts with only 100 or so words in a second language. It gives them great satisfaction, as well as many contacts which would otherwise have been impossible.

A basic contact consists of 10 parts: (1) calling CQ, (2) acknowledge reply, (3) name, (4) QTH, (5) signal report, (6) equipment used, (7) weather, (8) QSL via bureau, (9) 'Thanks for contact', (10) 73. Nearly every contact comes over in that order and all 10 parts usually come over in three of four transmissions, grouping two or three parts together in each one.

Every language can be found on the 14MHz band. For familiarisation and pronunciation of any of these four languages, search around the band for someone calling CQ who is speaking clearly and slowly with a strong signal. Do not waste time with weak signals or trying to understand a ragchew!

After some listening practice, make out the memory page with your name, QTH, rig etc. There are eight types of weather to choose from and the numbers down the side will cover station reports and temperatures up to 30°C. The memory page is just a prompt so that you do not forget your words in the middle of a transmission and so that you are able to give the other operator the information required correctly.

When ready to start transmitting, you will find it easier to contact an English-speaking station. After the preliminaries are established, tell your contact that you wish to practice his language and change straight over, reading from the prepared memory page. Do not be put off if your contact continues in English - he may wish to practice as well!

When you advance to calling CQ it is advisable to tell the other station that you "only speak the language for the QSO". This should prevent questions coming across which cannot be understood; if they do, repeat the same statement and continue to the end of the contact.

While four foreign languages are given here, you are strongly advised not to attempt more than one at a time - probably the second language which you learned at school - as it is very easy to get the words mixed up, particularly when you start to rely on memory.

FRENCH

0	zero
1	un, une
2	deux
3	trois
4	quatre
5	cinq
6	six
7	sept
8	huit
9	neuf
10	dix
11	onze
12	douze
13	treize
14	quatorze
15	quinze
16	seize
17	dix-sept
18	dix-huit
19	dix-neuf
20	vingt
21	vingt et un
22	vingt-deux
23	vingt-trois
24	vingt-quatre
25	vingt-cinque
26	vingt-six
27	vingt-sept
28	vingt-huit
29	vingt-neuf
30	trente
40	quarante
80	quatre-vingts

Calling CQ, CQ, this is G	*CQ, CQ, (SAY KOO) appel général, appel général, ici G . . . . . .*
calling CQ on the . . . . . . metre band.	*qui lance appel bande . . . . . . mètres.*
G . . . . . . standing by.	*G . . . . . . pass a l'écoute.*
F . . . . . . , G . . . . . . returning.	*F . . . . . . , G . . . . . . qui revient*
The name here is	*Le prénom ici est . . . . . .*
and the QTH	*et le QTH (KOO TAY ASSH) . . . . . .*
I spell	*je vous épele*
Your report here is . . . . . . and	*Votre rapport ici est . . . . . . et . . . . . .*
F . . . . . . , G . . . . . . over to you.	*F . . . . . . , G . . . . . . à vous.*
F . . . . . . , G . . . . . . returning,	*F . . . . . . , G . . . . . . de retour*
the rig here is	*la condition de travail ici est . . . . . .*
with a . . . . . . antenna	*avec une antenne . . . . . .*
and a . . . . . . microphone	*et un micro . . . . . .*
the WX here is	*Le WX (DOUBLA VAY EKS) ici est . . . . . .*
1. sunny 5. fog	*1. ensoleillé 5. du brouillard*
2. cloudy 6. warm	*2. nuageux 6. chaud*
3. raining 7. cold	*3. il pleut 7. froid*
4. windy 8. snowing	*4. du vent 8. il neige*
and the temperature C	*et la température . . . . . . dégrées Centigrad*
F . . . . . . , G . . . . . . back to you	*F . . . . . . , G . . . . . . à vous*
F . . . . . . , G . . . . . . returning for the final	*F . . . . . . , G . . . . . . qui revient pour le final*
I will send you my QSL card via the bureau,	*Je vous enverrai ma carte QSL (KOO ES EL) via le bureau,*
Thank you for the very good QSO,	*Merci bien pour le très bon QSO (KOO ES AW)*
73, OM,	*Soixante-treize, cher OM*
F . . . . . . , G . . . . . . closing,	*F . . . . . . , G . . . . . . qui termine*
cheerio.	*maintenant, au revoir.*

ADDITIONAL PHRASES WHICH MAY BE REQUIRED

I only speak French for the QSO.	*Je parle français seulement pour le QSO.*
Please speak slowly.	*Parlez lentement, s'il vous plâit.*
Please give me my report again.	*Donnez-moi mon rapport encore une fois, s'il vous plâit.*
Please give me your name again.	*Donnez-moi votre prénom encore une fois, s'il vous plâit.*
Please give me your QTH again.	*Donnez-moi votre QTH encore une fois, s'il vous plâit.*

GERMAN

0	null, zero
1	ein, eins
2	zwei, zwo
3	drei
4	vier
5	fünf
6	sechs
7	sieben
8	acht
9	neun
10	zehn
11	elf
12	zwolf
13	dreizehn
14	vierzehn
15	fünfzehn
16	sechszehn
17	siebzehn
18	achtzehn
19	neunzehn
20	zwanzig
21	ein und zwanzig
22	zwei und zwanzig
23	drei und zwanzig
24	vier und zwanzig
5	fünf und zwanzig
26	sechs und zwanzig
27	sieben und zwanzig
28	acht und zwanzig
29	neun und zwanzig
30	dreissig
40	vierzig
80	achtzig

English	German
CQ, CQ, CQ, ... metres	*CQ, CQ, CQ (SEE KOO), ... meter Band*
This is the English station G	*Hier ruft die englische Station G . . . . . .*
calling CQ	*mit einem allgemeinen Anruf*
G . . . . . . going over to receive,	*G . . . . . . geht auf empfang,*
stand by	*bitte kommen*
D . . . . . . , G . . . . . . returning	*D . . . . . . , G . . . . . . zurück*
My name is	*Mein Name ist . . . . . .*
and my QTH is	*und mein QTH (KOO TAY HAA) ist*
I spell	*Ich buchstabiere*
Your report here is . . . . . . and	*Ihr Rapport hier ist . . . . . . und . . . . . .*
D . . . . . . , G . . . . . . back to you	*D . . . . . . , G . . . . . . bitte kommen*
D . . . . . . , G . . . . . . coming back	*D . . . . . . , G . . . . . . zurück*
My station is	*Meine Station ist . . . . . .*
with a . . . . . . antenna	*mit eine . . . . . . Antenne*
and a . . . . . . microphone	*und ein . . . . . . Mikrophon*
The weather here is	*Das Wetter hier ist*
1. sunny 5. foggy	*1. sunnig 5. nebelig*
2. cloudy 6. warm	*2. bewoelkt 6. warm*
3. raining 7. cold	*3. es regnet 7. kalt*
4. windy 8. snowing	*4. windig 8. es schneit*
and the temperature . . . . . . degrees C	*und das Temperatur . . . . . . Grad*
back to you D . . . . . . , G	*zurück zu Ihnen D . . . . . . , G . . . . . . bitte kommen*
D . . . . . .,. G . . . . . . Thank you for the QSO	*D . . . . . . , G . . . . . . Dankeschön für das QSO (KOO ES OH)*
I will send you my QSL card via the bureau	*Ich werde meine QSL-Karte via Bureau senden*
Best wishes and good DX	*Die besten Grüsse und gut DX*
73 until we meet again	*drei und siebzig, auf wiederhören*
D . . . . . . , G . . . . . . cheerio	*D . . . . . . , G . . . . . . Tschuess*

ADDITIONAL PHRASES WHICH MAY BE REQUIRED

I only speak German for the QSO.	*Ich spreche Deutsch nur für das QSO.*
Please give me your callsign again.	*Bitte, geben Sie mir Ihr Rufzeichen noch einmal.*
Please give me your name again.	*Bitte, geben Sie mir Ihr Name noch einmal.*
Please give me your QTH again.	*Bitte, geben Sie mir Ihr QTH (KOO TAY HAA) noch einmal.*
I give you back the microphone.	*Ich gebe Ihnen das Mikrophon wieder zurück.*

ITALIAN

0	zero
1	uno
2	due
3	tre
4	quattro
5	cinque
6	sei
7	sette
8	otto
9	nove
10	dieci
11	undici
12	dodici
13	tredici
14	quattordici
15	quindici
16	sedici
17	diciasette
18	diciotto
19	diciannove
20	venti
21	ventuno
22	ventidue
23	ventitré
24	ventiquattro
25	venticinque
26	ventsei
27	ventisette
28	ventotto
29	ventinove
30	trenta
40	quaranta
80	ottanta

CQ . . . . . . metres, this is the English station
G . . . . . . standing by

Chiamata generale . . . . . . metri, questo è la stazione inglese G . . . . . . e vi ascolto, avanti

I . . . . . . , G . . . . . . returning,
many thanks for the call.
The name here is . . . . . .
and the QTH is . . . . . .
Your report is . . . . . . and . . . . . .
Mike back to you, I . . . . . . , G . . . .

I . . . . . . , G . . . . . . ritornando
tante grazie per la risposta.
Il mio nome è . . . . . .
Il mio QTH (KOO TEE ACCA) è . . . . . .
Il vostro controllo è . . . . . . e . . . . . .
Vi ripasso il micro, I . . . . . . , G . . . . . .
avanti, cambio

I . . . . . . , G . . . . . . returning
The rig here is . . . . . .
with . . . . linear
The microphone is . . . . . .
My antenna is . . . . . .
The WX here is
1. sunny 5. foggy
2. cloudy 6. warm
3. raining 7. cold
4. windy 8. snowing
The temperature is . . . . . . degrees
I . . . . . . , G . . . . . . over to you

I . . . . . . , G . . . . . . ritornando
Il mio apparechio è . . . . . .
con amplificatore . . . . . .
Il micro è . . . . . .
La mia antenna è . . . . . .
Il tempo qui è
1. bellissimo 5. nebbioso
2. nuvoloso 6. caldo
3. piovoso 7. freddo
4. fa vento 8. nevica
La temperatura è . . . . . . gradi
Vi ripasso il micro, I . . . . . . , G . . . . . .
avanti, cambio

I . . . . . . , G . . . . . . returning for the final
I will send my QSL card via the bureau.

Thank you for the excellent QSO, best wishes and good DX.
The mike to you for the final. Bye-bye.
I . . . . . . , G 73

I . . . . . . , G . . . . . . ritornando, per il finale.
Vi mandero la mia cartolina QSL (KOO ESS ELLE) via bureau (associatione).
Molti grazie per il QSO eccellente, tanti saluti e buon DX.
Il micro a voi caro amico per il finale. Ciao (CHOW).
I . . . . . . , G . . . . . .
Avanti, cambio, 73 (settanta tre)

ADDITIONAL PHRASES WHICH MAY BE REQUIRED

I only speak Italian for the QSO.	*Parlo Italiano soltanto per il QSO.*
Please speak slowly.	*Prego, parlate lentamente.*
I did not get your callsign.	*Non ho capito il vostro nominativo.*
What is my report?	*Cos' è il mio controllo?*

SPANISH

0	cero
1	uno
2	dos
3	tres
4	cuatro
5	cinco
6	seis
7	siete
8	ocho
9	nueve
10	diez
11	once
12	doce
13	trece
14	catorce
15	quince
16	diez y seis
17	diez y siete
18	diez y ocho
19	diez nueve
20	veinte
21	veintiuno
22	veintidos
23	veintitres
24	veinticuatro
25	veinticinco
26	veintiseis
27	veintisiete
28	veintiocho
29	veintinueve
30	treinta
31	treinta y uno
40	cuarenta
80	ochenta

Calling CQ CQ CQ, this is G . . . . . . calling CQ on . . . . . . metres, G . . . . . . standing by.	*Llamada general, G . . . . . . llamando, CQ . . . . metros, y G . . . . escuchando.*
EA . . . . . . , from G . . . . . .returning,	*EA . . . . . . , G . . . . . .retornando.*
Thank you for returning my call.	*Gracias por haber contestado a mi llamada.*
My name is . . . . I spell	*Mi nombre es . . . . . . , como*
My QTH is . . . . . . ,. I spell	*Mi QTH es . . . . . . , como*
Your report here is . . . . . . and	*Su control es . . . . . . y . . . . . .*
EA . . . . . . from G . . . . come in.	*EA . . . . . . de G . . . . adelante*
EA . . . . . . from G	*EA . . . . . . de G . . . .*
Thank you for your message.	*Gracias por su mensaje.*
My station is	*Mis condiciones de trabajo . . . . . .*
my antenna is dipole/multiband/beam.	*mi antena es dipolo/multibanda/directional.*
My microphone is crystal/dynamic.	*Mi microfono es cristal/dinamico.*
The weather here is	*El tiempo aqui*
1. sunny 5. fog	*1. hace sol 5. niebla*
2. cloudy 6. warm	*2. nublado 6. hace calor*
8. raining 7. cold	*3. lloviendo 7. hace frio*
4. windy 8. snowing	*4. hace viento 8. nevando*
The temperature is . . . . . . degrees.	*La temperatura . . . . . . grados.*
EA . . . . . . from G . . . . . . , come in	*EA . . . . . . de G . . . . . ., adelante*
EA . . . . . . from G . . . . . . for the final.	*EA . . . . . . de G . . . . . . por el final.*
I will send my QSL card via the bureau.	*Me enviaré la tarjeta de QSL via el bureau.*
Thank youfor the QSO, 73, Cheerio.	*Gracias por el QSO, 73 (setenta y tres).*
	EA . . . . de G . . . . adios!

ADDITIONAL PHRASES WHICH MAY BE REQUIRED

I only speak Spanish for the QSO.	*Hablo el español solamente por el QSO.*
Please speak slowly.	*Por favor hable despacio.*
Please repeat my report/your name/your QTH.	*Por favor repete mi control/su nombre/su QTH.*
Can you QSY . . . kHz higher/lower.	*Puede Usted QSY . . . kHz alto/bajo.*
I am sorry, I cannot copy, bad QRM.	*Lo siento, no puedo copiar, mucho QRM.*

Index